MAMMALS OF NORTH AMERICA

MAMMALS
OF NORTH AMERICA

By VICTOR H. CAHALANE

WITH DRAWINGS BY FRANCIS L. JAQUES

1961

THE MACMILLAN COMPANY · NEW YORK

To My Mother and Father

Contents

	PAGE
INTRODUCTION	1
1. THE WILD PIG	10
PECCARY	10
2. THE DEER FAMILY	15
ELK	15
WHITETAIL DEER	23
MULE DEER	33
BLACKTAIL DEER	40
MOOSE	44
CARIBOU	53
3. THE HELIOGRAPHER	62
ANTELOPE	62
4. ORIGINAL AMERICAN LIVESTOCK	71
BUFFALO	71
MUSKOX	82
BIGHORN	88
MOUNTAIN GOAT	98
5. SURVIVORS OF ANCIENT ORDERS	104
OPOSSUM	104
ARMADILLO	108
6. THE INSECT HUNTERS	114
MOLE	114
SHREW	119
7. THE FLYER	126
BAT	126
8. THE BEARS	134
BLACK BEAR	134
GRIZZLY BEAR	144
POLAR BEAR	150

PAGE

9. THE BEAR'S SMALL COUSINS 156
   RACCOON 156
   COATI 161
   RINGTAIL 165

10. THE MUSK–CARRIERS 170
    MARTEN 170
    FISHER 175
    WEASEL 180
    MINK 188
    WOLVERINE 193
    THE OTTER 198
    SEA OTTER 203
    STRIPED SKUNK 209
    HOG-NOSED SKUNK 216
    SPOTTED SKUNK 218
    BADGER 222

11. THE WILD DOGS 228
    RED FOX 228
    KIT FOX 235
    GRAY FOX 237
    ARCTIC FOX 241
    COYOTE 245
    WOLF 256

12. THE CATS 264
    THE COUGAR 264
    JAGUAR 273
    OCELOT 278
    JAGUARUNDI 282
    LYNX 284
    BOBCAT 290

13. THE FINFEET 298
    FUR SEAL 298
    SEA LION 303
    THE EARLESS SEALS 308
    SEA ELEPHANT 318
    WALRUS 322

PAGE

14. THE 'CHUCKS AND GROUND SQUIRRELS   328
    WOODCHUCK   328
    MARMOT   336
    COLUMBIAN GROUND SQUIRREL   341
    STRIPED GROUND SQUIRREL   349
    ROCK SQUIRREL   355
    ANTELOPE SQUIRREL   359
    GOLDEN-MANTLED GROUND SQUIRREL   363
    PRAIRIE DOG   368

15. THE CHIPMUNKS AND SQUIRRELS   377
    EASTERN CHIPMUNK   377
    WESTERN CHIPMUNK   383
    RED SQUIRREL   389
    GRAY SQUIRREL   400
    TASSEL-EARED SQUIRREL   406
    FOX SQUIRREL   410
    FLYING SQUIRREL   416

16. CHISEL–TEETH (PART 1)   425
    POCKET GOPHER   425
    SPINY MOUSE   434
    POCKET MOUSE   437
    KANGAROO RAT   442
    BEAVER   452
    GRASSHOPPER MOUSE   462
    HARVEST MOUSE   466
    WHITE-FOOTED MOUSE   470
    RICE RAT   479
    COTTON RAT   483
    WOOD RAT   487

17. CHISEL–TEETH (PART 2)   501
    LEMMING   501
    MEADOW MOUSE   508
    WATER RAT   519
    MUSKRAT   523
    HOUSE MOUSE   538
    HOUSE RAT   544

PAGE

17. CHISEL-TEETH (Part 2)—(Cont'd)
    Mountain Beaver   550
    Jumping Mouse   556
    Porcupine   563

18. THE HARES AND RABBITS   577
    Pika   577
    Varying Hare   583
    Arctic Hare   594
    Jack Rabbit   601
    Cottontail Rabbit   612

19. THE VANISHING MERMAID   626
    The Manatee   626

20. TWO SEAFARERS   631
    The Whale   631
    Dolphin   642

    LIST OF REFERENCES   647
    General References   647
    References to Specific Mammals   652

    INDEX   677

INTRODUCTION

Introduction

MILLIONS OF MAMMALS

When the first colonists from Europe arrived in North America, they found a multitude of mammals comprising many species. Deer, elk, caribou, and moose roamed the forests. Wolverines, lynx, mountain lions, and wolves stalked and killed them. Mountain sheep with magnificent horns, and shaggy, white-bearded goats lived on the high western mountains, and here also were the snowshoe hares and little rabbitlike animals called pikas.

The number of mammals found on the grasslands of central North America surpassed anything that man had witnessed since the dawn of history. For days explorers pushed their way through apparently endless herds of buffalo, antelope, and elk—more than a hundred million of these animals! Countless bands of deer also lived along the water courses, and bighorns watched from the buttes of the badlands. For thousands of years these staggering numbers of game animals had been preyed upon by great grizzly bears (the largest carnivorous mammals on earth), wolves, stealthy coyotes, and savage men. But the spectacle had not diminished, nor did it, until the nineteenth century.

Less conspicuous, but amazingly numerous were the rounded earthen mounds of prairie dogs. In places, they dotted the plains as far as eye could see. Some of their "towns" harbored more inhabitants than any human city of that time.

EXTERMINATION

Thirty years of slaughter, during the 1850's, sixties and seventies, climaxed the near-extermination of the larger animals. They were gone completely from vast areas where they had lived in countless numbers. Only a few remnants of the former millions managed to persist where they were secluded in wild areas of the western mountains, or in the far-off, inhospitable northlands.

RESTORATION

By the opening of the twentieth century, an aroused and fearful public realized how drastic the exterminating process had been and hastily sought to have the damage remedied. Today, after half a century of trial and error in conservation, most of the larger land mammals are no longer in immediate danger of becoming extinct. Many of them are perhaps as populous as they ever can be in a man-modified continent. With some notable exceptions, as the prairie dogs, the smaller land species have been little harmed by the activities of man. Many of the seed-eaters may have benefited. Not as much can be said for the majority of the great marine mammals that live in the surrounding oceans, as some of these seem likely to disappear before we know enough about their habits to conserve them intelligently.

HOW MAMMALS AFFECT HUMANS

Most of us have a deep interest in mammals. Sportsmen and trappers want to know more about the "game species" (hoofed animals, bears, squirrels, and rabbits), their predatory enemies, and the many fur-bearers. Farmers are vitally concerned about the multitude of native rodents and practically everyone may be troubled by those introduced foreigners, the house rat and house mouse. The products of native mammals such as meat, hides, fats, bones, furs, perfumes, and fertilizers are worth many millions of dollars each year. Many species are of great aesthetic interest and are worth more alive than dead, while the activities of others help to improve soil and to control injurious plant and animal life. Such services are priceless. Others may do immense damage to agricultural crops and products, to forage and forests, to livestock and poultry. Some species harbor diseases that may be transmitted to man or to his domestic animals.

SCOPE OF THIS BOOK

Because mammals are so important to mankind, much study has been given to them and a great many volumes have been written about them. Several popular books on the habits of North American mammals have appeared. One of the first of these works which attempted to cover the subject, Stone and Cram's *American Animals*, was published forty years ago. Seton's *Lives of Game Animals* appeared more recently, in 1929. It is a very fine work originally in four volumes which include most of the information then available concerning the animals whose biographies appear. Although somewhat broader in scope than the title indicates, the volumes describe comparatively few of the smaller mammals.

Information on these species as well as results of recent studies on other mammals are scattered in many publications. Much of this literature is of a technical or semi-technical nature, and is limited to regions, states, or smaller areas. There is a need, therefore, for a popular book which will summarize existing information on the principal kinds of mammals of North America.

This book attempts to meet that need. It devotes a minimum of space to morphology and taxonomy, for excellent publications are available on these phases of mammalogy. Instead, the book is intended to reveal the intimate lives of mammals: how they come into the world and grow to adult stature; their daily routine; the food they eat, and how they get it; their courtships, mates, and offspring; their enemies and how they escape them. These and many other details of existence through the four seasons of the year are related.

As so many of the mammal species of Mexico belong to the assemblage that has its roots in the tropics rather than in the temperate zone, they are not described here. The region treated is that part of continental America north of the Mexican boundary, and the islands in the Arctic Ocean between the continent and the North Pole. The mammals that live in or commonly visit the oceanic waters immediately surrounding the American continent north of Mexico also are included.

OPPORTUNITY FOR MORE RESEARCH

Because federal and state agencies have financed much research, knowledge of many economically important mammals has grown rapidly in the last two decades. Nevertheless, a great many vital facts about a large number of species remain to be discovered. The life histories of some of our commonest mammals which live close to towns and cities, or even on vacant lots near factories and skyscrapers, are not yet fully known. Some of our largest animals which are difficult to observe still have many mysterious ways, while other small and common species such as ground squirrels and cottontail rabbits have been watched, measured and weighed with meticulous care. Yet undoubtedly much still remains to be learned even about these animals whose privacy has been so thoroughly invaded. None of the following life-history sketches, therefore, should be regarded as complete, as many important features are lacking in some cases because they are as yet unknown or unpublished. There is still a wide-open field for young naturalists who would like to discover more of the secrets about American mammals.

WHAT ARE MAMMALS?

Mammals are a predominant form of life on the earth. Of the estimated one million species of creatures known in the entire animal kingdom, the thirty-five hundred species of mammals are a tiny minority. Yet, because they are so highly specialized, so efficient in their ways of life, and so capable of coping with circumstances as they arise, the mammals have risen to the highest strata of Nature's social order. They are so diversified and often so beautiful that, to many humans, these fellow mammals are the most fascinating of living things.

In popular everyday language, mammals are "animals." The British call them "beasts." "Quadrupeds" does fairly well, although bats and seals are hardly four-footed in the ordinary sense of the word, and the hind limbs of whales, dolphins, porpoises and manatees no longer emerge from their bodies.

Mammals are vertebrates or backboned animals, and the name "mammal" comes from the Latin *mamma,* meaning breast. With the exception of two egg-laying mammals, the Australian platypus and the echidna, all mammals bring forth their young alive and helpless. During a period of infancy the young must be nourished on the mother's milk until they can get food themselves. Most backboned animals, exclusive of the mammals, hatch from eggs and are largely able to make their own way in life. However, the young of all but a few birds are dependent on parental help for one to several weeks after hatching.

Mammals are warm-blooded, which permits them to be notably independent of changes in air temperature, unlike the cold-blooded fishes, lizards, and reptiles which become sluggish and finally torpid when chilled. Each mammal has a four-chambered heart which pumps blood through a double circulatory system, consisting of arteries, capillaries, and veins. The chest, which contains the heart and lungs, is separated from the abdomen, containing the stomach and other organs, by a thin sheet of muscle called the diaphragm.

The typical mammal has four legs although, as mentioned, the hind pair of the whale allies and the manatee are mere remnants buried in the body or lost altogether. An outstanding feature of all mammals is the hairy coat, which ranges in different species from stout bristles to very fine fur. Some adults may be almost barren of hair, but even they are hairy at some stage of development. Practically hairless sea mammals like the whales have furry coats but lose them before birth. Backboned animals other than the mammals have different types of covering: feathers (birds); scales (reptiles and fishes); or bare skin (amphibians: toads, frogs, and salamanders).

There can be little question that, as a class, mammals are more intelligent than other vertebrates. In some the brain is much bigger in proportion to body weight, and is more highly developed in the "thinking" centers.

MAN AND OTHER MAMMALS

It is customary for humans to set themselves on a plane above that of their fellow-mammals. Scientists recognize similarities of organs and development of body structure in man and in the "lesser" mammals. But many of them are loath to acknowledge a likeness of actions and feelings, and vigorously object to the use of human terms in describing an animal's habits.

Some adherents of the mechanical school believe that only man can have "feelings." They assert that the mother deer cannot experience affection for her fawn, or the woodchuck a sense of enjoyment when it suns itself on the mound in front of its den. The dog that obeys his master's command to "sit up," according to them, is only reacting automatically to familiar sounds much as a dummy responds to the strings pulled by a puppeteer.

At the other extreme is the sentimentalist who "anthropomorphizes" or "humanizes," attributing all human characteristics to the "lower" mammals, which may carry on prolonged conversations, expressing ideas and emotions analogous to our own. Finally there is the "nature faker" who invents happenings or actions that never occurred.

At the risk of being considered a "humanizer," the author has described mammals and their habits in familiar terms. A portion of the burrow in which an animal sleeps is called a bedroom, and the nest may be termed a bed. The space that it reserves exclusively for body wastes is called a toilet. If the first period of feeding comes soon after a diurnal mammal wakes up, the meal corresponds to a person's breakfast. When animals signal or call to each other by a series of vocal sounds, I have sometimes termed it "talk" or conversation. I have not attempted to interpret it except rarely when it was an obvious "Go away!" or an apparently derisive snort.

I hope this effort to describe the lives of North American mammals in everyday language will not be annoying to any scientist, and that it will not give false impressions to laymen. The mammals that are below us in the zoological scale are believed to be more limited than humans in their intelligence and reactions. It is certain, however, that many of them are perceptive of matters which are beyond our sensory range or understanding. How can we claim justifiably that we are exclusive proprietors of such qualities as courage, cleverness, affection, or the ability to enjoy life and to communicate with others of our own kind?

HISTORY OF MAMMALS

The mammals are an extremely ancient division of the animal kingdom. They probably developed from reptilelike ancestors in the early Triassic period —about 200 million years ago. Ever since, to meet different and constantly varying conditions of climate, habitat, enemies, and many other factors, they have been changing. Some mammals took to the sea; others went up to the mountains or down to the plains of the early continents. Some went underground, some to rocky cliffs, while others sought safety in trees. Each mammalian strain "specialized" for its particular kind of environment. Those which evolved the most efficient physical equipment lived a little longer than those that did not, and so produced more progeny which eventually supplanted the others. The survivors developed into many groups and kinds or species. The mammals reached their peak of size, diversity, and abundance during the Miocene epoch, which began some 30 million years ago and lasted for about 18 million years. By comparison with the mammals of the world in that faraway time, the present-day fauna is small in number of species. Speaking in terms of geologic time, the big mammals of the present era appear almost to have reached the end of the trail to extinction.

HOW ARE MAMMALS CLASSIFIED?

To describe the surviving fifteen thousand varieties of mammals and to show their relationship to each other, zoologists have devised a classification system. Based on physical characteristics, it begins with the most important and striking features of the bony structure and works down to minor characters such as shades of coat color or variations in size. Thus, first of all, the mammals are divided into two classes—the egg-laying and the viviparous. The latter (which includes all of the North American kinds) is split into orders. Examples of these are the Insectivora (moles and shrews), the Rodentia (rodents, including the squirrels and mice), the Artiodactyla (even-toed, hoofed mammals), and the Cetacea (whales and dolphins).

Each order is divided into families. For example, in North America the order Artiodactyla comprises the families Tayassuidae (peccaries), Cervidae (deer), Antilocapridae (pronghorn or antelope), and Bovidae (wild cattle, sheep and goats).

The families are divided successively into genera, species, and subspecies or geographic races. Speaking broadly, a genus is so definitely different that one would not confuse a member of it with an individual of a closely related genus. Deer of the genus *Alces* (moose) can be distinguished easily from those of the genus *Rangifer* (caribou). The differences in the skulls, antlers, shoulders, length of legs, and general proportions of the bodies of moose and caribou are so pronounced that even the black silhouettes of the animals against a distant skyline can hardly be confused.

The several species of a genus are recognized by distinctions in size or color, and often by comparatively minor differences in one or more parts of the body. The value of these characteristics is often relative. For example, the woodland caribou (*Rangifer caribou*) is "larger and darker," the barren-ground caribou (*Rangifer arcticus*) is "smaller and paler."

Differentiation between subspecies of the same species is based on more subtle technical points of color and body measurements. While members of two species very rarely interbreed, those of subspecies of the same species do so wherever their ranges join. This means that in the zone where the subspecies meet, the animals intergrade. Their characteristics are a blend of both subspecies and their exact identification may be impossible even by an expert.

1,500 SPECIES UNDER 94 HEADINGS

At least 1,500 species and subspecies of mammals have been identified in North America north of the Rio Grande. Some are known only from a few museum specimens, while information on the habits of many others is only fragmentary. Even if the life histories of all of these mammals were known, the details in many instances would be repetitious and of interest to only a limited number of researchers. To keep this book within the limits of one volume, therefore, these more than 1,500 species and subspecies have been combined under 94 headings.

An attempt has been made to treat each of the main groups of North American mammals. The true marine mammals, the whales, dolphins, porpoises, sea lions, and seals, and the aerial mammals (bats) have been described rather broadly. The terrestrial species have been given relatively more space. In general, a chapter has been devoted to each of the genera of the land mammals. This has been done partly because they are closer to the lives of most of us, and partly because much more has been learned about them than about those which live chiefly outside of our element.

Each chapter on the terrestrial mammals includes all species and subspecies. Although, because of their similarity, many of these subgroups are not particularized. In the case of some far-ranging forms, however, it is often impossible to generalize. Closely allied species, which dwell in radically different environments, often develop specialized habits to meet the peculiar conditions under which they live. Whenever important distinctions of this type occur, the specific or subspecific form of the mammal has been identified by name. Otherwise, for simplicity, the names of specific subgroups so far as possible have been avoided. A brief review of the genera, subgenera, or important species has been given at the close of each chapter concerning especially diversified "kinds" of mammals. For a complete systematic account, however, the reader should consult Miller's "List of North American Recent Mammals" or Anthony's "Field Book of North American Mammals." The latter also contains detailed descriptions of each species and subspecies, which it is not feasible to give in this book.

MAMMALS ARE INDIVIDUALISTS

No real naturalist assumes that he knows all about any mammal species. If he ever reaches that point, he is promptly disillusioned by acquaintance with an individual that behaves as no other of his kind has acted before. Although mammals have certain racial tendencies, even the least intelligent of them sometimes exhibits originality. The certainty that mammals of a given species will react in a variety of ways is one of the things that makes their study fascinating. It also makes it impossible to write a book about the lives of mammals that will generalize their actions with invariable accuracy.

ACKNOWLEDGMENTS

In writing these accounts, I have drawn on the observations of many able naturalists as well as my own experiences. The majority of those whose writings I have used are named in the list of references which begins on page 647. A great many minor items have been gleaned from the writings of other biologists who are not listed.

Others have been generous with their time in furnishing information and references. Among these persons are Dr. W. B. Bell, formerly Chief of the Division of Wildlife Research; Mr. Leo K. Couch, Assistant Chief of the Division of Wildlife Research; Mr. Frank G. Ashbrook, In Charge of the Section on Fur Resources; and Mr. W. L. McAtee, Technical Advisor, all of the Fish and Wildlife Service; Dr. Carl P. Russell, Chief Naturalist, National Park Service; Dr. Remington Kellogg, Curator of Mammals, U. S. National Museum; Dr. W. H. Osgood, Curator Emeritus; Mr. Karl P. Schmidt, Chief Curator of Zoology, and Mr. C. J. Albrecht, formerly staff preparator, all of the Chicago Museum of Natural History; Dr. J. Eric Hill, Assistant Curator of Mammals, American Museum of Natural History; Miss Caroline A. Heppenstall, Assistant Curator of Mammalogy, Carnegie Museum; and Dr. E. Raymond Hall, Head of the Department of Zoology, University of Kansas, who furnished me with the classification of the weasels (pp. 187–188).

A number of my friends have reviewed portions of the manuscript and have made comments and suggested improvements in it. I am grateful to them for their criticisms. It should be understood, however, that the responsibility for statements and for such errors as may now exist is solely mine and not theirs.

The following have very kindly given their time and advice for the improvement of chapters on the mammal groups named: Mr. Frank G. Ashbrook (the mustelids: weasels, skunks, etc.); Dr. Hartley H. T. Jackson, In Charge, Section on Biological Surveys, Fish and Wildlife Service (the insectivores and cats); Dr. Remington Kellogg (marine mammals except the sea otter); Dr. Adolph Murie, Biologist, Fish and Wildlife Service (bears and wild dogs); and Mr. Olaus J. Murie, Director, The Wilderness Society (hoofed mammals and sea otter). Various chapters on the rodents were read by Mr. A. E. Borell, Regional Biologist of the Soil Conservation Service; Dr. C. H. D. Clarke, Biologist, Department of Lands and Forests of the Province of Ontario; Dr. E. Raymond Hall; and Dr. H. B. Sherman, Professor of Zoology, University of Florida.

Finally, I am indebted to my wife for criticism and much typing on the manuscript. Without her able and willing assistance, this book would never have been written.

1. The Wild Pig

PECCARY—*PECARI ANGULATUS*

Pigs is pigs. But the peccary is different. This little salt-and-pepper-colored pig should not be confused with domestic hogs that have gone wild. It is much smaller, more active, and nervous. It is a native American, while the barnyard porkers are of foreign origin.

Scooting through the desert mesquite or the scrub oaks of the low southwestern mountains, the peccary pops out of sight before one can get a good look at it. It leaves behind a strong, musky odor that is disagreeable to human noses. To other peccaries, it shouts: "Trouble! Watch out!"

On the arched back of this little pig, about eight inches in front of his absurdly short tail, is a large musk gland. Buried in the coarse grizzled hair, the opening in the skin looks like a misplaced navel. When the peccary becomes excited, the hair rises on his back and neck. The gland opens and exudes a little of the secretion. Very powerful, the odor of a small band of peccaries can be noticed even by human noses at a distance of several hundred feet.

The musk is also an identification. As peccaries pass under overhanging branches of trees and shrubs, they may rub against these, leaving some of the musky odor behind. Probably all sorts of information is gleaned from these scent posts by later-passing peccaries. The human hunter, with his dull and limited faculties, can only tell that one or more "musk hogs" have gone by.

Peccaries are found only in the Americas. Although numerous in Central and South America, they are comparatively scarce in the United States. Because they occur in so few places along our southwestern border, many well-informed Americans have never even heard of them.

Very little is recorded about the personal life of the peccary in this country. Instead of producing six to twelve offspring at a time like the barnyard porker, the peccary usually bears only twins. Because the climate of their habitat is so mild, the babies may be born through at least six months of the year. In the tropics, adults may breed during any month. The nursery is in a hollow log, or a burrow, or even on top of the ground in a thicket.

About the size of cottontail rabbits, the babies are reddish or yellowish brown mixed with black, and wear a black stripe running down the center of their backs. At the age of a few hours, they are able to stand on wobbly legs, and can even dodge about in the underbrush fast enough to avoid a man with collecting ideas.

When captured at an early age, the little peccary makes an interesting and very affectionate pet, becoming attached to people that it knows, and whining and crying when left alone. It is not afraid of the larger domestic pigs and often runs them away from their food.

When only a day or two old, the young peccaries, with their mother, join a band of males and females—from three or four up to twenty-five, or even more animals. Running energetically this way and that, they keep up a conversation of grunts and soft yaps or barks. They can be heard more frequently than they can be seen. When at peace with the world, their grunts are in monotone. If trouble threatens, an alarm is sounded with a deep, sharp note, and the animals immediately speed away with gruff ejaculations at every jump.

The peccary never gets as fat as the porker. It is too busy, but has the same eating habits—anything and everything edible will do. The members of the

PECCARY

band feed mostly in the morning and evening, but by no means fast the rest of the time. Their long snouts grub up roots and tubers, insect larvae, worms, lizards, toads and snakes. Eggs of turtles or ground-nesting birds are devoured. They like every available fruit: juniper and manzanita berries, cactus fruits, mesquite and catclaw beans, pine nuts and acorns.

The prickly pear seems to be the peccaries' favorite food during the summer. They gobble down the fruit, needlelike spines and all. Their stomach linings are stuck with spines like pincushions. In years when oak mast is abundant, the peccary gets quite fat at the end of the summer. Only infrequently does a choice bit of food occasion a brief quarrel. A quick bite and a sharp squeal of pain terminate the disagreement, for they are too busy to argue.

The peccary has never learned to do without water as many desert dwellers have. Water holes are scarce in our Southwest, and the margins are often hacked to bits by the sharp little hoofs of thirsty peccaries. Deeply beaten trails radiate in every direction and over all hangs the distinct odor of musk.

These little wild pigs are preyed upon by the jaguar, ocelot and wolf, and sometimes by the coyote and bobcat. The jaguar seems to be especially fond of peccary meat, and against this powerful cat the peccary has little chance. One peccary is known to have put up such a fight before being killed that the jaguar lost one of its claws. The sharp canine teeth of the peccaries are reenforced by plenty of spunk, and a sense of teamwork. A predator like the coyote may find a band of peccaries too dangerous to tackle. They have been known to tear to pieces a coyote caught in a trap.

When brought to bay by dogs, the peccary backs against a large tree or rock wall and fights gamely. Inexperienced dogs are sometimes killed, and even old, wily hounds may be badly slashed. Unless attacked and cornered, however, the little pig's foremost thought is to run.

Tales of peccaries attacking hunters, and even men on horseback, are numerous but often exaggerated. Men have been treed; but in some cases their fear was probably needless. The rush of a divided band coming together may look like a mass attack when it is only a casual meeting. The fighting ability of the larger white-lipped peccary is regarded with much respect in South America, and this may have colored accounts of our own species.

A century ago, the peccary, also called javelina, ranged as far north as southwestern Arkansas. Unrestricted hunting almost exterminated the species in the United States, but under protection the javelinas have recovered within their present restricted range. Their numbers in this country are now estimated roughly at about fifty thousand. Regulated hunting has been resumed, but is regarded as a difficult sport. Javelinas are small, elusive targets and are hard to kill. It took an average of four and one-half shots apiece to kill seventy-seven peccaries in a hunt near Tucson, Arizona, a couple of years ago.

The flesh of the peccary, when well fattened on oak mast, is fairly good, but otherwise may be rather tough and dry. The large musk gland in the back, if not removed shortly after the peccary's death, is supposed to ruin the meat. No bad effects were noticed in one case when the gland was left for two hours. As a sporting trophy, the mounted head of an old male is picturesque. The tanned hide also makes an effective wall or table decoration.

In southwestern New Mexico, a favorite pastime of the cowboys some years ago was to try to lasso lone peccaries as they crossed openings in the mesquite. Peccaries are hunted with packs of dogs in Mexico and countries to the south, and when brought to bay are killed with clubs. The hides, which are thin and very durable, are used in making the finest "pigskin" jackets and gloves. In the raw state the hides bring about fifty cents each.

Although domestic hogs were first brought to the New World by the Spaniards, the peccaries belong to one of the oldest American families. Their piglike ancestors probably migrated from Europe or Asia many millions of years ago. Their fossilized remains have been found embedded in rocks laid down during the middle Eocene. Through geological time, the animals slowly increased in size until in the Pleistocene the biggest species was considerably larger than present-day peccaries. These larger and more adventuresome beasts seem to have wandered into South America where the greatest number of peccaries are now found.

Zoologists point out certain technical differences between the peccaries and domestic swine. The "dewclaws" of swine reach the ground, giving them four toes to stand on. Peccaries, however, have very small, useless dewclaws; two well up on each front leg and one on each hind leg.

We all know the big tusks or canine teeth of the swine, the two uppers of which curve outward and up, well away from the jaw. The canines of the peccary are straight and grow in a vertical direction. Although not large, they are effective weapons.

Peccaries are divided into two groups. Our species is called the "collared" peccary, from the light-colored streak on the shoulder. In the Southwest, it usually goes by the name of javelina. The "white-lipped" species, which ranges from central Mexico southward, is larger and blacker, and has whitish patches on the side of the head.

In the tropics, the collared peccary lives in dense forests and usually in the valleys or on low plains. Within the United States, it selects several kinds of habitat. It may be found in the low dense thickets of the Rio Grande, the desert scrub farther west, or the mixed live-oak clumps and grassland of the southern Texas coast. Because of lack of shelter, extensive open grassland is avoided. In Arizona, although found on the flat desert, it seems to prefer the foothills and lower mountains. In New Mexico, I have found comparatively few signs of the peccary on the plains, but observed numerous tracks at six thousand feet on the tops of the Peloncillo Mountains.

General description. A piglike animal with long snout, thick neck, compact body with arched back, rather short legs, small sharp hoofs, and very short tail. Hair long and coarse, forming an erectile mane on neck, shoulders and back, grizzled black and gray with a grayish "collar" from throat to shoulder. Total length, 34 to 40 inches; height at shoulder, 21 to 22 inches; weight, 40 to 65 pounds.

Distinguishing characteristics. Our only native pig. Easily distinguished from the domestic hog "gone wild" by the peccary's small size and coarse, grizzled coat.

Range. Southern Texas and Arizona and southwestern New Mexico, south through Central and South America to Patagonia.

2. The Deer Family

ELK—*CERVUS* SP.

The sun was going down. Shadows of the Engelmann spruces reached across the little meadow and etched queer shadows on a band of cow elk and their calves. Restlessly one of the cows moved away, and then one could see that she was followed closely by a bull. Tall as a saddle horse, his tawny olive body was sleek and rounded from a summer of good living. The great branched antlers rose slantingly four feet or more above his head. His pale buffy rump disk looked brighter in the dusk than in the sunlight. It was late September in the northern Rockies, and the mating season was at its height.

The elk is a sultan—the greatest of them all except, perhaps, the fur seal and the caribou. An exceptionally powerful bull may have sixty or even many more mates. This elk was just an average master. One by one, by blandishment or bullying, he collected merely a dozen cows. The number and membership of the little harem varied slightly from week to week as he acquired new cows or permitted the old ones to wander away. The latest addition, with her calf, had been crossing the lower meadow that morning. In high excitement the bull had charged upon her and, with a few gentle antler prods and a kick or two, had herded her into the little company. After a summer of calf rearing and feminine society, she was more willing than not to accept the new relationship.

As yet, she did not feel much affection for her new master; in fact, she was bored by his repeated attempts to thrust his attentions on her. To this demonstration, his mates of longer standing paid not the slightest heed. Only the calves ceased their feeding or their brief games of tag to whine uneasily.

Suddenly, just before dark, a clear bugle note sounded from beyond the spruces. It was a stirring, clear, loud call. Starting on a low note, it rose to high pitch, then dropped abruptly and broke into a harsh, jarring scream followed by a grunt. The bull, startled by this challenge, did not hustle his harem off out of sight as some more timorous bulls do.

"Eeough!" His loud, harsh answering bark was defiant. He trotted a few steps in the direction of the challenger, then stopped. After several moments another bull, perhaps slightly larger than the first, stepped from the deep shadows and walked slowly into the meadow. As they met, the manes of the two

15

bulls rose. Their swollen necks throbbed, and their antlers clashed together like great rattling sabers. The weapons squealed as trees might, rubbing against each other in the wind. There were a couple of shoves, a twist, a grunt, then suddenly the defending bull broke back, wheeled and galloped heavily away.

ROCKY MOUNTAIN ELK

The newcomer was accepted by his easily won harem with only a curious glance or two, then indifference.

Sometimes the struggle between bulls is more serious and spectacular. It may end in a broken neck or a fatal horn-thrust for one contestant or locked antlers for both. More often the smaller bulls give up without any attempt to defend their rights.

As the autumn frosts intensified, the tender herbs shriveled, and the golden leaves of the aspens fell in showers. This typical band of elk moved southward across the mountain ridges toward the central canyon which ran into the wide low valley. Migrating mostly at night, they often stopped a day or two to take advantage of good grazing. Behind them, on the peaks, the early snow became more compact nightly. Finally a sudden white blanket covered the lower ridges to the depth of a foot or more, and the elk quickened their pace.

The little band merged with other bands, and the herd, now numbering a hundred or more, moved on into the grassy valleys. Dotted about in the distance were other herds, some larger, some smaller. Twenty thousand elk were drifting south. Many of them would never return.

As the nights of early winter grew long, the cold increased and the snow piled deeper. Hunters continued to shoot until five thousand elk had been killed. The breeding bulls that survived had lost their ardor, were thin, worn, and exhausted. No longer were they interested in the cows for which they had battled so furiously.

While the snow remained loose and fluffy the elk could paw it readily. They swept it back and to each side with strokes of the front feet used alternately. Several warm days occurred, the snow settled, and then came rain, followed by a hard freeze. The grasses were sealed under a four-inch shell of crusted snow so hard that the deer and antelope walked on the top without breaking through. By striking vigorously, the elk were able to break the crust to feed, but the sharp, hard edges cut their pasterns, and their legs and sometimes noses were soon raw and bleeding. For several weeks they were forced to depend almost wholly on browse foods: Douglas fir, juniper, aspen, serviceberry, sage, and bitterbrush. Under the attacks of hungry animals, the foliage of the coniferous plants and the tender twigs of other species quickly vanished. Gradually, feeding progressed to more and more indigestible woody stems and to unpalatable kinds of browse.

The deer and antelope began to starve first, crowded out by the voracious elk. The latter, because of their greater size, were able to reach higher for food and thus to eke out existence a little longer. Day by day the open space between snow and lower foliage of the firs and junipers grew wider, and even the lodge-poles began to lose their pitchy needles. The "elk-line" on the forest became distinct. Straight across the trees it ran, as high as the elk could reach. They became weaker and weaker.

Night by night the coyotes quarreled and snarled over the carcasses of the dead. The eerie howl of the wolf preceded his nightly hunt. His chases were short, for the elk could hardly maintain, even for a short distance, their normal top speed of about thirty-five miles an hour. Mountain lions came down from the rimrocks for the feast of easy kills. Many elk succumbed to hunger and cold, the casualty list beginning with the calves and the sick and crippled adults. Normally the elk carry numbers of wood ticks, bot fly larvae, tapeworms, and roundworms. The weakening effects of these and other parasites made the animals more susceptible to starvation. Continuous chewing of coarse, woody fiber caused mouth cuts and lesions. Through these openings, the organisms causing necrotic stomatitis gained more ready entrance. Results of this disease were bone decay, pneumonia, arthritis, pleurisy, and "blood poisoning."

Starving elk crowded around the ranchers' haystacks. Earlier in the winter they could have jumped fences seven or sometimes nine feet high. But now they were too weak. One of the bulls lifted the wire of an electrified fence with his "non-conducting" antlers and let the rest of the herd walk through. Others managed somehow to break down the fences and reach the hay and fruit trees. Alarmed settlers appealed for state compensation or took the law and their rifles into their own hands. Hunters shot into the bands by day, forcing them back to the hills where the snow was even deeper. Until much disturbed, the elk moved away from humans slowly.

By late winter the bulls began to lose their stately antlers. Except for their larger size, they looked much like the meek cows. Male and female, big and small, they were a hungry, weakened lot.

Spring came at last. To the elk that remained, its arrival was announced by a shift of the wind that brought a trace of warmth to the pre-dawn blackness of a morning in early April. By late afternoon the snow was soggy, and the air across the valley was misty and blue with moisture. In a few days many ridges and south-facing mountain shoulders were bare. The elk were able to dig out some forage that had been buried during the winter. Although their ribs remained prominent, their eyes gradually lost the glaze that had dulled them, and the movements of many of the animals became a little more lively.

The snow was forced at last into its final stand in ravines and under the spruces, but the earth seemed reluctant to give up its dark brown dress. Finally, one sunny day a trace of green became evident. In a few days it was distinct, and the creeks were outlined by the deep green of watercress and cowslip leaves.

The elk, eager for the sharp acid juices after their winter diet, sought out the developing sprigs of cinquefoil, mountain dandelion, sedges and grasses.

Slowly the animals moved upward in the valleys and on the mountainsides, looking for this food and tonic. Many of the weaker elk continued to die. Their carcasses dotted the migration routes back to the summer range, and the ragged coyotes gorged as they followed the herds. Besides the five thousand elk shot by hunters, fifteen hundred had perished during the winter. Another thousand died on the way back.

The bonds of companionship between the cows and their yearling calves were now tenuous, or, in most cases, broken completely. One by one, the remaining pairs separated. Some of the cows, heavy with calf, stayed quietly in little valleys or parks. The others, with the youngsters, the bulls, and the few non-bearing cows, went on. Bushes along the trails were whitened with bunches of hair as the elk rubbed off their faded, heavy coats.

Most of the births took place in open country, sometimes on grassland so bare that the single calf had no concealment whatever. Now and then a new mother was so satisfied with her calf and herself for having produced it, that she burst forth into a triumphant bugle. Similar but not as powerful as the bull's call, it may have expressed even greater emotion. In an hour or so, after having nursed her young, she urged it to walk on wobbly legs to shelter among clumps of grass or sagebrush or perhaps a small aspen thicket. The light tawny-brown fawn was conspicuous while standing, but not when it dropped flat on the ground. Then its neck and head curled along its body, and the white spots on its back and flanks broke up the outline and looked like sunflecks on a small stump. Very unsuspicious at first, it would have permitted a human being to handle and fondle it, but soon learned better. If in pain or in distress at being left alone too long, it called to the mother in a rather high-pitched bleat. She answered reassuringly, with a deeper voice, or sometimes, if the fawn moved away and was temporarily lost, she would call repeatedly for it.

Gray-brown coyotes, their sharp yellow eyes blank but watchful, searched the meadow for ground squirrels, early insects and fawns. A tender elk calf, weighing perhaps thirty-five pounds, whose bones were soft and filled with marrow, would be a juicy windfall. The bears, both blacks and grizzlies, knew that a lone cow here and there was not lingering about just to graze. Systematically they crisscrossed the meadow in search of calves, eagerly shuffling on huge flat feet. Occasionally they reared upright on their hind feet to get a better view or wind.

The adult elk had plenty of courage when dealing with other mammals. Last fall a bull elk, pulling back his lower jaw and grinding his teeth with rage, had driven three great buffalo off their own feeding ground. Another had charged an automobile. During the rutting season, bulls had chased a man occasionally, and at least once they had kept a pretty girl on a bridge for two hours. Only once was a human being actually attacked. A ranger, who had chopped a cow elk free from river ice, was kicked in the rear for his trouble—but that was only because she was maddened with fright.

When Dr. Adolph Murie gently examined a calf, he looked up to see nine elk mothers approaching him. Advancing and retreating, they were obviously torn between worry over the calf and fear of the man. Most of the elk mothers took a great interest in each other's offspring. If a calf were in danger, one or more of the cows would join the worried parent. They helped either to drive away a coyote, to look for a lost calf, or just to offer moral support. With or without assistance, every mother occasionally had to charge the coyotes and drive them off about their business.

Some elk mothers were probably more easily frightened than others. Heavy traffic kept one cow from her calf all day until sundown. Somehow it had managed to get on the other side of the road. Superintendent Edmund Rogers of Yellowstone Park watched a cow elk stride into a neighborhood where two Canada geese were building their nest. Immediately she was attacked by the comparatively small home-makers. Furious at the intrusion, they beat at her with their beaks and bodies. Traveling at a lumbering gallop, the big creature fled downstream fifty feet and up the opposite bank.

When it came to attacking grizzly bears that were hunting her calf, the elk mother was hard put. She had no antlers, and the grizzlies were much heavier and considerably more powerful. Sometimes she gave a sharp bark of distress that warned the other mothers. She did her courageous best to tantalize the bears into chasing her, recklessly venturing within thirty feet of the mammoth creatures before dashing away. Although they continued to search and sniff carefully, they were handicapped by their poor sight and the slight body odor from the calf. They generally abandoned the hunt after an hour or less of fruitless search.

In a few days the calf was strong enough to leave the meadow and follow the mother, and by short journeys they reached the summer range in the high mountains. Scattered through the glades and parks were other mothers and their calves. The pair joined a small herd, in which were a number of yearling cows and bulls. The calves varied in size, for some were born as early as the middle of May, while the youngest arrived as late as June 10th after their mothers had almost or quite reached the summer range.

For the first four to six weeks they were nourished entirely by their mother's milk. Then, beginning about the end of June, the older calves nibbled more and more at the leaves about them. The irregular intervals between nursings became longer. Instead of nursing for two to three minutes, the calves, with loud squeals of protest, were brushed off more quickly. By the first of August they had grown so much that they had to drop to their knees to suck. The weaning process went on into the late autumn when practically all of the cows' energy would be expended in developing the next year's embryos.

Many of the calves had lost their spots by August. Their bodies were now a uniform pale tawny olive, and the rump patches were conspicuous. Temporarily, their coats were quite shaggy, but this long hair would be shed in September to reveal their first trim, neat, adult dress.

Through the summer days, the bulls quietly poked about, frequently solitary, sometimes in groups of two, three or possibly more. Their antlers were growing and, being very soft, they were easily injured if carelessly carried through the woods. Those of last season's male calves were simple spikes, six or eight to perhaps fifteen inches long. Older bulls grew branched antlers. These generally were larger and had more points with increasing age, until a four- to five-year-old animal had about six tines on each beam. There were exceptions, of course, as a particularly vigorous elk would have seven or eight. A "freak" head might have many "points," while a weak, sick or very old bull (aged twelve years!) could grow only small antlers.

In spite of the attacks of mosquitoes and many other insects, the elk prospered through the summer. The restless calves grazed and investigated the vicinity. They played tag and follow-the-leader. Sparring with each other, they bounded about like mule deer, and loved to splash and swim in the water. A bull up the lake swam a little more than two miles in twelve minutes one day. Young and old conversed noisily at times with squeals, bleats or barks.

Every morning, for several hours, beginning before daylight, and again in the later afternoon until after dark, the elk fed on herbage, mostly grasses. It did not take them as long to harvest full meals as it had in the lean winter and they enjoyed lying in the shade and chewing their cuds. They lie like horses, with their heads and shoulders erect. Their front legs were drawn up while their hind quarters were tipped to one side with the hind legs stretched out. Sometimes they slept, with neck and head turned back along one flank or, again, stretched ahead and lying on their extended forelegs dog-fashion.

Like other animals, the elk had short memories. In the pleasant warmth they had forgotten the privations and misery of the winter season. Faintly, the mating urge stirred again.

In the old days, when walking between Asia and Alaska was good, the elk came over and helped to colonize America. The Shawnee Indians called them "wapiti," which is still the name insisted upon by many naturalists. When the English came to Virginia, they proclaimed them to be "elk" which is what the Europeans call their moose. That has remained the most popular name for our largest deer.

The history of the elk race since the coming of the whites four hundred years ago has been as tragic as this account of a typical herd in the northern Rockies.

Elk once ranged over much of the northern two-thirds of the United States from the Berkshires and southern Appalachians to the Pacific Coast (except the Great Basin) and from northern Alberta to southern New Mexico. By 1900 the "Great Slaughter" had exterminated all the wapiti from about ninety per cent of that vast area. Sizeable herds remained only in Saskatchewan, Manitoba and Alberta in Canada, and in the Yellowstone Park region and Olympic Peninsula of the United States. Since that time, elk have been restocked in many localities.

In spite of disastrous winters, the race has increased and become too populous for its own good in some areas. For example, whitetail deer have disappeared in Yellowstone Park largely because of lack of food. If the elk were allowed to continue to increase there, it is conceivable that they could do such great damage to the range that the deer, buffalo, mountain sheep, antelope, and eventually the elk themselves would follow the whitetail deer. Yellowstone Park and other elk refuges can well afford to cut down the elk population, for the total number of elk in the country was estimated in 1943 to be 233,700.

Three distinct types of wapiti are recognized:

(1) The Rocky Mountain elk (*Cervus canadensis canadensis*) inhabits that part of the original range between northern New Mexico and north central Alberta, and a large area in Saskatchewan and Manitoba. Most of the restocking —notably northern Michigan, the southern Appalachians, Pennsylvania, the Black Hills, Arizona and Nevada—has been accomplished by using this type. Sometimes this race is further subdivided.

(2) The Roosevelt or Olympic elk (*C. c. occidentalis*) is larger and distinctly darker than the Rocky Mountain form, with heavier but shorter antlers. The animal is an inhabitant of the dense forests of the Pacific coastal belt from Vancouver Island to northern California, and has been introduced into parts of western British Columbia and southeastern Alaska. Its habits are adapted somewhat to the different conditions of the humid habitat. Plants most often eaten

are sedges, grasses (in summer), vine maple, hemlock, salmonberry, alder, willow, salal, huckleberry, and various ferns.

(3) The tule, dwarf, or California elk (*C. nannodes*) is a much smaller and paler animal than the wapiti of the Rockies. At one time it was almost extinct. Today dwarf elk exist in a wild state only in Owens Valley, Kern County, and in Inyo County, California. In 1945, the total number in the two herds was somewhat more than four hundred.

General description. Large, heavy, deerlike, with a conspicuous neck mane. Bulls have branching antlers. Head deep brown, neck brownish black, body brownish gray in summer and yellowish gray in winter; a large buffy or whitish patch on rump; legs and belly deep brown to blackish. Total length, up to 115 inches, height at shoulder, up to 60 inches; weight, up to 700 or even 1000 pounds. Females are about 25 per cent smaller.

Distinguishing characteristics. Larger than the deer, and with a heavy brown mane which the deer lack. The pale yellowish rump patch distinguishes the elk from other hoofed mammals, except the bighorn and antelope which have white rump patches.

Range. Chiefly the Rocky Mountains from northern New Mexico to northwestern Alberta, Manitoba and central Saskatchewan; Vancouver Island and northwestern Washington; northwestern California and southeastern Oregon; central California. Once present over much of the United States and southeastern Canada, and has been transplanted to most states with mountainous wild land where the animals are well established.

WHITETAIL DEER
ODOCOILEUS VIRGINIANUS AND O. COUESI

Standing straight up, the white tails of these deer flash signals of alarm as they whisk through the woods. No other big game in North America is as widely known and hunted as the whitetail deer. There are almost four and one-quarter million of them in the United States.

Why does the whitetail continue to overpopulate certain parts of the country? In the first place, he needs very little range in which to make a living. Under normal circumstances, it seems to be no more than one-half mile square. In the second and third place, the whitetail is very polygamous, and the normal doe continues to have twin fawns every year after her first one. With progeny

WHITETAIL DEER

producing more progeny, each doe is theoretically responsible in ten years for one hundred offspring.

The fawns are born in May or early June with their eyes wide open. I have found them in ferns among scattered trees, but ordinarily they are hidden in a thicket. Although twins are usual, triplets are not rare. One or two cases of quadruplet embryos have been recorded, and I once saw what I believed were four fawns with a doe on Drummond Island, Michigan. Occasionally a doe adopts a fawn. An older doe in Nebraska, thin and worried, insisted on nursing a two-year-old's fawn in addition to her own. The plump young mother protested, but in vain. Perhaps the older doe was distressed at having only one offspring that season, or she felt that the inexperienced mother was doing a poor job.

Weighing four or five pounds at birth, the little fawns are weak and unsteady on their legs. They are easy to care for since they stay in or near the nursery for the first two weeks or more. (Some deer don't travel more than thirty feet from their birthplace for the first twenty-five days of their lives.) During her half-dozen daily visits for nursing, the mother warns her little ones to stay quietly flat on the ground. If they are inclined to be disobedient, she pushes them down with her muzzle. White polka dots spatter their reddish brown coats, and lying on the ground, the young pass easily for sun-splashed bumps on the forest floor.

Like all children, they get restless during their mother's absence and must amble about for at least a few feet. If anything strange occurs, they immediately drop outstretched to the ground. Almost every meat-eater down to the red fox in size is a potential killer. Except at nursing time the doe remains away, and frequently is out of hearing. Concealment, therefore, is often the fawns' only defense during the first weeks of their lives. Their protective coloring, as well as lack of strong scent, is a great help.

The fawns that I have handled have kept silent, unless an accidental bump or rough squeeze brought forth a short bleat. However, very young twins have been heard to "converse" in calls like the "mew" of the cat bird. Their cries of distress are much shorter and louder. Adult deer are usually voiceless except in extreme terror. I have heard a deer shriek with a loud, hoarse, high-pitched voice when chased by coyotes, but ordinarily it will save its breath for running. I also once heard a deer scolding very loudly as though in pain when he trotted by. Now and then a doe may bleat for lost fawns. Occasionally a deer will signal by blowing violently through the nostrils. From personal experience, I think it does this at times to startle suspicious-looking objects into moving and so identifying themselves.

Many mammal mothers constantly watch over their babies. The doe has several good reasons for leaving her fawns alone. By staying away she avoids attracting attention to the nursery. She must also get plenty to eat in order to nourish herself and to produce enough milk for the youngsters. She cannot stock up her larder, or have her meals brought to her by her mate as some of the predators do. Instead, she must eat wherever the food grows.

She dines on leaves of the various maples, willows, oaks, dogwood, sassafras, raspberry, blackberry, grape, greenbriar, witch hazel, shadbush, elderberry, blueberry and rose; many herbs such as goldenrod and ferns; and fungi. When going to a pond to drink, she feeds on water lilies and other plants that grow in shallow water or along the shore. In spring and early summer she eats considerable grass. At that time she frequents mineral "licks" and eats the salty mud and drinks quantities of the flavorsome water. In fact, she patronizes these places off and on until early fall. At times, seemingly out of curiosity, anything from garbage to a leather belt will be eaten.

In several instances she has been known to eat fish that had been caught by fishermen and left on the bank or hanging up at camp. Sometimes she will go fishing for herself, continuing to strike at running black suckers or even trout in a small stream until she disables one, perhaps fourteen inches long. Turning the still-wriggling fish head foremost into her mouth, she will chew, swallow it, and proceed to catch another.

Both the doe and buck have a great antipathy for snakes, especially the rattler. Several times I have seen a whitetail circle and dance around a garter snake, breathing heavily and snorting with excitement. Sometimes it will jump on the snake with all four feet bunched together and mangle it.

By the time the fawns are about four weeks old, they are strong enough to travel with the doe. They like "watering places" for several reasons. The margins of streams and ponds are open to the wind, which blows away the deer flies, black flies and mosquitoes. Water plants, like pondweeds and burreed, grow there and are good to eat. The deer also enjoy lying in the water, which they sometimes do for hours. They like to swim and for short distances can go as fast as four miles per hour. If a little deer gets tired, it has been known to hang on to its mother's tail.

All summer, the buck stays by himself, or perhaps with another. They live a quiet, rather furtive life, methodically feeding, going to the lick for minerals, and to the stream or lake for water, food and swimming. A buck whitetail can be found almost invariably in the same place at the same time day after day. He even uses the same trails with little variation, a whitetail characteristic which hunters frequently use to advantage.

As with all male deer, the buck's principal accomplishment during the summer is the growing of a new set of antlers. These decorative weapons start in April or May as a couple of bulbous swellings, just in front of his ears. Covered with skin or "velvet" through which courses a multitude of blood vessels, the antlers grow rapidly. The owner is very careful of them, for they are now soft and sensitive. Any real injury to them at this stage results in a permanent mark or deformity. If cut, they bleed freely like any other part.

By late August, the antlers are fully formed. The blood supply dwindles and the skin commences to shrivel and turn brown. This is believed to cause an annoying itching, for before the skin dies, the buck starts rubbing the antlers against trees, beginning with the lower parts of the beams, and fraying the velvet into bloody shreds. Finally the antler tips are draped with these streamers that flutter crazily in the wind. The bony antlers, blunt and round until almost the last, finally harden and come out of the velvet nearly as sharp as pitchfork tines.

Ordinarily a buck's antlers are larger with more tines each successive year until there are twelve. He is then five years old. From that time until he passes maturity, three years later, his antlers grow out a little heavier each autumn, but the number of points remains about the same. During old age the number of points and massiveness of the antlers decrease with waning vigor until a very old, feeble deer, aged perhaps twelve, may carry only simple spikes.

You can't be sure about a deer's age by the number of antler points. Up to maturity, the diameter of the antler beam just above the burr or basal swelling is a fairly reliable indicator. It must be remembered, however, that the size of antlers really reflects the physical condition of the animal. A well-fed deer will grow heavier horns than a poorly nourished buck of the same age. Tooth succession is probably the best index to age.

A well-developed set of antlers, with their gracefully arched beams each carrying four to eight long tines, makes a prized trophy. The finest head on record was taken forty years ago in British Columbia. The longest beam measured thirty and three-quarters inches in length, the set spread thirty-three and one-half inches at its widest extent, and the total number of "points" was twenty-six.

Sometimes things go wrong, probably a glandular disturbance, and the horns grow into queer shapes. Occasionally they are flattened or palmated, somewhat like those of the caribou. More often all sorts of queer spikes develop. I have seen whitetail antlers with as many as twenty-five or thirty of these irregular "points." A number of mule deer have been seen bearing more than fifty. At least one had as many as sixty.

Once the antlers are clean and polished, the buck's disposition alters markedly. No longer is he retiring, content to live on perhaps one hundred acres of land. His neck enlarges, becoming twice its normal size. Boldly he stalks through the woods looking for mates. The does are located and followed by scent, sometimes by several bucks at a time. Unlike the elk and some other deer, the whitetail does not accumulate a harem. One mate at a time is all that he cares to manage. However, he runs with her only a few days and then dashes off to seek another. For the individual male, the "rut" or breeding season lasts about a month, which gives him plenty of time to find a number of mates. The rutting season for the entire group (in the north) may extend from early October to the middle of December, and is at its height in November.

When two bucks meet at this time, there is likely to be a battle. The animals dash at each other, meeting on their horns, and then engage in a shoving contest. Eyes rolling and muscles straining, each strives to throw the other or to rush him backward. Sometimes a half acre of ground is ploughed up by the sharp hoofs. Fighting deer do not make repeated charges like bighorns, but struggle with concentrated fury. Now and then, one buck succeeds in goring his opponent. Occasionally the tines and tips of the antlers interlock, and the two rivals starve to death.

Most male deer do not find mates before their third autumn, when they are about two and one-half years old. The majority of females breed a year earlier. There seem to be many exceptions, however. In the Adirondacks it has been found that forty per cent of the female fawns attain sexual maturity when they are only six or seven months old, and mate in December, a month later than normal adults.

Like most mammals, the adult whitetail changes its coat twice each year. The summer reddish dress is a light-weight one made up of fine short hairs that lie close to the skin. These are gradually shed over a space of several weeks in October, and each fine summer hair is neatly replaced by a coarse hollow bristle. Because of the much larger diameter and greater length of the winter hairs, they form a coat sometimes two inches thick. It is gray, and the deer is said by hunters to be "in the blue." The innumerable air spaces in the hair act as additional insulation and help to keep the animal warm in the biting cold of the northern winter. Deer that live farther south need and have less protection.

A whitetail doe in Pennsylvania once grew a fine silky winter coat with hairs about one-twentieth the normal coarseness. Had she not been killed in the fall, she probably would have perished.

Beginning in early December, the deer drop their solitary habits and band together in small groups. Bucks, does and fawns are mixed promiscuously, although each family unit of doe and fawns is still intact. The bucks are no longer arrogant after losing their antlers.

What becomes of the millions of stately antlers that are cast off each year? Why aren't they found more often? The heavy bone structures seem almost indestructible. Usually they suffer the ignominious fate of being eaten by rodents. Porcupines, squirrels, rabbits, even mice gnaw away at them to satisfy their craving for calcium and other minerals. Pregnant mothers of these species, especially, need these minerals to build up the tiny frames of their developing offspring. If not eaten, the antlers slowly disintegrate under baking heat and leaching rain. In the humid range of the blacktail deer, cast antlers rot away much faster than those that are dropped on the arid plains and deserts.

Where the snowfall is heavy, the deer winter on low ground where the cover is dense, in cedar swamps or in patches of pine and hardwood brush interspersed with swales and marshes. Farther south, where the sun settles the scantier snow cover, the deer take to the south-facing hillsides. From the middle of January until March, a typical band of a couple of bucks and four or five does and their fawns will stay within an area of about three hundred acres, frequently not requiring over one hundred.

It is said casually that deer "yard" in the north because it is easier for a number of deer to break trails through the snow between feeding grounds and to keep these places accessible. Probably they gather where the snow is lighter and where protection can be secured from cold north and northwest winds. In winters of exceptionally little snow, the deer do not yard but instead are scattered over the hills.

The hoofs of all the deer are so small that they are not of much use for pawing. After the snow gets deep, therefore, the animals must feed entirely by browsing, sprouts or suckers and normal growth that is soft and watery, such as the twigs of basswood, being eaten most freely. The list of winter food items is very long, varying, of course, with the region. The tree species that are liked best are apple, mountain ash, maples, black, white and yellow birch, oaks, aspen, willows, black cherry, fir, juniper, and white cedar. Among the shrubs, the deer prefer yew, dogwood, sumac, rose, buckbrush, bearberry, chokecherry, blueberry, serviceberry, viburnum, snowbrush, witch hazel, and American hazel. Incidentally, all deer are very fond of acorns and stuff themselves with the rich nuts in the fall and early winter as long as the supply lasts. Until buried by snow such low-growing plants as sweet fern, horseweed, dewberry, and wintergreen are eaten.

Food preference is largely a matter of habit, depending upon the abundance or scarcity of various palatable plants. Sometimes a plant that is heavily eaten by deer in one locality is scarce in another yard, and there a substitute will be taken. Where deer are too abundant, the browse is eaten as high as the hungry animals can reach. If the winter is prolonged, the smaller and weaker ones may die by the score. The animals often rear on their hind legs to stretch for mouthfuls and this can result in horrible entanglement. I have seen the carcasses of such deer whose front feet, or even heads, had slipped into forks of limbs or tree trunks. Unable to extricate themselves, the victims had perished of heart failure, nervous exhaustion, or broken necks.

Whitetails, as well as blacktails and mule deer, have much the same enemies as other big game species. Their most common four-footed enemies—coyotes, wolves, bobcats, lynxes and cougars—vary in importance with the region. Adult, healthy deer can usually protect themselves with striking hoofs or take to flight successfully. Probably few animals live to become senile. The deer reach their prime at about six or seven years and are old at ten. Sometime during the following five years the surviving animals fall prey to disease, starvation or predators. One of the deer's numerous parasites is the nose fly. I have examined deer that were slowly choking to death by reason of the fifty or even more larvae that crammed the rear nasal passages and even sinuses and throats.

In early economy, deer were highly important. To the American Indian, venison was a staple food. He used practically every part of the animal—buckskin for clothing, tepee coverings and bedding; sinews for sewing, for fish lines, for stitching bark utensils; deer brains for bleaching and tanning; bones for awls, needles, scrapers, and ornaments. Deer were an essential support for pioneer white culture. They were extremely abundant in places. During the early 1800's in central Ohio, for example, bands of twenty deer were not unusual. A man was a poor or unlucky hunter if he could kill no more than four or five in a day. Venison was as important to the early whites as to the Indians and was sold in the public markets. Buckskin was a common article of commerce for several centuries. In 1880 a firm in northern California shipped thirty-four thousand skins of mule and blacktail deer, paying the hunters fifty cents each. Two independent hunters in the same region were said to have shipped three thousand deer hides in one year.

In region after region, the slaughter moved from east to west across the country, until the deer were almost exterminated. Then the pendulum swung to the opposite extreme of absolute protection. In the East, provided with an abundance of food in millions of acres of sprout growth following the lumbering period and the decline of agriculture, the deer population increased beyond the sportsmen's wildest dreams.

Only in the West have the whitetails not continued to increase. On the Great Plains and in the mountains the species lived in thickets mostly along stream courses. As the valley bottoms were cleared for farming, the whitetails were deprived of the first essential—a place to live. They were exterminated from wide areas, in many of which they have never become reestablished. Even in and immediately north of Yellowstone Park, overpopulation of game animals reduced the browse to such an extent that this was largely responsible for extinction of the whitetail deer there.

In the East, the whitetail has become far too abundant in many places. It loves the brushy slopes and the forest border, and since the shrubs that furnish the bulk of the food cannot survive in heavy shade, it dislikes the deep forest except in emergencies. Man's farming activities, if not too widespread, are actually helpful; the unbroken forest is opened, and escaping fires are followed by the growth of grass, sprouts and shrubs. The whitetail is quick to learn that tender vegetables, green alfalfa and twigs and buds of apple trees are good to eat. Even frozen apples have helped to make man's settlements attractive to deer.

When very abundant, deer may do much damage to truck crops and orchards. If properly constructed and maintained, electric fences may keep the animals out of gardens and other places where they are not wanted. Scarecrows and shotguns fired at night are sometimes successful, but are generally much less dependable. One man effectively used bags of mothballs tied to his fence.

For several decades the famous "buck law" permitted the killing of males only. But the surviving polygamous bucks were so active that the does produced as many offspring as ever. Finally, even the most single-minded hunters were forced to admit the many evidences of too abundant deer—depleted ranges, starving animals, and stunted survivors. In numerous instances, state game commissions have since been given authority to open the hunting season on does and fawns, and to take other steps necessary to balance the deer with their food supply.

The annual hunt has become a rather important economic factor. The hunters spend lavishly in purchasing licenses, outdoor clothing, camping equipment, meals and lodging, transportation, guns and ammunition. The total annual kill of three hundred and seventy-five thousand whitetails probably weighs some twenty-eight million pounds hog-dressed. The value of the meat alone is estimated at $11,400,000.

Artificial feeding is just as unsatisfactory for wild deer as it has proven to be for other wild hoofed mammals, as this tends to destroy their initiative and to spread disease. An emergency ration has been developed in New York State to tide the deer over unusually difficult periods where natural food is scarce. In cake form, it consists of forty-five per cent cane molasses and fifty-five per cent coarsely ground soy beans. Browse is scattered over each cake to induce the deer to try it. A fifty-pound cake lasts fifteen deer about a week under average conditions. In certain parts of the country where salt is not available, blocks of salt have been dropped by airplane. Airplanes have also been used to count deer and to determine the locale of overpopulations.

With a single exception, the whitetails of the United States belong to one species. The subspecies vary considerably in size, from the big northern deer that average two hundred pounds in weight to those of Florida that run only half as large. Several Central American varieties scale less than forty pounds. In the northeastern states and eastern Canada, the summer coat color is bright chestnut, but this becomes paler and more gray in the West and South. As a result of the varied conditions under which these deer live, they have adopted diversified habits.

The Coues deer (*Odocoileus couesi*) is also called the Arizona, Sonora, or dwarf whitetail and is distinct from its numerous relatives. It is abundant in some mountainous places from southwestern Arizona to the Big Bend of Texas, and south through Chihuahua and eastern Sonora into Durango. This little deer has big ears, a pale brownish coat in summer and a grayish one in winter. Bucks rarely exceed one hundred pounds in weight and have correspondingly small antlers.

General description. A graceful deer. Antler beams of male curve forward bearing unbranched tines. Color in summer reddish brown with a white band across the nose, indistinct eye ring, and white inside of ear; belly, throat, and inside of upper legs whitish; tail large, bushy, and white underneath. In winter the "red" coat is replaced by grayish to grayish brown. Size variable with the species: total length, 60 to 75 inches; height at shoulder, 30 to 40 inches; weight, 75 to 300 pounds; rarely 400 pounds.

Distinguishing characteristics. In summer the whitetail deer is much redder than its relatives, the blacktail and mule deer. Its tail is bushier, the same color on top as its coat and conspicuously white and flaring on the under side, which is often raised. (The blacktail's tail is black on top, not as bushy, and therefore not as startling when the white under side is raised. The mule deer's tail is rounded, all white, with a black tip. Of course, where these two latter species intergrade, the characteristics may be combined.)

The antler tines of the whitetail buck do *not* branch as do those of the blacktail and mule deer. The beams also curve forward and turn inward more than those of the other two deer. Another distinction is the metatarsal gland below the hock on the outside and rear of the hind leg. The gland of the whitetail deer is about 1 inch long, that of the blacktail deer is 3 inches, and of the mule deer 5 inches.

Range. Most of the United States and southern Canada, from Nova Scotia west to eastern British Columbia; south to the Florida Keys, west to southern Arizona, eastern Utah, southwestern Washington; eastern slope of the Cascades and lower Columbia River, Oregon; also south through Central and South America to Peru and Bolivia.

MULE DEER
ODOCOILEUS HEMIONUS

When the mule deer raises its head to attention, the great ears twist forward. Then the reason for the name is as plain as the ears. They spread fully twenty-five per cent larger than the whitetail's. No one knows the reason, for any hunter will tell you that the whitetail's comparatively modest ear trumpets can pick up the sound of a pin dropping into a bed of moss a thousand feet away—almost!

As it plods along at a walk with head down and mule ears flapping, this deer of western America is not nearly as shapely as the whitetail. The body seems heavy and the legs stocky and less trim. Even the feet are larger. But when something startles the animal, it becomes vibrant, alive, and graceful. The head comes up, and it bounds away with high leaps that seem to be powered by steel and rubber levers instead of flesh and bone legs. These leaps carry it over the rocks and brush. In Manitoba, this gait has given it the local name of "jumping deer."

Each running bound clears four feet vertically, and gives it a chance to look back and see what is coming. When necessary to escape from a trap, the mule deer has been known to jump eight feet from a running start of only a few feet. In full flight, a mule deer has made horizontal leaps of twenty feet on ground that was slightly uphill. It can run as fast as thirty-five miles per hour for a fraction of a mile at least. Perhaps its jumping gait makes it short-winded, for in a run of one-half mile in open country, it will be panting heavily.

This big-eyed, big-eared animal is not as timorous as it looks. The buck **as**

MULE DEER

well as the doe must often take after hungry coyotes and drive them away. If angry enough, it may jump on an over-rash coyote with all four feet until the predator is dead or at least its bones broken. One mother doe was so furious when she found that two coyotes had chased one of her offspring into the water that she attacked both of them. While the fawn swam about and caught its breath, she went after the attackers with flailing hoofs and drove them off into the woods.

Some deer are braver as well as stronger than others. I once saw a doe temporarily beat off three coyotes that were successfully attacking a yearling. The other members of the band did not offer to help. With two coyotes threatening her in front and a third ready to leap on her flanks, she finally abandoned the yearling which was probably fatally injured already. Apparently it is only when the fawns are in danger that the adult deer really get up their fighting ardor. Even a buck has been seen to drive off coyotes that were menacing a fawn.

The mule deer buck does more bluffing and less actual fighting than the male whitetail during rutting season. They are more restless and obstreperous than at other times. This keeps the does and their half-grown fawns moving about, and sometimes the youngsters get lost temporarily in the confusion. When the fawns get underfoot, the buck that is courting at the moment will become exasperated and lunge at them with a low, deep "baaa," but he seldom or never does them any harm.

He does not waste any time on an unwilling female. Scent tells him when a doe is ready and he gives chase through the densest of forests until he finds her. She does not, of course, respond immediately, but makes a play of running off and he usually continues after. If he is tired and gives up, she flutters back to lure him on again. Once having succumbed to his addresses, she is quite affectionate and nuzzles him fondly until he goes off to find a new mate.

Although easygoing in courtship matters, enterprising bucks will sometimes acquire harems of perhaps three or four does. The does may leave or stay but usually prefer to stay. If a rival comes about, he is quickly chased away, unless he looks bigger and fiercer. In that case the buck in possession makes a few perfunctory gestures and then philosophically departs to find some more mates. There are always enough to go around.

A buck has no sense of chivalry at any age. Even a yearling with two little spike horns can be overbearing. One of these upstarts was once seen following a single file of does as they made a trail through the snow. Unerringly they led him into the open to a dry salt lick. He did not care for any himself, but neither would he permit them to enjoy it. With his little horns he kept pushing them away and pestering the fawns. At last the does gave up and went ahead, meekly breaking a new path for his young lordship, so that he dined in the cedar swamp that evening.

By the middle of December in the North, and about a month later in the South, the deer have settled down to the quiet routine of winter. The bucks become thin and spiritless, and a few weeks afterward lose their antlers. The young bucks with only spikes may hold on to them a few weeks longer, but even they must soon part with these weapons. Then in the mixed bands only the fawns can be distinguished by their smaller size and immature, shorter faces. The biggest animals are probably bucks, but there are small bucks and big does. At any rate the males, without their antlers, and worn out by their fall cavortings, are not of much account. They may strike with their forefeet, but ordinarily the does need no longer fear any of them. More than likely, it is a wise old doe that leads the clan to its winter home.

Instead of hanging around its birthplace all its life as the whitetail does, the mule deer uses different ranges for the two seasons. It spends the short summer in the mountains at seven thousand five hundred to eight thousand feet among the aspens and pines. Under the pressure of the fall snowstorms, the bands drift down to the sheltered valleys where food is still available and where their movements are not hampered by too deep snow.

The annual autumn journey is a slow, leisurely one for the most part. Not until a heavy snowstorm reminds them of the penalties of getting caught in a thick white blanket, do they hasten. Often the summer and winter ranges are fifty miles apart. In a few instances mule deer are known to make a round trip of three hundred miles on their annual jaunt from one range to another and back.

Life is not easy in their winter homes. Food may be very scarce, and slipping on ice may result in unpleasant predicaments or even broken bones. Two employees of the Tule Lake Wildlife Refuge in California once found twenty-six deer that had fallen on the ice and were unable to get up because it was so slippery. The men worked hard to drag them ashore where they could get footing and dash away. One buck was very ungrateful, or more likely badly scared. After he had been brought ashore and had time to recover his composure and his breath, he arose to his feet and went after one of his rescuers. Quick-thinking, the man fled out cn the lake. The deer chased him, fell down and had to be rescued all over again!

As if reluctant to face the long upgrade trip into the mountains, the deer dawdle through the spring. After the dull winter fare, they enjoy lingering over the new green grass. When they reach their summer quarters toward the end of June, the snow has disappeared and the slopes are green. The bucks usually arrive first, for the does are heavy with fawn.

The fawns are born in late June or early July, soon after the does reach the summer range. Most does have twins, and occasionally triplets, although young mothers and those in poor condition generally have only one. The little animals weigh six to seven pounds at birth. When about a month old they are strong and go running around with their mothers. At this time their home range covers about a square mile. At top speed, the fawns have been clocked at twenty-eight miles per hour, and have held that pace in front of an automobile for three-tenths of a mile before veering away.

Fawns begin to nibble at forage about the time they start running with their mothers. They are soon eating considerable amounts of green stuff and are weaned in late September or October. A little earlier their spotted coats are replaced by the gray winter dress. Young deer at this stage are quite shaggy instead of being dressed in the neat close-fitting coats of their elders. Possibly the first winter coats are extra long and heavy because this is the most critical season of their lives.

Mule deer are found over a vast expanse of western America and in a variety of habitats from the high mountains of the north to the plains and deserts. Naturally their diet varies somewhat with the locality. Although grass and herbs are preferred when new and tender, they are eaten to some extent the year round, and considerably more than by the whitetail. The remainder of the mule deer's food consists of a great variety of browse.

Leaves and twigs are not a monotonous diet, for they have a multitude of delicious flavors. In summer, the food includes mountain mahogany or buck-brush, sagebrush, dogwood, buffaloberry, elderberry, raspberry, manzanita, Oregon grape, cliff rose, chokecherry, gooseberry, currant, serviceberry, hack-berry, thimbleberry, and the leaves of oaks, aspens, willows, and mountain ash. Like whitetails, mule deer are fond of mushrooms, and feed on them at every opportunity. On some of the high mountain ranges of the Southwest, fungi of many kinds are sufficiently abundant to be a prominent food item. In that region, mistletoe is also an important and palatable food.

In the north, there is not nearly as much nor as great a variety of good things to eat. Deer do not paw through snow as vigorously as elk, and must winter on windswept slopes, or wade into drifted areas to reach tree limbs, such as juniper and Douglas fir, that are bent down by the snow load. In the south, grass is even less eaten, either because it is buried under the mountain snows or, in the deserts, it may be scanty at that season.

Spring comes and goes again. The bucks, that are growing new antlers as usual, are living by themselves or with a few companions. They are great pals at this time and one would never guess that in a few months they would be fighting and running off with each others' mates. Ticks are a nuisance through-out the summer, and thousands of them may burrow into the skin and feast on blood. Sometimes one buck will bite at the parasites on his companion's throat while the other will reciprocate by chewing on the first one's shoulder.

Even the magpies and mountain jays help. They perch on the deer's back and gently probe around in search of the pests, apparently being very careful not to startle or hurt the deer with their sharp bills. Occasionally they will perch up in the antlers as if to get a better view of their work.

With the coming of colder nights in late August the northern mule deer begin to need warmer coats. The thin brownish hair is gradually pushed out by the growing gray coat, and by the end of September the thick winter pelage is complete. This change takes place two to four weeks later among southern deer. It is finished, usually, before the deer arrive on their winter range and the mating season begins again. Throughout the year the mule deer's tail remains the same, comparatively thin, rounded, and white with a black tip.

Deer, like many other animals, may not always distinguish a stationary strange object. The slightest movement, however, is detected at once. Their big eyes are efficient gatherers of light, and they are effective considerably earlier in the morning and later in the evening than the human eye.

Smell is the best of all the deer's senses. They often use their nose when they do not trust their eyes. Numerous times I have been stalked by deer that worked around to my lee, picked up my scent, whistled disparagingly, and were off.

Of the two million mule deer and half a million blacktails, about two hundred and twenty-five thousand are shot by hunters each year. Among the beasts of prey, the cougar or mountain lion is probably the most important enemy of the mule deer. Hunters and others commonly assert that a cougar's toll is about a deer each week. No one knows for certain. It is probable that many cougars are not as successful as that. There is some evidence that a large percentage of the deer killed by cougars are the weaker animals, perhaps crippled by encounters with human hunters, or weakened by disease or age.

During the fawning season, bears, both blacks and grizzlies, spend considerable time hunting for fawns, and very likely are rewarded fairly often. Badly crippled, sick, or very careless adult deer may be killed and eaten by bears, but ordinarily deer are too alert and fast to be caught by these clumsy carnivores.

Coyotes hunt deer at times and being numerous throughout the West undoubtedly account for more deer than the far less abundant though much more powerful mountain lions. Under ordinary circumstances, most of the coyote-killed deer are crippled, diseased, or young animals. Bobcats, lynxes and wolverines kill a few deer, usually in deep snow and during times of food scarcity. Golden eagles are believed to take some fawns.

Mule deer are subject to most of the parasites and diseases that affect their cousins the whitetails. Screwworms also are present at times. The famous epidemic of hoof-and-mouth disease in California in 1924–5 was responsible for the deaths of many thousands of mule deer. More than twenty-two thousand in addition were slaughtered in a campaign to check the malady. Eyeworms, which are tiny white round worms twenty-five hundredths to eighty-five hundredths of an inch long, are sometimes found in their eyes. These parasites live in the liquid between the eyeball and the lid and set up an irritation that may result in blindness.

When a small hard object lodges in the stomach of any of the deer, calcium and other salts may be deposited around it, resulting in the formation of a hard, smooth, round "stone" called a calculus or "madstone." Sometimes the base is a nail, a pebble, a wad of hair, roots, or a bullet. According to early superstition, if a "madstone" were laid on a wound caused by a rabid dog, it would draw out the poison and prevent rabies. Similar calculi are found in many mammals, including man.

The high branched antlers of the mule deer are greatly prized as trophies. Normally, a full head has a total of ten tines, although abnormal sets of horns have been recorded with sixty or more "points." The largest head ever taken which had a regulation set of tines had a spread of thirty-six and one-quarter inches, measured thirty-three and three-quarter inches along the outside curve of the beam, and tallied nine points.

Occasionally does grow antlers. These structures are usually malformed, covered with velvet, and result from disease or other aberration of the sex organs or glands. In a few cases horned does produce young and are otherwise normal.

General description. A rather stout-bodied deer. Antler tines of the male are usually pronged or branched. In summer, the body, neck, and upper legs are pale, dull yellowish brown to yellowish tawny; upper throat, inner ear, and inside of legs whitish; forehead dark brown; a large patch of white on the rump; tail white with a black tip; belly dark brownish to blackish. In winter, the color is dark gray instead of brownish. Size variable with the locality: total length, 56 to 68 inches; height at shoulder, 36 to 42 inches; weight, 145 to 200 pounds, up to 400 pounds as an extreme.

Distinguishing characteristics. Ears large and broad. Antler tines branched (as are the blacktail's) instead of single like the whitetail's. Tail whitish and rounded with black tip instead of all black on the outer surface (blacktail deer) or bushy and completely white beneath (whitetail deer). See also this section (pp. 32–33) of the chapter on whitetail deer.

Range. Western United States and southwestern Canada, from western Minnesota to north-central Alberta and eastern British Columbia; south through eastern Colorado and western Texas to the Tropic of Cancer in Mexico; west to central Washington, Oregon, and the Pacific Coast south of San Francisco Bay.

BLACKTAIL DEER
ODOCOILEUS COLUMBIANUS

Life in the humid forest belt along the Pacific coast has darkened the coat of the blacktail. It is a little smaller than the mule deer, the antlers generally have fewer points, and the ears are shorter and slightly broader. Instead of the rounded whitish tail with the black tip, this deer's tail is broader, entirely black on top and whitish underneath.

Nevertheless the two deer look much alike and often consort together when

BLACKTAIL DEER

occupying overlapping territory. The resulting progeny may have characteristics of either parent, or a combination.

Ordinarily the blacktail has little use for the high bounding gait which carries the mule deer away from danger. The typical blacktail lives on the floor of the great redwood or spruce-fir forests where the undergrowth is dense and rank, hence it is sometimes called "redwood deer." It can't leap high enough to clear the great blueberries, salal, salmonberry, and other shrubs that grow as much as eight or ten feet high, and doesn't try. It jumps only to clear the great trunks of fallen trees that lie rotting in such profusion on the spongy ground. The blacktail's gait, therefore, is between the flat run of the whitetail and the high bounding gallop of the mule deer.

Having learned from experience that the thicket is a shield against enemies, the blacktail just remains quiet when he hears something poking about. The chances are that, whatever its identity, the intruder is practically blinded by the green blanket that presses down everywhere. Panicky flight would be heard and give the clue for which the enemy is searching. So the deer keeps calm and still. If it seems best, finally, to seek another refuge, it steals silently away through the labyrinth of trails that it knows so well. But it will stop and hide again within a couple of hundred yards.

Next to man, the blacktail's most serious enemies are the cougar, the wolf, and the coyote. On the northern coastal belt the cougar's place as a predator is partially taken by its smaller but potent kinsman, the lynx.

In the lowlands, the deer stay on the same area the year round. Inland, and in the far north, there is a distinct although generally short migration twice a year. By summer the most venturesome blacktails have climbed to the heights where the forest is no longer dense and towering, and is broken by alpine meadows. It is here, as well as at the southern extremity of the range in California, that the blacktails and mule deer may meet and exchange courtesies. Occasionally mountain-dwelling animals of the two species migrate to the same valleys and winter together.

The habits of the blacktail and mule deer are generally similar, with differences which are determined by the various conditions of climate and vegetation.

The blacktail buck sheds his antlers in January and February. New antlers start growing during April and are hard about four months later. He mates as early as September, in the south, but not until November in Alaska.

The fawns, generally two but sometimes one or three, are born any time between April and July. They are reddish brown, with more numerous and conspicuous spots than the young mule deer.

Blacktails are typically browsing animals. Those that inhabit the dense lowland forests almost never eat grass, because there isn't any. At least very little can grow in the deep shade of the vast trees and thick undergrowth. In the openings, of course, the deer find it together with sedges, clover, skunk cabbage, fireweed, hedge nettle, and other favorite herbs. They like huckleberry, blueberry, wild lilac, salal, dogwood, mountain ash, mountain maple, elderberry, hazel, buckbrush and other shrubs, as well as salmonberry, raspberry, and thimbleberry. Moss and mistletoe are plentiful in the humid "rain forest" and are eaten in large quantities. Fungi spring up in the autumn rains and are greatly relished. Acorns fatten the deer for winter, and oak browse is an important food the year 'round. The high winds and wet, heavy snow of winter break many branches and so actually help provide food. This may be leaves or twigs of cedar, hemlock, red alder, and other trees. The deer generally eat at sunrise and sunset. They may be active on moonlit nights, but are very quiet during the daylight hours. Because of the thick cover, they are seldom seen even where a good-sized population exists.

Along much of the Alaskan coast where blacktails live, the mainland mountains rise steeply from the Inside Passage. Only a narrow strip below the glaciers and the heavy winter snow belt is habitable. Most of the deer, therefore, live on the offshore islands. Winter is a critical time. While snow is never heavy on the island beaches, it increases rapidly in depth as one goes inland. Sometimes for weeks, the deer cannot get more than two hundred yards away from the water's edge.

Food occasionally becomes depleted and great numbers of animals, especially the smaller ones, may die of starvation. The survivors, as a last resort, are said to forage along the water's edge for seaweed and kelp. Wolves, coyotes and lynxes find easy pickings. When winter breaks, the remaining deer follow the retreating snow line back to the open barrens above the forest. Here the fawns are born and the tenacious race starts toward another peak of overpopulation. The hard fact is that this northern land is "sub-marginal" habitat for deer where only the most rugged can subsist.

The deer that are born in a big burn or cut-over region are the favorites of fortune. Those that live in the deep shady forest have two strikes against them from the beginning of their struggle for existence. The undergrowth may be dense and the deer's stomachs crammed with palatable food. Still, in late winter, many of them die. On brushy areas where the mature forest has been burned or logged off, the deer thrive amazingly. The largest animals are found here, and all the deer seem fat and healthy.

The reason has been explained by Arthur S. Einarsen. When he examined the chemical and nutritive content of the browse that grew in the shade and that in the open, he found an astonishing difference. The shade-grown leaves and twigs in winter were low in protein value. A deer might stuff its belly with them, but it would still be hungry and spiritless. Browse that grew in the clearings, however, was packed with proteins and bone-building ash. No wonder that the deer that pasture here continue to be "fat and sassy" despite bad weather!

Forest fires sometimes kill individual blacktails, but they benefit the race as a whole by stimulating a luxuriant growth of energy-foods. They also destroy many of the deer's most harmful parasitic enemies.

All deer swim well, but the blacktails that live in the coastal and insular region of British Columbia and Alaska are amazingly venturesome and intrepid. They strike out across channels between islands, and across fiords whose waters are chilled by icebergs. A rugged human swimmer would die of cold in a half-hour. Fairly often deer are seen crossing Icy Strait between the Glacier Bay mainland and the islands such as Inian and Chichagof.

Through this well-named channel and Cross Sound Passage, at least two miles wide, the tide sometimes runs so swiftly that a strong oarsman in a dory may be swamped in the chop or swept out to sea. Probably some of the deer suffer these fates and are drowned. Once, when I was passing through Icy Strait on a large steamer, we intercepted two deer near the middle of the channel. Frightened by the bow wash of our ship, they turned back toward Inian Island.

As a hunting trophy, the antlers of the blacktail buck do not measure up to those of its two larger relatives. Less than a half-dozen sets of antlers with a spread of thirty inches or more have been recorded. Even big blacktails may have only two points on each side. A record head with beams thirty and one-half inches long carried a total of six points.

General description. A dark-colored deer with antlers much like those of the mule deer. In summer, the upper parts are reddish to reddish yellow; in winter, rich brownish gray becoming dark along the backbone; forehead, nose and chest blackish; belly and inside of forelegs and ears white. Total length, about 60 inches; height at shoulder, 38 inches; weight, up to 150 pounds and, rarely, to 310 pounds.

Distinguishing characteristics. Darker and smaller than the mule deer, and with antler tines less often forked. Ears shorter and proportionately broader. Tail broad at base and tapering toward tip, entirely black on the upper surface, instead of only at the extremity as in the mule deer. The gland on the hind leg is near the middle of the shank and is only about 3 inches long, or one-third the length of that bone, while in the mule deer the gland is about 5 inches long and extends nearly to the heel.

Range. Forests of the Pacific Coast and parts of the western slope of the Sierra Nevada and Cascade Mountains, from central California (Point Concepcion) northward to the region of Glacier Bay and Cape Spencer, Alaska.

MOOSE
ALCES AMERICANA AND A. GIGAS

The moose is the largest antlered mammal that ever lived on earth. The bull is crowned with a magnificent set of broad-bladed antlers that spread perhaps six feet or more. He may be seven and one-half feet high at the shoulders and weigh an extreme of one thousand eight hundred pounds, but he can turn and fade into the forest as quietly as a mouse.

His four-and-one-half-foot-high stiltlike legs support a high-humped dark body. Thrust forward on an awkward neck is a great head with a pendulous muzzle. Hanging about six inches below his throat is the bell or ropelike flap of skin covered with long hair. This varies in length from a few inches to three feet, twelve to fifteen inches being most usual. Reaching its best development in young bulls, it becomes a mere dewlap in old animals. The cow's bell is generally smaller.

Once in a great while you may see a moose on his knees. Pushing his head and antlers ahead of him like a very slow lawn mower, he chops off the tender grasses for a series of salads. He is much more likely to be rising toward the sky, tearing down foliage. It is nothing at all for him to reach eight or nine feet from the ground for food, far higher than any deer could stretch. By standing on his long hind legs, he can pull down foliage growing *twelve feet* above the ground. Even this is still not very high, for by running his chin up and along saplings and branches, and so forcing them lower, he can strip off the leaves that were growing *twenty feet* above the ground. Frequently he snaps off the saplings, or rides them down between his fore legs and eats the leaves in comfort. I have seen brittle trees, like aspen, up to three inches in diameter and twenty feet high that had been broken down by a moose for dinner.

Despite its long legs that could travel great distances if necessary, the moose has no desire to travel and usually spends its entire life in a relatively small area. The only time that a bull takes a trip is during the mating season when he may bestir himself out of his little territory of five square miles to track down a cow or two. At this time the cow moose is bolder than the doe deer. She runs around in circles and gets very excited. With low hoarse calls, she invites any male within hearing distance to come to see her. Then, when he arrives, she may pretend to be shy and run off. Her calf continues to hang around, but this does not dampen her ardor. She tries only half-heartedly to drive him off, and the visiting bulls simply put up with him.

Big and powerful as he is, the bull moose does not assemble a harem like the elk. He is content with one female at a time. He stays with her for perhaps ten days and then departs to find another. During the four to eight weeks rutting season, he may have several mates.

During this period he is ready to fight any bull whom he suspects of being a rival. His great ears are on the alert for every sound—the crackle of footfalls, the beating of antlers on a dead branch, or the deep grunt of another bull. Then caution may be forgotten. Off he goes in a shambling but rapid trot, crashing through the branches, swinging his antlers furiously. Sometimes he stops and beats them against trees as if warming up for action. If his rival is equally pugnacious a mighty battle may develop. The ground is torn up, small trees and brush are trampled. Antlers are nicked and broken, and hides are gashed and bleeding. Usually one bull or the other gives up and runs away. Occasionally the pair lock antlers. A broken neck may then end the life of the weaker bull, but the other is fastened inextricably to the corpse of his victim. He either starves to death, or is killed by wolves or a late roaming bear.

When two moose in western Alaska once locked horns, Jack Benson, famous game warden, happened to notice them from an airplane. Immediately he ordered the plane to land. The smaller bull was already dead but the other continued to struggle with the carcass to which he was bound. Jack and his assistants lassoed him and after herculean efforts succeeded in sawing off an antler. This dislodged the dead bull. Free, but annoyed by the loss of his antler and the whole situation, the great moose took after his benefactor.

Generally there is not a great deal of fighting. A smaller bull hesitates to dispute with a larger one. He may look longingly, but seldom attacks.

By the middle or end of November the rut is at an end, and the moose revert to their usual drowsy routine of eating browse and chewing their cuds. They eat day or night whenever they feel like it. Erstwhile rivals forget their differences and sometimes spend the winter together. A little group may include a cow or two with their gangling, growing calves. The band generally uses a thick swamp as headquarters, feeding daily out over the neighboring ridges. Their heavy winter coats, which are nearly an inch thick over their backs, keep

MOOSE

out the cold. Dense conifers help to break the wind. Their long legs permit them to wander as they please unless the snow becomes very deep. Then they make something like a deer's "yard," where crisscrossing trails are kept open by the passing individuals or groups of moose.

Sometimes, of course, deep snow restricts them and their available food becomes scanty. Weakened by starvation and cold, they may fall victim to pneumonia, or to their only serious four-footed enemies, the wolves. In the northern Rockies the cougar occasionally makes a meal of a moose. Moose may suffer from liver flukes, tapeworms, roundworms, degeneration of the brain, liver and kidneys. One poor old moose had cataracts of the eye and went around charging imaginary objects. Sometimes these great deer acquire Bang's disease from domestic cattle.

By early May the cow begins to find much fault with her yearling calf. It certainly is grotesque—gangling, awkward and possessed of very little sense. The mother's suddenly determined attitude, however, stems from another cause. She lowers her ears, raises her mane, and makes short rushes at the yearling. Although she does not strike him, he is bewildered and frightened, and retreats hastily. After a few days, he either gives up, or is successfully evaded by the cow which desires only solitude. She picks out a thicket or, if available, a small island, for a safe, secluded delivery room and nursery. Here her new calf is born in late May or June.

The little calf, sometimes a twin and very rarely a triplet, is a skinny caricature of its mother. It has a bell, but the legs are even longer proportionately, and it lacks the high shoulder hump and overhanging upper lip. Unlike the deer fawn, it is not spotted. Except for the black muzzle, and a mark over each eye, the coat is a uniform light bay color. After the first few weeks spent in or close to the birthplace, it travels about with its mother. The two are almost inseparable for nearly a year. Only the impending arrival of the next little calf the following spring will send it out to shift for itself.

A yearling newly thrown on its own resources is plainly adrift. It has not learned to depend on its wits, and seems a little foolish. I once met such a youngster on Isle Royale in Lake Superior. Seated on a log in a clearing above a beaver pond, I was eating my lunch. A yearling moose ambled out of the woods on my left, heading for the water. It was almost past before it saw me. Then it turned and trotted directly toward me. When it was only thirty feet away and still coming on I leaped to my feet and shouted. The youngster recoiled in fright, then stood in such evident dismay and uncertainty that I regretted my rudeness. Fully three or four minutes elapsed before the bewildered creature slowly and hesitatingly turned and fled back into the timber.

Bungling through the windfalls, it crossed behind me and emerged about two hundred feet away. Wading into the pond to feed on water plants, it looked back wonderingly at me from time to time.

Ordinarily, and especially when hunted, an experienced adult moose is cunning and wary. While its sight is not too keen, the sense of smell is excellent and the hearing phenomenal. A moose that is on the alert keeps its big ears in almost constant motion, turning them this way and that to catch the faintest sound from every direction. It is able to detect the presence or approach of another moose or a person long before the human ear can pick up a footfall.

Such a moose was the huge bull that I once tried to stalk near Naknek Lake on the Alaska Peninsula. He was standing at the edge of some woods overlooking a marsh, alternately drowsing and then beating a dead spruce snag with his great shovel horns. Keeping well concealed, and walking in the deep tundra moss, I made a careful approach upwind. Yet, when I neared the spot over a little ridge, the moose had vanished. A red squirrel overhead exploded into a shower of invectives. Perhaps the moose was curious. He stalked me for the next twenty minutes, and I could hear him occasionally as he circled; but I never saw him again.

The moose can move swiftly, with scarcely a sound. On a wooded slope on Isle Royale I once startled a bull moose, apparently out of his siesta. He ran a little way groggily, then stopped to watch me. After a few minutes I started to follow. I looked down for a second to step across a fallen log. In that moment he disappeared. I went to the spot, less than a hundred yards away, and found his fresh tracks and trail where he had run down the hill. The slope was littered with dry, dead brush in which my every step created a loud crackling, but the moose had not made a sound that was audible to my perfectly normal hearing.

Through the long days of the northern summer, the moose cow and her calf wander along the streams and lakes, feeding on the lush grasses and water plants. Hordes of flies and mosquitoes suck their blood. To avoid the stings, the moose wade into the water, sometimes until they are submerged. They may take rather long excursions by water, frequently preferring to swim across lakes rather than to walk around. If the calf tires, it can rest its neck on the mother's withers or throw a front leg over her neck. She then tows it alongside her shoulder.

Moose are strong swimmers. No one knows how far they can travel by this means. There are tales that moose have been seen crossing frigid Lake Superior between Whitefish Point, Michigan, and the Ontario shore, an air-line distance of sixteen miles. I know of a cow and calf that chose of their own volition to swim across a bay of Lake Superior on a December day when the thermometer stood at four degrees above zero. Moose occasionally drown, when swimming, and sometimes break through thin ice and are unable to regain the shore.

In summer, another favorite resort of moose is the wallow and lick. This is a muddy spot, usually beside a stream, well trampled and worn by the animals that have frequented it to eat the tasty muck and to roll in the ooze. Some of them come at least once a day from spring until fall. A good coating of mud certainly helps to discourage the blood-sucking flies, but it does not improve their looks. Sometimes they even patronize a lick during winter when they have to scrape at the snow and mushy ice with their hoofs to get at the muddy water.

Apparently these unwieldy giants have no fear of being mired in the mud or quicksands of the northern swamps and lake borders, but occasionally an unfortunate is drowned in them. Sick or aged moose may not estimate their strength correctly and bog down, while others have entangled their feet in submerged roots, and died of exhaustion or starvation.

I have watched moose cross deep mud holes buried to their withers in muck. They plunged laboriously until tired, then rested with complete unconcern. A more nervous animal, such as a deer, would have gone into a panic. I have seen the deep tracks of moose emerging from the swirling delta of the Ukak River of southwestern Alaska—a quarter mile of soupy volcanic ash that is churned into quicksand by the shallow rushing stream that drains the Valley of Ten Thousand Smokes. The great animals apparently plunge in and cross without hesitation.

Through the summer, while the cow moose is caring for her calf and the yearling is learning more about the wilderness, the bull dawdles about, growing a new set of antlers. One would think it a difficult job, for he rests a great deal! Early in May, two swellings had begun to appear, one on each side of his forehead. Covered with black fuzzy skin through which the blood supply courses, the swellings become knobs and finally antlers. The maximum size depends on many factors, the chief of which is the health and vitality of the individual bull. Generally the yearling grows a set of spikes six to eight inches long, a two-year-old develops a fork-horn, and a three-year-old moose has a narrow palmed antler with three or four points. After that the antlers become heavier and broader each successive year until the bull passes maturity at perhaps twelve years. Then his waning vigor is indicated by smaller and weaker antlers.

Like other deer, moose occasionally have abnormal antlers. One of the strangest cases was that of an Alaskan moose that grew two soft lumpy structures, with a hard outer shell, like a pair of big mushrooms.

When the antlers are fully grown in August, the velvet begins to die and is rubbed off by the bull. A fir tree about three or four inches in diameter whose trunk is free of lower branches makes a favorite rubbing post. When the velvet is first removed the antlers are bone-white, streaked with blood. They become brown as the bull continues to rub them against saplings and to vent his growing ill temper by beating shrubbery and dead trees.

A fine bull moose grows heavier antlers than any other antlered mammal living in the world today. A record "head" of a Canadian moose may spread seventy inches or more, while the great antlers of a fine Alaskan moose (*Alces gigas*) will be over seventy-five inches from tip to tip and weigh eighty-five pounds. The largest authenticated head taken in the United States is from near Kendall, Wyoming. That Shiras moose, shot October 16, 1941, had antlers with a spread of fifty-eight and one-half inches. The broad sweeping shovels, with their many short prongs along the front edge and outer end, are magnificent. They are among the most prized of all hunting trophies.

How dangerous is a moose to man? The mother moose on Isle Royale has at times abandoned her calf to save her own skin. But I know of one moose that repeatedly chased a big black bear up into the treetops when she and her calf were feeding in the neighborhood.

Music hath charms—sometimes. A quick-thinking ranger in Yellowstone Park had heard that the European moose can be lured into target range by a hunter playing a violin. In fact, he knew of a moose right in Yellowstone which beat time to radio music with his head. This ranger was confronted by a moose whose picture he wished to take. Resourcefully, the ranger began to whistle, and the moose stopped dead in her tracks. Valiantly, the whistler kept on, his emotion now and then causing false notes. Fascinated, the moose applauded by wiggling her ears. While she stood there, apparently thrilled by the solo, the intrepid ranger backed slowly away for twenty-five feet. Coolly he proceeded to take pictures of the musical-minded moose and then sprinted off to more complete safety.

During the rut, the bull moose is much more likely to be disagreeable. He has driven many a man up a tree and kept him there, sometimes for hours. One of my friends was chased across a creek, up to his neck in water. Even a snow plow and tractor has been charged.

As a matter of fact, a moose under most circumstances is very unlikely to make an unprovoked attack. I have studied and photographed a good many moose from a reasonable distance and evoked nothing more than a gnashing of teeth.

The legs of a moose are only long enough to reach the ground. But they are too long for it to reach conveniently the sedges, grasses, horsetail and many other herbs that it likes, without getting down on its knees. However, it can readily reach the tall plants, such as ferns, asters and jewelweed while standing. It is very fond of water plants. Where moose are numerous they may almost denude the lakes of water lilies. Floating duckweeds (*Potamogeton,* etc.) are scooped off the surface, while submerged plants such as burreed and duck-potato require going underneath the water.

The moose isn't built for diving. It doesn't like to feed where the water is more than six feet deep. Even then, when its feet leave the bottom, it may roll over on one side most ungracefully. Usually it dines in shallower water, plunging its head underneath to grasp the plants. Sometimes it even pulls up the thick, scarred bases of the water lilies. I have never seen it keep its head under water more than a minute at a time, although it is said to be able to hold its breath twice as long.

Even in summer, it eats more browse of woody plants than anything else. The leaves of aspen, white, gray, and black birch, hard and soft maple and the striped (often called "moose") maples, cottonwood, mountain ash, willow and cherry are especially delectable. Many shrubs such as viburnum, dogwood, honeysuckle, blueberry, hazel, alder, currant, raspberry, and thimbleberry are also taken.

During the long cold winter the herbs are withered and the grass is buried under the snow. The moose then eats the buds and twigs of the browse species, but most of the food consists of conifers, especially fir, which it usually ignores in warm weather. Willow is an important cold-weather food in many localities.

In the eastern part of its range, the moose is said by some naturalists to browse extensively in winter on white cedar. My own observations indicate that it does not like cedar and takes it only occasionally. Ground hemlock (a yew) is eagerly sought at all seasons. On Isle Royale the great numbers of moose there have almost exterminated ground hemlock and it is difficult to find plants of more than a single sprig about a foot high. A vivid picture of the effect of this dense moose population may be obtained by going from Isle Royale about ten miles east to Passage Island. In the absence here of any moose whatever during historic times, suitable areas are covered by a dense "jungle" of ground hemlock about five feet or more in height.

During winter and spring some aspen bark is eaten. The moose removes this from the trunks of standing trees by a slanting, upward gouge with his lower incisors. (The moose has no front teeth or incisors on his upper jaw and so cannot bite out chunks of bark as the horse does, for example.) More often, however, this food is obtained from the upper parts of aspens that may be wind-thrown or broken down by snow, ice or avalanche. Such bark is more tender, and perhaps more tasty, than that on the lower trunk of the tree. It is often stripped off completely from many feet of the branches. Moose visit and revisit a fallen live aspen numerous times during the winter and spend much time standing around and nibbling at the "heaven-sent delicacy."

Once almost or quite exterminated from most parts of the original range in the eastern United States, moose now seem to be recovering. An estimated two thousand five hundred animals inhabit the Maine woods. A few live in New Hampshire, Vermont, and the Berkshire Hills of Massachusetts. Individuals have even wandered recently across the Connecticut Valley to the Mount Tobey region. The species has been reestablished in the Upper Peninsula of Michigan by transplanting from Isle Royale. On that island the animals are abundant. Considerable numbers also occur in northern Minnesota.

Some hunters imitate the amorous call of the cow moose for her lover. This moose "calling" as a means of enticing the bull within rifle shot range is frowned upon by many sportsmen as unfair and as bad as shooting over a salt lick. Others consider it quite legitimate. North-woods guides jealously prefer their own individual fashion of horn-making. Each has his peculiar routine of grunting or whining through it, with hands helping to vary the volume and resonance. Whether the long quavering whine of the cow or hoarse barking "uh—uh—uh" of a rival bull is well or poorly imitated, any unattached bull within a mile or two is likely to investigate. Skeptics insist that he is as easily attracted by the mere breaking of branches. They claim that any noise that might indicate the presence of an unmated cow will bring the bull running.

Moose meat is dry, like other venison, but tastes more like beef than deer meat does. In Alaska and northwestern Canada it is a staple food among trappers and other woodsmen. Small-town restaurants and hotels keep it on hand for emergencies and tourists. Along the Pacific Coast and where meat cannot be kept frozen, moose flesh is canned or corned. The fat is sometimes said to be inedible. It is very strong, but I have known Alaskans who could eat quantities of it when traveling in sub-zero weather. Moose muzzle (the gelatinous nose and upper lip) is a great delicacy. As a rich stew it is said to taste much like green turtle fat.

During the Middle Ages, the European moose was used at times as a draft animal in Scandinavia. For the carrying of mail in winter this moose could draw a sled through deep snow for long distances far faster than relays of horses could. The American moose, in a few cases, has also been "broken" to harness.

General description. A large, ungainly deerlike animal with humped shoulders, heavy pendulous muzzle, and long legs. A growth of skin and hair, called the "bell," hangs from the throat. Males have very heavy, flattened antlers. Color of upper parts blackish brown to black, belly and lower legs brownish gray, muzzle gray. Total length, 100 to 122 inches; height at shoulder, 66 to 92 inches; weight, 900 to an extreme of 1800 pounds. Females are about 25 per cent smaller.

Distinguishing characteristics. The size, grotesque appearance, pendulous muzzle, throat "bell," shoulder hump, and broadly flattened antlers of the adult bull distinguish the moose from all other deer.

Range. The coniferous forests of northern North America; south of the limit of trees, from Nova Scotia and the Adirondack Mountains west to northern Minnesota, central Saskatchewan, southern James Bay, and the Mackenzie River delta to Bristol Bay and Kenai Peninsula of Alaska. South in the Rocky Mountains to central Wyoming, Idaho, and (occasionally) northern Washington.

CARIBOU

RANGIFER SP.

Thousands of caribou surge over the tundra day after day. The Great Trek is on. At least once they have been seen to form an unbroken line four miles long, walking twelve and fifteen abreast. At other times the whole country as far as one can see is alive with caribou, all moving in the same direction. They eat as they travel. Continuously they push on, impelled by a mysterious urge to go beyond the horizon.

Click! Click! Click! The movement of the small ankle bones or the shifting of the tendons makes a continuous sound as they walk or trot. The mass of many-forked antlers bends and tosses with their moving bodies.

Rivers that are in their way are crossed without hesitation. Sometimes they swim directly across, sometimes upstream or downstream.

Where do they come from? Where are they going? No one ever really knows. Thousands of them may appear in one week and be gone the next. Several times since the settlement of Maine, waves of caribou have flooded in from the North. Almost as suddenly the tides receded and the woods were deserted.

What causes these unpredictable migrations? Why do they invade a region? Why do they suddenly depart and perhaps not return for years? Many theories have been advanced: avoidance of the mosquitoes, need for shelter, some magnetic attraction. The most reasonable explanation is based on the need for food.

BARREN-GROUND CARIBOU

Lichens, a favorite food, grow extremely slowly and once over-pastured require twenty to forty years to renew themselves completely. Trampling does even more damage than grazing, so it is logical that the caribou should not follow age-long migration routes like most other game species.

The bull caribou has a clumsy build according to our standards of beauty, but in his fresh winter coat he is magnificent. His brown body is set off by the white neck ruff which forms a "beard" on his upper chest. The white runs back over his shoulder and rather indistinctly along the lower flank as far as his hip. White bands circle the lower legs above the hoofs.

His antlers are quite different from those of any other deer. They are made up of two great, heavy beams. Along their upper, forward-pointing ends, they bear a number of points or tines which may be up to a foot long. Just above the base of each beam is the flattened, vertical brow tine or "shovel" which extends forward over his face.

Caribou antlers have a multitude of shapes and forms, and some are more flattened than others. The largest ever known measured sixty-seven and five-eighths inches along the beam and had a maximum horizontal spread of forty-eight and one-half inches.

The female caribou is the only female of all the American deer that wears antlers. They are smaller than the bull's, with fewer points, and the brow tine is a mere round stub, or at best a small shovel. She grows them each year and keeps them until the fawns are born. The bull discards his weapons earlier in the season. The coat of the doe is paler than that of the bull, and her neck is also demurely gray instead of the bull's startling white.

During spring the caribou is no longer handsome. He looks like a tramp with his old coat torn off in shreds and tatters. Ragged patches of faded hair flutter in the breeze. Great streaks and blotches of black skin are laid bare. Later he is clad in a neat, smooth suit of short hair that is dark brown or grayish. This does not last long. It is gradually replaced, hair by hair in a much more orderly process than in the spring, by the thick winter coat.

The caribou has big feet. They are specialized for his particular needs. In mud, spongy tundra, and snow, the two halves of the hoof spread to support his weight. It is said that the great rounded hoofs and pasterns, as much as four inches wide by seven inches long, give him one square inch of foot support for every two pounds of weight. The mighty moose has only one inch for every eight pounds. The sharp outer edges of the concave hoofs enable the caribou to travel sure-footedly over crusted snow, slush ice, or rocks that would be almost impossible for other deer.

Where do the caribou live? All the way around the North Pole in the northern parts of the Old and the New Worlds. We can roughly divide them into the reindeer of Europe and Asia, and the caribou of North America, the west coast of Greenland and the intervening islands of the Arctic Ocean.

Two types of caribou are recognized on this continent:

1. The barren-ground caribou which lives on the Arctic tundra from Labrador to Unimak Island, Alaska.

2. The woodland caribou immediately to the south from Nova Scotia and Newfoundland to British Columbia.

Probably two million of the barren-ground caribou roam Alaska and the Yukon. Except in western Alaska, the herds are still basically intact.

The woodland caribou have not fared as well. They are in some danger of fading into oblivion. When they were exterminated from a great area of western Quebec and eastern Ontario, the bands in Newfoundland, Labrador and eastern Quebec were practically isolated from those of the West. The animals are still fairly numerous in western Alberta.

Today the only resident caribou in the United States are a small remnant band of the woodland caribou in northern Minnesota. Bands occasionally wander south from Canada into western Montana, Idaho and eastern Washington, but they seem to be only temporary visitors. Maine, northern New Hampshire and Vermont, the Adirondacks, Isle Royale and the Upper Peninsula of Michigan, and northern Wisconsin and Minnesota were always on the southern margin of their range.

The characteristics and life histories of the two caribou are generally similar, with differences in details caused by long residence in contrasting habitats.

The woodland caribou lives in the evergreen forests which alternate with open bogs. Except in Newfoundland, it is darker in color, and is supposed to have longer legs than its northern relative. Its antlers are generally more flattened and shorter. It is rather solitary in summer and rarely bands together in herds larger than a half-dozen until autumn brings the animals together. In warm weather, it stays under cover during the day, coming out to feed in the bogs and around lakes in the evening.

The barren-ground caribou is rarely solitary. Living where night does not come in summer for many weeks, it can not afford to wait for darkness to do its foraging.

During the Arctic winter, the older bulls begin to wander away from the cows until by spring they are in separate bands. The mother caribou usually, but not always, drive away their yearling calves who gravitate together in disconsolate "tenderfoot" clubs. All this is in preparation for the birth of the fawns in late May or June.

Among the woodland caribou, twins come fairly often. The barren-ground animals usually have only one. The little fellows, unlike many young deer, are not spotted. Their coats are a uniform buffy brown; their muzzles and lower legs are black.

The birthplace is anywhere that the cows happen to be when their time arrives. They often do not pick out a secluded spot in advance, for as soon as their fawns are dry they are able to follow. The youngsters' legs are wobbly, but they have surprising strength and speed. On the soft spongy tundra they can outrun a pursuing man. A wolf, however, is another and more serious menace.

Through the summer the mothers and their calves wander about. They talk rather seldom—in piglike grunts, in "sign language," and by their actions. They feed on the grassy lowlands and mountain slopes, stripping leaves from willows that grow along the streams and over the flats, and from the dwarf birch. Grass and sedge are mainstays, but they never pass by lichens even though these plants were their main diet all winter. They also eat blueberry, mountain cranberry, crowberry, Labrador tea, woodrush (*Luzula*), and horsetail. Fungi, which are abundant in the far North during July and August, are great delicacies.

All this fine fare makes the caribou fat, and by the end of summer they are in top-notch condition. The bulls, particularly, have been getting ready for the rutting season. They have acquired a great deal of fat, especially over their rumps, where it may be as much as three inches thick.

By the end of September, their necks are much swollen, their cleaned antlers are being put to heavy use in sparring matches, and fighting becomes bitter. The antlers of the big bulls are sharp and long, and can easily slash through the hides of opponents. Bruises and cuts are inevitable. Sometimes they lock antlers and starve to death or are eaten by predators.

As promiscuous as the elk, the caribou bull rushes about day and night guarding his cows and looking for new ones, but seldom keeps more than a dozen or so at a time. Weaned calves and sometimes even yearlings are attached to the successive harems. As long as a female provides any interest for her master, she is kept in the harem, jealously watched, and guarded from any rival. Eating little or nothing, a successful bull loses his reserve of fat and is very thin by the beginning of winter. Fortunately his fur coat keeps him warm during the icy blasts and temperatures as low as sixty degrees below zero.

Even the muzzles of caribou are now covered with extra-thick hair. Protruding through the thick layer of fine wool underwear are the many longer guard hairs that form their outer coats. These guard hairs are formed like delicate quills. Each one is hollow and is filled with air. Since dead air is an efficient nonconductor of heat and cold, they give the caribou superinsulated comfort. Very little of their body heat is lost.

These air-filled coats act like rubber boats when the caribou want to cross a stream or lake. Floating high in the water and paddling vigorously with their big hoofs, the animals make good time.

Like many other hoofed animals, the caribou have a strong curiosity. They have been known to follow a pack train all day, usually at some distance but at intervals approaching within a few feet of the horses. Hunters have sometimes lured the animals into rifle range by waving a rag, or their feet, in the air. I have never been able to get the same result. My caribou in Alaska have merely stared and shifted about uneasily before finally trotting off. Their eyesight does not seem to be much if any better than that of other deer. They depend largely on the sense of smell, which is acute.

The caribou appear to be stupid. Certainly they are not very difficult to shoot. Being highly gregarious and accustomed to traveling in large herds, they frequently depend on "the other fellow" to detect danger. A number of times, caribou have been found sleeping so soundly that men have walked up and photographed them at close range.

When an unusual danger presents itself, the members of a caribou band generally are uncertain how to cope with it. There is much uneasy shifting and dashing about. The caribou may trot away together. Then various animals may run this way and that. Or, like Lot's wife, stop and look back. With black noses held so high that their faces are almost horizontal, they run with a high-stepping trot. This looks clumsy, but is an efficient, ground-consuming gait. If they are pressed further, the trot becomes labored. The big feet swing wildly and awkwardly and the animals soon tire. If trapped, they become panic-stricken and gallop madly about, becoming so exhausted that heart failure is a common result.

In a normal lifetime, each doe produces about a half dozen fawns. If Nature did not impose rigorous checks on this increase, the herds would double every three years. Soon the northland would be full of caribou. They would eat up all the food, which would be disastrous for the race.

Bothered by mosquitoes, individual caribou often stand on a hill with their rears to the breeze and desperately swipe their faces with their forelegs. The mosquitoes bite and drink the animals' blood, making the weak still more susceptible to other troubles. Warble flies lay their eggs on the hair. The larvae hatch, bore into the flesh, and migrate into the back muscles where they develop. Finally they work out through the skin and drop to the ground to pupate. A large buck may serve as an unwilling host to several hundred of these big "grubs." Nose fly larvae live in the nasal passages, where they set up irritation and absorb blood. Bladderworms settle in the liver, and tapeworms and roundworms infest the lungs. It is unfortunate that Nature cannot devise a pleasanter means of population control!

The wolverine and Canada lynx kill young caribou on occasion. Bears, both blacks and grizzlies, hunt fawns systematically at calving time. They probably get a good many meals for their efforts. Unwary or sick adults may be killed as well, at any time of year. The most potent enemy is the wolf. This animal, which sometimes weighs one hundred pounds or more and stands three feet high at the shoulder, has great speed and endurance.

Nevertheless the two species—caribou and wolf—have lived together for centuries. A normal caribou can run faster than his ancient enemy. Even the fawn, after it is a couple of weeks old, can race as fleetly as its mother. The wolf must test band after band, perhaps for hours, before spotting the crippled or diseased caribou, or even an occasional healthy one that makes a square meal. Man—the game hog, the wasteful native, or the traveler with many dogs to feed—has reduced the herds of caribou more in the past three hundred years than has the wolf during the historic period.

The long winter is the lean season for the caribou. Then and through the rest of the year the caribou eats whatever is available. It digs deep holes into the snow if necessary to get at the lichens, grasses and mosses which constitute the bulk of its food. The twigs of willow and dwarf birch also make good browsing. South of the barren grounds, woodland caribou live on the same plants, plus aspen and red osier as well as other shrubs.

Tradition says that the caribou digs away snow with its shovel—the brow tines of the antlers. But even the largest brow tines do not extend beyond the buck's nose, and they are set so nearly parallel to the animal's face that they would be awkward to use for that purpose. The antlers of does and yearling bulls are considerably smaller, while calves have only spikes without any brow tines at all. The truth is that all caribou dig through snow with their feet, just as do other deer.

Despite their apparent clumsiness, their serious demeanor, and the harshness of the climate and the region in which they live, the caribou like to play on occasion. Fawns gambol with each other and their parents, just as do the young deer of pleasanter climes.

In the old days, the Eskimos, Aleuts, Chipewyans, and other northern Indians hunted caribou with bows and spears, lying in wait for them at river and lake crossings and stalking them on the tundra. They also killed the animals at simple fence traps, and in pits that were covered with brush and thin slabs of hard snow. Another method was to set rawhide snares among willows at river crossings. When they first acquired rifles, they slaughtered the animals to the last one at every opportunity. Often many of the carcasses were wasted, only the tongues being taken.

In our Alaskan country where reindeer have been introduced, caribou are detested and killed at every opportunity because the wild bands are likely to attract and toll away the reindeer. Sometimes thousands of reindeer are thus "lost" from the domestic herds, especially when they are not systematically watched. This results in hybridizing the native caribou with the smaller and less rugged reindeer.

Reindeer are the domesticated Old World barren-ground caribou. They were introduced into Alaska from Siberia. The one thousand two hundred and eighty animals imported between 1891 and 1902, chiefly to the Seward Peninsula, have increased to well over a million. They are now spread over western Alaska from Point Barrow to the Alaska Peninsula and the south end of Kodiak Island. A large herd was established in 1935 near the mouth of the Mackenzie River in Yukon Territory for the benefit of the Canadian Eskimos.

The objectives of the project were to provide the Eskimos with a dependable source of food and to establish an industry in western Alaska. The reindeer now furnish a vast quantity of meat for humans, dogs and fur-farm foxes, as well as hides and other products.

Where they have been in captivity for generations, reindeer are much more tractable than the wild caribou. When tamed and herded like cattle, they learn to depend upon man for food and protection. Even some of the cows seem to take less responsibility for their offspring.

The uninvited caribou stand out conspicuously in a herd of reindeer. Their larger ears and longer legs make them look much taller. They have more white on their undersides, and the buck antlers average larger than those of the reindeer.

General description. A large, rather awkward-looking deerlike animal with thick hairy muzzle, maned neck, broad flat hoofs that are concave underneath, and rather long, loose hair. Both sexes have slightly flattened antlers. Color, brown in summer, grayish brown in winter, with yellowish white on neck, belly, feet, and rump, including tail. Total length, 60 to 90 inches; height at shoulder, 40 to 60 inches; weight variable with the species, 200 to 700 pounds; average about 275 pounds. Females are about 30 per cent smaller.

Distinguishing characteristics. The combination of blocky form, maned neck, large hoofs, and slightly flattened antlers of both males and females.

Range. Most of Canada, and many of the islands of the Arctic Ocean, except Nova Scotia, southern Quebec and Ontario westward to the mountains, and the Pacific coastal belt; Alaska, except the extreme western portions adjacent to Bering Sea. A small herd in northern Minnesota apparently comprise the only resident caribou within the United States.

3. The Heliographer

ANTELOPE—*ANTILOCAPRA AMERICANA*

The antelope can travel almost a mile a minute when necessary. Although it cannot keep up this speed for long, it is probably the swiftest of all our American mammals. When in good condition, it can run forty miles an hour for several miles.

At the first appearance of danger anywhere on the horizon, the antelope throws up its head and stares. The great black eyes dilate, the pointed ears, five inches high and three inches broad, are thrown forward to scoop in the faintest sound. For an instant the beautifully marked body is tense. At the same moment, the twin white disks on the buttocks serve as heliographs. The alarm causes a contraction of special muscles, and the multitude of white hairs at the rear rise instantly. These flaring patches reflect an astonishing amount of light. Other antelope may see these signals a couple of miles away. They immediately repeat it, and the warning is then spread far and wide. Even fawns a few hours old erect their rosettes, although theirs are dulled by a tinge of brown. The whole plains landscape seems to be dotted with flying white rump patches.

Simultaneously, as the rump signal is flashed, a strong musky scent is released from a set of twin glands located in the muscles that erect the glistening hairs. It is so strong that some human noses can smell it several hundred yards away down wind. Antelope probably detect the odor at a far greater distance, perhaps a mile or even more.

As soon as the members of a band see and smell the warning signals, and repeat them for the benefit of others, they dash to a rallying point. Then the bands act as one unit, galloping, wheeling, and stopping to look back as if on command.

Antelope make tremendous horizontal leaps at times. Rarely do they make high vertical jumps. They can go through the strands of a wire fence, or under the bottom wire, with astonishing ease and speed. I have seen running antelope flash through a space no more than a foot high between the ground and lower strand of a fence, with hardly a pause.

Coyotes and wolves by running in relays sometimes tire and pull down antelope. One of the carnivores will chase an antelope for some distance, and then

ANTELOPE

turn it over to a waiting companion that is freshly rested and takes up the chase. When tired, it turns the flagging prey over to another member, and this continues until one of the pack can overtake the victim.

The antelope does not depend entirely on flight for defense. It has stout sharp hoofs and does not hesitate to use them. I once watched two coyotes chase a large buck antelope. The trio came running, a coyote on each side and about twenty feet away from the buck's hind quarters. I drove my car off the road and up over the hill after them. From time to time, one of the coyotes would make a move to close in or to head off the antelope. At each attempt, the antelope jabbed furiously at the coyote with a front foot. Each time the coyote recoiled hastily. Galloping, then stopping to strike off his tormentors, and galloping again, the antelope disappeared over another ridge where I was unable to follow because of an intervening fence.

Coyotes are believed by many hunters to be deadly enemies of the antelope. In the above instance, however, the antelope seemed to be taking care of himself. I also know of a lone antelope buck with a broken hind leg that lived for two years unmolested on a range where coyotes were numerous. On a number of occasions I have watched bands of antelope as they tagged along after coyotes, watching them hunt for smaller fry. The coyotes seemed to be annoyed by this inquisitiveness, but did not do anything about it. I have found several antelope carcasses in the dead of winter, untouched by coyotes. Undoubtedly, if a coyote is hungry enough, fast enough, strong enough, and smart enough, he will kill an antelope. But under most circumstances there are many other foods easier for him to secure.

Disease is perhaps a greater factor in antelope existence than predators. Several parasites are dangerous: ticks, lice and mites, externally; flat worms and round worms, internally. The antelope seems to be subject to lung ailments, such as pneumonia and ulcers. A very serious and frequently fatal malady is actinomycosis or "lumpy-jaw." This disease may be transmitted to man, and sometimes it is fatal. In confinement, the antelope is very delicate and rarely lives longer than a year. Its extreme nervousness and tendency to bolt blindly on the slightest unusual noise, sight, or smell also make it a difficult ward in the zoological parks. Under natural conditions, it reaches maturity at five years and may live for three to five, or even eight, years longer.

The antelope is smaller than our deer, but much more striking in appearance. The beautiful tawny body has immaculate white underpinnings and buttocks. Black horns, dark markings on the face, and bands around the throat are decorative accents. The shining black eyes, with black eyelashes, are bigger than those of the much larger horse.

Prominent and set well to the sides of his face, the eyes can cover a wide range without any movement of the head. Their "binocular" qualities are amazing. All the antelope asks is a ridge or knoll as a lookout over open country. Sometimes it lives in open pine forest, as in parts of the Southwest, but its typical home is on the vast grassy plains and valleys where the shrubs grow sparse and low. There the wolf or coyote, practically its only four-legged enemies, can be seen while a long way off.

Most hoofed animals have four toes on each foot, but the antelope has only two. It has lost all bony remnants of the lateral toes (dewclaws) of its ancestors.

September and October is mating time in the antelope world, possibly a little earlier in the South. The buck is satisfied with a small harem. You will rarely see him with more than three or four does, and often with only one. It takes a very enterprising buck to control eight mates. Each doe leads him a long chase before allowing him to catch her. Most does can run faster than the portly bucks, if they wish!

The bucks that spent their summer alone, or in bachelor groups, gather on the fawning range and try to lure away the mates of the older bucks that have stayed with the does the year round. Fights are usually mild. A couple of males will knock their heads together a few times until the weaker one flees precipitately with the other after him. The "victor" keeps up the chase perhaps a half mile and then returns to his apathetic mates.

Once in a while a fight between two equally matched and ardent males may be vicious and terrible. In Yellowstone Park a buck was badly wounded by his rival. With blood streaming, he fled and disappeared over a knoll. The victor followed and found him lying flat on the ground by a fallen tree. Ruthlessly he dug his horns into the prostrate animal again, and, as the tormented creature writhed in agony, the pronged horns twisted and tore out its vitals. Satisfied, the vainglorious antelope bounded away.

After the rutting season, the antelope gather into larger bands. Since the antelope population has been reduced so greatly, these present-day bands will probably not number more than fifty or one hundred.

The interval between the mating and fawning seasons is slightly over eight months. As winter approaches, the antelope's thin coat of fine hair is replaced by a thick warm blanket made up of coarse, hollow hairs. This in turn is shed during March and April, beginning at the muzzle and working back over the body to the rump patches.

The American antelope or pronghorn is the only animal in the world that annually sheds the horny coverings of the permanent horn cores.

Headgear that is solid, like that of the deer and elk, is called antlers. These are discarded every year. The hollow forms, like those of domestic and wild cattle and mountain sheep and goats, are called horns. They must last a lifetime, for if they get broken the damage is permanent. The antelope, however, can repair damage to the outer portions of the horns by growing new sheaths each year.

Shortly after the end of the rut, both does and bucks begin the process of acquiring new horn coverings. The old black horn sheaths loosen at the base as the new sheaths grow and push underneath. Finally the old coverings are shoved so far out of place that they fall off. Then it can be seen that the permanent cores, three- or four-inch fingerlike spikes, are coated with a soft thick membrane. Near the base this is densely covered by upstanding coarse hair.

The membrane and hair harden into horn, beginning at the tip of the core and working down. At the same time, new horny material grows upward, beyond the tip, putting out a backward spike or prong. The new sheaths are complete about four months after they first began to push off the old ones.

The horns of the female antelope are hardly worth mentioning. They are rarely longer than four or five inches and but very slightly forked. Sometimes they are so small that they are invisible at a distance. The horns of both sexes grow longer and heavier each year until the animal reaches maturity at the age of five years. A set of buck's horns measuring more than twelve or thirteen inches along the outer side of the curve is considered remarkable. The all-time record for this measurement is that of an antelope killed in Arizona in 1899. The length along the outer curve was twenty and five-sixteenths inches, while the greatest spread between the horns was sixteen and three-sixteenths inches.

The spikes of the fawns start to grow when they are about ten months old. By the following autumn, when the first shedding takes place, those of the young bucks are two or three inches long.

Since the antelope's horn sheaths are not nearly as substantial as the solid antlers of the elk, deer, or moose, they disappear relatively soon after shedding. Even in a very arid climate such as the Arizona deserts, these relics rarely last more than three years. When softened by rain or snow, they appeal to hungry coyotes or badgers that make good meals out of them. Hard or soft, they are gnawed by porcupines, ground squirrels, mice, gophers and prairie dogs which in this way renew their supply of calcium. Even the antelope have been seen chewing their own horns after shedding them.

Fawning time follows the full greening of the plains, as early as the first of May in Mexico and a full month or six weeks later in western Canada. The little fawns are frequently two in number after the doe's first accouchement, when she has only one. She may deliver them in a little "park" in a pine forest, or, more likely, she may choose the top of a knoll or ridge on the open plains, perhaps only one hundred to two hundred yards away from the band. Most likely, they are just dropped anywhere.

The little fawns appear to be all ears, eyes, and legs, and measure about sixteen or seventeen inches high at the shoulder. Paler and grayer than their mother, their color pattern is very faint. The forehead of the little female shows no indication of future horns, although small whorls of hair mark the spots on the male. Another mark that distinguishes the male, at birth, is a black streak on the lower edge of each of his lower jaws. This lasts throughout life. It starts at the angle of the jaw and runs about halfway to the muzzle.

Little antelope develop much faster than deer fawns. When only a day or two old, they can run at the rate of twenty-five miles an hour for a short time. Hiding is the preferred method of avoiding trouble, however. During the first week of their lives, they spend most of the time flattened out on the ground with their ears folded back. How do these delicate creatures stand the extremes of blazing midday heat and the cold nights of the high plateaus?

The mother takes the precaution of stationing her twins separately, seventy-five to one hundred yards apart. She stays at a distance except when it is time to feed them. Then, after looking around to be sure that no possible enemy is watching, she saunters apparently aimlessly to the first little dun-colored bump on the plain. The fawn gets up eagerly and nurses for a few minutes. It may then drop down again, or walk with its mother to the brother or sister which nurses in turn. As the youngsters grow stronger, they travel more and more with their mother. When they are a few days old, she takes them to her band consisting of other mothers and their kids, perhaps six to twelve yearlings, and a buck.

The golden eagle is supposed to kill young fawns at times. The wolf, coyote, even bear and fox, search for them diligently. When a mother sees one of these predators in the vicinity, she does not get excited, but cannily pretends complete indifference and lack of concern. She is smart enough to stay away from her fawns, even if they must go hungry for a little while. She knows that her youngsters have almost no scent and the odds are against the predators finding them.

When an enemy approaches, the little fawns instinctively "freeze," but if the predator comes too close, they are off like a shot and the marauder is lucky if he catches them. Usually, if the predator gets dangerously near his quarry, the mother takes action. When the hunter is a coyote or fox, she dashes in and puts an end to the hunt. Even a coyote, if alone, rarely puts up much of a fight against an aroused mother antelope. He can't afford to risk serious crippling from her sharp front hoofs.

When the hunter is of greater strength, she turns to strategy, trying to lure him away by getting near enough to be tempting prey herself. An exceptionally artful doe is said to feign injury. Of course, some mothers are more devoted and smarter than others.

Fawns are very playful when out of danger, and their antics often have the appearance of games of tag. Even grown-ups like impromptu sprinting contests. A notable characteristic of the antelope is the overpowering impulse to outrace and cross in front of any swiftly moving object.

Numerous times my attention has first been drawn to an antelope by having it gallop in from a distance to speed alongside my automobile or horse. After traveling parallel for a little way, the antelope would unleash a burst of speed and cross the road just ahead of me. Then it would slow down as if completely satisfied with its demonstration of superiority.

The antelope swims when necessary, but not for the fun of it. It has been suggested that the antelope does not have to seek water for relief from flies, since the secretion of musk is so odorous that it drives them away. My experience has been that the flies are not so particular.

The antelope has many scent glands—on the rump patches, on the jaw, at the base of each horn, on the lower back, and on each hind leg near the hock. All these secretions may serve as messages to other animals. Small glands between the claws of each hoof also leave an identifying trail that may be read by antelope that pass.

Occasionally one will see an antelope feeding or resting alone or sometimes there will be a pair. Generally these animals are bucks, perhaps grumpy bachelors bored by feminine company. Most antelope, however, are sociable. Sentinels seem to be posted to keep watch while the band grazes or rests. Probably they are only individuals that are especially cautious. As a rule everyone takes a look around occasionally. The fawns seem to be as suspicious as their elders.

During summer and winter, the antelope depends on browse. In the north, the staple shrub food is sagebrush. Atriplex, rabbitbrush, greasewood, and Russian thistle are also important. At all times the antelope is a dainty eater. It feeds thriftily, and does not trample down and discard undesired plants as do some other big game species. Like all hoofed animals it relishes the salt licks.

Tender grasses are a major item of the antelope's summer food, although they are also taken in winter if green. The antelope prefer such varieties as grama and buffalo grasses. Nosing down into the heads of bunch grasses, they seek out the green sprouts. Fond of alfalfa, they sometimes do considerable damage to irrigated fields of this plant and of grains such as oats. Their ability to squeeze through fences makes it difficult to keep them out of cultivated fields.

In spite of their ability to run fast and far, antelopes are not erratic wanderers. If food is plentiful, they will normally stay within a circle no more than three or four miles across. Sometimes they get along for months on much less than that area. However, they make seasonal migrations. Those that live in the mountains in summer move down to the valleys in autumn to escape the deep snow. That is a "must" for antelope. Unlike many other animals, they seldom paw for their food. Wind-swept slopes provide feeding space in the north.

In early days, antelope on the northern Great Plains congregated in enormous loosely organized herds in the fall. A general movement took the animals to favorable wintering areas, away from the flat prairie. These were not necessarily in the south; the southern lee of the Black Hills of South Dakota, for example, is much milder than the country to the east and west of that range, and was a favored cold-weather region. Most animals moved but a few miles to find shelter from the cold winds in coulees or draws and low hills.

Early travelers and naturalists estimated that the antelope multitudes were nearly as numerous as the buffalo, or perhaps even greater at times. Seton calculated one hundred million, and there must have been at least thirty to forty million and perhaps many more. For centuries the species furnished meat, hides, and tableware for the plains Indians. Then the whites came, and for a few decades antelope steaks were the most common palatable meat on the bill-of-fare along the covered wagon routes from the Mississippi to California and Oregon. By 1908, the millions of antelope had melted to about nineteen thousand animals north of Mexico.

Fencing, plowing and livestock grazing cut up the antelopes' habitat and depleted their supply of food. Thousands of the animals were surrounded by companies of mounted men and driven together where they could be slaughtered. Driving antelope was a favorite method of the Indians, particularly after they acquired horses. Many other antelope were shot down from ambush, at river crossings and passes through the hills.

Frequently individual hunters took advantage of a fatal weakness in their prey. The antelope has an overwhelming curiosity about any strange object. Hunters disguised themselves in outlandish garbs. They crept on all fours, covered themselves with skins of buffalo or antelope or even bed sheets, waved flags, or lay on their backs and kicked their feet in the air to lure the animal within rifle range.

I have tried this latter method, after making sure that no one was around to report me to the insane asylum, but the antelope kept right on going. If I had continued these antics long enough for them to overcome their fear, they might have returned. However, the modern antelope is apt to be too sophisticated to be fooled by man and his tricks.

Conservation practices were applied in time to save the antelope race from extinction. Rigid protection of the surviving bands has resulted in an estimated population in the United States of a quarter of a million animals (1945). With a limited area and food supply, some ranges in New Mexico, Colorado, Wyoming, the western Dakotas and Montana have become fully stocked. An annual hunting kill of approximately ten thousand antelope is now safe. Methods of capturing and transplanting surplus antelope to new ranges have been worked out. It appears that this graceful animal with the colorful past may become a common sight again in many parts of the West.

This is the only native American of all our hoofed animals. It has no close relative, nor has it ever had any, on the other continents. Although called the American antelope, it is not even a second cousin of the African or Asiatic antelope. Scientists have traced the pronghorn's ancestry back to a practically identical American forebear in the early Pleistocene, between one and two million years ago. The other American hoofed animals of that time—the great giraffe-camels, the hornless deer, and the antlered deer-antelopes—have become extinct long since. Our modern deer, moose and elk are all immigrants!

General description. A medium-sized, graceful hoofed mammal with rather chunky body, slightly curved single-fork horns, long pointed ears, slender legs and short pointed tail. Color varies with the habitat from light tan to rich reddish brown; whitish to yellowish white under parts, rump, side of head, and two broad bars on the underside of neck; dark brown to black on muzzle and below ear. Total length, 4 to 4½ feet; height at shoulder, 32 to 40 inches; weight, 100 to 125 pounds. Females are about 10 per cent smaller than males, with horns much smaller, or vestigial.

Distinguishing characteristics. The contrasting pattern of brown or tan, black and white. Rounded white rump. Both sexes have single-forked horns without distinct slender tines, situated directly above the eyes. Small, slender form as contrasted with most deer.

Range. Western plains areas from southern Saskatchewan and Alberta to Baja California and southern Coahuila; central Nebraska and western Texas to central Oregon, western Nevada, and the Sacramento Valley of California.

4. Original American Livestock

BUFFALO—*BISON BISON*

A mountain of a beast, the buffalo seems to be perpetually brooding. The mighty head with its solemn short beard is low. The humped shoulders appear bowed with the sorrows and wrongs of a continent. It personifies in its vast, sombre hulk, and dull, inattentive eyes all the wildlife that was wastefully slaughtered in the Era of Exploitation.

Fact lies behind this fancy. The buffalo has had a tragic history. It has come perilously close to passing into the shadowy land of extinct species.

According to De Solis' account, the first white man to see one of these great mammals was Cortez. It was 1521 in Mexico City. Montezuma was nervously showing his dangerous pale-faced guests through his zoological park. There in a paddock was a great bull, which Montezuma said had been brought from many leagues to the north. Cortez recognized it as a kind of cattle or wild ox, and he ordered his official historian-artist to make a drawing and description to impress the King of Spain.

Later American explorers found buffalo in widely separated parts of the vast continent. Western Pennsylvania, westward to southern Idaho, the Pecos River in New Mexico, and possibly across northern Nevada to the eastern side of the Sierra Nevada and the Blue Mountains of Oregon. North, around Lake Athabaska and Great Slave Lake in northwest Canada. Southeast, near the headwaters of the Potomac, and in central Georgia and northern Florida.

In some regions there were vast numbers. Blue Licks, in Kentucky, attracted thousands. Daniel Boone and others of his generation said that the trails leading from all points of the compass to the Licks were cut deep in the earth "like the streets of a great city."

It was on the vast central prairies and the high plains to the westward, however, that the buffaloes found their best habitat and reached the peak of their abundance. Uncounted millions! Beginning with Coronado in 1542, three centuries of explorers marveled and exhausted their stock of adjectives in trying to describe the spectacle.

The plains were not covered everywhere with buffalo. The herds were ever shifting as they wandered for fresh grazing. Unlike cattle, the buffalo did not

BISON

feed thoroughly; they wandered erratically, and could range much farther from water. So there were times when a given "township" of prairies might be entirely devoid of buffaloes, or perhaps might have only a lone misanthrope or two.

The vast herds came and went. As they passed, they blackened the grass-lands, and their numbers seemed limitless. Wagon trains creaked on for days without passing beyond sight of buffalo for a single moment.

No one ever counted the buffaloes. Guesses have ranged as high as hundreds of millions. Most naturalists and historians, however, agree that Seton's estimate is based on reasonable assumption of various factors such as total range, abundance in various regions, and areas of scarcity. The result: sixty million buffaloes. It seems certain that civilized man has never seen a greater aggregation of animals anywhere on the earth. Not even the teeming myriads of antelopes, zebras, wildebeests and other grazing animals of southern Africa approached the multitudes of bison and antelope of colonial America.

But civilization steadily rolled westward like a tidal wave. The buffalo was in the way, and despite its huge bulk and vast numbers, it was overwhelmed. By 1820 not a bison was left east of the Mississippi River. Through the fifties and sixties the slaughter went on. With the Civil War out of the way, the nation turned to the West. Like slender steel tentacles, the transcontinental railroads stretched toward the Rockies and out through the buffalo range. They brought men to slaughter buffalo and antelope and cattle to devour grass as no grasshoppers or crickets had ever done.

Buffalo Bill Cody contracted to supply the Kansas Pacific construction crews with an average of twelve buffaloes daily. In eighteen months Cody killed four thousand two hundred and eighty animals and earned the nickname which became world famous. Railroads advertised special excursions, "with refreshments," and practically guaranteed a kill from the car windows. General Phil Sheridan got up a hunt for the Grand Duke Alexis of Russia. By 1889 Hornaday was able to account for only five hundred and forty-one buffaloes remaining alive in the United States.

The greater number of these millions of slaughtered buffaloes were wasted. Many were killed merely for their hides, or for their tongues alone. Thousands were shot for sport and never touched. Buffaloes in the northern plains region were killed for the express purpose of destroying the principal food supply of the Sioux, the Crows, and other tribes, in order to starve them off the warpath. Soon the grasslands were empty. The hordes of big game had vanished, and only their bones lay bleaching in the sunshine.

For a number of years, a few bison bands persisted in a wild state, existing precariously in inaccessible canyons or mountainous regions. Head-hunters slowly decimated these to sell their scalps to taxidermists, and the hides to tanners to make sleigh robes. Only one primitively wild band survived in the United States, about twenty-two animals in Yellowstone Park. In Canada the plains buffaloes were reduced to a handful; and the wood bison by 1900 were down to about two hundred and fifty animals.

The rest of the surviving buffaloes of the plains were in captivity in the United States, in zoos and on ranches of old-time cattlemen. The future of these animals was no more secure than the lives and fortunes of a small group of mortal men. Conservationists were aroused to action. Under the auspices of the federal government, a buffalo restoration project was started in 1902 in Yellowstone Park. This and a number of other preserves and refuges were successful, and a similar program was put into effect in Canada.

The buffalo was saved. Today, about five thousand buffaloes are found in the United States. Some were introduced into central Alaska, and that herd now numbers more than two hundred (the first that have lived there since the Pleistocene Age). Canada has at least fifteen thousand buffaloes. It seems that as a species the buffalo is now as safe as human forethought and limited range can assure.

Only one important step remains.

A big national monument should be established in the Great Plains area where a moderate sized herd could live under primitive conditions, together with other plains species. This would ensure the perpetuation of the animal as a wild species, free from danger of domestication.

The buffalo is the most gregarious of all the wild cattle. Cows and bulls graze together throughout the year. The bands vary in size from small groups of six or eight animals to herds of a hundred or more. The basic unit of buffalo society seems to be the family, consisting of the mother, several generations of her calves, and a more or less interested bull. The latter may be a roving, carefree fellow. In any case the clan revolves about the old cow. Any number of these family groups may join forces, and divide again as grazing, fancy, or numberless other factors decide. During cold weather, buffaloes seem more gregarious than in summer and have a tendency to form larger herds. Even then, groups of one or more clans may leave temporarily to follow their own course.

The only exception to this custom of bison sociability is the older bull. Young males stay in the band, apparently loosely tied to their mothers' apron strings. As they approach maturity they tend more and more to break away. Some naturalists blame much of this on jealousy. Undoubtedly the ambitious upstarts try to steal an older bull's cows and are thrashed and thrown out in the cold. I believe, however, that many bulls leave of their own accord. Perhaps, like other males, they get tired of communal life and want a change.

Frequently two, three, or even more mature bachelor bulls will form a little club. Wandering about together, they seem to get just enough companionship without manifesting any visible camaraderie. Other buffaloes are solitary hermits, and have nothing to do with their kind. On several occasions I have stepped behind trees to let one of these majestic old fellows walk by, less than fifty feet away. They ignored my presence or were unaware of it.

Normally the buffalo is a timid animal, but it is unpredictable. On one occasion a band of bison may stand and stare for some time, allowing a person to approach in plain view within a hundred yards. The next time, the same herd may stampede while the approaching person is still a half mile off. Cows are much more "scary" and alert than bulls. The signal to run is almost always given by a female, whereupon all the animals gallop off as a unit, snorting and hoisting their skimpy tails in the air.

Rarely the buffalo is bold and aggressive, but then it can be as dangerous as a rhinoceros. Weighing up to a ton or more, it lowers the heavy sharp horns and plunges after an enemy. For a short distance it moves as fast as the swiftest cow pony, and is almost as agile. Unlike a domestic bull, the wild bison does not shut its eyes when charging. More than one unfortunate man has been killed by taking chances with captive buffaloes.

I have hiked many miles on buffalo ranges, but I have always planned my course sufficiently close to stout trees, on the assumption that I might need them. Another "must" to remember: buffaloes seem to bear a grudge against horses and will sometimes go out of their way to attack and try to gore them. A crusty bachelor bull, or a cow with calf should always be assumed to be dangerous.

The bull that accompanies the herd is almost as willing to defend a calf against attack as is the mother. Most of the young are born in May, but numbers of them may arrive in late April or in June. They have no nursery area. When the mother feels that her time has come, she merely moves a short way from her companions. Like the domestic cow, she has taken nine to nine and one-half months to produce her calf.

A single calf is the rule; twins are exceedingly rare. It looks much like a domestic calf but is shorter, less gangling, and has a much shorter neck. There is only the faintest suggestion of the humped shoulders of the parents. The color is completely different, a bright yellowish red which becomes paler on the belly and legs. Only a blackish smudge on the muzzle and lower face prevents the bison calf from being really handsome. This gives it a dull, blunt-headed appearance, but actually it is a gay, lively little animal. In two or three days it is strong enough to join and follow the band, which has fed around in the general vicinity. It sometimes takes the whole herd to chase away a lurking wolf effectively. The young calf plays with others its own age, bouncing stiff-legged, dodging through games of tag or follow-the-leader. They like to butt and shove head-to-head to show how strong they are.

Every little while the calf's stomach overpowers its love of fun and it runs to the mother for a quick lunch of milk. Buffalo nursing is always an enthusiastic, vigorous matter. I have seen good-sized calves bunt their mothers so heartily as to lift the hind quarters off the ground. If the grazing is good, the mother's milk supply may last practically through the year, and weaning is sometimes deferred until a new calf is due.

Albino buffaloes occur, but very rarely. They were eagerly sought by the Indians, for a prayer uttered over one of these skins was practically assured of a favorable answer. A Mandan would offer the equivalent of ten to fifteen horses for a white buffalo hide, and consider himself lucky to close the deal. In recent years, two or three albino buffaloes have been raised on the National Bison Range in western Montana. Although mother buffaloes are usually devoted, a mother in Yellowstone Park abandoned her albino calf the day after it was born, and it was too blind to follow her.

There are said to be only three albinos among the five thousand buffaloes in the United States today. A true albino, blind from birth, is in the National Zoological Park; another was reported seen in an Alaskan herd, and the third is on the National Bison Range of Montana. This latter animal is a magnificent bull, all white except for a shaggy black crown on his head. Instead of being handicapped, as are most albinos, he is the leader of the herd. What he says, goes. When he moves, the other bulls, the cows, and the calves follow after.

The calf changes greatly. The horns of the male appear in a couple of months as twin bumps on the forehead, but those of the female are a little slower. The shoulder hump begins to be quite definite at about the same time. During the autumn the reddish coat is gradually shed and replaced by a rich brownish one. Through the following years more changes occur. The straight spike horns gradually curve inward and become heavier, and the shoulder hump, especially of the bull, grows enormously.

Although the buffalo is not a fully mature animal until it is about eight years old, it begins to look for a mate at the age of three. Cows may breed for many years. When the buffalo herd in Wainwright Park, Alberta, was slaughtered in 1940, it was found that a number of the original cows were accompanied by calves. The mothers had been earmarked *forty* years before, yet they still were productive.

While the weight of an average full-grown bull is around eighteen hundred pounds, exceptional animals may be considerably larger. Several wild buffaloes have been weighed after being killed that tipped the scales at over a ton. According to Garretson, an authority on the plains buffalo, a monster shot in western Kansas weighed three thousand pounds gross. The largest bison ever killed for scientific purposes, and accurately weighed on the spot, was a wood bison on Peace River that totaled two thousand four hundred and two pounds. The average wood bison is supposed to run a little larger than the plains buffalo.

The record head is that of a bull from the Yellowstone Park herd; the skull is now in the Park museum. The greatest spread between the horns is thirty-five and three-eighths inches; the longer horn measures twenty-two and three-eighths inches along the outer curve, and is fourteen and seven-eighths inches in circumference at the base.

The females are somewhat smaller and less bearded. Their horns are more curved and slender, and their humps and shoulders are less massive.

I have mentioned the concern for the calves shown by the entire herd as well as the mothers. Early travelers on the plains noticed that the mothers and calves are practically always in the interior of the group, while the bulls are ranged around them. While this gallant maneuver may have a defensive value, the bulls probably do not plan it. Rather, the cows and calves are more gregarious and bunch together, while the bulls tend to spread out more widely to get a better selection of grass. The older bulls are notoriously careless lookouts. Hunters in early days found it comparatively easy to crawl past them, in brush or a little arroyo, to get to the interior of the herd and come within range of the younger and better meat animals.

The buffalos' sight is not very keen, which makes them appear stupid at times. Since their hearing and sense of smell are good, they seem to depend particularly on the wind to bring indications of danger.

I have known bison to feed and move about on dark nights, especially in summer, but this is probably out of the ordinary. Their usual routine is more like our own than most animals. An hour or two after sunset finds the herd lying down, each calf beside its mother, with the majority of the bulls toward the outer edge. A bedground may be used for several nights or be abandoned forever after one sleep.

They may feed in a restricted area for days or as much as a week. Then the wanderlust may seize them, and the herd will move five or ten miles in as many hours, stopping only for a mouthful here and there before settling down once more. They are much more sedentary in winter. A siesta is usually taken for four or five hours in the middle of the day, especially in warm weather.

Normally the buffalo moves at a plodding, dogged walk which seems slow but actually covers ground at the rate of four or five miles an hour. Next fastest is a swinging trot, which on slight urging becomes a stiff-legged, lumbering canter or a fast, rolling gallop.

The buffalo's clothing is oddly distributed. In summer, especially, it is practically all bunched up on the head, neck and forequarters. After the animal has torn and rolled off the faded, yellowish brown winter coat that hangs in tatters and matted patches for weeks, the hindquarters and much of the middle are barely covered with short hair.

Mosquitoes and flies of many kinds find this near-bareness a happy hunting ground. The desperate buffalo's short tail is a most inadequate defense, and the more easily frightened insects merely move forward and burrow into the deep wool on the neck and hump. Sharp-awned seeds of squirreltail and foxtail grass attach themselves to this fur and work down to the hide. The sun beats down and adds heat to the buffalo's misery.

To get some relief the buffalo lies on the ground, going down front knees first. Here it squirms and rolls furiously, going completely over in spite of its hump. Kicking and thrashing, it wears off the grass and sod and works the fine dust into its coat and burning skin. Lying on its side, it kicks bushels of dirt onto the upper surface by means of the front feet, and drives off the flies temporarily.

After a few dust baths, the wallow is a saucerlike depression from eight to fifteen feet across and as much as sixteen or eighteen inches deep toward the center. In places, wallows may be so numerous that they overlap, and some are used for generations. Rain may fill the depressions, whereupon the rolling buffalo delightedly plasters itself with mud. It may also wallow in the mud along a stream or at a marsh for the same purpose of fly control or to soothe an itching skin. Rubbing against trees or rocks also affords relief. Around wallows, particularly, the trees are likely to lose their bark and lower branches by the rough treatment. Saplings may be beaten to death by the thrashing of buffalo heads and horns.

Magpies, blackbirds and cowbirds come to the rescue at times. Usually not more than one or two, but occasionally as many as a dozen at a time may perch on a buffalo's back and eat up the flies and other insects. At other times they hop along a few inches from the great cloven hoofs, watching for the insects that are stirred up.

Grass and sometimes a few herbs make up the buffalo's normal year-round diet. Occasionally this is varied by a few leaves or twigs of low shrubs such as willow.

While the buffalo can stand thirst better than domestic cattle, it must drink eventually, especially in hot weather. In early days the approaches to streams that were lined with high bluffs excited the wonder of explorers. Some of these "roadways" were cut many feet deep in the clay by uncounted generations of trampling hoofs. In some instances, these gave wagon trains the only opportunity to cross deep arroyos and saved many miles of detouring. Some of the trails on high, steep bluffs were extraordinarily steep and necessitated leaps of six or eight feet down. Despite its enormous bulk and clumsy appearance, the buffalo is surprisingly agile and sure-footed.

It is a ready swimmer, sufficiently buoyant so that head and the upper ten or twelve inches of hump stay above water. Before the "Great Slaughter," many buffaloes were drowned at times when trying to cross swift rivers in flood. There are also records of many hundreds crashing through weak ice and drowning. In January or February, 1945, thirty-eight buffaloes tried to cross the Yellowstone River about five miles below Yellowstone Lake. Crashing through the thin ice, they were unable to climb the steep wall of ice on either bank, and all perished.

Boggy ground is sometimes a deathtrap. Rangers in Yellowstone Park have found buffaloes hopelessly mired, especially in early spring. If the animals were still alive, the men usually tried to drag them out with ropes and the help of a saddle horse or truck. All too frequently the enraged and exhausted buffalo has misunderstood the rescuers' intentions and, after release, tried to kill them.

In one instance a misguided but loyal buffalo prevented the rangers from pulling its comrade out of a bog. Not until the drowning animal died, did the stubborn champion depart.

Numerous times, buffaloes have chased rangers and hikers up into the tree-tops and kept them there for hours at a time.

July and August are the months of the mating craze. Gradually the placid tenor of life changes, and both cows and bulls become more and more restless. Whatever camaraderie exists between the herd bulls is replaced by suspicion, and later by active hostility. As each male reaches the breeding stage, he challenges the authority of a herd leader, or tries to break into a family group. Most of these attempts are brief and are discouraged with no more than a glowering threat from the reigning monarch.

I once witnessed a battle royal between two evenly matched bulls at Wind Cave National Park. The whole surrounding region seemed to be shaken by their deep-pitched, rumbling bellows. Standing about twenty feet apart, the mammoth animals kicked dirt high in the air with quick backward strokes of the front hoofs. Suddenly they lunged together, meeting head-on. Their combined two tons of weight came together like a couple of piledrivers. Their foreheads, rather than their horns, took the impact. Despite the thick mat of hair, the sound was as if two vast bare skulls had crashed. Again and again the infuriated beasts backed away, then came together again like colliding locomotives. In the dust that covered the battlefield, the rest of the herd stood around and watched, apparently indifferently. After it seemed as if the skulls of both gladiators must be shattered, one bull turned groggily and staggered off. The victor took a few slow steps in pursuit, then stopped and stared glassily into space, too stunned to enjoy his triumph.

Apparently very few of these combats result in injuries or fatal goring by the sharp horns. Many of the vanquished bulls are not actually driven from the herd, but they mind their manners and avoid giving the boss any reason for additional punishment.

A stampeding herd of buffalo is almost an irresistible force. When thoroughly frightened, the animals may run for miles in a blind, unheeding, compact mass. It seems that no obstacle, alive or inanimate, will stop them. The thunder of hoofs shakes the ground, and the rush of galloping bodies sounds like Niagara. Calves, each one beside or almost underneath its mother, appear from time to time as rusty flashes among the enormous black adults. It is miraculous that the youngsters are not trampled into pulp, but casualties are rare.

The western Indians took advantage of this tendency of the bison to dash blindly. Purposely they startled herds and then directed the fleeing animals into prepared enclosures where they were easily slaughtered. In some places, bluffs or cliffs were used so that the buffaloes cascaded over the edge before perceiving their danger.

Such a natural trap was the famous Buffalo Jump-Off in the Yellowstone River valley about twenty-five miles north of Gardiner, Montana. Excavations at the foot of the sandstone cliff have revealed a great mass of buffalo bones, hair, bits of dried skin, other remains, and many spear and arrow heads of the hunters. This layer, which is a number of feet thick, extends from the foot of the cliff down the talus slope to the plain below.

Exceptionally fierce, swiftly running prairie fires probably destroyed whole herds. Such catastrophes may have been rare, occurring only at times of high winds when the grass was tinder dry.

A cow buffalo at Wind Cave National Park, South Dakota, was once found to have numerous porcupine quills in her face and neck. It would have been interesting to watch the encounter of the quill pig and the great bison, and the latter's discomfiture!

Although the buffalo was of great importance in the economy of the aboriginal Plains Indians as food, shelter, clothing and utensils, little impression was made on the size of the immense herds. Other predators—wolves, cougars, coyotes, and grizzly and black bears—probably often acted as scavengers or killed cripples and senile animals and young. Under exceptionally favorable circumstances these four-footed flesh eaters caught and killed healthy adults, but extreme hunger must have been required to spur even the most powerful of them to tackle a grown cow or bull in fighting trim.

Under absolutely normal conditions, as in Wood Buffalo Park, aged buffaloes have been found dead of natural causes, not killed by the numerous predators that occur there. These buffalo patriarchs, that seem to be almost too tough for the wolves, may be over forty years old. Their coats are hoary with age, and they are almost toothless and blind.

The buffalo is well prepared by its heavy frontlet to face the winter storms and weather them out. Its great head sweeps away the snow in a semicircle, and uncovers cured grasses three feet or more below. It rarely paws the snow with its feet. As it works, it breathes out great geysers of frost from its nostrils. In spite of its endurance, winter weather, a combination of icy crusts and intense, prolonged cold, or food depletion may have been the greatest factor in keeping the bison herds within bounds before the white man came.

Two living races of buffalo are recognized:

1. The plains buffalo (*Bison bison bison*) which originally ranged over much of the United States (except the arid Southwest and Pacific coastal region), northeastern Mexico, and the Canadian extension of the Great Plains as far north as central Alberta.

2. The wood buffalo (*Bison bison athabascae*), which some authorities say is larger and darker in color, while others claim that the two cannot be distinguished. It was once found over a considerable area around Great Slave Lake and Peace River in Northwest Territories and northern Alberta. The surviving herd, in Wood Buffalo Park, has been mixed by the addition between 1925 and 1929 of six thousand six hundred and seventy-three plains buffaloes from Wainwright Park. The wood bison as a pure race already may have vanished through hybridization.

General description. A very large species of wild cattle with heavy head, short, curved black horns, short neck, high, humped shoulders, and short tail ending in a tuft of hair. Fur on head, neck and shoulders brownish black, long and rather wooly (as much as 14 to 16 inches long on top of head and forming a beard on the chin). Fur on body and hindquarters short and close, grading into brown to light brown. Total length, 10 to 12½ feet; height at shoulder, 5½ to 6 feet; weight, 1600 to 2000 pounds, to an extreme of possibly 3000 pounds. Cows are considerably smaller: length, about 7 feet; height at shoulder, 5 feet; weight, about 700 to 900 pounds.

Distinguishing characteristics. Easily told from other mammals with cleft hoofs by large size, dark uniform color, humped shoulders and simple short horns like those of the domestic cow.

Range. In the wild state, in Wood Buffalo Park south of Great Slave Lake, and in Yellowstone Park in northwestern Wyoming; maintained in numerous fenced refuges, parks, and other preserves throughout the United States and southern Canada.

MUSKOX
OVIBOS MOSCHATUS

The muskox is one of the hardiest hoofed animals in the world. It is built and upholstered for glacial climates. The bleakest, most barren tundras of the North American hemisphere, north of timber line, are its home. Here the surface of the thin, rocky soil barely thaws in summer, and temperatures of fifty below are common through the long winter. This animal never migrates.

The muskox looks somewhat like a buffalo, but is not as large, weighing only five hundred to nine hundred pounds. It has the longest hair of any animal in America. The hair varies in length from about six inches on the back to two feet—or even three feet in exceptional cases—on the neck, chest and hind quarters. Hanging like a mane from its belly and sides, this "skirt" of its coat is usually ankle length, but may brush the ground. It is dark brown to black, and the "saddle" and socks are paler to whitish. The hair is perfectly straight, except on the shoulders where it is curly.

The massive horns curve down, out and then up. Sharp, vicious weapons, they get bigger and better every year. An exceptionally fine set of horns may have a spread of twenty-eight to twenty-nine inches.

When the muskox tears off the old underwear each spring, it probably looks more ragged and moth-eaten than any other animal in the world. Long streamers and great patches of the dense soft wool work out through the long hairs of its overcoat. Some of it lies in loose mats on top. Other pieces flutter in the air. New underwear grows in simultaneously so that it is not embarrassed by flies nor does it catch cold. The tundra is littered with these cast-offs, and rocks and shrubs are festooned with them.

The muskox looks placid and kindly when its world is going smoothly. But when it is disturbed, look out! It snorts, the eyes become bloodshot, and it lowers its great head and charges with a swift dash.

No other animal has a defense method like that of the muskox. Instead of trying to run away, the whole herd backs into a rough circle, with their heads turned outward. The calves are pushed into the center, or they cower under their mothers' curtained bellies. Occasionally a precocious calf will stand with its head

MUSKOX

out toward the enemy also. The packed mass of horned heads threaten the invader from every angle. The bulls rub their massive heads against their fore-legs. Apparently this distributes the musk from a small gland just below each eye. The odor may be noticeable more than a hundred yards away.

From time to time, one or more bulls will dash out of the circle to attack the enemy. The muskox is exceedingly nimble and a single sweep of the pointed horns can cripple or kill. Woe to the wolf or dog or Eskimo that trips and stumbles. The infuriated ox will gore and trample him to death, or will endeavor to fling the unfortunate creature so high than the fall will smash his bones. If the rush fails, the ox backs into the formation, thus protecting flank and rear.

This method of defense is almost impregnable against natural enemies. Even the great wolf of the tundra has a healthy respect for the muskox, and usually finds it much more profitable to hunt hares or to follow the caribou bands.

A lone muskox, on scenting danger, tries to find a large rock or steep bank. Backing up against this shelter, it attempts to keep an enemy from attacking the rear. If grabbed by a wolf, it will buck and kick like a Texas steer. Suddenly it may leap into the air and crash down on its side, crushing the life out of any creature foolish enough to be clinging there.

Not even the great Barren Ground bear can attack the muskoxen with impunity. A black bear once tried to feast on one of the muskoxen confined in a pasture near Fairbanks, Alaska. Ripping and tearing, the muskoxen fought it out. Although it succeeded in breaking the neck of one, the bear was badly cut up by the maddened animals, and was later shot by the caretakers.

The defense formation and bravery of the muskoxen are formidable even to primitive man. Many a hunter has lost his life to charging bulls or infuriated cows with calves. The temper of muskoxen becomes more and more unreliable as they grow older, and it takes correspondingly less trouble on the part of a rash traveler to provoke a charge.

Unfortunately this method of defense that is so successful against predators is a complete failure against modern man and the rifle. Bunched together, they are an easy target, and can be wiped out in a few minutes.

The female muskox is about thirty per cent smaller than the bull. Her skull is not as thick, the hair on her chest and neck is not as long, but she has a pair of horns that may be even sharper than her mate's.

Her one calf is born into a bleak cold world in April or May. The Arctic night, still much longer than day, fights with frost and icy wind to keep the ground frozen and snow-covered. The sun stays above the southern horizon only a few hours each day. The low, rounded hills, stony and barren of trees, are little protection against the wind that streams off the Polar Sea. The calf has real need for its birth coat of short, curly, dark brown hair. It weighs sixteen to twenty-five pounds, is twenty inches long from nose to tail, and stands eighteen inches high at the shoulder.

During the first few hours, if the weather is extremely cold and windy, life is a nip-and-tuck affair. The calf may be frozen to death before it dries. On weak, shivering legs, it huddles under the mother, seeking warmth from her body. At the time, she may be foraging by herself or with another cow or two. More likely she is still with a band of ten to twenty oxen. Perhaps half of her company are adult cows, with four or five mature bulls and several immature animals and yearlings making up the remainder. Even in a good year, three calves or perhaps four will be all that a band of that size will produce. The muskox cow may bear a calf in succeeding years, but frequently breeds only every other year. Rigorous conditions of life in the Arctic impose a rigid system of birth control.

For the first three months of life, the calf lives on its mother's milk, which is rich and nourishing. Within a few weeks it begins to nibble at grass and tender herbs. It must learn to eat solid food soon because food conditions in that bleak habitat make it difficult for the mother to support herself alone. At the age of four months it is munching plants for a steady diet.

As spring comes and leaves, to the tinkle of innumerable streams from the melting snow, summer arrives with a rush. Mosquitoes and blackflies swarm on the tundra and hang in the willow thickets in clouds. They drive the caribou into frenzies and even suck the blood of the mice and lemmings. Due to the new thick underwear and the long, fringed overcoats, the muskoxen are almost immune. Only the edges of the eyelids and the upper halves of their ears are vulnerable, and these are sometimes raw from fly bites.

Except for the flies and mosquitoes, the short Arctic summer is a pleasant time. The flowers bloom and seed prolifically. Many species of plants grow on the tundra, even on the great islands of the Polar Ocean. The muskoxen wander slowly, methodically feeding and stopping in the best pastures until they have eaten everything in sight. Their mainstay is grass and sedge, but saxifrage, horse-tail, mountain avens, blueberry, dwarf birch, alder, and willows are also impor-tant food plants. In places the ground is covered for acres with tiny lichens. Like other bovines, the muskoxen have no upper incisors. They gather food with their strong lips, tearing it loose with sharp lower teeth and tough upper palates.

As the summer sun warms the passions of the bulls, they compete for numer-ous mates. Bulls that have stayed with harems the year round now put a more rigid control on their cows. July and August see some mighty combats. Two jealous monsters will square away and rush together, their heads meeting with a mighty crack. The bony frontlet takes the brunt of the collision, but occa-sionally even that may be cracked and broken. Time after time the bulls ram each other. Sometimes the collision drives each animal straight up on his hind legs as he paws madly in the air. Eventually one gives up. Muskoxen are vindic-tive, unlike the chivalrous bighorns. If the vanquished bull can run away, he is fortunate. If too weak or weary, he may be prodded and pounded unmercifully. Bulls have been found with chests and shoulders slashed by the sharp horns of their opponents. Some of them succumb on the field of battle with fractured skulls, or are gored to death.

By September the rut is at an end and so is summer. The first storms of winter powder the willow bottoms with snow and the muskoxen move into the hills. Here their food consists of the dried, frozen plants of the same species that are eaten in summer. The animals feed on exposed ridges from which the snow is driven by the fierce wind. They can also paw away snow with their broad hoofs.

These hoofs are remarkable aids to the muskoxen. Although the animals are large and clumsy looking, they can run over hard crusted snow and rough rocky ground at great speed. The hoofs spread and their sharp edges cut into or grip the ground, furnishing their owners with non-skid traction. A herd of these ungainly looking muskoxen can sweep like a flying carpet over steep rocky slopes. The hills may be covered with loose debris, and avalanches of rocks will pour from beneath their feet. Their trails cross steep slopes covered with snow so hard that a person could scarcely walk without cutting steps. They can easily run faster than man.

For as long as paleozoologists can discover, muskoxen have lived in this barren environment and icy climate. When the great ice sheet covered much of the northern part of the world, these oxen grazed across the snowy plains in front of the glaciers. At that time, perhaps twenty thousand years ago, they lived in what is now northern Mongolia, Germany, Pennsylvania, and Kansas.

As the world grew warmer, the glaciers melted back until a comparatively modest ice cap around the North Pole is all that remains. Many of the mighty animals could not adjust themselves to warmer climate and lush vegetation. Some, such as the mammoth and the woolly rhinoceros, died out. The reindeer and the muskoxen, being more adaptable, followed the retreating ice. Only in America, certain Arctic islands, and Greenland were the muskoxen able to persist down to the present time. In Europe and Asia the species retired to the shores of the Arctic Ocean and died out in prehistoric times. Even in America they have not been allowed to occupy the entire tundra belt. They were exterminated from northern Alaska before the coming of the first white explorers about a century ago. Apparently they were also wiped out on the shore of Bering Sea rather recently, for the Eskimos and Aleuts of that region still have accurate descriptions of them.

The high-powered rifle has almost eliminated the muskoxen from their last stand. Explorers have depended on them for much food, both for men and dogs. Some of the early expeditions were large, with as many as a hundred men who required great quantities of meat. The various Peary expeditions, it is said, probably accounted for more than six hundred of these animals. Bands consisting of more than fifty were slaughtered for the fine nutritious steaks which were much like beef. Only old bulls, those killed in July and August, or those that were carelessly butchered had a musky flavor.

Eskimos and Indians, acquiring rifles for the first time, had an orgy of killing. Since time began for their races, they had prized muskox meat and fat for food and fuel, the skins for bedding and other purposes, and the horns for making dishes, spoons, dippers, bows, spearheads, blubber- and skin-mauls, and many other implements and tools. Now they could bring down almost any number of muskoxen with practically no risk and only the effort that it took to seek out the animals. The ancient circle formation was no longer an impregnable defense. On the contrary, it meant their death, for a hunter could stand at a safe distance and kill at leisure while his prey glared and rubbed noses along their forelegs in futile anger. Unless hit in the heart or spine the animals can withstand many bullets before dropping. The killing is sheer slaughter and not in any sense "sport."

Calf hunting has also accounted for the destruction of many muskoxen. During the first quarter of the twentieth century nearly two hundred and fifty calves were recorded as captured for zoological parks throughout Europe and America. The first to be shown in this country arrived at the Bronx Zoo in March, 1902. Any zoo director would pay at least a hundred dollars apiece for the strange shaggy little brutes, and as much as sixteen hundred dollars was given for one animal. Because the calves could not be lassoed or entangled in nets until the protecting adults had been killed, many bands were wiped out for this purpose only. Perhaps five or six adults were killed for every calf secured.

Possibly the primitive Eskimos and Indians were right. They passed on from generation to generation a legend that if any muskoxen were allowed to go or be taken South, all of the oxen would follow. To prevent such a catastrophe to themselves, Eskimos crept into Buffalo Jones' camp on the Canadian tundra in 1898 and cut the throats of the five muskoxen he had captured and was taking back to civilization. After little more than a century of exploration of the Arctic by the white man, the muskoxen have been reduced to dangerously low numbers. The total population for all the vast range of mainland and islands under the Dominion of Canada is only thirteen thousand. Perhaps eleven thousand more live along the north and east coasts of Greenland.

Apart from its interest to civilized man, the continuance of the muskox is of vital concern to the Eskimos and other people of the Arctic. It is one of the few animals that can thrive there. In an effort to rebuild the population, Canada has forbidden the killing of these animals under any condition by either natives or whites. Possession of skins is accepted as evidence of guilt. The Royal Canadian Mounted Police carefully investigate any signs or reports of killing. The Thelon Game Sanctuary, an area of fifteen thousand square miles northeast of Great Slave Lake, has been established especially for protection of the largest remaining group on the Canadian mainland, about three hundred oxen.

Through the efforts of the Fish and Wildlife Service and the Alaska Game Commission, the species has been reestablished in southwestern Alaska. In 1930 a band of thirty-four animals, nineteen females and fifteen males, were captured in Greenland. After shipment to New York, via Oslo, Norway, they were sent by railway express to Seattle, by boat to Seward, Alaska, and then by rail to Fairbanks, a trip of about fourteen thousand miles. Five years later the survivors of the original herd and their progeny were transferred to Nunivak Island in Bering Sea. By 1943 a count showed that more than a hundred muskoxen were roaming over the grassy tundra of the island. Eventually it is planned to remove the surplus and restock them in suitable places on the species' ancestral range on the Arctic slope of Alaska.

The time may arrive when some muskoxen will be domesticated as the reindeer have been. Then they can furnish meat, skins and rich good milk to the people of the Northland, as does the yak to the dwellers of the high barrens of central Asia. Their wool, when spun, is said not to shrink, but there is at present no feasible way of eliminating the many coarse guard hairs mixed with it. It makes up best when mixed with the wool of domestic sheep.

General description. A large, shaggy, oxlike animal with short neck and legs, stocky body, slightly humped shoulders, and very short tail. Horns of adult male are broad, downward curving, and nearly meet over the forehead, while those of the female are not as long, broad, or expanded. The fine, woolly undercoat is covered by very long thick hair that is dark brown to black, paler across the middle of the back and on the feet and lower legs. Total length, 80 to 100 inches; height at shoulder, 56 to 70 inches; weight, 500 to 900 pounds. Females are about 30 per cent smaller.

Distinguishing characteristics. The oxlike, blocky form, long shaggy coat, and broad flattened horns.

Range. Northwest Territories from northern Boothia Peninsula south to Chesterfield Inlet, west to Great Slave Lake, and north to Coronation Gulf; north of Great Bear Lake; a number of Arctic islands, especially Prince of Wales, Melville, Bathhurst, Cornwallis, Axel Heiberg, and Ellesmere Islands, and Grinnell Peninsula of Devon Island; the northern and eastern coast of Greenland as far south as Scoresby Sound. Introduced to Nunivak Island, Alaska.

BIGHORN
OVIS CANADENSIS AND *O. DALLI*

High on its throne, the bighorn looks down on the vast world that, from the crags of the bleak mountains, seems deserted. Possibly the white thread of a highway or a pastel patchwork of ranch fields can be seen on the distant valley floor. These works of puny man, the earthling who crawls slowly on the flat places but fears the cliffs, are lost in Nature's immensity. More likely than not, even these intrusions are lacking. The brown and black mountains, with their glistening snow patches or bright desert heat reflections, stretch away in wave after wave to the horizon.

The wild sheep of North America do not have wool like domestic sheep. Their hairy coats are more like those of the deer. Excepting the white Dall sheep of Alaska, they are pale brownish to nearly black in color, depending upon their environment and species. They are usually found in the mountains. At times they go down to the plains or deserts nearby, but rarely more than a mile

ROCKY MOUNTAIN BIGHORN

or so from the rocks. Valleys for them are dangerous places that must be crossed to go from one mountain range to another. Ledges, cliffs and steep slopes of broken rock mean greater safety from all except man armed with his rifle. They can easily outclimb every other enemy in such a habitat.

In this world-on-edge, the bighorn is born. Sometimes, perhaps about once in ten times, it is one of twins. It may be an early arrival. March in the desert ranges is a pleasant time of warm days that stir the spring flowers, but in the north, snow and ice may prevent the early lamb from surviving. A late lamb that is born in July is in an even more precarious position. It may not have time to build up enough strength and size to fight through the following winter. The most favorable period for the lamb to arrive is late March in the south and around the first of June in Alaska.

When the momentous event is about to take place, the ewe desires solitude. She leaves the band with which she has been feeding and climbs to a ledge or foot of a cliff. Here there is shelter from wind and storms, and a lookout that will easily cover the one approach possible for an enemy. Sometimes she remains there for several days without moving away to eat or drink.

The newborn lamb does not remain helpless for long. In an hour after birth the mouse-colored coat with a dark stripe down the back is dry and the young-ster is standing on tottering legs to nurse. (The Dall sheep lamb is white like its parents.) The lamb is so small that it can walk under its mother's belly with several inches clearance, and has to stretch its little neck to reach her udder. When a month old it has grown so fast that it frequently must kneel to nurse.

During the first week of its life the lamb stays on the nursery ledge. Taking barely enough time to drink and to snatch a few bites of grass, the ewe spends most of this period on guard. Even while the lamb sleeps beside her, she stands alert, watching for any intruder. The threatening whirr and whistle of a golden eagle's wings will bring her over the baby with one leap. She nurses the infant frequently, oftener than once every hour, with feedings that last two or three minutes.

When the lamb is about a week old it follows close to its mother as she wanders about the mountain in search for food. They may join other families and yearlings, until there are twenty-five to over sixty animals forming a loose band. The youngsters begin to nibble at the most tender foliage and flowers. By the time they are a month old, they are getting substantial nourishment from this source. Their feedings of milk become less and less frequent, and quite brief. The mothers try to wean them by walking away quickly after a half-minute's nursing. Nevertheless, some lambs manage to persuade their mothers into giving them milk well into their first winter.

Lambs have surprising endurance and speed. Dall sheep only two weeks old can easily keep up with their mothers that are running at full speed—at least for a while. A Dall lamb at McKinley Park was once picked up by some rangers when the animal was only a few hours old. It became attached to its "foster parents" and at the age of two and one-half weeks followed them for thirty miles over rough slopes and through glacial streams.

While the mother bighorns are grave and watchful, their lambs make merry. Like human children, they enjoy each other's company and are every bit as lively. They play games of tag and follow-the-leader, jumping over rocks and running around pinnacles. Sometimes there are butting matches as two lambs meet head-on and test out the tiny horns that are sprouting from their foreheads. Occasionally a ewe will unbend and play with the lambs.

The site is chosen carefully so that any approaching predatory animal can be seen at a distance. When the band stops to rest, at least two ewes seem to still stand guard. A favorite trick of the mischievous lambs is to fake an alarm, perhaps to enjoy the fright that it gives their elders. Bighorns have extraordinary sight. They rely on their eyes, almost to the exclusion of their ears and noses, to warn them of danger.

Frequently, some of the ewes go off to feed and take a respite from their rambunctious offspring. At this time one of the mothers or possibly a dry ewe takes charge of the youngsters. Besides keeping some semblance of order, one of her duties is to chase off yearlings and two-year-old bighorns that want to play too roughly with the lambs.

Bighorns ordinarily are silent animals. Ewes and their lambs in summer, however, are exceptions. There is a good deal of talking back and forth in "blatts" that are almost indistinguishable from the "baas" of domestic sheep. But they are not the vapid repetitions of the wooly species.

Usually the calls are rather faint, although they "carry" far in still air. However, a lost lamb or an excited mother on the search lifts up her bleats loudly and without restraint. Mothers also raise their voices to call their lambs from play in order to nurse. It is interesting to see how each lamb recognizes its mother's voice. After late summer, the bighorns seldom call, although they use a signal, a combination of snort and sneeze, to warn each other of danger. Rams rarely if ever make any sound except to grunt or snort. When angry, they gnash or grind their teeth.

Nonconformists among bighorns, just as among human beings, are inclined to be solitary and keep all kinds of hours. Most bighorns, however, are highly sociable and keep a regular daily schedule. During the summer they get up and start breakfast before daybreak, or about four o'clock. By the middle of the morning they have eaten their fill, and are ready to lie down, chew their cuds, and rest. It is amusing to watch the cud, a wad of hastily swallowed food, travel back up the gullet for a thorough chewing. The movement is plainly visible along the neck. After the animal has masticated the food for a minute with a steady rotary movement of the lower jaw, it swallows it again. This time it is digested. This procedure is continued until the entire breakfast—perhaps a peck of grass and herbs—is brought up from the first stomach (the rumen), chewed, and sent down to the three remaining divisions of the stomach for digestion.

After a brief lunch during early afternoon, the bighorns take another siesta. Up comes their food again for another proper disposal. From late afternoon to dusk, they dine long and well. It is then time to retire. All good sheep go to bed early.

Day beds are quite simple. Some bighorns, standing on a fairly level spot, paw three or four times with each front hoof and then lie down. Others, particularly the younger sheep, just flop down anywhere when they feel sleepy, without any preparation. Night beds, however, are chosen carefully, usually on the lee side, just under the crest of a ridge where possible enemies may be heard approaching from any direction. The beds that I have seen in the foothills of the Alaska Range and elsewhere have been depressions about two feet wide by three feet long, and as much as six inches deep. Such beds are probably used regularly for a long time. They smell decidedly "sheepy" from the animals' habit of defecating at each end of the bed, as well as the ram's custom of urinating in it each morning as he leaves to graze.

Each band of bighorns has a home range within which it moves back and forth irregularly between bedding and feeding grounds. The size of this range, as well as its shape, depends on many factors such as the topography, location of water holes or streams, and amount and distribution of food. In Yellowstone Park, bighorns in summer were found to live within a circle of a mile radius.

The bighorns are usually grass eaters. But in the dry mountains of our southwestern deserts, the grass is sparse and the bighorns here have adopted a different diet. They have become chiefly browsers and live on shrubs such as mountain mahogany, Mormon tea, buckbrush and the bark of ocotillo. They also eat the center and flowering parts of sotol, and the fruits and fleshy portions of sahuaro, organ pipe and barrel cacti, and prickly pear. In this land of little rain, the bighorns drink only once every three or four days, or even less often, and must get moisture from plant pulp. Along the Camino del Diablo in southern Arizona I have seen where they have chewed as much as six inches deep into the trunks of sahuaros. How do these tender-nosed bighorns avoid the wickedly sharp spines with which all the cacti are so heavily armed!

Mountain sheep farther north have a softer diet. Grass makes up ninety-five per cent of their food. For a fillip, they eat sedges, clover, tender herbs and a little browse. This latter includes the tender opening buds of aspen, spruce, Douglas fir, willow, currant, rose and juniper. These bighorns may be very finicky eaters. Sometimes they take merely the young flowers of some herbs such as wild buckwheat and smartweed, and leave the rest of the plant untouched. The Dall sheep of Alaska live principally on grasses, sedges, and willows, with smaller amounts of mountain avens, woodrush, horsetail, locoweed, cottonwood, blueberry, raspberry, alder, birch, cinquefoil, lichens, and other plants.

Like other hoofed animals, bighorns eagerly patronize salt licks. They do so most often in spring and early summer, but sometimes even in winter. I once visited such a spot on Ewe Creek in central Alaska. The grayish clay was exposed in a high bluff which was cut, trampled and gouged by the animals that came there. Many smooth spots and cuplike depressions showed where they had been licking. As we approached, four rams clambered over the bluff and disappeared. Following them to the bench above, we found many sheep droppings composed entirely of clay. Narrow trails were beaten three inches deep in the hard gravel, testimony of the thousands of hoofs that had traveled those trails for decades.

Sometimes they get salt by eating rock, decomposed rhyolite to a scientist, but salted rye crisp to the sheep. They chew down this sulphur-salt-flavored rock with great enjoyment.

The sure-footedness of the bighorn, while perhaps not as famous as that of the goat, is the envy of all mountaineers. The bottom of each cloven hoof is concave and the edge is sharp, enabling the animal to stick to the rocks with suction cups. One old ram in the Sierra Diablo of west Texas is known to have gone down a nearly vertical cliff fifty feet high, where only three footrests were possible.

Another sheep jumped four feet high and covered sixteen and three-quarters feet all in one leap, probably not an unusual one.

On Sable Mountain in the Alaska Range, I once startled a group of five Dall sheep rams. After milling around and watching me for several minutes they suddenly turned and, closely bunched, fled down the fifty-degree slope. As they raced at full speed, I expected one of them to stumble and the entire band to roll to the bottom of the gulch, a thousand feet below, in a flying pinwheel of broken legs and necks. Instead, the rams never faltered. Their white legs moved like blurred pistons as they sped on down to the very bottom and dashed up a slope opposite me. Here they stopped and immediately fell to grazing, apparently not even out of breath. Their poise and nonchalance were superb. They were neither excited nor flustered. They had merely, and casually, put me at my proper distance.

Bighorns cannot ordinarily maintain much speed for any length of time. However, one desert bighorn was found to have run at the rate of thirty miles per hour for a quarter of a mile.

All summer the rams loaf in their bachelor clubs, taking no part in the upbringing of the lambs. In late autumn, about the middle of October in the Rockies, their placid manner vanishes. They become jealous of each other, and vastly interested in the ewes. By the middle of November they are exceedingly restless and quarrelsome, and are chasing the ewes almost constantly. The rut becomes a craze. The ewes take to the cliffs for partial protection. They are sometimes almost surrounded by overeager admirers whose necks are extended and whose curled noses are lifted in the air. On the ewe's slightest movement, they rush at her. To get rest she may be forced to crawl out to the end of a narrow rock, or to hide under an overhanging tree or ledge. She, too, has horns, but they are only slender spikes. Sometimes as many as nine rams may chase a desirable ewe.

Many rams do not bother to make up harems. Those who do are occasionally quite lenient if a friendly ram comes to enjoy the society of his four to seven mates. Other harem masters are less generous, especially if a stranger attempts to intrude. Resulting battles are among the most spectacular in the animal kingdom.

Sometimes these duels seem to follow a definite routine with certain rules for position and movements. Two rams may open action by standing side by side, but facing in opposite directions. With ferocious grunts and snorts, they strike sideways and upward at each other with a sharp front hoof. For a few minutes (sometimes up to twenty), they tell each other off in this manner. Then they each walk away for about twenty feet. Suddenly, as though at a signal, they turn, rear simultaneously, and charge. Each ram is nearly upright and rushing forward on stiffened hind legs. Without pausing they drop to all fours, crouch, and the two heads crash together. The terrific crack of the heavy, hollow horns can be heard a mile away. The collision causes a ripple or "shock-wave" to roll the entire length of each muscular body. For a few moments the impact dazes the rams. Then they back away and crash again. The battle may be over quickly, or it may last for a couple of hours. It usually ends with both warriors on their feet. They may even walk away, side by side, in an amiable manner. The difference of opinion has been settled satisfactorily between one gentleman and another.

Sometimes a number of rowdies will jump into a free-for-all. This may become a most exciting battle and continue until the last two contestants are exhausted. No holds or blows below the belt are barred. Sideswipes with wicked hoofs cut deep bloody gashes, nosebleeds are common, horn tips splintered and sometimes entire horns are broken off short. These will never be replaced. Some rams push their opponents over the cliffs. Others are killed in combat by fractured skulls. By the end of the two-month mating season, many bighorn rams are battered, bruised, and limping.

Butting matches and, rarely, serious combats may be staged between rams in winter, spring or summer. As a rule, these are much more genteel arguments than the vicious fights during the two-month rutting season.

The gestation period of the bighorn has been determined to be one hundred and eight days, or almost exactly six months. The ram is not sexually mature until he is three and one-half years old, but the ewe mates for the first time a year earlier.

On the southern desert mountains the bighorns may frequent the same area the year round. Or they may migrate to a region of reliable waterholes during the summer. In the north the animals usually move twice each year between summer and winter range. This may be a shift in altitude to reach a locality where snowfall is of moderate depth, or it may be to find an area at a similar altitude where constant wind keeps the ground somewhat clear of snow. In the central Rockies, bighorns depend largely on grass in winter. They often paw through six or eight inches of snow to reach the short tender blades. At times they browse heavily, eating quantities of the twigs and buds of such shrubs as sagebrush, rabbitbrush, wild cherry and willow. Dall sheep in the Alaska Range subsist in winter on grasses, sedges, willows, blueberry, Labrador tea, sage, cranberry, and other plants. Their preferences are indicated by the order of listing the species.

By the beginning of winter the lamb is about three-quarters as tall as its mother, and weighs in the neighborhood of eighty pounds. Its frowzy baby coat has been shed and it is dressed in the double winter dress of all adult bighorns. Next to the skin is a loose layer of very fine fur, while over this extends a dense layer of coarse hair about two and one-half inches long.

Winter, which crowds the northern bighorns together on restricted ranges, is likely to test the animals not only with hunger but with disease. Parasites— ticks, scab mites, and lice—live on the skin. Internally there are lungworms and bacteria that cause pneumonia, nematodes that live in the intestines, and sheep bots that are found in the nose. Stomach worms cause diarrhea.

A very virulent disease of hoofed mammals, hemorrhagic septicemia, results in a pneumonic condition and a high death rate. Necrotic stomatitis, another disease of big game animals, often brings swift death, especially to the younger sheep. The organism causing it frequently enters the body through cuts and lesions in the mouth resulting from eating rough, coarse forage. Older animals that recover are frequently left with deformed jaw bones and missing teeth, which is a serious handicap to browsing and grazing animals that must eat huge quantities of forage.

Although exceedingly sure-footed, the mountain sheep live in a dangerous home and are subject to accidents. Bruises, cuts from jagged rocks, and broken ribs and even legs are more common than is supposed. Bighorns have been found dead with tough snags penetrating the abdomen and intestines, the result of a mad dash through a windfall at timber line.

Few bighorns live to be thirteen or fourteen years old. These aged sheep are unfortunate. (By the time they were ten or eleven, they were already far past their prime.) Their teeth are worn down, sometimes below the gums, and they are probably sick and hungry.

Wolves and coyotes hunt sheep of all ages. In the broken rock of the sheep's real home, these meat-eaters are left hopelessly behind, but out on the rolling mountain slopes, the foothills, or at valley crossings, they have the advantage. Among the cliffs, the cougar and possibly a wolverine may wait in ambush. When the snowshoe hares fail, the desperate lynx may turn to the bighorn, but he is only an occasional enemy. Both the lynx and the wolf have learned that the best way to catch a bighorn on a mountain is to climb above the prospective victim and then chase him downhill. The golden eagle is thought to be a serious menace to young lambs, but scientific investigations have cleared it of suspicion in a number of cases.

If the predators had been such important enemies that they controlled the numbers of bighorns, we might expect that the bighorns would have increased when the predators were in turn reduced. However, the extermination of the wolf, cougar and wolverine in several bighorn areas seems to have had no beneficial effect on the bighorn population.

In Wyoming, several bighorns are known to have perished as a result of quills from the ubiquitous porcupine. Apparently victims of their own curiosity, these vegetarian sheep must have poked their faces too close and a swish of a porcupine tail left the faces of the bighorns stuck full of fiery barbs. Noses and mouths swollen by the festering sores, the sheep were not able to eat, and starved to death or died of infection. Quills have been found in bighorn noses in Nevada, also.

Man has been by far the most destructive enemy of the mountain sheep. His attack has been indirect, by driving domestic sheep into the mountains to eat up the bighorn's forage; and direct, by shooting. The great curling horns of the wild sheep are the most coveted trophy in the world of sport. If fairly earned, it takes days of hard climbing, exposure to cold, wind and hail, clever stalking, and marksmanship of the highest order to kill an alert master of the crags.

The finest head of the Rocky Mountain bighorn on record was taken in British Columbia. The horns measured forty-nine inches along the front curve, with a circumference of sixteen inches at the base. Their greatest spread was twenty-four inches. The biggest head ever taken of the northern bighorn was a Stone sheep also from British Columbia. It had horns that measured fifty-one inches along the front curve, fifteen inches around the base, and spread a maximum of thirty-one inches.

A combination of disease, competition with domestic stock, and overhunting has decimated the bighorns over the southern half of their range. They have been extirpated completely from many mountain ranges, especially in the arid Southwest. Legal hunting for them, except in a few restricted localities in Idaho and Wyoming, was abolished from the United States years ago. Heavy fines and jail sentences are meted out to the convicted poacher, yet the magnificent head of an old ram is so tempting that unscrupulous men still take the risk of jail and fines.

Building a little rock blind overlooking a spring or seep, a poacher may wait days for the desert sheep to come in to drink, as they must eventually. Whether he kills for his own trophy, or to sell the head for money, the poacher of a rare bighorn is one of the meanest of outlaws. This human should be shot, stuffed and mounted for all to see.

The bighorn are divided into two species as follows:

1. The Rocky Mountain bighorn (*Ovis canadensis*) are heavy-bodied animals. Their massive horns are tightly curled. They live all the way from southwestern Alberta and southeastern British Columbia to northern Mexico. Their coats vary from the thick, dark grayish brown apparel of the northern mountain bighorn to the comparatively thin, pale buffy dress of the desert mountain bighorn.

2. The northern sheep (*Ovis dalli*) are perhaps more beautiful. They are somewhat smaller and more lightly built. Their long, slender horns are not as tightly curled and often flare away from the head. These sheep are divided into two kinds:

(a) The Dall or white sheep wear the striking white coats of their snow-bound home. They are found over most of Alaska and east in Yukon almost to the Mackenzie River.

(b) The Stone or black sheep are less spectacular in their brownish black coats. They inhabit south-central Yukon south to central British Columbia.

General description. A large, chunky, hoofed animal with dark brown horns, those of the adult male heavy and curling almost a full circle while those of the female and young male are small and only slightly curved. Hair much like that of the deer. Color varies with the locality—upper parts pale grayish brown to blackish brown or nearly black, darkest along the back line and on legs; large rump patch and under parts yellowish white. The Dall sheep of Alaska is completely white, and its dark horns are slender and flaring. Total length, 54 to 70 inches; height at shoulder, 38 to 42 inches; weight, 175 to 225 pounds. Females are considerably smaller.

Distinguishing characteristics. The combination of distinct rump patch and simple curved horns.

Range. Mountainous areas of western North America, from Chihuahua and Baja California, Mexico, north through the Rockies and Sierra Nevada to Brooks Range and Kenai Peninsula of Alaska.

MOUNTAIN GOAT
OREAMNOS AMERICANUS

The mountain goat is not a true goat; it is an antelope. It looks something like a goat and acts like one. However, its shoulders and neck are far heavier and the horns are smaller and do not twist into spirals. Although it goes by the name of goat, it is more closely related to the European chamois.

White, long-haired and bearded, the mountain goat walks stiffly and with dignity. Its chunky body with short tail is set on short legs. Ruminatively, it chews its cud. Its yellow eyes are round and solemn. If it sees something strange, it is likely to sit up on its haunches to get a better view. With its white beard waving sedately in the wind, it reminds one of a professor looking over the top of his spectacles.

From the broken cliffs and almost barren slopes above timber line, it looks down on the rich, sheltered valleys. It disdains their easy existence. The tall meadow grass to feast upon is not for it, nor the tall spruce to cut off the biting winds. It is an ascetic, tough and hard.

MOUNTAIN GOAT

Strong icy winds and shallow stony soil stunt and flatten the few hardy plants that manage to survive. The sun shines but the home peaks of the goat are so high that warmth is radiated off into space and lost.

Living in the Arctic zone of the northern Rockies, the mountain goat keeps comfortable in a suit of underwear of very fine wool, three or four inches thick, under the long shaggy overcoat. In the winter the goat's black horns, lips and hoofs stand out in striking contrast with his white coat. In the summer, at least in some localities, the horns and hoofs turn grayish white.

The heavy, fleecy coat is not a disadvantage in wet climates. Many goats live close to the coast from Puget Sound north and west to the Seward Peninsula in Alaska. Here fog and rain are more usual than fair weather during most of the year.

Naturalists have much to learn about the goat, especially what it does in winter. Man can seldom endure the conditions which to the goat are just everyday winter weather.

During the pleasant days of spring, in late April, May and June, the kids are born. Usually the nanny has only one, but twins are not rare and at times and in favorable localities they may occur rather commonly.

A few minutes after birth, the kid stands up and reaches for its first meal. Thus fortified, it may even jump about, in the peculiar stiff-legged goat style, at the tender age of half an hour. It weighs about seven pounds, and stands about thirteen inches high at the shoulders.

Although the kid is so precocious, its mother keeps it hidden in the isolated birthplace. She goes out to feed, but returns every couple of hours to let it nurse. If danger appears, the kid "freezes" immediately. After a few days, the pair joins a mixed band of mothers with kids, other females and young billies. There may be twenty to thirty or even more goats in a group.

During the summer months the nursery area is surprisingly small. The band may be found almost any day on a single mountain slope, browsing on the leaves and succulent new sprouts of dwarf shrubs and other plants, including grasses, sedges, phacelia, and mountain sorrel. The adult males wander over much larger areas, and are solitary more often than not. Sometimes, however, a billy may be seen accompanying a nanny with her kid during the summer.

Ordinarily the goat is not quarrelsome with its kind. In the November rutting season, however, the billies get pugnacious. They beat the shrubs with their horns, and rub them against rocks, leaving behind an oily secretion from the large gland that lies just to the rear of the base of each horn. Perhaps this is an attraction to the nannies, which have their own scent posts.

A goat is apt to keep his dignity even when angry. He and his rival walk stiff-leggedly around each other, sparring awkwardly but with grim determination. Successful thrusts of their daggerlike horns may result in peritonitis, a not uncommon cause of mortality. After the mating ardor has subsided, the goats move together in large bands. Only the older males avoid their erstwhile mates. The goats seem able to subsist on very little forage. They live for long periods wherever the wind blows the snow from small areas on ridges or slopes where palatable plants are exposed. Ordinarily, except for this slight shift to wind-cleaned spots, the animals use the same range throughout the year.

A principal hazard in winter is the avalanche. White goats seem to pay little heed to the frightful torrents of snow that occasionally thunder down the mountain sides, sweeping trees and boulders in their path. These snow-slides may kill more goats than any other single factor.

The mountain goats that have been moved to the Black Hills, South Dakota, often descend to the bottoms of ravines during the heavy snows of winter.

The goat is a deliberate creature. Ordinarily it walks slowly and with a certain stiffness due to the relative shortness of the front legs and the weight of the shoulders. An old animal with arthritic joints walks even more stiffly, and often has real difficulty in getting up from the ground and hobbling downhill.

It is a careful mountaineer, rarely taking a step until certain about the trail beyond. If, because of some emergency, the goat chooses a narrow, crooked ledge that "peters out," it doesn't get panicky. Perhaps it is possible to back very slowly until it can turn around, but if that is impossible, it cautiously rears up on the hind legs. With its weight pressed against the cliff, the goat carefully turns inward and around and then drops down on all fours, or it may grab a rock shelf with its short forelegs and pull itself up to a higher level.

An enemy cannot count on setting an ambush for a goat. Although it travels the same cliffs many times, it does not always pick the same trail. Perhaps it likes to figure out new routes and combinations of footholds. Several goats climbing together often scatter instead of following a leader.

It is not true that a goat never makes a misstep. Falls sometimes result in broken bones, and even death.

When frightened, the goat shifts into a slow lumbering gallop. Going uphill on good footing, a man has been able to almost catch up with a fleeing goat. In spite of his clumsiness, the goat is a good jumper, and one leap may cover twelve feet at a time.

Sheer cliffs and great heights seem to have no effect on it. It has a cool head, and probably little imagination. The hoofs are marvelously adapted for rock work. The sole of each toe is concave so that each one acts as a suction cup when pressed down hard. The clefts between the two toes on each foot open toward the front. When descending a smooth rock surface, the weight of the animal spreads the toes wider and they clamp down even more firmly on the ground.

A goat can swim, and swim well when it wants to. It probably crosses lakes and the long coastal bays of southeastern Alaska in this way.

Most mountain men believe that the golden eagles kill large numbers of kids. The remains of kids are sometimes found on or below eagle nests. Whether or not these were dead before being picked up by the big birds has never been determined, as the golden eagle is a notable scavenger. One point against this theory of kidnapping is that after the first couple of days in hiding the kid is continuously close to its mother. A wise old nanny has little fear of an eagle.

On their rocky ramparts, the goats are almost immune from attack by any four-footed enemy except the big climbing cats, the cougar and the lynx. Unfortunately there is only a small amount of nourishment there in the form of lichens and mosses. The goats must graze the smooth slopes of the mountains for the bulk of their food and occasionally descend into the valley to visit mineral licks. Sometimes they pass through several miles of forest in moving from one mountain range to another. At these times, they may be attacked by a grizzly, a black bear, a pack of wolves, or a wolverine. Even the big mountain coyote, out after ground squirrels, is always glad to take advantage of a goat.

The goat, however, has considerable pugnacity, and an adult buck or doe can do a lot of damage when cornered and desperate. The slender, slightly curved horns of the male average about nine inches long, but have been known to measure twelve and one-half inches. The doe's are smaller, but are also effective daggers. They have killed black and grizzly bears by thrusts into the heart, lungs or abdomen.

Some naturalists in northern British Columbia once watched two wolves try in vain to secure a meal from among a band of eleven goats. Showing little or no concern, the goats stopped twice to drink at pools of water before going on to the security of the cliffs. Of course goats would rather run than fight if given a choice.

When stopping to feed for any length of time, one goat usually appears to stand guard. Sometimes it will stay in one spot without moving its feet for over an hour. Looking this way and that, it keeps its feet planted far apart as if ready for an immediate attack.

The goat is occasionally curious about man, for bipeds are almost unknown in the high mountains. It is seldom aggressive. In one instance, an over-bold and inquisitive naturalist followed a goat onto a rock ledge that terminated in empty space. Made desperate, no doubt, the goat charged, bunted its annoyer over the cliff and walked angrily away. Fortunately for the man, a rock shelf about ten feet below saved him from anything worse than severe bruises and a bad scare.

Goats are subject to a number of ailments, including pneumonia and that notorious plague of the big game, necrotic stomatitis. Heavy infestations of tapeworms and stomach worms have been found. The thick furry coat may serve as shelter for great numbers of ticks which sometimes plug the ears so solidly as to cause deafness. Carcasses are rarely found because the sick animals crawl into crevices that are almost never penetrated by man.

The Indians of the Northwest Coast once used the goat's fine underfur in making choice blankets. The dyed and natural wool was rolled into yarn by hand and then woven on looms. The wool was pulled from dead goats, or gathered from bushes or from the ground where it was shed naturally. I have seen several places where the wool was so thick that several bushels could have been raked up from a few square yards.

Goat hunting is a difficult sport, chiefly because the animal lives in such rugged, inaccessible places. But unless the region is much hunted, the goat is not wary, nor particularly difficult to approach within rifle range. As a trophy, the head is unusual but the horns are not impressive.

The mountain goat has been far less adversely affected by man than any other North American big game. The meat of young goats is good, but that of older animals is tough and "strong." With very minor exceptions, goats still inhabit the same range that their ancestors occupied when Captain Cook sailed his ship into Prince William Sound more than a century and a half ago. Man has found no use for the home of the mountain goat.

General description. A large goat-like animal with humped shoulders, small, slender, backward-curving black horns, and bearded chin; tail short. Hair long, shaggy, white with a slight yellowish tinge. Total length, 60 to 70 inches; height at shoulder, 35 to 40 inches; weight, 150 to 300 pounds. Females are about 15 per cent smaller.

Distinguishing characteristics. The white, shaggy coat and goat-like appearance.

Range. Mountains of northwestern North America, from south central Idaho, western Montana, and the Cascade Mountains of southern Washington north to the Copper River region, Alaska.

5. Survivors of Ancient Orders

OPOSSUM—*DIDELPHIS* SP.

The opossum is our only native North American mammal that carries her young in a pouch. Very premature, the little opossums are born just thirteen days after their conception. Smaller than a bumblebee, each baby weighs one-fifteenth ounce. Its eyes and ears are still developing in the body covering; the stomach, heart and other organs can be seen through the transparent body wall, and the tiny legs are nothing but pegs.

Formerly it was supposed that the newly born opossum was picked up by the mother and placed in her pouch. Only within comparatively recent years have biologists learned that it reaches the mother's pouch by dragging itself up by the front paws.

The first trip in the little opossum's life is a hazardous one. During spring, the cold may be chilling. In the forest of hairs of the mother's abdomen, the opening of her pouch is hard to find. Small, it can be almost closed by muscles to keep the infants from falling out once they are inside.

Feeling its blind way, the little opossum must rely solely on instinct to climb higher. If it misses the entrance at first, one of its many brothers and sisters may beat him to the last of the mother's teats. She has about twelve (depending on the individual), and sometimes as many as eighteen young are born. Six of them, being cut off from food, must die.

Crawling into the warm dark pouch, the first dozen offspring feel for a teat, which is about the diameter of a pin. Taking a firm grip, the infants hang on for weeks without letting go. Their sole concern is food. In the first week their weight increases nearly ten times, and at two months of age they are as big as mice. By this time, accidents and the mother's limitation of milk will have reduced their number to an average of seven to nine.

Even earlier, at the age of a month, the youngsters start to peek out of the mother's pouch at a new world. Probably the first glimpse is of the nest—a leafy grass-lined burrow in the ground or a cavity in a tree or fallen log. Or it may be of the tree tops while the mother is hunting for sleepy birds or a batch of eggs. The young find it great fun when they are old enough to ride on their mother's back with their toes firmly grasping her coarse fur. They leave her to fend for themselves when they are about three months old.

OPOSSUM

Most opossums are born during the months of January and February in the South, somewhat later in the North. However, a few litters may be delayed a month or even two, if the females do not meet the males at the first opportune time. Most southern opossums produce a second litter of young, which are born in May or early June. South of the United States border there may be time for three families in a season.

The first conscious effort of each young opossum is probably to find a new home. It is not an expert digger and is glad to take any vacant den. Sometimes it repairs and adds more leaves to an old squirrel nest in a treetop. It may even move in with another animal that is too phlegmatic to protest, perhaps an armadillo or a skunk.

Even a half-grown opossum knows how to gather its nesting material. Picking up mouthfuls of dry grass or leaves, it pushes them under the abdomen to the prehensile tail which is expectantly curved in a loop. Six or eight mouthfuls fill the loop. The opossum then moves into its den, dragging the load of leaves with the tail.

Although solitary except at mating time, the opossum is not very particular about its home territory or hunting range. The neighboring opossums wander over, without causing any ructions, in their search for food. They eat everything: flesh, fruits, vegetables and even carrion, although flesh is preferred. One opossum is known to have eaten a bat. Whether it actually killed the bat, or came across the dead body, is not told. Opossums like insects (including scarab and ground beetles, squash and stink bugs, ants, grasshoppers and crickets), worms, mice, moles and other small mammals, snakes, lizards and skinks, frogs and fishes, crayfish, snails, birds and their eggs, mushrooms, fruits such as pokeberry, hackberry, mulberry, grapes, blackberries, green brier (*Smilax*), haws, apples, wild cherries, persimmons and pawpaws. They sometimes eat cultivated grain, particularly field corn.

Life is one gastronomic excitement after another! In the South at least, lack of food is hardly one of the factors that limit the numbers of opossums. They do not have to travel far from home, for ordinarily they find plenty to eat on an area of between fifteen and forty acres. The species seems to have a wanderlust, however. In the cooler months, most opossums wander about. A forest from which opossums are hunted out will soon be restocked by immigrants.

Next to the minutes following the birth of the tiny opossum when it must struggle to its mother's pouch, the days following weaning are the most critical of its life. Hawks, owls, foxes, dogs, bobcats, coyotes, ocelots, wolves and all other meat-eaters are looking for it. Minor enemies, ticks and fleas, seem not to pester it much. Roundworms (nematodes) usually inhabit its stomach and intestines.

When cornered, the opossum may show its teeth. The traditional protection is to feign death, "play 'possum." It falls limply on one side, shuts the eyes and lolls the tongue from partly opened mouth. If picked up, it is limp as a rag. Pulse and heartbeat are reduced. Presumably this is a state of true shock, but if the enemy leaves, its "victim" recovers almost immediately. Apparently these wiles are not very successful, for the opossum's life expectancy is short.

The opossum likes wooded streams. It is quite adaptable, however, and does very well in farming country providing there is enough cover left for shelter and hunting for food. Even in settled country it is rarely seen, for it sleeps all day and forages at night.

Climbing is second nature, and it hunts as readily in the tree tops as on the ground. The hind feet are even better "hands" than the front ones because they have a very long flexible first toe. This "big toe" can meet any of the other four toes of the same foot like a kind of superthumb. So the opossum goes around grabbing things with the hind feet the way people use their hands. Its naked, scaly tail is also prehensile and very useful to carry loads or to hang itself up on a tree.

Although we usually think of the opossum as an animal of the deep South, it ventures much farther north. For a retiring animal, the opossum has shown a surprising tendency in recent years to extend its range. It has been found living as far north as Warner, New Hampshire; Bellows Falls, Vermont; Albany and Binghamton, New York. It has also been seen in southern Ontario, central Michigan and southern Wisconsin. A convenient habit of wrapping up in leaves in a hole and becoming torpid for several weeks at a time helps it to ignore the cold winters. During very cold weather, females especially are likely to remain in their dens. The species does not truly hibernate. At most, the body temperature does not vary more than three and one-half degrees Fahrenheit between the hottest and coldest times of the year.

With the help of man, the opossum has become established in California. Between 1905 and 1910, captive animals escaped or were liberated near Los Angeles and at Santa Clara. Their descendants are now found at many places south of Sacramento, and west of the mountains and deserts. At least one has even climbed up the Sierra to Giant Forest in Sequoia National Park. Other opossums are known to have become established near Pendleton, Oregon. In 1943, they were also reported in Washington State.

Opossums belong to the "Ancient Order of Marsupials, or Pouched Mammals," whose best known representative is the kangaroo. Theirs is a very old family which had its beginnings back in the Mesozoic era. They probably spread over all of the continents. Eons later, but still a very long time ago, something exterminated all of the opossums in North America. But you can't stop the opossums from traveling, and in the Pliocene or early Pleistocene they wandered north across Central America from the southern hemisphere.

Opossums come in three color phases. The normal coat is the well-known 'possum gray, in which the black-tipped under fur is overlaid with long white guard hairs. "Black" opossums, in which the white hairs are almost lacking, are rather common in some localities. The cinnamon phase results when brown pigment occurs instead of the black. White opossums have been seen with fancy trimmings—black-tipped ears and toes—and albinos are not rare.

In spite of a large infant mortality and a short life expectancy, the opossum belongs to a hardy race. He shows an amazing vitality and ability to recover from injuries that would finish weaker creatures. Of ninety-five skeletons of animals taken near Lawrence, Kansas, thirty-nine had broken bones that had completely healed. Many had survived broken ribs and shoulders. They are extraordinarily careless! One animal had recovered from a total of two broken shoulders, eleven ribs (two of which were broken in three places and two others had two breaks each), and a badly damaged vertebral column. Not being very intelligent, the opossum must be both prolific and tough to survive.

The fur, while coarse, and seldom worth more than fifty cents a pelt to the trapper, is always in fashion for trimming inexpensive cloth coats. The better pelts are made into whole fur wraps. Farmer boys find opossums easy to trap and the number of skins sold each year is enormous. It has been estimated that, in Missouri in 1934–5, trappers and night-hunters killed three hundred and thirty-three thousand. During 1937–8 in Iowa, eleven thousand seven hundred and fifty-five pelts were sold for a total over three thousand five hundred dollars. It is said that an opossum usually has enough fat to fire five 37-mm. antiaircraft shells!

General description. A bushy-furred animal about the size of a house cat, with long, sharp muzzle, short legs and long, naked scaly tail. Fur grizzled gray becoming yellowish white on the head. Total length, 2½ to 3 feet; height at shoulders, 5¾ to 6½ inches; weight, 8 to 15 pounds.

Distinguishing characteristics. The sharp muzzle, generally with many teeth exposed when the animal is frightened; grizzled fur and long, naked tail.

Range. Central New England to Florida and westward from the Atlantic coast to Wisconsin, Colorado and Texas; also established in the Pacific Coast states.

ARMADILLO

DASYPUS NOVEMCINCTUS TEXANUS

A Pig in Armor!

Dressed up like a knight of old, this long-snouted, short-legged creature shuffles about in a coat of "chain and mail." Only the ears are naked. Fore and aft it is encased in form-fitting bony coverings that are joined over the ribs and backed by nine flattened hoops. One flat plate covers its head from crown to tip of nose. The tail is protected by a series of rings. Even the short legs are covered with many hardened scales.

With all this display of armor, it is astonishing to discover that the front of the upper and lower jaws are toothless! True, it has molars, but not a pre-molar, a canine, nor an incisor in its head! Even the molars are mere rootless pegs with no enamel covering.

Nevertheless it is a juggernaut to the world of insects. Its long sticky tongue darts back and forth sweeping in its victims. It can lap up sixty or seventy ants, their eggs or larvae, with a single swipe and practically no effort.

This small armored tank is a "fire eater." At least it devours fire ants, scorpions, tarantulas and roaches. It has been widely accused of destroying the eggs of quail, turkeys and other ground-nesting birds. Proven instances of such raids, however, are rare, and as a matter of fact, its appetite for the ants that attack the newly hatched chicks has greatly benefited the quail population. It actually has little or no interest in eggs unless they belong to insects or snakes. Only occasionally has it been known to raid a poultry house for eggs. Certain captive armadillos positively refused to eat hens' eggs until the shells had been broken for them. A nest of bantam eggs placed in a cage with five armadillos was ignored although it lay there for three weeks. Possibly only the most experienced foragers get the egg-eating habit, and they are few and far between.

Ninety per cent of the armadillo's food is of the insect type. Besides those species already mentioned, the animal eats sugar cane borers, termites, the larvae and adults of scarab beetles, wireworms, centipedes, grasshoppers and

ARMADILLO

other destructive insects. Sometimes it eats a few fungi, especially puff-balls; and fruits such as blackberries, mulberries, and wild plums. A careless or torpid salamander, toad or lizard furnish an occasional meal.

Eons ago, an animal belonging to the Ancient Order of Armadillos was as large as a modern rhinoceros. It roamed the plains of South America. Other much smaller cousins of this behemoth lived as far north as the present boundary between Canada and the United States.

Time was not kind to the family. Armadillos now range only from Patagonia to Texas and Louisiana. The nine-banded armadillo, the only species entering the United States, is one of the larger members of the present family. It is scarcely two and one-half feet long and weighs twelve to fifteen pounds. The smallest of the tribe lives in South America and is only about five inches long. Nine-banded armadillos of several races inhabit a vast area: all of South America east of the Andes and from northern Argentina to the southern United States.

In 1870 armadillos were unknown in Texas outside the lower Rio Grande Valley. As civilization spread, and their natural enemies were reduced, the armadillos had leisure and opportunity to travel. They pushed their way farther and farther northeast until by 1895 they had reached the Brazos River. Soon after 1925 they invaded northeastern Oklahoma and Louisiana. Then, even before bridges had been built across the Mississippi, they mysteriously appeared on the east bank. Now they are well across the state on their way to Mississippi and points east. Colonies have been established in Florida and Mississippi, probably from escaped or released pets. Alive, or dead with their shells made into baskets, armadillos have been shipped and sold for years. By natural means, the species has spread to southwestern Arkansas and eastern Oklahoma.

All goes well for these northern pioneers until an unusual cold spell occurs. A few frosty days do not matter; the armadillos merely stay in their burrows. A more extended period may be fatal. Armadillos do not hibernate and eventually they must seek food. Those that do not freeze to death in their dens come out. They cannot dig into frozen ground, and their surface-dwelling prey is destroyed by the cold. The unfortunate creatures starve or succumb to exposure.

There is some reason to believe, therefore, that the armadillo is now near the northernmost limit at which it can survive. Sooner or later, a succession of cold winters may shrink the range southward for hundreds of miles.

Heat is not such a serious problem. The armadillo does not like too much of it, but it can get relief by staying below ground. On very hot days it hunts only in the cooler night hours. If the ground is baked too hard, the creatures on which it feeds retreat deeper in the soil, and then the armadillo may starve to death.

Do these armored tanks sink or swim? Did they cross the largest river in the United States under their own power or as hitch-hikers on ferries? In spite of its armor, the armadillo is a good swimmer, but if the waterway is short, it walks under the water, on the bottom. When one good deep breath of air is not enough for the crossing, it must come to the surface. Obviously it has serious trouble staying afloat at first. Weighed down by the heavy shell, it dog-paddles furiously with stubby legs and gasps desperately for air. Then, slowly, the heavy body relaxes. It breathes more slowly and self-assuredly. At last it has swallowed enough air to inflate the intestinal tract. Buoyed up by this internal life pre-server, it swims vigorously and well.

On land, the armadillo likes enough cover for protection. But not so much as to shade out its insect food. It lives in thickets, tall grass, patches of cactus, or chaparral, and particularly enjoys limestone rock formations where burrows are ready-made by leaching water. In one of these, or in a "hand-made" tunnel, the mother has her young. The home may be seven or eight inches in diameter and up to twenty-five feet long, but usually is much shorter. The tunnel is straight, unless it must go around an obstruction, and ranges in depth from a few inches to four feet. It generally forks two or three times. The enlarged end of each branch is about one and one-half feet in diameter, and is lined with grass, leaves of mesquite or other shrubs, or weeds. The nest is merely a bundle into which the armadillo worms its way.

One animal has several dens, sometimes as many as ten or a dozen. Some serve only for emergency shelters. Especially shallow tunnels may be most useful to attract the insects which form so much of its food.

While digging, the armadillo loosens the soil with its forefeet and pointed snout. When a small pile has accumulated under the belly, it balances on its forefeet and tail. Arching its back, it brings the hind feet over the pile. Then a quick kick backward sends the dirt flying a couple of feet and the armadillo is ready to dig several inches more.

When the excavator is ready to make a nest, it goes to the surface and gathers the material. With the forefeet it makes a small bundle and pushes it back into the angle between its raised body and the hind legs. Lowering its shell will clamp the bedding fast. Then the armadillo slowly shuffles backward into the tunnel, catching any loosened material with its mouth or front feet.

Apparently this animal does not have a special toilet. The feces are scattered along the trails. About the size and shape of a marble, they are made up mostly of the hard remains of insects. These are poorly held together by soil which the armadillo has carelessly eaten while probing for food.

Armadillos are monotonous. An ordinary observer can't tell a male from a female. They look alike and act alike. Even when grown, they are the same size and the same weight. With few exceptions, the mother gives birth to four babies which are all of the same sex. Neither more nor less, because the original cell, when fertilized, normally splits into equal quarters and the little quadruplets start on their prenatal development. Not only are they all of the same sex, but they are identical down to minute details of scales and numbers of hairs on their bellies. In rare cases five embryos have developed, or one or more of the normal four have degenerated before birth. Armadillos mate in midsummer, July or August. The cells do not start to divide until about fourteen weeks later. The young require only one hundred and twenty days for actual development. Born in February, March or April, their eyes are open, and they are well developed except that the "coat of mail" is soft as fine leather. They are miniatures of their mother and are able to move about with her a few hours after birth. Because armadillos do not change shells like lobsters or crabs, their armor cannot harden completely until they reach their full growth and are sure of a "perfect fit!" The young are nursed by their mother for about two months. She has just the right number of breasts—four.

Even before they are weaned they join her in foraging for insects. Erratically the animals move about, now walking, now trotting. The long pointed snout is pushed into the leaf litter and the loose top soil. Instead of constantly lifting it, the armadillo roots out a furrow three or four or even six inches deep. When a buried insect or grub is located, evidently by smell, the armadillo stops and digs a cone-shaped hole with its front feet. When working especially hard, it is likely to grunt softly. Quickly chomping down the morsel, it puts its nose "back to the grindstone" and plows ahead. The course is haphazard and it often goes over an area twice in a night.

Occasionally the armadillo sits up on its hind legs and, bracing itself with its tail, sniffs the air for danger. It also uses this stance when examining plants for insects and berries.

Armadillos are sociable animals. Sometimes as many as fifty may be seen foraging together. Although adults generally live alone, as many as five have been found in one den.

The armadillo is a favorite, in a different way, with coyotes, dogs, men and all other carnivores. Even peccaries eat it. Once you get under that hard shell, the flesh is delicious. Especially when barbecued with hot chili sauce. The meat is white and tender, and tastes like pork. In east Texas, the armadillo is often called "poverty pig" or "poor man's pig."

Its eyesight is bad, and, despite the uncovered mule ears, its hearing is not much better. Enemies can often creep up closely before the industrious armadillo notices anything wrong. In such a dilemma, some of its cousins in South America roll up tightly in their armor.

Unfortunately our armadillo's suit is not as complete, and it must take to its heels for safety. With amazing speed, this clumsy-looking little pig-tank races for its burrow or a thicket. It can outrun a man and outdodge many dogs. Once in a tangled thicket, its safest refuge, it digs furiously. The two great middle claws on each front foot slash at the earth and soon it is out of sight. Here, in this emergency tunnel, it arches its body and the plates of its "mail" dig into the soil. Pulling it backward only wedges the plates more firmly. An armadillo once buried itself in two minutes so firmly into the earth that it was necessary to use a pick to dig it out. If cornered, the animal's only defense is the raking claws and the odor. The latter originates in a pair of anal glands and is objectionable to most people. When captured alive, it is easily tamed and makes an unusual pet. It seems to be unusually free from external parasites such as ticks, fleas and lice. Armadillos have been known to share their nests with cottontails, cotton rats, and opossums. Their abandoned burrows are useful as shelters for many animals, including cottontail rabbits, opossums, skunks, burrowing owls and even an occasional mink.

General description. About the size of a small house cat but much broader and more squat. Entire body, except the ears, under parts, chin, throat and base of tail, covered with a dense hard shell which is mottled dark brown to yellowish white. Practically hairless except for a sprinkling on the under surfaces. Legs short, feet with well-developed claws. Total length, 28 to 30 inches; height at shoulders, 5¾ to 7 inches; weight, 12 to 17 pounds.

Distinguishing characteristics. Shell covering.

Range. Southwestern Arkansas, eastern Oklahoma and Louisiana, southwest through Texas, Central and South America.

6. The Insect Hunters

MOLE—FAMILY *TALPIDAE*

Few people have ever seen a mole. Most of the family seldom come above ground. But everyone knows when it travels under a lawn or golf course fairway. Long meandering ridges mark the roof of its tunnels. They ruin the appearance of the lawn and spoil the smoothness of the golf course. Prize tulips are felled, and golf balls are interrupted.

The common and western moles are almost blind. Their eyes have nearly disappeared. The eyelids have grown almost together over degenerate eyeballs, and the animals can only distinguish light from darkness. Many nerve endings on their nose, and sensory hairs on their hands keep them from bumping into the sides of the tunnels. Their hearing is also fairly acute.

A few moles, the hairy-tailed, shrew mole and star-nosed, can see more and are more venturesome. Their eyes are open, although very small. They frequently leave their burrows and travel about on the surface of the ground, but

COMMON MOLE

still disliking bright light, they keep under the cover of thick grass, ground litter and fallen logs.

Each species of mole looks superficially like the others. Built for digging underground, the animal has heavy shoulders with long-snouted head and short neck. The short front legs are stout and muscular, with large shovel feet and toes with big heavy claws. The hind legs and feet are small and the tail short. Except in the hairy-tailed and the star-nose, the tail is almost naked. Moles have no external ears to get in the way and the short velvety fur offers no resistance to their passage either backward or forward through the tunnel. Depending on the species, they vary from dark gray to black. Albino moles have been seen, as well as moles whose color was partly or completely cinnamon yellow.

Although the common and western moles usually prefer open country for their tunnels, the hairy-tailed mole may burrow in woodland if it is not too dense. Each of these three moles is quite particular about the quality of the soil. It must not be too sandy and loose, or the tunnels would collapse. Besides, its food, insects and worms, would be scarce. The most desirable habitat is soft, moist soil with considerable humus. The mole may live on hillsides, or on valley bottoms if these are not subject to regular flooding. Although it can get through a flooded burrow that is not too long, it would be likely to drown if all of the tunnels were inundated regularly.

The venturesome star-nosed and shrew moles not only leave their tunnels, but like water and are good swimmers. Their burrows are in swampy places, frequently in mucky soils and ending in a stream or pool. A very large part of the food of these moles consists of aquatic insects. Sometimes a stream bed is thoroughly plowed up by moles for the annelid worms that live there. The moles' broad front feet and the smaller hind ones serve as oars, while the tail is used slightly as a rudder.

Moles caught above ground don't run. They dig down underground and disappear almost immediately. In the water they try to escape danger by diving rather than by fleeing to land. Trappers sometimes catch these water-minded moles in traps set under water at the entrances to muskrat dens. A hardy individual, the star-nosed mole is quite likely to travel in water, under the ice.

The tunnels of all the moles are of two kinds. The deep tunnel, from six inches to two feet below the surface, is used as "living quarters" in which the mole spends the winter as well as periods of heat and drought. The surface tunnel, whose visible roof annoys housewives and golfers, is chiefly a means of reaching food. If worms are abundant, the mole will return to an old upper runway again and again. If not, it is used only a few times or perhaps but once.

Sometimes the surface tunnel is quite long and can be traced for more than half a mile. Perhaps such long passages are highways between nest and feeding grounds. They may also be the work of more than one mole.

If the soil is soft, surface tunnels are made quite easily. Apparently the mole uses its snout to find a suitable place to dig. Then it shovels the dirt aside with the big front feet. Going ahead, it twists the forward part of its body sideways and pushes upward with the forefeet. Thus the passageway is made by pushing alternately against the sides and the roof. The little miner seems to have a sense of location, at least in respect to the surface, for it goes over ridges and across ravines without breaking through to the top, or varying the thickness of the tunnel roof. In fairly compact soil it digs at the rate of twelve to fifteen feet an hour, including halts to feed or rest.

The deep tunnel is made in more compact soil and requires much more time and labor than the upper system of passages. First the hard soil is clawed loose with the front feet, thrown back under the body, and kicked to the rear by the hind feet. When a load has accumulated, the mole must turn around in the narrow passage. It has no turn-out. An able contortionist, it makes a slow half somersault. Now headed back to the opening, it pushes the dirt ahead of itself through the tunnel to the surface, where the mole spills it out in what we call a "molehill."

Even in cold climates, the common mole seems to be active throughout the winter except during periods of the lowest temperature. It cannot construct new surface tunnels where the ground is frozen, but the deeper system may be extended by carrying the excavated dirt into old side passages. Probably its activity depends upon the activity of its animal food.

I have occasionally seen tunnels that the star-nosed mole has made through the snow. Sometimes it comes out impatiently, and runs along on top of the icy crust. One of the peculiarities of some star-nosed moles is the curious enlargement of their tails in winter. At its greatest thickness, an exceptionally swollen tail may be as large in cross-section as a ten-cent piece. Nobody knows why the tail should swell at this time, nor why some star-nosed moles have it, and others do not.

Our moles are not known to store food, but a European mole is said to paralyze earthworms by biting them in the head and keeping them in cold storage for the winter.

Most moles work day and night, probably hardest in the daytime when the earthworms and insects are stirring. Perhaps because they labor so strenuously, the moles have an insatiable appetite. They often eat the equivalent of one-third to two-thirds of their own weight in a day. For a one hundred and eighty pound man, that would be sixty to one hundred and twenty pounds of meat and vegetables every day.

Not even the approach of death can destroy their appetites. Mortally wounded by sharp-pronged traps, they have been known to eat earthworms when placed within reach.

They prefer worms and insects, including ants, insect larvae, millepeds and centipedes, also snails, slugs and sowbugs. Occasionally, however, they must fill up the crannies with small amounts of vegetable matter such as seeds of corn, wheat and oats.

Apparently the eastern mole does not eat tulip bulbs, or any roots or tubers. It is likely to cut through them on its endless journey for other food, and the mice, that follow, finish them. The western mole, however, often devours tulip and iris bulbs as well as many other garden plants even when more usual food is abundant.

Earthworms are grasped in the mouth by one end and chewed down like spaghetti. The mole makes no effort to wipe off the dirt. As the two front paws slide down the worm's length, however, they occasionally clean the worm inside and out. The mole often kills beetles and other active prey by crushing them against the side of the burrow with front paws. At other times it piles earth on them and bites off their heads while they are thus imprisoned.

Do moles live together? Morose, underground creatures, most of them do not. Occasionally two or three common moles have been known to use the same tunnel in summer. Apparently the males live together more amicably than do females. In one case two females actually occupied a tunnel together for some time. But the inevitable quarrel took place. Plugging up a passageway with a wall they isolated themselves into separate tunnels.

The star-nosed and hairy-tailed are probably the only moles that really like a bit of company. It is not uncommon to find some numbers of them using a community system of runways.

Moles propagate only once a year. Mating in March, or earlier in the South, the one to five young are born six weeks later. This low replacement rate is an indication that the mole has comparatively few enemies. Many of the other small mammals have three or four or even more litters a year.

The birth chamber is in the lower tunnel. About eight inches in diameter and five inches deep, it may be lined with dead leaves, dry grass, or not at all. It may be located under a stump, boulder or bush for added protection, and have several entrances from as many tunnels.

The young are comparatively well developed when born. The fleshy nose fringe of the star-nosed mole is conspicuous at birth, and in fact can be discerned in a half-grown embryo. The youngsters grow rapidly. At the age of two months they are nearly as big as their parents and are demolishing lawns and golf courses with almost equal skill. They are ready to mate the next spring at the age of ten months.

Three years later, if accidents have not overtaken them, they are in their dotage. The common mole and western mole lead such subterranean lives that they are free from many troubles that beset the moles that venture on the surface. Most of the carnivores, such as the skunk, fox, and coyote, and the birds of prey such as the barn, barred and great-horned owls and the broad-winged and red-tailed hawks, will eat moles when they have an opportunity. The strong musky odor is some protection, however. Snakes sometimes pursue moles in their own runways. The star-nosed mole, while swimming, is in danger from rapacious fish like the pike.

Lice, fleas and mites may live in the fur, and threadworms in the stomach. Man kills great numbers of moles when they invade his premises, disfiguring lawns and gardens. Most commercial mole fur is imported from Great Britain and Canada. Once worth thirty-five cents each, the pelt of our own western mole is now seldom traded. It is good-sized but does not take dye satisfactorily.

The western mole at times feeds on flower bulbs and farm crops. It is also accused of spreading plant pests and diseases, and of providing easy access via its runways for mice to reach and destroy garden and orchard plants. In such cases, it can be caught and killed by traps set in the runways.

It should be accepted with enthusiasm in many other areas. It is one of the important soil-forming organisms, for it works over and aerates the soil, and destroys important crop enemies, such as cut-worms and Japanese beetles. It is interesting because of its peculiar way of life.

The North American moles are divided into two groups—eastern and western. The former range from the Atlantic and Gulf coasts, between Labrador and northern Tamaulipas, Mexico, west to Manitoba and eastern Colorado.

These eastern moles are divided into three groups or genera:

1. The common mole (*Scalopus*) has a naked tail and is best known and most widely distributed. It is found from Massachusetts west to central Minnesota and western Nebraska, and from Florida to southern Texas. It is between 5½ and 8 inches long.

2. The hairy-tailed mole (*Parascalops*) which lives from New Brunswick and southern Ontario south to the mountains of western North Carolina. Length 6 inches.

3. The star-nosed mole (*Condylura*) has a peculiar fleshy fringe around the

nose and lives from southern Labrador west to Manitoba and south to Georgia and northern Illinois. Length 7 to 8 inches.

The western moles are divided into two groups:

1. The western mole (*Scapanus*) is much like the common mole of the East, but larger. It is abundant from the west coast to the high mountains between British Columbia and northern Baja California. Length 6 to 9 inches. The Oregon member of this group is the largest and has the handsomest coat of all the moles. Nearly black, it brings a higher price than other skins.

2. The shrew mole (*Neürotrichus*) is the smallest of all the moles, about 4½ inches long. It is found on higher ground west of the Sierra Nevada from southern British Columbia to Monterey County, California.

General description. A small, stout-bodied, burrowing animal with pointed nose, short legs, and large flattened front feet; eyes and ears very small (hardly visible without close examination); tail short. Fur soft, brushing in any direction like velvet, gray to black in color. Total length, 4½ to 9 inches; height at shoulder, about 2 inches; weight, 2 to 4 ounces.

Distinguishing characteristics. Larger than the shrews and mice, which spend at least part of their lives on the surface of the ground; different from the pocket gopher in that the latter, although a burrowing mammal, has a rounded nose and small but readily discernible eyes and ears.

Range. Labrador to Florida and Tamaulipas, Mexico, west to Manitoba and northeastern Colorado; also west of the Cascades and Sierra Nevada from southern British Columbia to northern Baja California.

SHREW
FAMILY *SORICIDAE*

The smallest of all our North American mammals is the shrew, and it is also one of the fiercest. Even when it is only three inches long, it is as ferocious as a small tiger. It does not hesitate to leap upon a mouse that may be twice its weight. Almost anything smaller than a weasel that crawls, runs, or flies is tempting to this insatiable little assassin.

Most of its victims do not have a chance. If it is the short-tailed shrew, it poisons them when it snaps its tiny jaws. The secretion from the salivary glands, flowing into the wounds made by the long lower incisor teeth, slows the heart action and breathing of the victims. Then it easily tears them limb from limb and devours skin, bones, and all.

Several centuries ago, our European ancestors knew that the bite of the shrew was poisonous. Gradually this knowledge was lost until it was regarded as an old wives' tale. Very recently it was found that our forebears were not so stupid. Saliva from the glands in the lower jaw of the short-tailed shrew was injected into captive mice. They quickly lost their alertness and began to breathe heavily. Soon their hind legs became partly paralyzed, and they moved with great difficulty. Larger doses of the saliva brought on convulsions and finally death from failure of the lungs. The effect of the poison in the mouth juices of the shrew is very similar to that of snake venom—especially cobra.

In experiments, six milligrams of ground-up salivary glands of the short-tailed shrew proved sufficient to kill a mouse weighing twenty grams (almost four-fifths ounce), or about the same size as the shrew. The entire glands contained enough poison to kill two hundred mice! A naturalist bitten by a shrew

COMMON SHREW

reported an instant burning sensation, followed by shooting pains in his arm. Considerable discomfort lasted for over a week.

Not all species of shrews can depend upon poison. The saliva of the long-tailed shrew (*Sorex*), for instance, seems to have only a slightly crippling effect on its victims.

When the shrew is not butchering its almost continuous meals, it is fighting with other shrews. If it lives to be a year old, it is likely to have lost a tail, a toe, a finger, or all three, and the hide may be badly scarred.

Some trap records seem to indicate that males are twice as numerous as female shrews, which may explain why they are such savage fighters.

Extremely nervous, the shrew is the most high-strung of all our animals. Every movement is quick and jerky. First a little dash forward, then a quick turn and a lunge at right angles. All this action is accompanied by a twittering series of short exclamations. When fighting, it fills the air with continuous high-pitched squeaks. Its feints and passes are almost too swift for the human eye to follow.

Even during the rare intervals when it is standing still, its nose is working and the tiny ears seem to be strained to catch the slightest sound. Frequently a movement or sound will send it scurrying for shelter. Sometimes, however, it will come to a stop completely in the open, quite unlike most small animals that rush from one shelter to another.

Repeatedly I have found shrews dead in my "catch-'em-alive" mouse traps. They were apparently uninjured and had been provided with plenty of food. Because they were so high-strung, they had fretted themselves to death in a few hours or even minutes after being caught. If bedding is not provided in traps, they die quickly of exposure unless the weather is quite warm.

The appetite of the little shrew is enormous, much greater than that of the hungry mole. It burns up a terrific amount of energy, and can eat the equivalent of its own weight in meat on an average of every three hours.

Dr. C. Hart Merriam once placed three shrews under a glass tumbler. "Almost immediately they commenced fighting, and in a few minutes one was slaughtered and eaten by the other two. . . . One of these then killed and ate his only surviving companion." Having eaten two companions of its own size within eight hours "its abdomen was much distended," Dr. Merriam staidly concluded.

Though the shrew is not limited to a special ration, it is at times reduced to eating vegetables. Berries and nuts are the least objectionable. I have trapped many hungry shrews in winter with oatmeal as bait. During this season when meat is scarce, oatmeal seems to be as effective a lure as bacon. In the summer, however, nothing less than odoriferous bacon will attract them to a trap. In the Northwest they eat quantities of Douglas fir seeds. Because the animals are abundant, they may be one of the natural checks on the reproduction of this important forest tree.

In spite of its passion to get somewhere, anywhere, always in a great hurry, the shrew finds an opportunity to be well groomed. First it may clean its face with its hind feet. Then it washes its fur with its tongue and combs it with the toes. When kept in a cage, it fastidiously uses only one corner for a toilet.

The only other animal with whom the shrew can get along is his mate. He may live with her peaceably, even devotedly, for some time before and during the mating season, and until the young are born. Although he is found once in a while with as many as five or six adults in one nest or covert, the others are probably his mate and grown offspring. Usually the young are thrown out on their own resources by the time they are a month old. At this age they have become competitors for food and ordinarily are no more friendly than total strangers.

The typical little shrew is born in a covered leaf and grass nest in a hollow stump, under a log, or in a burrow near the surface of the ground. The outside diameter of this bundle of loose material is six to eight inches, but that of the interior is only two or three inches. The entrance is a small opening in the side of this ball-shaped nest.

There may be three to ten, usually six or seven, young in the nest. Tiny, pink and wrinkled, they are about the size of honey bees. Their combined weight is less than that of a twenty-five-cent piece, but is nearly or quite half of their mother's weight. She is very busy trying to satisfy her appetite which has now become voracious, and receives no help from her mate. In fact, just before the young are born, she takes the precaution of chasing him out of the nest.

At the age of a week, the little shrew begins to acquire its coat of fur, and can crawl about in the nest. In another week the body is well furred, the ears are open, and a few days later the first teeth appear. Within three or four weeks the eyes open. Its mother now feels that it is old enough to be weaned, and it is put out on its own for the rest of its short life. Meanwhile the mother gets ready for the next bumper crop of babies as she has two or three litters each summer.

The young shrew becomes wise to the ways of the world in a hurry. Although it is thrust into the world of competitors and enemies without experience, it learns quickly to be a successful hunter. Instead of the mother's milk, it gulps down crickets, ants, beetles, the larvae of flies, butterflies, moths, grasshoppers, slugs and centipedes. With the strong, hooked incisor teeth, it bites off the apex and spire of shells and pulls out snails and other mollusks. Earthworms and small salamanders furnish easy prey. Lizards are nabbed by their tails, but occasionally escape if the tail breaks off. The young shrew philosophically eats the tail and tries to work faster with the next one. Any carrion, no matter how rank, is a find. If maggots are working in it, so much the better!

Young mice are readily killed. An animal as active as a grown mouse has a good chance to elude the killer because of the shrew's poor eyesight. In a cage, where it cannot get away, it is a different matter. Even if the mouse were able to fight back before being affected by the poison, it has little chance to kill its smaller attacker. The shrew's skin is thick and tough, especially on the neck, and even a large mouse is unable to bite through it.

In captivity, the shrew appears to be playful. Or maybe it is just keeping in practice. Captives have frequently pretended to have a hard struggle to kill small insects put in their cage. Throwing them into the air, they worry and tug, rush and jump, as a cat may play with a mouse.

Just as these fierce little shrews leap upon and devour insects, so are they in turn leaped upon and devoured by many larger meat-eaters. Their skulls and bits of their bones are often found in owl pellets. Hawks and shrikes pounce upon them, and snakes, weasels, foxes, bobcats and coyotes hunt them. If it is hungry enough, even the great timber wolf may not disdain the tiny, strong-flavored creature. A pair of glands, one on each flank of the shrew, secretes such a strong-smelling musk that some predators do not relish their flesh. When not hungry, they will occasionally leave the little carcasses untouched. House cats especially are apt to kill and play with the remains of shrews, but are not hungry enough to overcome their repugnance to the rank odor.

You might think the water shrew would be comparatively safe from the usual enemies. It swims, dives, and walks on the stream bottom, catching small fishes and sometimes eating fish eggs which it digs from the gravelly spawning beds. The fur holds many tiny globules of air, so that under water it appears to be covered with a silvery sheath of little bubbles, but the inner fur does not absorb any of the moisture.

It walks on the water! Holding air bubbles in the feet, it runs blithely across the surface of a quiet pool. But this astonishing feat is no great protection, for the species is captured by fish, herons, and even mergansers.

Every shrew leads a fast life and a short one. It has no time to hibernate! Propagating two or three families of three to ten offspring a season, it has finished its mission in life at the age of fourteen or sixteen months. It has lived and eaten too hastily and too much. Rather frequently it is found dead without any mark of violence, dead of old age—at sixteen months!

Don't ever think a shrew is a mouse. It is an insectivore, like the mole, and in a general way has many mole characteristics. Its body is more slender, but like the mole's is covered with dark gray, velvetlike fur that brushes easily either way and never sticks up. Occasionally it has white patches on its flanks, and one shrew is recorded to have had a white belt around the middle. Only one in many thousands is an albino.

The shrew has short legs, tiny feet, insignificant tail, and a long head drawn out into a probing snout. It can see better than the mole, but the eyes are very sub-normal—perhaps 2/20 on an optician's scale. Because it is far quicker and more active than the mole, its diet is more varied.

Some of the Indian tribes distinguished shrews from mice. The Eskimos knew that a shrew that chanced to stray onto the sea ice was a distinct species, and they believed it to be a veritable demon. If disturbed, they thought the little creature would dart at the intruder, burrow into him and kill him by entering the heart. E. W. Nelson tells of an Eskimo hunter who, meeting such a shrew, stood like a stone for several hours until it disappeared. On reaching home, his friends all congratulated him on a very narrow escape.

Shrews inhabit most of North America. They are classified in five groups, several of which are difficult to distinguish except on skull and teeth characters.

1. The common, long-tailed, and water shrews (genus *Sorex*) have rather long tails and, with the exception of (2) and (3) below, are the smallest North American mammals. They live in damp places all the way across the northern part of the continent, and from the Arctic Ocean south to northern Florida, Illinois, Nebraska, central California and in the western mountains south to Guatemala. Length, 3½ to 6½ inches; weight, ⅓ to ⅘ ounce.

2. The pigmy shrew (*Microsorex*) is very tiny and has a short tail. It is found in dry open woods from northeastern Quebec to west central Alaska, and south to the District of Columbia, Ohio, and northwestern Washington. Length, 3 to 4 inches; weight, about 1/14 ounce.

3. The "little" shrew (*Cryptotis*) is much like the short-tailed shrew but is smaller and is brownish instead of gray. It occurs in swamps from southern New York to the tip of Florida, westward to eastern Nebraska, Texas, and into northern South America. The shortest American mammal: length, 3 inches.

4. The short-tailed shrew (*Blarina*) is a rather stocky, dark gray animal with a short tail. It lives from southeastern Canada south to southern Florida and west to Oklahoma and Manitoba. Length, 4 to 5 inches.

5. The Crawford or gray shrew (*Notiosorex*) is a slender animal about 4 inches long with a rather short tail and large ears. It is very rare within its

range: eastern Texas to southern California and south into Mexico for an unknown distance. Length, 3½ inches.

General description. A very small, darting mammal with pointed muzzle, minute or hidden eyes and ears, slender body, and small delicate feet; tail varies from short to long. Fur soft, brownish or grayish. Total length, 3 to 6½ inches; height at shoulder, ¾ to 1½ inches; weight, 2 to 20 grams, or 1/15 to 4/5 ounce.

Distinguishing characteristics. Usually seen briefly only while darting across the surface of the ground, when it may be confused with mice. The latter are usually proportionately "fatter" and their pelage is coarser and grizzled or more fawn-colored. Although similar in color, moles are much larger and normally live underground. The shrews are not only much smaller, but more slender, quicker of movement, and spend a portion of their time on the surface of the ground.

Range. Practically all of North America.

7. The Flyer

BAT—SUBORDER *MICROCHIROPTERA*

The bat is the only mammal that has wings. It is covered with fur, and has big ears and a tail. It suckles its mother's breast for milk. It bites, has the face of a tiny bull dog, the body of a mouse, and the wings of a miniature airplane.

Of the nearly 2,000 kinds of bats in the world, it may be the demure little pipistrelle only two inches long, or the great flying fox of the East Indies with a wingspread of more than four feet which eats fruits and flowers.

The bat does not try to get into women's hair. If it does, by chance, it does not result in death or a disastrous love affair within a year, as some writers would have you believe. Some bats—vampires—are said to suck human blood, but these bats do not live in the United States or Canada.

What is this mysterious flying mammal? Its furred face, the little eyes almost buried in wrinkles, pug nose, determined chin, and wings have erroneously symbolized evil for centuries.

Probably its ancestor began life like any other mammal. Perhaps it was a little shrewlike creature living in the tree tops. But see what determination can do! For countless ages, each new generation spent much of its energy trying to fly. Each bat even went to sleep hanging upside down. At last the little creature's legs and arms became stiff and sticklike. Slowly the hands and fingers grew fantastically long. A membrane of hairless skin covered and connected them, and they became the ribs of wings. It took many millions of years for the bats to learn to fly. The flying squirrels are still trying!

Since the bat's legs and arms have been imprisoned by a wing-membrane and its knees and elbows bend only backward, its feet and hands are of little use except to hang itself up when it goes to sleep. On the end of each free, short thumb is a long claw which helps the bat when alighting and when crawling over the ground. The female uses it in giving birth as is shown later.

Bat ears are leathery and usually are bare of hair. Some are small, while others are so large that they have to be supported by thickened ribs. The ears of the pale bat, for instance, are twice as long as its face.

You wouldn't think there would be anything very remarkable about a bat's pug nose. A strange erect membrane or "leaf" rises on the nose of our leaf-nosed bat. This fellow has numerous relatives outside this country whose "leaves" take many different forms.

Is there a purpose for this leaf? One supposition is that it is a sensitive recorder of air vibrations set up by insect wings or reflected from stationary objects, or the echoes of supersonic shouts made exploratively by the bats themselves. Proceeding upon this assumption, it is said, Sir Hiram Maxim invented the echo sounder for finding obstacles hidden from a ship by darkness or fog. This device and the related depth finder, which determines the ocean depths by "bouncing" sound off the bottom, are among the most useful aids to navigation. Radar, the device by which the pilots of World War II found enemy aircraft and other targets on the blackest of nights, utilized a similar adaptation, this time of electrical waves.

A bat cannot compete with falcons, doves or many of the waterfowl in a race against time and distance. Nevertheless the bats which migrate south for the winter travel many hundreds of miles each autumn. While pursuing prey,

BROWN BAT

many a bat can twist, turn and dodge in full flight with much greater agility than almost any bird.

Different bats have different techniques of flying. The little brown bat is extremely erratic, dodging and twisting with great speed. The pipistrelle flutters irregularly and slowly as if it couldn't make up its mind. The leaf-nosed bat swoops in long, very swift, apparently purposeful arcs. Although most bats' wings describe almost a half-circle in making each beat, the free-tailed bat flies like a bird with short, swift beats.

These marvellous fliers usually drink while flying. I have often watched them passing back and forth just above a pool. On each pass they scooped up a tiny tongue-full of water. Silver-haired bats falling into swiftly-flowing streams have proved to be excellent swimmers.

"Blind as a bat" is not completely blind. They can see well enough and are not dazzled by sunlight. Apparently, however, they depend largely on their "hearing."

Experiments were carried out with bats flying in a room hung with criss-crossing silk threads. The bats had been blinded but they flew about without touching the threads. Other blinded bats have been able to fly under chairs and other furniture to escape capture. Although not infallible when flying through an experimental maze of wires, blinded bats have been fairly successful. The little brown bats hit wires only about once in every four or five flights.

When the bats had their ears stopped with plaster, they blundered into obstacles two-thirds of the time. Apparently they guide themselves by the echoes of vibrations thrown back from objects. In this way they can chase their food at full speed through the darkness and dodge all sorts of obstacles.

Bats have voices which cover a wide register. In the upper range, the frequency of the sounds is in the neighborhood of fifty kilocycles, or fifty thousand sound waves a second. This is within the band used by commercial radio, and of course is far beyond the perception of the human ear. The bats listen for the echoes of their high-pitched cries to locate objects which they cannot see as they fly through darkness. In their ordinary conversations, and when expressing fear or pain, bats use "deep bass" tones which are audible to our ears as shrill squeaks.

As a race, bats eat a great variety of food. As families, they have highly specialized diets. The vampires are famous, or infamous, for living on blood. Some bats prey on frogs, mice, small birds, and lesser bats. These are all tropical animals, and none of them ever come to the United States except in the cages of collectors for zoos. Other bats, including the flying foxes of Australia, subsist on a fruit diet. There are even fish-eating bats! They catch fish by scooping them up in their tail membrane, or grasping them with their sharp-nailed feet, or both. Our own bats, as well as a host of others throughout the world, live almost entirely on insects.

At times bats may look for food on the ground. They have been known to feed on scorpions, and on Jerusalem crickets and their flightless relatives. Most of the time they capture their insect prey while flying. The click of their sharp white teeth snapping shut on a hapless moth can be heard for twenty feet. Sometimes they catch their meals in their mouth, sometimes in their tail membrane. When this membrane is dropped so that it curves back of the hind legs, it forms a net or pocket. If the captured prey is too large and powerful the bat takes it to a tree, where it bites the victim in the head several times and then devours it. The bat eats moths head-first and discards their wings.

The tiny bat has a big appetite. It will eat a quarter of its weight at one meal and more than half its weight every night. We owe it a debt of gratitude for its share in keeping the insect world in its place. The hordes of bats at Carlsbad Caverns eat several tons of insects in a single night. Estimates of the number in this colony range from one-half million to nine million. Most of them live in one vast room, a quarter of a mile long and up to one hundred and fifty feet high. It is located in what is probably the greatest and most thrilling chain of caves in the world. On summer evenings about sundown, on a signal that perhaps is given by a change in the air currents, the bats stream forth from the mouth of the cave to feed in the Pecos River Valley. For fifteen to twenty minutes the crowded column of bats pours upward and away until it seems to be a mile long. The clicking of wings as they strike accidentally, the squeaking protests of the animals, and the draft of air stirred into movement can be heard and felt a hundred feet away.

The deposit of their guano in the Caverns was at one time about one-quarter mile long, over one hundred feet wide and up to one hundred feet deep. Over one hundred thousand tons have been shipped for commercial fertilizer. At present, this valuable deposit is being replaced at the rate of a little less than an inch per year.

The value of guano, ranging from $60 to $90 per ton in the past, led opportunists to build artificial roosts to attract the animals. These towers, most of which are in Texas, are about twenty feet high, twelve feet square at the base and six feet square at the top. Only a few of them have been occupied by large numbers of free-tailed bats. The guano that accumulates on the floor of the tower is emptied by a chute. Ardent bat-fans claim that these animals control malarial mosquitoes but this has not been proven. We do know that they eat vast quantities of insects that are injurious to crops.

Most bats spend five-sixths of their life hanging upside down in the dark.

The bats that sleep through the summer days in caves, hollow trees or similar dark places usually spend the cold weather in caverns in the same general region. Brown bats and long-eared bats have been found hibernating in caves as far north as Port Arthur, Ontario, on the north shore of Lake Superior where the outside temperature frequently is colder than twenty degrees below zero. The winter homes of all cool-climate bats must be deep enough to maintain their temperature above the freezing point. Sometimes they put up in buildings —at the risk that the human owners will shut off the heat and migrate south.

If the temperature of their winter retreat stays between thirty-four and forty degrees above zero the bats go into a sound sleep. They breathe at five-minute intervals and stir only occasionally. Their body temperature becomes only slightly higher than that of the surrounding air. If necessary, they can arouse themselves, may move a bit, and if water is available drink a little. Sometimes bats choose poor hibernating places. In such cases they have been known to fly as far as one hundred and twenty-five miles between caves during cold weather. When spring brings out the early insects, all the bats rouse, and start flying and feeding.

A few species, such as the red, the hoary, and the silver-haired bats, migrate south in autumn and return in spring. These bats roost in treetops or against tree trunks. They do not like to enter caves and they winter luxuriously in the southeastern states. Most of them migrate over land, largely at night, but several great flights in the daytime, usually in cloudy weather, have been recorded.

Sometimes the travelers take short cuts over the ocean. Flights of several hundred bats have passed ships that were ten to twenty miles off the Atlantic coast, or have alighted wearily for a rest and free ride. Others have taken refuge on ships or lighthouses from twenty to one hundred and fifty miles from land. Red bats sometimes reach Bermuda, but probably these are wanderers that have lost their way or have been blown off their course by winds.

The bat often can find its way home after being kidnapped. In one experiment, little brown bats were taken from their colonies in southern Ontario and, after being banded, were released at distances of sixty-eight and seventy-six miles. Six nights later, some of these bats were found back at home. In another instance, bats of the same species were taken from their roost on an island in Lake Winnepesaukee, New Hampshire. Some were released seventy miles away to the northwest, at Lyndonville, Vermont. Others were set free at New Haven, Connecticut, one hundred and eighty miles to the south and west. A check of the colony about a year later revealed some of these tagged bats.

Most females have but one young; a few species may have two, three, or four in a litter. The embryos develop very slowly after the August, September, or October mating. In fact their growth is suspended completely through the winter while the mother can get little or no food. Little brown bats (*Myotis*) have been seen mating in winter during the hibernating period. The gestation time of this species has been estimated at fifty to sixty days. Dr. H. B. Sherman has learned that development in the Florida free-tailed bat (*Tadarida*) requires between eleven and twelve weeks.

When it comes time to give birth in May, June or July, bat mothers usually retire to "maternity wards." In most species the prospective fathers live for the time in bachelor clubs.

Hanging from a wall or tree by her feet and thumb hooks, the mother spreads herself into an apron to catch the new baby. Like human babies, most bats are born head first and crying at the top of their squeaky voices. Others come feet or knees first. The mother efficiently cuts the umbilical cord and eats the after-birth.

The new baby is tiny, blind and naked. Nevertheless, it is one-eighth to one-third the size of the mother. Singlets are larger, of course, than twins, triplets or quadruplets. The bat mother is most affectionate and devoted. Hanging head downward during the day, she partly holds the babies in her folded wings as they cling to her breasts. When she flies out in the evening, she may at times carry her family along. This is a tremendous load for such a small animal. A hoary bat has been known to carry two young that totaled twenty-five per cent more than her own weight. Other females have flown some distance with even heavier burdens. By the time such a mother has eaten half her weight in food, she really has a load. No small bird could equal this feat. It is possible only because of the bat's comparatively great wings.

The mother bat will brave considerable danger to protect her children. One bat is known to have fought off a blue jay with teeth, wings and hisses. Others have even been known to alight on human beings who were carrying off their babies.

By the time the young bats are two weeks old, they are half-grown and too heavy for their mother to carry any great distance. The young of some species are precocious and reach this stage in about three or four days. Since the youngsters now support themselves on the roost the mother no longer has qualms about leaving them home at night. At the age of three weeks they begin to practice flying and in a few days are out every night hunting their own meals.

Bats have comparatively few enemies and often die of old age, which is not very long in coming. Old World fruit bats in captivity have lived to the advanced age of almost twenty years. Most bats in the wild are probably worn out in a few years.

Owls capture some bats, probably by luck rather than by skill because, if given warning, most bats can easily avoid any predatory bird. The bats are subject to the usual run of accidents. Wind storms may beat an unlucky bat to the ground or against a tree trunk, or blow it too far out at sea. Migrating bats, like birds, are sometimes fatally attracted to lighthouses. Hail is a hazard to tree-roosting species, and sudden snows may overtake cave bats before they can reach shelter. In 1940 a storm in Minnesota closed a cave entrance with drifted snow. Afterward more than a hundred dead bats were found outside the blocked entrance. Bats have been found inextricably caught in burdock burrs, other spiny plants, and barbed wire fences, but such accidents are probably rare.

Most unjustly, the bat has the reputation of being unclean and of harboring bedbugs and all manner of crawling things. It is actually one of the cleanest of animals, including man. It spends much time preparing its toilet while hanging upside down. It licks and cleans thoroughly every bit of the body and wings that it can reach with its long red tongue. Moistening the hind foot, the bat runs it through the hair on the back, the top of the head and other spots that are out of reach of the tongue. To clean its valuable ears, it licks a thumb and, sticking it into the ear, twists and shakes it. Little brown bats have been seen to spend a half-hour on their baths.

Of course some bats are parasitized, but this is true of almost all animals and birds. I have seldom found more than two or three fleas or lice on a bat, and many that I have examined have been entirely free of parasites.

A few bats have been kept successfully as pets in captivity on a diet of finely chopped raw or cooked meat, honey bees, hard-boiled eggs, bananas, bread or crackers, cottage cheese and similar protein-rich foods, all slightly moistened with milk. Plenty of drinking water is essential. At first the little animals are resentful of handling, but soon will permit it, and even seem to like to have their heads stroked gently. Bats are edible but strong in taste.

Scientists have named almost two thousand different kinds of bats in the entire world and grouped them in seventeen families. These in turn are divided into slightly over two hundred genera. Our North American bats that range north of Mexico belong to one of three families:

A. The leaf-nosed bat (*Macrotus*) has a tall growth or "leaf" on its nose. It is a medium-sized brownish bat of the arid Southwest.

B. The "Molossids" are narrow-winged, fast-flying bats whose tails project beyond the interfemoral membrane. Most of the family inhabits the tropics and only two genera reach the United States. These are:

1. The free-tailed bat (*Tadarida*). This is a medium-sized brown bat found across the southern United States occasionally as far north as Iowa.

2. The mastiff bat (*Eumops*) is the largest bat found in this country (southern Texas to southern California). It is sooty brown and has such long ears that they droop over the face.

C. All of our other bats belong to the family of "Vespertilionids," which contains ten principal subdivisions or genera.

1. The little brown bat (*Myotis*) is small, dull-brown, and is found over most of North America.

2. The silver-haired bat (*Lasionycteris*) is medium-sized and dark with a "frosting" of white. It occurs throughout the United States.

3. The pipistrelle (*Pipistrellus*) is very small, pale yellowish brown, and lives in the eastern and southwestern states.

4. The big brown bat (*Eptesicus*) is found over most of North America.

5. The red bat (*Nycteris*), medium-sized and bright rufous, lives in southeastern Canada and all except the northwestern quarter of the United States.

6. The yellow bat (*Dasypterus*) is quite like the preceding, but is pale yellowish brown instead of red. It is uncommon and ranges into the United States only in the Southeast.

7. The Rafinesque bat (*Nycticeius*) is small, dull brown, and is found uncommonly in the southeastern states.

8. The spotted bat (*Euderma*), a rather large dark brown animal with a large white spot on each shoulder and on the rump, is very rare. Only eight have been recorded, in California, Arizona and New Mexico.

9. The lump-nosed bat (*Corynorhinus*), which takes its name from a wartlike growth on the muzzle, is fairly large and brown. It lives throughout the United States except the Northeast.

10. The pale bat (*Antrozous*) is large, pale gray, and has big ears. It is common in our western states, especially in the arid Southwest.

General description. A mouselike, brownish or grayish mammal with large "leathery" wings. Total length, 3 to 5 inches; wing expanse, 6 to 12 inches; weight, 1/5 ounce to 2 ounces.

Distinguishing characteristics. The wings, and power of flight, distinguish the bat from all other mammals.

Range. Practically all of North America.

8. The Bears

BLACK BEAR—*EUARCTOS AMERICANUS*
AND RELATIVES

The black bear resembles man more than any other North American mammal. Ordinarily it is an independent creature that works hard for a living and generally minds its own business. It can climb trees and shake down apples as well as anyone. If it wants a better view, or wind, or to wrestle with a rival, it stands erect on the hind legs. It may even take a few shuffling steps with this human posture. Its mate is a good mother that trains her children with affection and severe discipline.

The Indians noticed the bear's resemblance to a big, shaggy, short-legged man, a similarity which became startling when the dead creature's enormous fur coat was removed. They respected this fellow-denizen of the woods. Sometimes they killed it for food and for warm bedding, but they were careful to apologize and to speed its spirit to the Happy Hunting Grounds with prayerful chants and propitiatory offerings. Among the ghosts that peopled the spirit world, the bear was too powerful not to be appeased. After cleaning the flesh from the skull, they placed it at the top of a tall pole where it was taboo. In Athabaska, northern Canada, such skulls have been seen with a fringe of skin and hair remaining in place around the back of the head, giving an eerie look to the face.

With leisure and opportunity, the black bear becomes very sociable, sometimes too sociable. It acquires a taste for apple pie, chocolate cake, and coca cola. If refused, it may take these delicacies by force. It loves applause and will clown and squint up its eyes with pleasure when admired.

It has some of our best traits, and some of our worst. It succumbs easily to temptations that have little appeal to a grizzly bear. When it discovers that a little acting will bring forth food, it becomes an inveterate cadger. No human beggar with tin cup and whining voice was ever more ingratiating or obsequious than a panhandling black bear. It stands up on its hind legs some seven feet into the air, scratches itself, looks around and holds out one or both hands.

When being a panhandler fails, it may become a robber. It breaks into cars and cabins, smashing doors and windows. It tears open tin cans, and goes off with sacks of sugar, flour, hams and bacon. It has clawed and wounded numerous persons, and killed some of them. In the national parks where some

BLACK BEAR

of the thousands of visitors have taught bears disrespect for man, all artificial feeding, including the popular garbage pits, has been discontinued. The Park Service hopes that these bears can be induced to give up their tourists, ham sandwiches and apple peelings, and to earn their own living again.

Black bears are quite individualistic about their clothes. A black bear may be really black or may be any shade of brown, from yellowish and silvery to red-dish cinnamon. A very black mother may have a blond, redhead, and brunette in the same litter. And a "blue" bear may occur in southeastern Alaska or an albino in British Columbia. All this diversification caused the original describer of the genus to call them "short-clawed American bears." This is really accurate because the grizzlies have much longer toe nails.

You seldom see a dirty bear. It may be faded and ragged when its seasonal coat is wearing out. In summer it sometimes takes mud and dust baths to get relief from insects that burrow deep into its heavy fur coat. But ordinarily it keeps clean. It scrubs itself on the grass, and licks and grooms the corners and creases of its coat. It has even been seen taking a warm tub bath in a hot spring pool that was only eighteen inches deep and four feet in diameter. It seems to manicure its nails. The result is an amazing amount of sartorial finish consider-ing the thick coat it has to wear.

The male and female adults have nothing to do with each other except during mating season in early summer. At this time they are quite affectionate. Sometimes they stand upright and hug and paw each other fondly. It is all very pleasant while it lasts, but the idyl is usually over in less than a month. For the next two years or more the female is interested only in making a living for herself and young. The male is ignored, or driven off if he dares to make a threatening gesture at his offspring.

Cold weather makes the bears drowsy and they very sensibly hole up for varying periods of time, depending upon the climate in which they live. A pregnant female takes more pains with her winter dwelling. The male bear just turns in almost anywhere. Of course there are exceptions. Some females are more slovenly about their housekeeping and some males are inclined to be fussy. These latter are very particular about leaves for their bed, the draughts and so forth. In regions where the winds come from the north the bears select their bedrooms with a southern exposure. The winds then accommodatingly pile the snow around them and they are well insulated.

The winter home may be a den, a cave in a ledge or among broken rocks, or a hollow in a large tree or fallen log. Sometimes they have to dig it out themselves. In Yellowstone Park, fortunate bears may spend the cold season in steam-heated rooms among the hot spring formations. More careless bears just go to sleep in a windfall, in the lee of fallen tree trunks, under an especially dense and drooping crown of a conifer, or in a thicket. Bears have been known to spend weeks of cold winter in the open, among small trees in a swamp. In these cases, perhaps natural dens are scarce and are already taken by early hibernators. Even with a thick fur coat and a three- to four-inch blanket of fat, these bears must get chilled in extreme weather.

In the south, the bear retires for merely a few days or a week at a time. In the far north, the bear may disappear in October and never poke his nose outside until the following April or early May. This period of inactivity in the northern or colder parts of the United States occurs from about the middle of November to early April, but much depends on the weather, snowfall, sex, abundance of food, and probably other factors. A pregnant female, for example, retires earlier and is more apt to stay inside longer than a restless male without responsibilities.

Even the most soundly sleeping bear does not hibernate in the true sense. Its temperature remains normal and the breathing, which has been timed at four to five complete respirations a minute, is about that of a person in very deep slumber. At times the animal is semi-conscious and aware, but not disturbed by movements and sounds around it. Sometimes it is wide awake and resentful of intrusion. Then it may bite or send flying an investigator who thinks it is "hibernating." Even in the northern states and Canada, black bears occasionally come outside the snuggest dens in the middle of winter, generally during warmer spells, and wander about for a while before turning in again.

During this winter "twilight sleep," the mother brings her cubs into the world, perhaps about January. The gestation period therefore is seven to seven and one-half months. At her first delivery when she is three years old, she usually has only one young. Thereafter she ordinarily has twins and occasionally triplets. In a few instances, litters of four have arrived. Superintendent J. A. Wood of Prince Albert Park, Saskatchewan, once saw a bear cross a road through the woods followed by *five* cubs, all of the same size and presumably brothers and sisters.

At birth the cubs of a black bear are actually smaller than those of a Canada porcupine. About nine inches long, they weigh six to eight ounces each, only one five-hundredth of the weight of their mother. Blind, hairless, toothless and squealing, they resemble miniature bull dogs whose legs and ears are just barely indicated. But they know where to find milk, and the mother dozes on. Motherhood at this stage is very easy. She has no hunting to do, and the youngsters cannot wander off. Her small, warm bed is made of grasses, pine needles, leaves and bark, and may not be more than thirty inches across.

After about forty days and nights, the cubs open their eyes and begin to cut their teeth. They are then twelve inches long, weigh about two pounds, and are covered with soft black down.

When spring arrives, the mother takes her brood out for their first airing. Although she has drawn on her layers of fat for nourishment during the whole winter, she still seems to be as bulky as when she finished her last full meal of beechnuts. It is generally presumed that her fatty layer is spongy and that the cells are mere shells. According to this theory she shrinks rapidly and two or three weeks later is lean and ravenously hungry again.

All bears do not use up their fat in a winter's sleep. The famous biologist, O. J. Murie, tells me that he has killed bears in April whose fat was very oily and yielded large quantities of grease for cooking. These were not mother bears, however.

Like any bear that first comes out in the spring, the mother bear may merely nibble at cedar twigs or the early sprouting grass. But she will hardly refuse a big chunk of a winter-killed elk if she sees one. Her old coat, so sleek and glossy the September before, begins to shed. The itching drives her to rub against trees and rocks, until she is ragged and her dark skin shows through in spots.

The cubs weigh about four pounds when they first leave their nest. They can walk, but unsteadily like toddling human children. They climb much better. At the first sign of trouble, the mother sends them sprinting up into the tree tops. If they do not obey her hoarse grunt immediately, she cuffs them hard and they know better the next time. She does not permit them to come down until the danger is over, or, if she has errands to do, not until her return.

The new world is an interesting big place, but it is also a potentially dangerous one. Almost any meat-eater, down to and probably including the fox, would be glad to make a meal of a tender young cub. The devoted mother is the good reason that they don't. Only bigger and stronger bears dare to face her and usually they have sense enough to leave her alone. Once in a tree, the cubs can retreat to the ends of branches where heavy adults are unable to follow. On the ground, however, large renegade male bears have been known to kill and eat cubs despite valiant attempts of the mother to defend them.

Some mother bears have apparently adopted orphan cubs, but other mothers will drive them away. A hungry cub that had been taken from his mother in Yellowstone was chased up a tree continuously by a large female. After several days, the cub's own mother found him in a tree. Attracted to the foot of the tree by food, she had immediately recognized his scent on the bark. Rising up on her hind feet, she grunted urgently and affectionately to him to come down.

The reunion was very touching. She fondled him and talked to him with comforting sounds. Then she cleaned him and sat down to nurse him and his sister at her breasts.

The young of most mammals play with evident enjoyment, but none of them romp and get into as much mischief as black bear cubs. If one cub tires and goes to sleep, the other will bite its ear or jump on it. Every trick practiced by human children on their elders was tried out ages ago by young bears on their mothers. The bear mother is an indulgent parent and often enters into the games of tag and wrestling, but she is also a stern disciplinarian. By example and by help, she teaches the youngsters to hunt mice and ground squirrels, to dig for wild parsnips and other roots, and to swim. Too much foolery or rank disobedience makes her lose her temper. Biff! A quick swat from her strong arm lands on the little rascal's ear and he flattens out howling.

Bears are silent animals ordinarily, although the mother and her cubs converse by low indeterminate sounds that range from grunts to mumbles and squeaks. In times of stress, however, there is nothing more vocal than a bear. An angry male can be heard half a mile away. Hoarse, panting roars broken by snarls and violent "Woofs!" vent his rage. A bear in pain will bawl and sob like a human. Cubs that have become separated from their mother cry for hours with a peculiar whimpering, high-pitched moan that rises and falls and stops only from sheer exhaustion.

Once the bears leave their den, they do not return to it, at least before autumn. Within a range perhaps ten miles in radius they are nomads for the next half year. The solitary male has a home range of about fifteen miles. The mother and her cubs sleep where fatigue overtakes them, sometimes in the trees, sometimes on the ground. As bulky as she is, a two hundred-pound female can relax completely when sprawled lengthwise on a limb only four inches in diameter. Her legs hang down on each side and she sleeps soundly without falling off. On the ground where most of the real resting is done she selects a sheltered place in a thicket and scoops out a shallow bed from a few inches to a foot deep. If abundant food is found in the neighborhood, she and her family will probably use the same beds for a number of days before moving on.

All bears swim readily, occasionally five miles at a time. Sometimes in hot weather they do so just to cool off.

Viewed from the rear, the bear's hindquarters don't appear to belong to him —they look different, and seem to be going in a different direction from his forequarters. But this mass of muscle and fat and hair gets along, as fast as twenty-five miles an hour if the distance is short and the need is urgent.

Once again the cold winds whip the last leaves from the maples and the first real snow of winter begins to cover the ground. The mother, and her cubs which now weigh about forty pounds apiece, look for a place to spend the winter. They may sleep together as before, or in dens that are within a few yards of each other.

The following spring, when the young bears are about sixteen months old, they are husky fellows that know a good deal about the woods. Their mother usually feels that she can now disregard them. Occasionally she will go on nursing them for another season, but she is less likely to do this than the grizzly bear. By the middle or end of June, she will probably be too interested in a big male bear in the vicinity to bother with them. Maternal indifference and the intimidation of the newcomer at last break the family bonds, and the yearling cubs move on. They travel together another year, until they are about two and one-half years old, then disperse, mate briefly and become hermits like their elders. As with humans, some bears remain spinsters, or perhaps bachelors, possibly by preference.

When the bear is not asleep, it spends most of its time looking for food. This usually comes in small packages for such a big creature. Although it prefers meat, it is too clumsy and comparatively slow to catch a healthy big-game animal. It digs out burrows and eats mice, chipmunks, ground squirrels, pocket gophers and marmots or woodchucks. Occasionally it overtakes a porcupine. A quick flip of the huge black paw, and the porcupine is on its back. With one blow, the unprotected under parts are torn open, and the victim is scooped out of its skin. Once in a while the bear is careless or clumsy and gets its face full of burning quills. Weeks after its death, the porcupine may be avenged—a life for a life.

During fawning time, the bear spends a good many hours looking for young deer, elk, or antelope. Many hunters think that it gets quite a few, but this is yet to be proven. The young fawns give off little scent and blend so perfectly with the ground that it takes better sight than the bear's to pick them out. It probably gets some by chance and by smell. After the first few days of their lives, the fawns run with their mothers and can easily outspeed the black monster. Even where both bears and deer are abundant, practically all of the supposed "kills" are carrion. The bear is not particular; it likes rank meat just as well as fresh, and may even roll in it.

Largely by accident, the bear finds some eggs and young of low-nesting birds. Perhaps a brooding bird may be gobbled as well. It has been known to rip open the whole side of a dead tree when it smelled a brood of fledglings inside.

The long, pink tongue busily laps up thousands of carpenter ants as they swarm over their broken walls. Earth-dwelling species are licked off the mighty forearms when they boil angrily out of their tunnels to bite the intruder. The bear is impervious to their tiny stabs and is very fond of their piquant acid flavor. When crickets and grasshoppers are abundant, it fills its stomach with them for days at a time.

As a class, black bears are not noted fishermen like the grizzlies and big brown bears. In the Pacific Northwest and Alaska, however, where hordes of fish still swarm up the rivers to spawn, the black bears gorge on fish as much as their larger relatives. Over the rest of America, bears will quickly gobble down a dead fish but only an occasional one finds it worth while to try to catch the elusive morsels that dart through the water.

Most of the time the bear is forced to be a vegetarian. Throughout the part of the year that it is active, especially soon after emerging from its winter den, it eats quantities of grasses, tender sedges and clover. In the northern Rockies I have seen places where it has torn great hunks of bark out of lodgepole pines. The inner bark of this and other conifers is an excellent spring tonic. Sometimes one tree in every ten is scarred in this way. A little later it digs over acres of ground for roots: starchy thistles and camas, the tiny but tasty bulbs of dog-toothed violets, avalanche lilies, spring beauties, and wild onions.

The list of fruits includes everything he can find. Manzanita berries, buffalo-berries, snowberries, elderberries, kinnikinnik-berries, hackberries, serviceberries, blueberries, strawberries, wild cherries, the fruits of poison oak, thornapple, crabapple, pawpaw, and persimmon. In the far south, the bear breaks open and eats the big central bud from the top of the cabbage palm.

All bears take the easy way of storing food for the long winter. They gorge and become fat. It seems as if the longer and colder the winter is to be, the fatter they become. At this time, the black bear devours the later seasonal fruits, including mountain ash and grapes, and the mast of oaks, pines, beech and tupelo. Frequently its stomach is filled with acorns or beechnuts. It may even rob the stores of pine and fir seeds that the red squirrel has laboriously gathered. If frost does not bring the nuts to the ground fast enough, the bear climbs the trees and shakes them vigorously. Then it returns to the ground to pick up and swallow the nuts, shells and all, with swift "champs" of the heavy jaws. If the nuts are too tight to be shaken off, it may tear off entire branches. Then, sitting comfortably on the ground, the bear chews off its dinner.

With its sensitive nose and lips, it can select very small berries and eat them without the leaves. When feeding on fruits such as huckleberries or raspberries, however, it may run the whole top of the plant through its mouth, swallowing a mixture of berries, leaves, twigs and a generous assortment of insects for seasoning.

The black bear has a sweet-tooth. With great delight it robs the nectar-storing wasps and wild bees, and eats their larvae. "Honeydew" from plant scales and from aphids, along with the insects and the foliage on which it is deposited, is a delicious dessert.

It will overturn and mash bee hives, clean out the honeycomb and devour the bees themselves for a final fillip. The bee stings cause little discomfort and of course result in the deaths of the angry insects. In the mountains of California, where bee colonies are frequently established during the summer months, apiaries are often placed on high platforms so built that bears cannot climb their supports, or they are protected by electrically charged fences.

Occasionally, a black bear discovers that sheep, goats, calves, or even cattle are helpless, easy victims. Then it proceeds to banquet regularly at the expense of the stockmen. One twenty-seven-year-old bear killed twenty-six sheep in one day. Practically toothless, it kept fat on its easy prey.

Another bear became an epicure. It dined continuously on the udders of nursing ewes. Although the sheep were not killed, they died later of infection. Sometimes the predator ate the heart and liver of a victim, but would not touch the rest of the meat.

There is only one thing to do with such a bear. It must be destroyed. It is too intelligent and too stubborn to be frightened back to normal food habits. Unfortunately such stockkillers ruin the reputations of all bears. They don't deserve it. Sometimes the herder himself is responsible for starting a bear on the downward path. If he fails to bury deeply or burn the carcasses of his animals that die of disease or trampling, the bear finds them and acquires a new appetite. Stock interests frequently urge that all bears be placed on the predator list, and that rewards be paid for their destruction.

A full-grown bear, that is four or five years old, may get tapeworms from raw fish and sometimes have abscessed teeth. But it has little to fear from other mammals. It is doubtful that a cougar (the next largest predator) would tackle a black bear unless the latter were crippled or sick. In times of winter or spring famine, a wolf pack probably would attack a bear that was not well protected in a den with a small, easily defended entrance. Bears may be a menace to each other at any time. Fights begin over mates, food, or more trivial causes. Usually they are brief, and the damage is no more serious than a torn nose or ear. Occasionally, however, they continue until one of the warriors is fatally wounded. I have known of several cases when one of the battlers was killed outright.

Bears are cannibals and the meat of their own kind appears to be just as appetizing as that of deer or elk. A bear in Yellowstone once lumbered across a meadow with the carcass of a slightly smaller bear slung across its shoulder and the throat gripped in its teeth. The black bear has a deep-rooted respect for the grizzly. As many as eight or nine have been seen to climb trees when a grizzly arrived.

Modern man, with his pack of trailing dogs and heavy rifle, is a deadly enemy. Nevertheless, black bears still live in every state of the union except Rhode Island, New Jersey, Delaware, and Kansas. This is a tribute to their adaptability, persistence, and crafty intelligence.

The pelt is valued chiefly as a trophy, although it made a popular coat before the days of closed, heated automobiles. The meat of the young bear is very fine eating. Because of its cunning and elusive habits under natural conditions, the bear is most prized for sport-hunting, and is usually trailed with packs of dogs.

In the western half of the continent, the brown phase of the black bear is common, in many places outnumbering the black. The so-called glacier or blue bear of Alaska, which is found from Lynn Canal to the Malespina Glacier and Mt. St. Elias, is a very rare variant of the black. A skin that I once examined in Dundas Bay was a beautiful gray-blue. Its hair was short, crisply waved, and curled. Kermode's bear, comparatively small, found on the coast of British Columbia, is an albino of the common black bear.

General description. A medium-sized bear with long soft fur. Color: black, blackish rusty, or dark brown to pale cinnamon; muzzle brownish; large white spot on chest. Total length, 4½ to 6½ feet; height at shoulder, 25 to 40 inches; weight, usually 200 to 300 pounds, up to an exceptional 500 pounds. Females are usually about 20 per cent smaller than males.

Distinguishing characteristics. Can be confused only with the grizzly, which has high humped shoulders, larger, heavier and blunter head, usually a dished face, and long, broad, slightly curved front claws that generally are rather light-colored. The black bear has a smaller, more pointed head with a straight face profile; lacks a permanent shoulder hump; and its front claws are short, narrow, markedly curved, and black or (in the cinnamon phase) dark brown. Black bears are smaller than grizzlies on the average, but a large old black bear may be more bulky than a small adult female grizzly.

Range. Practically all of wooded North America, including the Mexican Plateau north of Mexico City. Not found, however, in the Great Basin, western Arizona, southern California and eastern Oregon.

GRIZZLY BEAR

URSUS SP.

The legend of the great, humpbacked, dish-faced grizzly has come down through the history of western America. In low tones, probably with backward glances into the blackness beyond the campfire, Indian warriors told early white explorers of the frightfulness and matchless strength of the King of Bears.

Civilization has almost exterminated this mighty monarch. There are less than six hundred survivors in the entire United States. Except in Yellowstone, Teton and Glacier National Parks, and the Flathead-Sun River region of north-western Montana, it is next to impossible to find a grizzly in the entire length of the American Rockies. Only in British Columbia, Yukon, and Alaska have they continued to roam, uninterrupted by the white man.

The grizzly bear is the largest carnivore on the earth. Its family includes the big brown, giant Alaska ("kodiak") and the Barren Ground ("white," *not* Polar) bears. The very largest of these grizzlies are found in southwestern Alaska, on Kodiak Island and the Alaska Peninsula. Bears have been killed there that measured as much as nine feet two inches from tip of nose to end of the absurdly short tail. The distance between claw tips of the front feet after the hide had been removed and laid flat was another nine feet. The heaviest wild bear weighed one thousand six hundred and fifty-six pounds. (Fat zoo specimens have scaled much more.) The skull of such an animal would be between eighteen and nineteen inches long. When standing on the hind legs, it could probably reach twelve feet into the air.

This enormous creature fears nothing that walks or flies, unless it be man or another grizzly. It has been seen walking off with the carcass of a great bull elk and even other loads that weigh the better part of a ton. If a grizzly is especially disagreeable, black bears will rush up into the tree tops when it appears.

During the early Spanish days in California, reckless vaqueros made a prac-tice of ambushing and lassoing a grizzly for the fiestas. After being tied up and transported to the Mission, the bear was turned loose in an arena with the wildest and most dangerous bull that could be obtained. Frequently the fun was not worth the trouble, for the first blow from the bear's paw might break the neck of the charging bull and end the spectacle abruptly.

Despite its enormous bulk, the grizzly is surprisingly agile. I have spent many hours watching big brownies fishing on Alaskan salmon streams, and have never ceased to marvel at their success. The bear wades the gravel bars

GRIZZLY BEAR

and bottom where the water is not more than two feet deep, and the frightened salmon dash wildly up or down like dark shadows. With great leaps and twists that send the water flying in spray, the bear tries to land on them with its front paws. Perhaps it makes four or five vain lunges. Then, in a flash, its open jaws with the four great fangs are around the salmon. Triumphantly, with water dripping from the fur, the monster lumbers ashore with the gleaming three-foot fish slowly waving its last.

Once when I was waiting for some of these bears to appear, I tried lying at the edge of the river to test my own skill. After lying motionless with arm poised for a few minutes, a salmon would move under my hand and hang there in the current about a foot below the surface. My quickest grab never even touched the watchful, lightning-fast fish. Yet these clumsy-looking giants catch many more than they can eat.

On the straight-away, these bears are also fast and have great endurance, compared to man. A grizzly in Yellowstone Park, running ahead of an automobile, was found to travel at a speed of thirty miles an hour.

I once startled two adult brown bears and two yearlings on the slopes of Mount Katolinat on the Alaska Peninsula. The rank grass, sagging under the autumn frosts from its original height of about five feet, formed a loose tangle about eighteen inches deep. It was a struggle for me to get through. I had to stop and gasp for breath every hundred yards. But not the bears! Probably never having seen a man before, they fled up the slope, then along the contour, crossing gulches and brushing through the alders as though they were straws. The animals' light, bounding gallop never faltered. When they disappeared from sight, more than a mile away, they were still running as if pursued by the devil and without any sign of slackening speed or of weariness.

When it is accustomed to humans and protected from shooting, the grizzly minds its own business and proceeds about it in a direct, purposeful manner. There is none of the easy-going nature of the black bear, that takes time to stop and observe the doings of the world about. This directness of purpose is never better illustrated than by the bear trails that lead across the open mountains of the Aleutian Range. I have seen bear paths that were so straight they might have been laid out with a surveyor's transit. Regardless of slope, many of them continue for a half-mile without the slightest deviation, through the tall grass, and across the water courses with their dense thickets of willows and alders. Some of these trails on Kodiak Island ran squarely up grades of fifty per cent or even steeper for two thousand to three thousand feet. Such trails can be seen from a great distance.

The grizzly, or brown bear, is a methodical animal. Once a good route is selected, every one of these bears going in that direction uses it. Furthermore, each one steps in the footprints of the one that went before. The great circular footholes may become ten to twelve inches deep. In time the rows of holes may merge into two parallel ruts. Trails laid out by humans and then abandoned are sometimes kept open for decades by traveling bears.

Along the bear trails, where the animals pass through timber, one often sees trees that are deeply scarred by bites and scratches. Frequently the deepest gouge, where more of the bears have bitten, is about six feet above the ground. The deepest scratches may be about twelve feet high. It looks as if every bear tried to stretch and leave its mark higher than anyone else. Some hunters believe that these trees are sign posts showing who has passed. Others think that the bears use them merely to stretch and relax their muscles.

As a rule most grizzlies are cautious and even timid. While their eyesight is very poor, especially for stationary objects, their hearing is excellent and their sense of smell unsurpassed. One has only to watch a black or grizzly bear to determine that it puts most reliance on its nose when it makes an investigation.

The fact that this plodding giant is not troublesome is no reason for pressing an acquaintance. It might be resentful and attack. Many persons ask how they may *always* tell a black from a grizzly. The distinguishing characteristics are given on page 143. Color is not a true sign by any means, although one can be sure that a glossy black animal is not a grizzly. The cinnamon phase of the black bear is very similar to the brownish or tan grizzlies. .

Grizzlies often differ widely from each other in exterior appearance, and even in the shape of their skulls and teeth which are the basis of most mammal classification. These various grizzlies may occupy the same valley or mountainside, and perhaps even mate. Yet a bear with an identically shaped head, or claws, or colored coat, may be found a thousand miles away. The grizzly's coat may be anywhere from blackish gray through any number of browns to a pale yellowish.

One scientist has described no less than eighty-four species and subspecies of grizzlies and big brown bears in North America, including five distinct species on one island only one hundred miles long and twenty miles wide. Probably no other piece of research has brought dignified mammalogists nearer to name-calling and nose-punching than the question of correctly classifying the grizzly bears.

If the over-rash amateur naturalist takes refuge in a tree and finds an angry bear climbing upward with the agility of a squirrel, he can be almost sure, belatedly, that his pursuer is a black bear. The grizzly rarely climbs, even as a cub. After it is a year or two old, the claws lose so much of their curvature that they are not efficient hooks for digging into the tree trunks.

However, there are always exceptions to every rule. Ranger Rudolph Grimm once looked out of his window in Yellowstone to see a mother grizzly and two cubs clambering about in an apple tree, busily shaking down the apples.

The grizzly's life is much like that of the black bear's. The female enjoys adult male society only once in every two or three years. At this time they may be very affectionate. A fond couple will often graze with noses close together. They wrestle in fun, hug and paw each other. The romance may last a month. If another male comes around to interfere, the female is likely to run away from him. However, if he is powerful enough and persistent enough, he may finally be permitted to join the couple and share the female's favor.

The cubs, generally two, sometimes three or one, and very rarely as many as four, are born in the winter den during January or February. They are about the same size at birth as the little black bears, but grow somewhat more slowly in size and self-reliance. Their mother not only takes care of them until their second June, but usually longer. Barring accidents, the cubs will be long-lived. They require eight to ten years to reach full size and weight, and in zoological parks have attained the age of twenty-five to thirty years.

Temperamentally, the grizzlies are even more solitary than the black bears. When two or more grizzlies chance to meet in a berry patch or on a salmon stream, they either ignore each other or snarl automatically.

The grizzly's menu is about the same as that of the black bear. It may eat almost anything that grows, but has definite preferences. On coming out of hibernation, it dines on the usual early vegetation and decaying flesh of winter-killed animals. It digs roots, and crops huge quantities of grass in early summer, grazing it by the mouthful much like a cow. Eating its way across a blueberry-covered flat, it strips the bushes as it goes and champs down fruit, leaves, twigs and all.

Its great strength and long, heavy claws enable the grizzly to dig deeper and faster than the black bear and it turns over great quantities of soil in its hunt for burrowing animals. I have crossed vast grassy slopes in southwestern Alaska that have been pitted with holes, each big enough to bury a piano, where hibernating ground squirrels had been rooted out and devoured. However, this is hard work, and many holes have no occupants.

Great strength and an aggressive intelligence have enabled grizzlies to make forays on sheep, hogs, cattle and even horses. Individual bears have gained wide-spread notoriety for their raids and eventually have been destroyed. These misdeeds of the few have resulted in the complete extirpation of all grizzlies from vast areas of the old range in the western states.

Caching surplus meat is practiced more commonly by the grizzly than by the black bear, although both species are thrifty. The larger bear quite often picks up its prize, even an elk or a moose carcass, and carries it bodily to a likely place. There the grizzly covers it with branches, rocks, dirt or leaf litter. Woe to any animal caught robbing this store!

To the sick or crippled elk, moose and deer, the grizzly is more dangerous than the black bear. It is more likely to ambush and kill them, or try to surprise them with an unexpected, swift dash. A fisherman in Yellowstone Park was astonished one summer day to see a bull moose dash out of the forest with a gray grizzly clinging and tearing at his hip. At the edge of the stream the moose succeeded in shaking off his attacker and escaped into deep water. The frustrated bear raged up and down the bank for hours, but finally left. The moose then came ashore but was so badly injured that he died a little later.

Even grizzly bears have to be vegetarians most of the time. It would take too long to find and dig out as many ground squirrels and mice as they would like. Carrion and some calves and fawns, their largest source of meat, are not frequent. Often the grizzly's stomach is filled only with grass.

In Alaska and much of northwestern Canada, the grizzly, including the big brown bear, is carefully conserved by authorities as a valuable wilderness asset. Bear hunting is the sport par excellence. A single trophy skin often represents an expenditure of several thousand dollars in traveling expenses (airplane), a guide, equipment and fees.

How dangerous is the grizzly to man? Occasionally human beings are terribly mauled and killed by grizzly bears. The bodies are seldom eaten. The bears seem to regard man as an antagonist, but not good to eat. Sometimes we learn the complete details of these tragedies, and almost always they reveal the possibility that the bear was not entirely at fault. Usually, after being wounded, it was defending itself. In other instances, the bear may have survived old hunting wounds and, crippled and crochety, had vented an understandable hatred against mankind. Sometimes the man had approached so quietly that the startled and frightened bear had reacted in supposed self-defense.

I have met quite a number of grizzlies and big brown bears. Not one ever offered to attack. With one exception, they were interested only in avoiding me, and fled in great haste. The sole exception, a grumpy old grizzly, merely continued on its course and expected me to do the same. That is good advice. Plenty of noise, to advertise one's presence and lack of evil intentions, is also a sensible courtesy. It is better protection than a gun in inexpert hands.

General description. A large, heavy bear with big head and long dished face; front claws are long, broad, little curved, and usually light brown in color. Fur long, varying in color with the individual: blackish-gray, brown, buffy or pale yellowish upper parts, often sprinkled with white hairs. Total length, 5 to 9 feet; height at shoulder, 2½ to 4 feet; weight, 300 to 1000, up to a maximum of 1,656 pounds. Females generally are considerably smaller than males.

Distinguishing characteristics. For differences between the grizzly and the black bear, see this section under "black bear" (page 143). In the tundra of extreme northern Alaska and Canada, a very pale, faded grizzly or brown bear may be told from a wandering polar bear by the heavy, deep head, humped shoulders, shorter neck and shorter legs.

Range. Western North America from the northern portion of the Mexican Plateau through the Rocky Mountains, Sierra Nevada, and Cascade Range to Northwest Territories (Great Bear Lake, Coronation Gulf, Great Slave Lake, and western half of Keewatin), all of interior Alaska and Umiak Island. Now extinct in the eastern portion of this range and south of the Canadian-United States boundary with the exception of a few isolated areas and national parks.

POLAR BEAR
THALARCTOS MARITIMUS

The muskox, the mountain goat and the tundra bear live in lands of sunshine and flowers compared to the polar bear. Their homes burst into bloom and green grass for two months out of a long, cold, barren year. But many a polar bear never sees a blade of grass during its whole life. It often lives by choice on the pack ice of the Arctic Ocean. The edge of the pack, where the icebergs and broken pan ice alternate with stretches of open water, may be a favorite hunting ground.

This indefinite boundary between the polar cap on the north and the open ocean to the south is ever shifting with the seasons and the winds. So the great white bear wanders southward in winter, back north in summer, and erratically according to the breaks and leads in the ice.

Almost as big as the Kodiak brown bear, the polar bear does not mate until he is about five years old. After a brief courtship in June or early July he resumes his solitary way.

POLAR BEAR

Early in the winter, the pregnant female looks for an area of "pressure ice," where the ice has been forced into great confused piles. Here she digs down into the deeply drifted snow. The wind promptly covers the shaft and she lies drowsily in a snug white bed completely surrounded by packed snow. The sun finally sinks below the horizon for the last time that year and the long night settles down.

In the dark January world of sub-zero cold below swirling snow, two cubs are born. Like the other bear young, they are little, blind, naked creatures, hardly well formed. While the mother may be a seven hundred pounder, the hairless cubs weigh less than two pounds, and are but ten inches long. It is only by snuggling into the soft fur of their mother's abdomen and between her front legs that they keep warm. Within a few days their wooly coats begin to grow and in six weeks their eyes open.

On the diet of their mother's milk the cubs grow rapidly. Aroused and made uneasy by the daylight that seeps dimly through the snow for a little longer each day, the family finally breaks out of its den in March.

By watching their mother, and eventually practising clumsily, the young bears learn to hunt. First they find out where to look. The whole chain of life in the Arctic is pegged to the little sea organisms of many species that are known as "krill." These shrimplike creatures swarm in greatest abundance in waters of low salinity. They find such places where icebergs, the cast-off chunks of glaciers, are melting and diluting the sea water. Here the fish live on the krill, the seals feed on the fish, and the bear stalks the seals.

Seal hunting requires real skill. It can be done only on the ice, for once in the water the seal is too fast to catch. For all its blank expression, the seal is watchful and cautious. It rarely moves far from the lead or blow hole, into which it will pop at the first hint of danger.

The polar bear must use every trick and take advantage of any hummock or drift to make an approach. Its year-round coat of white, slightly yellowish, is the best possible camouflage. If shelter is scant it lies flat on the ice. As its long, snaky neck and head thrust forward, the rear legs trail behind its body. Slowly it pulls itself along with the front paws. When close enough, it rushes and with one blow crushes the skull or breaks the back of the unfortunate seal.

It has another method of sealing if the blowhole is not too far from the edge of the ice pan. Taking a deep breath, the polar bear slips into the water and swims under the ice. Once at the hole, which is much too small to admit its shoulders, it probably makes a scratching sound. At any rate the seal is alarmed and dives headlong for supposed safety, and lands in the crushing embrace of the two mighty forearms of the enemy.

Young walrus is equally delicious to the polar bear. This hunt, however, is a hazardous one. The mother walrus keeps a close watch on her ponderous offspring. At the sight of her traditional foe, she screams for help and charges to the rescue. The whole herd of clumsy giants responds and the bear may have to abandon its injured victim before the menace of a row of flashing tusks. On the ice it can outdodge the walruses but sometimes the concentration of so many tons of flesh breaks the ice or overbalances the floe. Then the whole controversy is thrown into the sea where the walruses are much better swimmers than the bear.

Any of the numerous birds of the Arctic Sea, if injured or careless, may be captured by the watchful bear. It may find fish washed up or stranded on the ice, while an occasional bear will go ashore to catch spawning fish in the tundra streams. This bear will discover an exciting change of diet in the vegetation. A polar bear that is stranded on northern islands grazes great quantities of grass, just like its cousins, the grizzlies, brownies and black bears. If a whale or walrus becomes stranded or washed ashore dead, the bears may gather from miles around for a free banquet. In one instance, at Pitt Point on the Arctic coast of Alaska, twenty polar bears and nearly one hundred foxes were counted around a whale carcass.

The polar bear must be a tireless traveler in its perpetual search for food. Unlike the other bears, it has fur overshoes that protect the soles of the feet. Its sight is better than that of any of the other bears, and it has an extraordinary sense of smell. It can see an object a mile away and smell it even farther. Arctic travelers say that it pays little attention to sounds, perhaps due to the fact that the polar sea is frequently a noisy place. Great icebergs grind together in the waves and the ice floes crash and crack with thunderous reports.

The males and the females which are not pregnant do not hibernate as other bears of the cold north do. They hunt for their living throughout the entire winter night. Thus the mother bear and her family stay out all during the cubs' second winter. When they are about seventeen months old, they may weigh two hundred pounds and can take fairly good care of themselves. At this time, unless their mother is unusually doting, she drives them off. It is time to mate again and take on another two-year cycle of family rearing.

Either because of extreme hunger or total ignorance of man, or both, polar bears have been known to stalk and kill humans in winter. During the summer season, they are usually inoffensive and even gentle. Hunters who have wounded polar bears, however, have found them to be as savage and even mortal antagonists as other wounded bears. In that treeless waste a person is easily overtaken, for the bear can run as fast as twenty-five miles per hour for a short distance. In the old days the Eskimos had to hunt bears with only short spears. A white bear pelt was and still is a prize, and its possession indicates that the owner is a mighty hunter. Even with dogs and a modern rifle, a polar bear hunt is a dangerous undertaking.

The polar bear has to be a good swimmer to live on such an unstable, fragile platform as floating ice. Another of its several names is "water bear." It is streamlined for easy swimming and the legs are jointed so that they can be swung in a wide circle. In the water, it swims with all four feet or by dog-paddling with only the front legs. It seems to think nothing of striking off out of sight of land across the rolling ocean. If distant icebergs seem to promise better sealing, it jumps from its perch and swims away, perhaps fifteen or twenty miles. In its lighter moments it dives, twists, and turns in the water exuberantly. It is a graceful, strong swimmer, although it cannot keep up with the swift seals and walruses.

The range of the polar bear extends all the way around the northern world. It has no relatives in the Antarctic. The population at any one place may vary considerably. Bears are plentiful west of Point Barrow and in the general region of Franklin Bay on the Canadian coast. A ship captain who was frozen in, east of the Mackenzie River, amused himself by shooting thirty-five polar bears in an afternoon. Between Barrow and Cape Bathhurst the bears are not as common, and they are rare in Coronation Gulf. East of Victoria Strait toward Greenland, they become more numerous.

Although most of the "ice bears" spend their entire lives on the ocean, many come ashore at times and for varying periods. These animals rarely travel far inland, but there have been notable exceptions. One of these was a bear that was seen northeast of Great Slave Lake about seventy-five miles from the nearest salt water. In another case, a bear traveled up the Mackenzie River to Fort MacPherson, one hundred and fifty miles from the ocean.

Sometimes a polar bear will float southward far below the Arctic Circle, and even reach the southern end of Hudson Bay. It is more likely to ride the icebergs down the Labrador coast to Newfoundland, following the great herds of harp seals. As the ice melts, it may go ashore to start the long hike overland back to the Polar Ocean. On the return trip, it is apt to astonish and terrorize the Indians by its white strangeness. Persistent, exploring bears have been known to pass through the Strait of Belle Isle, between Newfoundland and Quebec, and follow the tidal currents along the north shore of the Gulf of St. Lawrence. One venturesome bear was killed by hunters at Lake St. John, Quebec, about one hundred miles up the Saguenay River from the Gulf.

On the western side of America, polar bears rather frequently drift through

Bering Strait. They may land on one of the large islands in Bering Sea and, after climbing to the higher peaks, stay for the summer. There they dig puffins out of their burrows, and eat grass and any carrion that can be found.

At times and in certain places, polar bears are so numerous as to be a substantial source of food for the Eskimos. Their hides make excellent mukluks, other small articles of clothing, and sleeping robes. Their teeth and claws are favorite ornaments and are frequently strung for necklaces. In the days of big houses when the Arctic was being explored, Americans paid as high as one thousand dollars for one of the enormous white pelts to be used as a rug, or wall hanging. Now that small apartments are more popular, the skin of the ice bear is worth about forty dollars. An average of sixty-five pelts are exported each year from Alaska. Somewhat fewer are traded in Canada.

Except for the liver, the meat of the polar bear is wholesome. Although it is delicious, the liver is said to cause nausea, dizziness, a splitting headache, and sometimes peeling of the skin.

Few people have ever been within hundreds of miles of the home of the polar bear and their sole acquaintance with it is through the bars of the city zoo. There it is, like a freak from another world, a huge white animal with a black tongue. Strangely, it takes to captivity and even summer heat better than many of our temperate zone animals. All it requires is food, a bathtub and plenty of cool water.

General description. A very large, elongated bear with a long neck, small, slender head and small ears. Fur very dense, uniformly yellowish white. Total length, 7 to 9½ feet; height at shoulder, 4 to 4½ feet; weight, 700 to 1000, up to 1600 pounds as the extreme. Females about 25 per cent smaller.

Distinguishing characteristics. Slender but bearlike form and uniform whitish color.

Range. Arctic North America, from the northwestern coast of Alaska to northern Labrador, and the islands and pack ice of the Arctic ocean.

9. The Bear's Small Cousins

RACCOON—*PROCYON LOTOR*

This intelligent little animal with a black mask and ringed, furry tail is astonishingly plucky. Unaided, it will beat off and cripple two or three husky hounds although they may have bitten and torn it badly. It has also been known to lead a pursuing dog into water, climb on its tormentor's head and drown it.

Frosty autumn and moonlight nights bring serious peril to the raccoon. Men with pistols, clubs and flashlights or lanterns, move into the woods. Their trained hounds pick up the coon's warm scent on the stream bank and baying with excitement take up the chase. Then the raccoon, especially a mother burdened with inexperienced youngsters, needs great craftiness and knowledge of the woods.

A wise old coon is as clever as a fox, and uses every trick of the trade. It wades along creeks or lake margins, walks fallen logs, employs adjacent trees as bridges to break the trail, and may even dive into the water. If it can finally enter its den without being overtaken, it is likely to be safe, at least until another night, when it must venture out for food. When it is deep in a rocky ledge or the hollow of a tree, the dogs apparently cannot smell it.

The aim of the hunting pack is to chase the raccoon and its companions into a tree top. This is the first place that an inexperienced coon will go. Led by the sound of the dogs' barking, the hunters arrive. The raccoons' eyes reflect the light·so that shooting is possible. No matter how scared they are, the treed coons are too curious not to look out from behind the branches to see what is going on. The light of the stars and lanterns is reflected in their eyes and makes them easy targets. If the hunters wish to save the hides, they may shake or prod the animals to the ground. While all this is going on, somebody has to hold back the dogs to keep·them from being hurt by their frightened quarry. Not until each adult coon is clubbed to death, are the dogs safe. Since the coon is a native of every state, this sport is widespread. Hunters gather around a blazing fire enjoying hot drinks and hunting tales, while the hounds chase down the raccoons.

Even more valuable than their roasted flesh, are the coons' popular and durable fur coats. The coats of the northern raccoons are much heavier than

156

RACCOON

those of the South. They are made into overcoats, collars, muffs and trimmings. Prime pelts bring an average of three dollars each, and as much as fifteen dollars in years of peak prices.

Raccoons thrive in captivity. Only their big appetites and the comparatively low return from their skins discourage raccoon farming.

In country districts raccoon oil is used to keep leather in good condition. During pioneer days it was a principal oil for many farm and home uses and, although very light, was used also for lubricating machinery. In those days the skins were used as money.

The raccoon's Latin name *Lotor* means "the washer." It is noted for washing its food when near water. Away from streams or lakes, it downs its rations as it finds them. If water is near, however, pieces of meat are washed and rewashed until there would seem to be no flavor left. It meticulously rolls berries between its long-fingered "hands" under water. Even a frog or crayfish that has just had its aquatic existence terminated may be sloshed repeatedly before it goes into the coon's mouth.

Why does *Lotor* wash so much of its food? Many naturalists believe that it does not *wash* but that it *dunks,* and derives pleasure from feeling the food under water through its sensitive hands. Perhaps this sensitivity has become an obsession, just as some beavers seemingly hope to flood the world.

The male raccoons are polygamous. However, their affection for mates is stronger than that of most polygamous animals. The female won't mate with just any male. He must be acceptable. After she has made her choice, she refuses to have anything to do with any other male that season. She may go out at night, but doesn't go far. The male travels much farther and may make several calls. The mating season is in December in the far South and in February in the North.

Nine weeks later the three to six, usually four or five, young are born. They come into the world with the family masks and warm fuzzy coats, but are still blind. The mother prefers a home in a hollow tree but will occupy a rock ledge or even an abandoned burrow if necessary.

One mother coon that could not find a conventional home along her chosen creek near Denver, Colorado, appropriated a magpie nest about twelve feet from the ground in a scrub oak. Another mother in Texas brought up her family in a nail keg that had been placed in a tree as a nest box for wood ducks. In this case, the tree was surrounded by water and it was necessary for the coon to swim about twenty feet when leaving or returning home.

Generally raccoons are not as amphibious as the female from Texas. They definitely like moist places, and their homes are usually located near water courses and along the margins of lakes or swamps. Forests or at least groves of trees are ordinarily a requirement. On the plains of central Texas raccoons are found far from trees and even water. In such places, if rocky breaks are not at hand, they depend on skunk and badger dens for shelter. In New Mexico and Arizona, they enjoy the water and shelter in the cliffs of canyons.

Although perfectly foot-sure in the trees, the raccoon uses them mostly as living quarters or places of refuge. Coming down either tail-first, or head-downward like a squirrel, it obtains most of its food on the ground.

The eyes of the little coons open when they are about three weeks old. By the time they are two months of age they are making short foraging trips with their mother. Although she may have three or four pairs of breast nipples, she is already weaning the youngsters.

It is very seldom that the journeys for food begin before dusk. At this time the coon family descends to the side of the stream. Here they hunt in the shallow pools for their favorite food, the crayfish. Rocks, when turned over, yield tasty water-insects, mussels and snails. These are cracked open and the meat devoured. As they grow more adept, the young coons learn to catch frogs and to trap the slower fishes. Their dexterous long black fingers are well suited to hold these slippery, wriggling creatures. Earthworms are dug up from the black loam, or are gathered easily when they come out of their burrows after summer rains. Rotten logs are pulled apart to get the white grubs that live there. Crickets are hunted in the grass. Turtle nests are found and their white paper-shelled eggs are dug out and eaten. Eggs of ground-nesting birds are gobbled whenever luck puts them in the coons' path. Even grown birds, the sick or unwary, may be captured occasionally. Mice are appetizing too.

Corn from farmers' fields is a summer and fall luxury. As fall approaches, other grains and fruits ripen. Persimmons, pecans, pokeweed berries, grapes, haws, plums, cherries, hackberries, raspberries, and dogwood and manzanita berries are relished. In fact, the animal's diet includes almost everything edible, although it runs more heavily to vegetables than to meat.

Travels of the coon family gradually lengthen until by late fall they may extend over a wide range. They often leave footprints that look astonishingly like those of small human children. The mother takes full responsibility and her progeny follow without question. Such slow, generally ambling animals cover surprising distances, from a half-mile to a mile from the den almost every night, and sometimes up to five miles. Unattached males, or females without young, may wander for many miles, investigating possible sources of food, and finding shelter en route just before daybreak.

Arkansas coons that were live-trapped and released in country that evidently was not to their liking, broke all records of coon traveling. They were recaptured twenty-seven, thirty-three and seventy-five miles away.

Young raccoons are usually safe from natural enemies as long as their mother is near. A large and powerful defender, she brings them up without any help from their absent father. When cornered by dogs, she will attack, injure and rout them, although she may be badly wounded herself. Sometimes she takes her progeny up the nearest tree, and then dashes away. The dogs follow her until she is able to throw them off and return to her family. She has been known to add an orphan to her brood. The cubs do not reach their full growth until two years old. Nevertheless, perhaps fifty per cent of the females mate when only ten months old. The males wait another year.

Coons are quite vocal in a surprisingly birdlike way. Although they growl in a deep voice when angry, their normal talk is a churring sound with many variations. One call is a long-drawn tremulo much like the cry of the screech owl.

All coons begin changing their clothes in April. They put on lighter underwear, and their coats of guard hairs are much thinner. By late August signs of the winter coat first appear.

When food gets too scarce in northern winters, they just give up and go to sleep. Several families may den together for warmth and for sociability. Their slumber is not real hibernation, since their respiration, heartbeat, temperature and metabolism are not lowered, as are the ground squirrels'. Any bungling intruder will awaken the animals and receive an inhospitable greeting. During milder spells, even in mid-winter, the coons often leave the den at night to satisfy reviving appetites on mice, rabbits, or any other prey that may be above ground.

The mothers keep their young with them for the first winter, including the pregnant daughters. The wandering fathers are more likely to live alone.

The winter mating season brings most of the adults out of their dozing. Once in a while a female mates, not in mid-winter, but in early summer. These young, born in August, weigh only about three pounds at the onset of cold weather. Probably their chances for survival are poor in the North, but the southern coons are active the year round.

Albino raccoons are beautiful animals with pink eyes, white claws, and whitish-cream fur faintly marked with the family pattern. They are not uncommon. The melanistic animals, almost black in color, are less numerous.

Economically, the raccoon is mainly beneficial. Occasionally one gets into a poultry house and slaughters the chickens, but this seldom occurs. In California it is accused of being the most destructive of native furbearers to waterfowl. It is said that in swampy regions the coon wades or swims to procure eggs and ducklings. It regularly explores cavities in willows and cottonwoods along rivers, perhaps in hope of finding wood duck eggs or young. A coon was once known to climb sixty feet to the nest of a red-tailed hawk. It devoured the eggs and then nonchalantly took a siesta in the raided nest. Perhaps the coon's fondness for corn and melons gets it into more trouble than any other appetite. Nevertheless, because of his great consumption of insects, and because of the value of his coat, it is generally a real asset.

Wild coons, if captured while still in the nest, make affectionate and intelligent, although mischievous, pets. As pet coons grow old, unfortunately, they are likely to become cranky.

General description. A stocky, bushy-haired animal with a pointed "masked" face and furry, banded tail. Ears large; toes long. General color grizzled gray, brownish and blackish; head grayish with a black band running across the cheeks and eyes, with a streak extending from nose to forehead; yellowish-gray tail banded with six or seven black rings. Total length, 30 to 36 inches; height at shoulder, 12 inches; weight, 10 to 25 pounds; reportedly up to 49 pounds for an extraordinarily large individual.

Distinguishing characteristics. The combination of stocky build, black face mask, and black-banded furry tail. The only other mammals north of Mexico having black-banded tails are the coati and the ringtail, but theirs are long and slender.

Range. The entire United States except northern Maine, the Rocky Mountain region south to southwestern Colorado, and the Great Basin; also found across southern Canada from Nova Scotia to southern Manitoba, and in southwestern British Columbia; thence south into South America.

COATI
NASUA NARICA

Looking like caricatured raccoons, a band of coatis scamper up an arroyo. They have short brownish hair and long snouts. Their long, thin tails with many black rings are waving high in the air. All told, they measure about four and one-half feet long. Hunting for insects, fruits, nuts, or nesting birds and their eggs, the animals run this way and that, pattering on their erratic course. A strange sound startles them! They dash up into the branches of the palo verde trees like a band of monkeys.

Leaping from tree to tree they hiss and spit and lash their long tails excitedly. If forced to the ground and cornered, their protruding canine teeth are as dangerous as a pair of little sabres.

A cowboy in Arizona reported a coati hanging down from a mesquite tree, gnashing at his pack of dogs, and severely injuring one of them. In the excitement the cowboy thought the animal swung by its tail. Although a coati usually comes down a tree head first and can hang from a tree by the hind legs, I have never known one to be able to suspend itself by the tail.

As long as the body and head together, the tail is apparently of no use except as a balance in the trees. Rather like a tabby cat's, it is slender and has many dark rings. You often see it before you see the coati. Waving above its body, the tail announces that the animal is from the house of Coati and no other. Held straight up while it is eating, the tail is often carried at an angle of forty-five to ninety degrees (or horizontal) at other times.

The male coati is almost twice as big as the female. He wants no society but his own, except during mating season. The female likes company and often

COATI

travels in bands with her offspring. No one has found out yet whether the courting season is long or short. About eleven weeks after mating the four or five young are born.

Young coatis make intelligent and gentle pets. Like their northern relatives, the 'coons, they are inquisitive and mischievous. In the tropics, they are common household pets, but must be held on leashes to avoid trouble. In keeping with their natural arboreal lives, coatis have shrill almost birdlike screams.

Coatis wear grizzled coats of harsh, rather coarse hair. There are two distinct color phases, brown and gray. They vary greatly in pattern and color from dark to faded shades according to whether their homes are in the humid jungle or the dry open desert, and depending somewhat on the individual.

Tropical America is the coatis' real home, from central South America northward. The hardiest coatis brave the comparative chills of the southern half of Arizona and southwestern New Mexico. During the past twenty years there have been enough records in those regions to demonstrate that coatis are resident in some numbers, not merely stragglers from Mexico. They are rather common in southeastern Arizona, where in 1939 a hunter reported seeing a troop of twelve or fifteen coatis. It is quite probable that they are extending their range northward.

The tribe is divided into numerous species. Several kinds in southern Mexico are much larger than our coati, while in South America most of them are smaller.

Because it is a strange-looking creature, the coati is more likely to be killed on sight than would be the case with a well-known game animal during the closed season. I was once directed to the remains of a coati about twenty miles north of Douglas, Arizona. The animal had been wandering over the mesquite flats along the highway when it was seen by a cowboy. The man promptly killed it "because he didn't know what it was!.' The coati should have year-long legal protection in this country.

During the last seventy years, only four coatis have been found on the north side of the Rio Grande in Texas. At least two and perhaps three of them had escaped from captivity. Coatis are often shipped from farther south to the Mexican border towns for sale to American tourists.

Very little is known about the coatis in the wild in the United States—or elsewhere, for that matter. In northeastern Mexico they live on the plains and foothills in the vicinity of rocky ledges, but not on the heavily forested mountains. Farther west in the mountains of Coahuila, they like the warmer, humid canyons.

Hungry creatures, they hunt day and night. and eat everything. They sleep during part of the night and through the midday heat. Curled up, they nap peacefully on the branch of a tree or on the ground. Their snouts have a keen sense of smell and are used frequently to dig out juicy grubs and insects. The rest of the time when digging, the animals use one forepaw after the other, arching their backs and letting their tails down to an angle of forty-five degrees.

Because they are as much at home aloft as on the ground, they pick many nuts and fruits from the trees. Sometimes when a band is leaping through the branches, another band will run below picking up the nuts that are shaken down from above. Perhaps because they are highly arboreal, coatis don't turn around like most other animals. Instead of turning on all fours, they usually pivot on their hind legs.

Lizards are a favorite food. In the tropics coatis expend much energy in climbing about the trees in search of sleeping iguanas. These big lizards are wary and usually drop to the ground and escape. Nevertheless the furry hunters are persistent and eventually surprise a sleeping or unwary animal for a meal.

Many predator-prey relationships are of this kind. No hunter is omniscient and no prey species is helpless. Only the capable predators make a living; while the watchful, fleet prey-animals survive, and the stupid, sick, and otherwise abnormal and unlucky individuals perish.

The coati is fond of birds' eggs. Not long ago, near Gila Bend, Arizona, a rancher stepped into his yard one morning to find one of his ducks protesting about the robbery of her nest. Broken eggshells lay about. Looking up in a nearby shade tree, the rancher saw the culprit—and his first coati.

In spite of its omnivorous tastes, the coati can be fastidious. One coati is known to have carefully cut out the stomach of a spiny rat and discarded it with the intestines, some skin, and the foot by which the rat had been caught in the trap.

Another name for the coati that is widely used by naturalists is *coatimundi*. In Mexico a common name is *choluga* or *cholla,* while in Central and South America *pisote* is the vernacular term. *Pisote solo* for the male who travels alone, and *pisote de manada* for the sociable female.

The fur of the coati is so coarse and sparse that it has little or no commercial value.

General description. A long, rather slender animal with long tail and harsh fur; head elongated, with a long movable snout that projects well beyond the lower jaw; legs fairly long; feet provided with long, rather straight, blunt claws. Color variable: grizzled brown, gray, black and yellowish, shading into white on chin and throat; a mask of pale brown across the eyes; tail not heavily furred, yellowish brown with, in young animals, dark brown rings. These become less distinct with age. Total length, 4 to 4½ feet; height at shoulder, about 10 inches; weight, 10 to 20 pounds. Females are much smaller.

Distinguishing characteristics. The only other animal north of Mexico having a long, slender, distinctly banded tail is the ringtail or cacomistle. The latter has soft, fluffy, rather thick fur. The larger coati has sparse, harsh fur, a much longer head and muzzle, a longer, more slender tail, and is found in the United States only in a restricted range in the Southwest.

Range. Southwestern New Mexico, southern Arizona, south through Mexico and Central America into South America.

RINGTAIL
BASSARISCUS ASTUTUS

The ringtail is the most appealing of all the furry mammals. Its delicate pointed face seems to be all eyes. Although the head is shaped somewhat like that of the marten or the gray fox, it does not have their sharp, sly expression. Instead, its great dark eyes surrounded by whitish circles, look out at the world with gentle wonder. The gorgeous, black-ringed tail, for which it is named, is as long as the head and body combined.

Although it is a common resident over a great area of the southwestern United States and southward to Costa Rica, few persons have ever seen it. Normally it is exceedingly shy, keeps to the dark caves, and does nearly all of its hunting at night.

Once in a great while the ringtail has been found in a tree almost out of sight, taking a sun bath. On one occasion I found a lone male inquisitively pulling up one of my cougar traps about four o'clock on a bright sunny afternoon. I had made the set the day before on his favorite promenade at the foot of a cliff. Fortunately for him, he pulled up the big trap with a delicate touch and escaped.

Only extreme drowsiness dulls the ringtail's vivid curiosity about everything going on around it. I once kept several ringtails in a large cage. The removable cover of their nest box was perpetually ajar, or even thrown off entirely, in spite of my pains to replace it each time that I entered the cage. Apparently the animals pushed their roof off deliberately in order to keep watch on their sur-

RINGTAIL

roundings. At any time of day or night that I entered the room except near the middle of the day, pairs of liquid black eyes were watching curiously. Even in full daylight at least one sleepy head would rise and the eyes, filmed with drowsiness, would open.

Few animals that are so little known have acquired as many names. Modern Mexicans frequently have used the Aztec title: *cacomixtle,* although in Baja California, *babisuri* is preferred. "Civet cat," a term often used in the Southwest, should be discarded because our ringtail is a very different animal from the civet of the Old World. *Bassaris* is better, because it comes from the Greek word for "little fox." The scientific title that we use today, *Bassariscus astutus,* means "clever little fox." The other common names arose from the bicolored tail: coon cat, band-tailed cat, and ringtail. To the last, "cat" is also frequently added, although the animal is not at all closely related to our tabby, which originated in Europe and Africa.

Broken ledges well supplied with caves and large crevices and a supply of drinking water are required by the ringtail. In this "rimrock" at the base of the cliffs that fringe the southwestern canyons, in ruins of ancient Indian dwellings, or sometimes in the pine forests, it lives with others of its kind.

Ringtails are congenial. My captive animals were kept in one cage and got along well from their first minute together. Their only disputes, which never lasted long, arose over a single piece of food. However, I have known of several male ringtails that apparently lived alone. Fathers are driven out of the nest three or four days before the young are born, but they probably move just around the corner until their progeny are a few weeks old. At least one ringtail father is known to have returned to the fold after three days, where he helped to raise the family.

The youngsters, from one to five, usually three or four in number, are born during May or early June in a nest in a rocky crevice or perhaps in a hollow tree. Sometimes the mass of sticks and other litter of a defunct woodrat's nest forms a barrier, and helps to keep out intruders. The blunt-nosed young are about the size of new-born kittens. They are blind, toothless, and their ears are closed. Their pink skin is covered with scant, fine, whitish fuzz. Black rings are faintly pigmented on the skin of their stubby tails.

When hungry, the young ringtails squeak like rusty door hinges. The mother may lie on her side to allow them to nurse, or may squat on her spread hind legs with her front legs propping up her forequarters. If she wishes to move the young to a safer place, she picks them up one at a time in her mouth. Usually she takes hold of the entire shoulder, or even the back, or the head, but rarely copies the "cat-carry" by the skin of the neck.

When the young are three weeks old, one, or both parents, brings them meat. A week and a half later their eyes open and in a few days they are crawling about by pulling-strokes of the front feet and then by staggering on all fours. They soon learn not to soil the nest. At two months they are allowed to travel on hunting trips. They have almost ceased their squeaking, and express emotion by a spitting bark instead. At four months, they are weaned and sent out into the world to make their own living.

Ringtails eat a great deal of meat, but they also like fruits and vegetables, and love sweets. Ringtails climb easily and hunt in the trees as well as on the ground. They enjoy lizards and any small rodents available such as mice, woodrats, chipmunks, ground squirrels, and perhaps even a pocket gopher surprised while cutting down forage.

When I was collecting specimens in the Southwest, Arizona ranchers advised me: "If you don't find fresh woodrat work, look somewhere else for ringtails." In that region I found that these "packrats" were the ringtail's staff of life. Abandoned mine tunnels and prospect shafts are favorite hunting grounds for ringtails, and here they are probably able to pick up occasional bats. Insects and their larvae, and centipedes are also eaten. Sleeping birds may be killed or their nests robbed of young. The birds most often eaten are the brush-dwellers such as the towhees, varied thrush, and some of the sparrows.

Ringtails like a great variety of fruits, including figs, the fruit of many low-growing cacti, madrone, yew, cascara, manzanita, and blackberry. My captive animals were fond of oranges. They would clean out all the pulp, leaving the rind clean and dry. Not a drop would they spill on their immaculate white vests. Then they would split open the orange seeds along one side, peel back the husks and eat the contents. From these actions, it seems that in their native canyons they may eat nuts such as pinyon, ponderosa pine and oak mast. They especially like green corn.

Like the rest of the musk-bearers, the ringtail's anal glands secrete a characteristic liquid. It is a clear amber color and has a sweetish musky odor. Fright causes the glands to function; the two or three drops of secretion that appear are not thrown but merely spread over the rear.

Wild ringtails that I caught in traps uttered a succession of piercing screams when I first approached. As I worked to release them, their great eyes regarded me with such seeming reproach, suffering, and appeal that I was utterly ashamed. Trying in vain to make amends later, I always spent too much time bringing them special fruits, juicy mice, and changing their cages.

The intelligent ringtails make delightful pets if caught when young. I once knew of an ingenious man who, having been sent to Arizona for his health, conceived the idea of catching and selling ringtails to eastern city pet shops. He had collected forty-two animals in a big wire enclosure when his doctor announced his cure. Forgetting his get-rich-quick scheme, he packed his bags, departed, and the ringtails were left imprisoned. Fortunately a tree fell across the fence shortly afterward and the animals escaped.

Ringtails that take up their residence in cabins generally are protected by the human owners, for there is no mammal more capable of ridding the premises of rats and mice. For this reason it has earned another name: "miner's cat." Two ringtails at Grand Canyon once moved into the garret of the El Tovar Hotel. Every night they dined fashionably and well at eight o'clock. Pretty waitresses served them luscious scraps, while admiring tourists watched.

Such quick, alert animals that normally move only at night probably have few enemies. The great horned owl may sometimes swoop on adults. Snakes, especially big rattlers, may crawl into the rocky crevices and swallow helpless young.

Only in "boom times" on the fur market, is the ringtail trapped intentionally on a large scale. Frequently, its curiosity gets it into traps set for more valuable furbearers. In 1927, good ringtail pelts brought up to three dollars, but ordinarily the price is about fifty cents. The fur, which on the living animal is fluffy and beautiful, mats down and loses its "life" and color and is used as trimming only on the cheapest cloth coats.

General description. A small, slender, cat-like animal with small pointed head, large ears, short legs and very long bushy, ringed tail. Color brownish-yellowish gray, much paler below; cheeks and lips whitish, with a black spot around the front portion of the eye; tail brownish black with 7 whitish bands. Total length, 25 to 30 inches; height at shoulder, 6 inches; weight, 2 to 2½ pounds.

Distinguishing characteristics. See this section under "Raccoon" (p. 161) and "Coati" (p. 165). As a further guide, it should be noted that the black bands on the tail of the ringtail do not meet on the under side; the black bands on the raccoon's much thicker tail are complete rings.

Range. Southwestern Oregon, California, southeastern Utah, western Colorado and eastern Texas south into South America.

10. The Musk-Carriers

MARTEN—*MARTES* SP.

Public Enemy No. 1 in the red squirrel world is the marten. It streaks through the treetops like a brown flash. It does the panic-stricken squirrel no good to retreat to the end of the highest branch for the marten will either rush the squirrel out of its refuge or shake it loose. The wildest leaps from tree to tree are of no avail for the marten can jump farther than the squirrel. Unless the little red rodent can quickly reach a den in rocks, or a hollow tree trunk where the entrance is too small for the marten to follow, it is lost. The long white canine teeth of the marten will speedily put an end to it.

The marten (also called pine-marten) is a tree-minded weasel. Large and golden-brown, it has a misleading, big-eyed squirrel expression. The ears are broad and rounded and the tail very bushy for a weasel. Constantly alert, it travels with swift, airy grace.

It is very wild. You almost never catch it robbing the farmer's poultry yard. Instead it is racing through the northern spruce and balsam forests catching its own food. Although it prefers to hunt in the tree tops, it is equally adept on the ground. Its prey includes the following:

Red squirrels	Mice	Fish (if thrown on to
Gray squirrels	Birds—including	the land when dead
(when present)	grouse, ducks	so that it doesn't have
Conies	Nestlings	to go into the water
Chipmunks	Eggs	after them)
Rabbits	Frogs (when it can	Insects
Young woodchucks	catch them without	Reptiles
Woodrats	getting wet feet)	Carrion
Shrews		Berries and other fruits
		(occasionally)
		Nuts (occasionally)
		Honey

The marten does not kill more than it needs as do the weasel and mink at times. What it doesn't eat immediately, it buries under the ground. If you set

MARTEN

a trap there, you will catch it for it always returns. Hunting day and night, it sleeps whenever it feels like it.

Although a full-grown, husky marmot is probably able to defend itself from a marten, a tender youngster provides a delectable meal. While a mother marmot was out gathering food, a marten once was seen to enter her den. A moment later it emerged with a squeaking, kicking, two-weeks-old young one about the size of a ground squirrel. After running some distance, the marten bit its prey through the neck to end its struggles. Not being satisfied with one kidnapping, the marten hurried back to the den. This time it was caught in the act by the mother marmot. It tore out of the burrow with a rush, ran to pick up the one victim, and fled.

At least one mallard duck took a marten "for a ride." He had been captured by the marten and dragged about forty feet toward a clump of firs. But the drake didn't give up. Struggling valiantly, he carried the marten off the ground and into the air several times. Each time the marten pulled him back to earth. Once the mallard carried it thirty feet. But at last the duck was killed, and the marten carried him into a hole under the trees and devoured him.

A savage soul, the marten usually hates everyone, including the members of its family. The only exceptions are man, when curiosity gets the upper hand, and its mate or mates. During pairing season, its spirit mellows as far as the latter are concerned, but it is more ferocious than ever if any possible rivals appear.

Imagine the surprise of a Yellowstone camper who woke up one morning to find a marten in his bed. Probably only one marten in a million will crawl into bed with a human! Another marten, however, could be persuaded to accept tidbits from a ranger's hand, and even to have its picture taken, providing a victrola was playing music records. The moment the music stopped, off the visitor would go.

Martens have very definite personalities. In captivity, males fight viciously whenever they meet, and are likely to bite off a female's head at the first opportunity. Nevertheless, if an introduction is made properly and carefully, at the right time, the relationship may be quite amicable. Some females show special liking for certain males. Others will accept several mates during a season. Smaller than the males, the females are equally warlike. They are more nervous and more on the *qui vive*.

Summer, from the middle of July through the third week of August, is the time of marten mating. As with several of the musk-bearers, marten gestation is suspended for a considerable length of time. The one to five, usually two or three, young do not arrive until nearly nine months later, during the following April.

The young are born in a decaying snag or hollow tree, very rarely in a burrow. Sometimes the mother usurps a woodpecker's nest, or that of a squirrel that she has eaten. It is comfortably lined with moss or grass. The infants are blind, with only a covering of very fine dun-colored hair. Their eyes do not open for a month or six weeks. In about three months they achieve adult weight and by fall leave their mother and become solitary hunters.

In spite of their natural ferocity, they can be entertaining pets if captured young enough. Young martens in the wild play like squirrels. Squealing with excitement, they chase each other up and down tree trunks. If the fun quiets down, one mischievous marten will slap at another, and the rough-and-tumble will begin all over again. Even an occasional adult may have moments of grim frivolity. It has been known to lead a coyote on a "merry" chase. Darting into a bush, and then through a hollow log, it would reappear seemingly just to tantalize the coyote into continuing the futile pursuit.

When angry, the marten doesn't hesitate to express itself. Snarls, hisses and growls assail the air. Trapped martens have screamed loud enough to be heard one hundred and fifty yards away. A female that wishes to attract a male will utter low clucking notes. All this sounds as if the marten were very loquacious, but actually it is a silent creature under ordinary circumstances.

The marten is consumed with curiosity. Where it is protected, as in our national parks, it pokes its elfin face into any business that comes its way. Sometimes it wanders into campgrounds, appearing absolutely unafraid, and watches tourists at their housekeeping. Any food left unguarded will be grabbed and hustled away into the trees.

In Yosemite, a ranger watched a marten which regularly examined a garbage can for left-overs. Instead of descending into the can it stretched across the opening and held on with three feet. Then it reached into the depths with its head and the remaining front paw. Once it lost its hold and tumbled in. Scrambling out with a rush, it looked around accusingly, evidently believing that someone had sneaked up from behind and pushed it in.

Another marten at Old Faithful ranger station in Yellowstone used to raid the refuse pile. Any discarded tin cans that offered promise were lugged to the roof of the cabin. Here it licked them out happily. Those that were only partly opened were shaken savagely. Sometimes the impatient animal lost its hold of the can in the shaking process, and would look utterly astonished as the can flew into space and disappeared in the soft snow.

The marten is rugged. It does not migrate to lower elevations during winter, nor does it hibernate. It stays inside during the most severe storms and picks up what game it can afterward. The hair on the soles of the feet grows long and completely covers the pads and toes so that even in soft snow its tracks are mere outlines. They show that it bounds along in the manner of the mink and fisher, making an average of thirty-two inches to the jump. It slows down to a walk when investigating something. Much of the hunting is done in the treetops and it may not descend to the ground for several miles if the forest canopy is complete enough to permit such travel. It may cover as much as ten to fifteen miles airline, on the ground and in the trees, in a single night. Much of this running is done apparently haphazardly. The trail crosses, circles and crisscrosses aimlessly.

A sun bath in the tree branches is greatly enjoyed, but not a water bath. It even hates to go out in the rain for food, and hustles back as soon as it can. No normal marten would think of going fishing. The water soaks and mats its fur and it will travel a long way to find a log or a bridge rather than swim across a stream. It carries this dislike of water to such an extent that in mountainous country it follows the ridge tops and descends into canyons only to cross from ridge to ridge.

Like the majority of the musk-carriers, the marten has a pair of anal glands filled with vile scent. It is not as objectionable as that of the weasel or mink, and cannot be thrown like that of the skunk.

In addition, it has a gland, about three inches long and one inch wide, between the skin and the muscular wall on the center of its abdomen. Through openings in the skin, scent is deposited on logs, stones and other objects over which it may rub its under surface. These scents are picked up by any marten following the same run or "trail."

Such a lightning-quick animal, well provided with intelligence, strength, sharp teeth and claws, does not have many serious enemies. The fisher is said to run down the marten in the same way that the marten runs down the squirrel. The lynx may make an occasional meal of a marten. In California, trappers believe that the golden eagle is an important enemy. In one instance in Yellowstone, tracks on the snow showed where a large bird, probably an owl or a raven, had attacked a marten. But the feathered hunter gave it up as a bad job and the marten ran off unscathed.

Very likely famine does much to keep down the marten population in the wild. On Anticosti Island, in the Gulf of St. Lawrence, this carnivore became nearly or quite extinct, apparently when rabbit disease decimated the once-abundant snowshoe hares. Tree squirrels do not exist on this island.

Overtrapping, and burning and lumbering of the marten's forest home have made great inroads on the population. A closed season has been found necessary to conserve the martens in Alaska. The same protection must be invoked eventually in the United States if the animals are not to be wiped out from most of their remaining habitat.

For durability, softness and beauty, the fur of the marten ranks very high. It is frequently called the American sable. The famous sable is only a larger marten that lives in the pine-fir forests of Siberia.

Over twenty thousand martens are trapped each winter in Canada, and perhaps ten thousand more are taken in the United States. About eight thousand of these come from Alaska. The total value of the catch exceeds a half-million dollars. Under ordinary market conditions the better pelts bring from twenty-five to fifty dollars.

Because of its curiosity, the marten is one of the easiest animals to catch. Bird feathers for bait will attract it, and a bird's head is irresistible. Trappers use ordinary small steel traps or a special device like an over-sized rat trap of the snap or deadfall type. This can be nailed to a tree where it will not be buried by snow. It also has the advantage of killing the victim instantly by a blow on the head or neck. A marten caught in an ordinary steel trap may twist or chew its foot off and escape.

Some success in marten fur-farming has been attained. The Fish and Wildlife Service is continuing experimental work on the best methods of management and it seems probable that eventually the industry will become important. Incidentally, two captive martens kept under electric light day and night produced a litter in four and a half months instead of the usual nine. This practice may greatly hasten the production of fur coats in the future!

General description. A large, tree-dwelling weasel with soft, rich yellowish or deep brown fur and a buffy patch on the chest. Head small, ears broad and rounded; legs short, and tail bushy. Total length, 22 to 30 inches; height at shoulder, 7½ inches; weight, 1½ to 3 pounds. Females weigh 30 per cent less.

Distinguishing characteristics. Resembles a large mink but has more prominent ears, bushier tail, a buffy spot on the chest, and displays great dexterity in climbing trees. The fisher is much larger, darker in color, and has very *short* ears.

Range. Coniferous forests from Labrador, Newfoundland, Nova Scotia, and northern New England and the Adirondacks west to western Alaska and British Columbia. In the western mountains, south to extreme northern New Mexico and the southern Sierra Nevada.

FISHER
MARTES PENNANTI

Who named the fisher? It does not fish! It will eat fish if somebody else will catch it. The fisher may even go into the water after a spawned-out salmon, or pick up a dead fish on shore. But it makes no vocation or avocation of fishing. Instead of pulling its meals out of water, it snatches them from the treetops. It is the fastest tree-traveler of any mammal. The marten can overtake the nimble red squirrel, but the fisher can overtake the marten, and can even outrun the snowshoe hare on the ground.

About the size of a fox, with dark, long, silky hair, the fisher lives mostly in low, damp forests, and sometimes in wooded swamps if necessary. Unlike the marten, it does not mind if its feet get wet. In fact it swims across lakes or any other body of water that is in the way.

It has the face of a weasel and the tail of a fox. With grandiloquence, it swishes this bushy appendage back and forth to express displeasure. When really angry, it arches its back and plunges furiously into battle.

Bounding along the ground like the big weasel that it is, the fisher covers four feet at a jump. It hunts by night, or if hungry, in daylight. No meat in any form is overlooked: squirrels, rabbits, marmots, woodrats, mice, mountain beavers, chipmunks, porcupines, and spawned-out, dead or dying fish. Even foxes, raccoons and an occasional lynx may be run down, for the fisher has all the persistent endurance of the weasel tribe, and is swifter and much more powerful than any of the others. It is said to kill deer by biting their jugular veins. If this is true, young bighorns and even mountain goats would be vulnerable prey. It will also eat fruit, vegetables and nuts when hard pressed.

The fisher is one of the mammals smart enough to eat a porcupine without getting hurt. With flashing paw or snapping jaws, it turns the quill pig over on its back. Ripping open the defenseless soft belly, it then proceeds to eat out the

FISHER

carcass from the inside. During many encounters, the fisher of course acquires some quills. Apparently the porcupine quills seldom injure this hardy killer. They often go through the outer hide without piercing the second layer of skin, or the muscles. Instead, they turn until they are flat against the skin and work their way out again. This usually occurs without causing any inflammation or festering sores. Quills have been known to pass through its digestive tract without piercing the delicate lining. Fishers are not always invulnerable, however. A number of them have been found with faces studded with quills and dying of starvation.

Here is a member of the weasel family that will not offend your nostrils nor your sense of economy. The odor is distinctive, but not at all offensive compared with that of the wolverine or mink. It stores all surplus food and invariably goes back to eat it.

April is mating time for the fishers. The young are born from eleven months to almost a year later. This very long gestation period results from what is termed "discontinuous development." The growth of the embryo is halted at a very early stage and is not resumed for months.

The mother fisher has to leave her blind, helpless young when they are only about a week old to hurry off to find a new mate. Because of the long gestation period, she must find a father for the next set of young while still occupied with the present set. She cannot afford to have a mate hanging around who might take a notion to eat up the young. So she goes out of an April night and then returns to her nursing and housekeeping. One night out may be enough, for she stays in heat only two or three days.

In British Columbia young fishers are born the last of March or first of April. The number in a litter varies from one to four, usually three. Their eyes open at the age of about seven weeks, and they are ready to leave the den and hunt with their mother when about three months old. The family breaks up in the late fall and each fisher goes its own way. The young ones look for mates when one or two years of age.

Winter is not a period of slumber for the fisher. It waits out the storms in a den in a hollow tree or log, or in a broken rock ledge, and emerges hungry "as a bear." Deep soft snow slows it down so that it must travel at a walk instead of the usual bounding weasel lope. It must also look more carefully, for food is scarce. The fisher that lives in the mountains usually descends to lower elevations for the winter in order to avoid the heaviest snowfalls. Here it hunts chiefly along the wooded ridges.

The fisher comes down a tree head first. When angry, it arches its back and gives a peculiar growl that ends in a snarl or hiss. It has been seen to defy a dog leaping around the base of its tree by pounding on the trunk with its forefeet used alternately.

Ordinarily the fisher will not stand and pick a fight with too formidable opponents. If cornered, however, it can whip any dog, even an experienced bear dog, and make an escape. In the ordinary run of events it has little to fear from any of the native neighbors. Such a swift climber could escape from an enemy of superior strength such as a cougar, a wolverine, or a wolf pack. A grizzly or black bear is probably too slow and clumsy. A coyote would be too wise.

Man, however, is an opponent from whom even the tallest trees are not a refuge. His traps seem to be everywhere. If given time, and not too badly wounded, the fisher will chew off its imprisoned foot and hobble away, badly handicapped for the rest of its shortened life.

The soft long silky fur of the fisher always brings a good price, for which trappers are willing to plod many freezing miles on the winter trapline. Exceptional pelts have brought as much as three hundred forty-five dollars. An average skin is worth fifty dollars in almost any market, or five times that of a red fox. The small, finely furred pelt of the female is most valuable and is valued at seventy-five to one hundred dollars, while the coarse skin of an old male may bring only twelve to fifteen dollars. Fishers are now kept in captivity, but the pelts produced by fur farms are numerically insignificant as yet. Being very timid and nervous, the animals seldom produce or bring up young unless great care is taken to provide the best of living conditions.

The fisher has become alarmingly scarce in the United States during the past twenty years. It must have complete protection if it is not to vanish entirely. In Canada, the average annual catch has decreased from five thousand six hundred and twenty-two in the decade 1920–1930 to only three thousand five hundred and ten in the period 1930–1940. This is a serious matter commercially, for fisher pelts represent about one per cent of the total value of furs taken in the Dominion, and almost as much as that of all the otters trapped.

We once had fishers in our eastern highlands—the Appalachians—as far south as North Carolina. Now the southern outpost of the species in the East is the Adirondack Mountains. In that wilderness island, fishers seem to be quite "numerous." That term is relative, as even under original conditions fishers were sparsely distributed. Throughout the nineteenth century the average catch each year in all North America was only eight thousand six hundred. Northeast to the Gulf of St. Lawrence and Nova Scotia, a very few fishers may still persist in the wildest, most inaccessible areas. About three-quarters of all the pelts taken in Canada come from Ontario and Quebec, with British Columbia contributing most of the remainder. Professor A. L. Rand has estimated that the total population of fishers in the Dominion is about ten thousand five hundred, or one to each one hundred and ten square miles of suitable habitat.

Fishers have a far-flung range, clear across Canada to the coast of British Columbia and south, in the mountains only, to Wyoming and east central California. Over this vast expanse of the continent, fishers, unlike most other mammals, are remarkably unchanged by their environment, and there is only one species.

Nevertheless, this species has many vagaries. It may weigh anywhere from eight to eighteen pounds. Its coat is slightly different from every other fisher's coat. Even the skull is different. One fisher may feel, think and act one way; another, the opposite. The variations are individual. California fishers as a group are not markedly different from those of Canada. Perhaps the uniformity of the fisher's chosen habitat, in cool coniferous forests, and the absence of insurmountable barriers have tended to prevent group variations from developing. Also, since the fisher is a great wanderer, there has been little inbreeding.

The fisher has many other names, equally inappropriate: fisher cat, black cat, Pennant's cat (after the Welsh naturalist), fisher marten, and pekan. It is not a fisherman and it has no close relationship to any cat. Perhaps these names originated to distinguish it from the marten. Many kinds of animals will eat fish with gusto, although they never went fishing in their lives. Thus the fisher has been caught in traps baited with fish. Since it often lives nearer water than the marten of the pine woods, it was assumed that since the fisher ate fish in traps, it customarily went after fish in the water. The Chippewa Indians were the most discerning naturalists. They named the animal "tha-cho," meaning big marten. This gives its description in one sneeze.

General description. A rather slender animal about the size of a gray fox. Head broad at rear, tapering to a sharp muzzle; eyes small; ears broad, low and rounded; tail long and bushy, tapering from the base; legs short. The long soft fur is dark brown to grayish brown, becoming grayer on the head and neck and black on rump, tail and legs. Total length, 36 to 40 inches; height at shoulder, 10 inches; weight, up to 18 pounds, although rarely over 12. Females are considerably smaller, weighing one-half as much as males.

Distinguishing characteristics. Much like the marten, but considerably larger and darker. Distinguished from the gray fox by darker coloration, shorter legs, and shorter, rounded (not pointed) ears.

Range. From southeastern Canada, northern New England and New York State, northwest to the lower Mackenzie River; south in the Rockies to northwestern Wyoming, in the Sierras to Sequoia National Park, and in the Coast Range almost to San Francisco Bay.

WEASEL

MUSTELA SP.

The weasel is the most bloodthirsty of all the mammals. Its favorite drink is warm blood sucked from the base of the skull or neck of its prey. It fills up on meat, bones, skins and feathers.

Apparently it kills for sheer lust of killing. Because it has sometimes slaughtered forty chickens in one night, people have believed that it lived only on blood. That was before naturalists began examining weasels' stomachs to find out what they really did eat.

The weasel has a superlative equipment for the profession of murder. The long supple body is a perfectly coordinated bundle of nerves and muscles. It is so strong that it can overcome animals several times its size, and so slender that it can follow even meadow mice into their burrows. In one flash, it can outmaneuver a garter snake. It is almost too quick for a bullet. I once saw cowboys in Arizona release a weasel from a trap to use as a target. There they stood, staring foolishly at a distant woodpile. It had vanished into the pile before they could cock their revolvers.

The weasel's long sharp canine teeth make its jaws as fearsome as those of

WEASEL

a tiger on a small scale. Back of them is a brain that is keen, quick, intelligent, and courageous. It fears no man, bird, nor beast. It does not hesitate to attack a creature thirty times its size. When a friend of mine stepped between a weasel and a chicken, the weasel, scarcely three inches high, flew at him in rage. Only repeated kicks saved the man from being severely bitten. Another weasel grabbed a man by the hand and bit so deeply that it could not be dislodged. The man was a naturalist and stubborn. He wanted the weasel alive. As the weasel bit deeper and deeper, the man kept trying to pry it off. At last he walked one-half mile to a creek, where he dunked the weasel loose.

The little brown terrorist uses its nose more than its eyes in stalking. When it is within a few feet of its prey, it rushes. The long neck waves back and forth. The eyes glitter, the serpentine body wraps around the victim, and the forelegs hug it tightly. In less than a split second, it has bitten the poor creature in the back of the neck or the jugular vein. The one or more bites are so swift that the eye can hardly see them.

Many a larger animal becomes uneasy when it sights a weasel. Cottontails in cages sometimes have died of fright. However, a smart snowshoe hare in Minnesota once made a new maze of tracks to keep the weasel busy each time that the weasel almost caught up with it. Patiently and accurately the weasel galloped up and down each cross and crisscross. The rabbit sat down and watched it, seemingly amused. Several times the weasel passed within a few feet of its prey, but the hare did not move. Intent on accurately following the tracks, the weasel did not look up. With its nose close to the footprints, it pushed on, tracing out the intricate pattern. When the weasel got almost to the end of the trail, the rabbit dashed off through the woods. The weasel followed in eager pursuit. About ten minutes later the rabbit would reappear and make another set of tracks in the little clearing. Back would come the weasel, its tongue practically hanging out. The whole procedure began again. Twice the rabbit dashed off, the weasel following after. After the third time, the weasel gave up, disgusted. The rabbit bounded off, with a big laugh, no doubt. Loudest and longest laughed Dr. Adolph Murie who had watched the whole procedure.

Although it can twist and dodge with great dexterity, the weasel is not a fast runner. In a foot race, even a short-winded person can overtake it.

Human hunters condemn the weasel as a game hog, an assassin, a mass murderer. They do not give it credit for courage. They usually forget that the weasel does not kill with a gun from a safe distance. It comes to close quarters and takes chances that it may be crippled or perhaps killed by bites from the sharp teeth of the desperate victims.

A male California weasel once tackled a king snake about three and one-

half feet long. He secured a firm grip on the snake's head, but the violent writh-
ings of the reptile threw the little killer off his feet. At last the convulsions of
the snake ceased. Frightened by shots from a spectator's pistol, the weasel
released his hold and slowly dragged himself into the grass, where he died.
There was no evidence of a bullet hole. The snake had bitten entirely through
the weasel's tough skin in six places, on the head, neck and body. The snake
died first, but had achieved its revenge.

By some unknown psychological or physical methods, the Kennicott's ground
squirrels of Yellowstone Park seem to have settled their weasel problem. Many
times they chase the weasel into a den or cranny and do not even bother to
follow. Wrestling matches, to the accompaniment of weasel growls and ground
squirrel chattering, have ended in utter rout of the fierce little meat eater.

Under favorable circumstances the weasel can and does kill full-grown
cottontails. Often, however, the rabbits are able to defend themselves successfully. Even in a cage where the prey is unable to get away, a weasel usually has
a hard struggle to subdue a healthy rabbit. It may be thrown off violently or
kicked away several times by the frightened animal before it is able to get its
teeth fixed in a lethal spot in the throat.

Why don't the weasels multiply faster? In spite of their agility and fearless
courage, they have many enemies. The black snake searches out young weasels
and eats them. Sometimes it gets an adult. Birds of prey kill numbers of weasels,
and remains have also been found in the stomach of the goshawk, rough-legged
hawk, barred owl, great horned owl, and snowy owl. Undoubtedly the great
gray owl of the Arctic captures a weasel occasionally. The hunting house-cat
accounts for weasel losses also. My successive cats in New Hampshire frequently
brought home weasels. Each time my pet had to be shut out of the house until a
several days' airing had reduced the potency of the weasel odor. It is much more
nauseating (to me) than that of the skunk.

A great many weasels are destroyed on sight by farmers, poultrymen, and
just plain people. Answers to a questionnaire that was distributed by the Michigan Department of Conservation indicated that seven out of ten weasels seen on
farms in the southern part of that state were killed on the spot.

Weasels have been found with short porcupine quills embedded in their
necks, heads and shoulders. Fleas and ticks live on their skins. Roundworms
and flatworms reduce their vitality from within. Weasels also prey on each other.

Abundance of food certainly exercises a rigid control. When mice are plentiful, weasels increase in numbers. When the mice die off, weasels become rare.

These quick-living little animals are easily killed by excitement. A least
weasel captured in a house near Chicago exhausted itself in a few desperate

dashes about its cage, and died. While helping a photographer to take pictures of another weasel, I saw the little mammal become unsteady from excitement (not fear) and the heat of our floodlights. The weasel never takes sunbaths like many other animals. If it is in a cage and left in the sun, it will almost immediately go into convulsions.

The male is much larger than the female, sometimes weighing twice as much. They probably mate in early summer. There is a delayed gestation period, and the young are not born until April of the following year.

The weasel has no penchant nor claws for digging. It picks out one of its victim's homes for occupation. If the nest is large enough, the weasel lines it with the remains of its former occupants and other prey. Or perhaps it builds a new bed. Rat and mouse fur and bird feathers provide downy comfort. Here it curls up, its nose under its tail, and takes a good sleep. As a rule, it uses only one den, although it often visits other holes and crevices in search of food or out of curiosity.

Having sanitary inclinations, the weasel deposits its scats in the entrance to its tunnel. Often it retains a separate room in the burrow or ledge for a toilet and for garbage. Much food is left or stored in the nest, however, and of course spoils.

In spite of their bloodthirsty pursuits, a number of weasel fathers are domestically inclined and devoted to their offspring. They work hard, helping to bring food to the little ones, disciplining them when necessary, and teaching them to support themselves.

The one to twelve young come into the world pink, wrinkled, toothless, practically naked and squeaking lustily. At three weeks they are still blind, but housebroken! At least, they will toddle several feet away from their nest to relieve themselves, and then find their way back.

When their eyes open about the fifth week, the mother feels that they are old enough to be entirely weaned. The males at seven months are much larger than their mother. No doubt the father has to discipline them thereafter.

The weasels eat whatever flesh is handy. But they prefer it alive and quivering. Carrion is less interesting unless it is some they have cached in their nest or storeroom themselves. Small mammals comprise the greatest part of their menu, and mice are the most common. Their food list runs as follows, being affected by location of their home:

Mice (meadow, white-footed, etc.)	Cottontails
Shrews	Snowshoe hares
Rats (house, cotton, wood)	Squirrels

Moles   **Many insects**
Pikas   Earthworms (when other food is
Young birds   scarce)
Small snakes   Prairie dogs (by the largest weasel
Frogs   —the black-footed ferret)
Lizards

Their fondness for small rodents should make the weasels more welcome on farms. It was found that, in winter in southern Michigan, sixty-five to seventy per cent of their food consisted of white-footed mice and twenty-three to thirty-three per cent of meadow mice. They killed a few birds—song sparrows, juncos, and other ground-frequenting species—and sometimes they climbed into bushes and low trees in apparent search of such tidbits. The total number of songbirds eaten, however, was insignificant. One quail was killed out of a flock of ten, but ring-necked pheasants were not molested.

Less hungry than the shrew for its size, the weasel will still eat about one-third of its weight each twenty-four hours. Young and growing weasels with healthy appetites, however, will down more than half their own weight in meat every twenty-four hours.

Imagine having a thirty-pound baby son who demands fifteen pounds of meat every day! Weasel parents may have to feed eight or ten such babies on the same ratio at one time. When food is scarce, they may come home empty-handed. Weary with fruitless travel, they must face the cries of all these hungry youngsters.

The parents may travel several miles each night to secure meat, but according to some naturalists they do not go far from home. Probably not more than one hundred and seventy-five feet in a straight line. However, four New York weasels that were watched in southern Michigan seemed to have more extensive hunting grounds. The travels of each animal blanketed about three hundred acres, or an average distance of three-tenths of a mile from the den. (Of course they did not cover all of their territories each night.) The distance that each of these weasels traveled in a night averaged one and twenty-seven-hundredths miles. Once the hunting trail was only about sixty feet long, while the longest trip was three and forty-three-hundredths miles.

Cold weather alone does not keep the weasel indoors, for it is often out on nights that are well below zero. It does stay in sometimes as long as forty-eight hours at a stretch. Probably it decides occasionally that a stored carcass and the comforts of home will be more satisfying than a long and uncertain quest in the cold. Or it may just not be as ravenous as usual.

Bounding or loping around with their tails held out stiffly parallel to the ground or raised somewhat, weasels explore every corner and grass tuft. They slow to a walk only when the trail becomes complicated or the prey near enough to stalk. When food is abundant, they may go berserk and kill until nothing within reach remains alive. As many as seventy chickens have been killed in a poultry run in one night of such orgy. Evidently they cannot bear to sit down and eat with a lot of live meat running around beside them.

The weasel sometimes stores excess food, mice and shrews, in a room of the burrow. The seeming rapacity of the weasel in killing more than he can possibly eat may be an instinctive precaution to provide for a future famine. He has often been seen running off with corpses that weighed twice as much as he did. Running!

Strangely enough, the weasels do not exterminate everything in their dooryards. Seven Michigan cottontails lived all winter on an area that was inhabited by four weasels. All was tranquillity—outwardly at least. In California, chipmunks have been seen inhabiting the vicinity of dens occupied by families of weasels. Juncoes and russet-backed thrushes have reared their young within a few feet of a weasel's home without being molested. Whether these particular hereditary enemies had reached an understanding and agreement to let bygones be bygones, we shall never know.

Pursuit of prey sometimes leads the weasel into water. In Sequoia National Park, a golden-mantled ground squirrel, desperately trying to escape from a weasel, rushed into a river. Hot after it dove the weasel. About four feet from shore, each animal suddenly forgot the other. Their one aim was to get back to dry land. I have seen weasels enter water merely to make shortcuts across the pool instead of walking around. They can climb trees, where they have been seen plundering birds' nests, but they are not interested in staying up in them.

In the north, or at high altitudes, the weasel puts on a royal white ermine coat with black-tipped tail every winter. (Only the least weasel is completely white.) Each brown hair is replaced by a white one. This does not happen all at once. For three to five weeks, the weasel appears in a kind of pepper-and-salt suit, followed by a piebald uniform. In the south, where snow rarely falls or quickly melts, the weasels wear plain brown suits throughout the year. Light ones for summer, somewhat heavier ones for winter. In the intermediate part of the range, some weasels manage to have white coats, but others do not.

On many occasions the weasel has been slow in getting around to making its seasonal change of clothes. It has been seen wearing its brown coat until the snow was deep. I know of at least one weasel that wore its white coat until July. Such dilatory behavior may mean that the animal is not in good health, or that some gland has failed to function properly. It has been suggested that the general factor causing the color change is heredity. Clearly, neither temperature nor the presence of snow is the immediate cause.

Curiosity is one of the strong family characteristics, and weasels will often disregard apparent danger to satisfy it. An Alaskan weasel barked at me and then followed for several minutes as I picked my way across a partially burned dock of a deserted cannery. It stayed within eight feet of me. Black eyes shining, it twisted and craned its neck so as not to miss a single movement.

This curiosity makes it easy to catch the first time, but it is difficult to keep it caged. After five months of captivity, an adult female at the University of Michigan managed to push out her water bottle and escape through the one-inch hole.

The weasel is quick to learn a lesson. Having been caught once, it is more wary. It took twenty-one days and thirty-two traps to recapture one weasel which apparently had been quite happy in captivity. Sometimes it even got away with the bait. Its footprints recorded its escapades.

There are many kinds of weasels—thirty-six species and subspecies, all the way from the big weasel to the least weasel. This does not include the larger weasel cousins, the wolverine, skunks, land and sea otters, badger, and mink.

Although small, the weasel pelt is soft and durable, and the skin is tough. In medieval times, common people were prohibited from wearing the white winter pelts, for this "ermine" was a badge of royalty. In these democratic times, it is highly fashionable. Fifty thousand ermine pelts are said to have been used in preparing for the coronation of King George VI of Great Britain in 1937. Although the average price is low, running from twenty-five to fifty cents, a good skin may bring a dollar. "Gray-backs," those changing from brown to white, are almost worthless.

It must be acknowledged that in a chicken yard a weasel is a dangerous guest. In a southern Michigan township, weasels killed nearly sixty per cent of the four hundred and seventy-eight poultry that were destroyed in twelve months by all four-footed enemies. During that time, most of the fowl were killed between early April and August. It seemed likely that under the stress of finding food for their young, mother weasels were looking for the easiest kind of prey.

Not that all weasels kill chickens, for they don't! But some night, rather than go hungry, a weasel may try it and find out how exhilaratingly easy it is. At the same time, he is America's best native ratter and he may be an asset to the poultry yard. One rat alone can kill one hundred and ninety chicks in a single night. The weasel is one of the principal factors in helping to check the upsurges of the small rodent population. It is a desirable citizen under most circumstances.

One of the rarest of American mammals, the black-footed ferret (*Mustela nigripes*), is a species of the weasel tribe. The largest of them, it wears black goggles and neat black socks. Its shoulders are heavier and it is about two feet long. The closest relative is actually the Siberian ferret.

Audubon described the black-footed ferret in 1851. Then, for almost twenty-five years, not another specimen was found. Audubon was called many hard names. Some naturalists accused him of inventing the species from a faked skin or just out of thin air. Even now, museums in the whole country contain very few skins, and living ferrets are extremely rare.

The ferret's habits are largely wrapped in mystery. Like the rest of the weasels, it is very inquisitive and will often stand up on its hind legs to see what is going on. This graceful animal preys on mice, rabbits, ground squirrels, and ground-nesting birds and their eggs. Its favorite meat is the prairie dog, but the near-extermination of this once numerous rodent has deprived the ferret of food and den shelter. Although it has been trapped in the mountains as high as ten thousand feet, its real home is the Great Plains from northern Montana to Texas and west to the Grand Canyon in Arizona.

Three species of weasels occur in North America. Each has several subspecies:

1. The ermine (*Mustela erminea*) varies in length from fifteen inches in the far north to nine inches in Colorado and New Mexico. Its tail is rarely more than two-fifths as long as the head and body combined, and is usually shorter. Chocolate brown above in summer, it turns white in winter throughout its range, except on the humid northwest coast from southern British Columbia to California. There it remains brown for the entire year.

2. The least weasel (*M. rixosa*) is the smallest of the tribe. The male is about nine inches long and the female only seven. Their tails are less than one and one-half inches in length, or approximately one-fifth as long as the head and body. The dark brown upper parts turn white in winter, except in the southern part of the range. At all seasons the tail-tip contains only a few black hairs among the brown or white ones. The end of the tails of other species of weasels is distinctly black throughout the year. The least weasel occurs from the Alleghenies to Alaska.

3. The common or long-tailed weasel (*M. frenata*) varies in length from twelve to twenty-four inches, depending on the subspecies and sex. The tail is two-fifths to seven-tenths as long as the head and body. The species ranges clear across the continent, and from southern Canada into South America. In the

northern part of this range the coat turns white in winter, but elsewhere the brown upper parts become only a little paler at that season. The subspecies of *M. frenata* in the southwestern United States has contrasting black-and-white markings on the face and so is named the bridled weasel. The subspecies on the Great Plains has a much longer tail than the species in the East and is called the long-tailed weasel.

General description. A very slender, short-legged small carnivore having a small flattened head with beady eyes and low rounded ears. Neck and body very long, and tail comparatively short. Underfur soft and close, overlaid with long glistening guard hairs. Colors: in summer, yellowish to dark chocolate brown above, with under parts and feet yellowish white; except in the least weasel, the terminal quarter of tail is black. In winter, in country where snow stays on the ground consistently, the weasel is white or slightly yellowish white except for the tail-tip which remains black. Size varies greatly with the species: total length, 6 to 20 inches; height at shoulder, 2 to 4 inches; weight, 6 to 12 ounces. Females are 20 per cent to as much as 50 per cent smaller than males.

Distinguishing characteristics. The greatly elongated form and short legs; rich brown coat in summer and (in the north) white color in winter. The other mustelids (mink, marten and fisher) having even a superficial resemblance are larger than the biggest of the weasels.

Range. Practically all of North America.

MINK
MUSTELA VISON

The mink is an aggressive, crafty killer. Although not as speedy in its movements as the weasel, it is fast by our standards. Its rapierlike thrusts have accounted for many small mammals. A versatile hunter, it can chase down and catch fish right in their own streams.

Its fondness for fresh muskrat is well known. The mink pursues these large rodents into their bank burrows and cattail lodges and kills them in short order. The big muskrats are able, vicious scrappers, but they are slow. In vain they stir up the muddy water so that their attacker cannot see them. They can dive deeper than the mink, but after all, they can't stay down forever.

When the muskrat mother is away, the mink may tear open the house and eat up the young. Like as not, it will then take possession of the house as one of its several homes. Sometimes a few minks will clean out a whole muskrat colony. On the other hand, there are many places where the two species are both numerous and seem to be mildly tolerant of each other.

One old, experienced mother muskrat near Hampton Falls, New Hampshire, could stand her own ground. She not only drove a marauding mink away from her family, but chased it away upstream. An occasional marmot can also get the best of a mink, or at least hold its own.

The mink seems to prefer to lug its meat home and eat it comfortably in bed. As a result the nest is always littered with scraps or even whole carcasses. A famous naturalist snooping around found that one mink had carted almost a month's supply to its den in a hollow ash stub six feet above ground. Stored in a corner were:

> 13 freshly-killed muskrats
> 2 mallard ducks
> 1 coot

Except for muskrats, crayfish and larger quantities of fish, the mink's diet is much the same as the weasel's.

MINK

Sportsmen, finding duck feathers in the mink's scats, have accused it of killing waterfowl. In Yellowstone a mink reached for a duck, missed, and grabbed it by the leg. The duck flapped its wings frantically and succeeded in rising clear out of the water and twenty inches above. But the mink held on. For a few moments the mink dangled in mid-air. Then its weight pulled the duck back down to the water and under. Most of the ducks eaten by the mink are those that are crippled or have died of wounds after escaping from hunters. Probably some nests are found and the eggs destroyed.

Although the mink does not usually kill as wastefully as the weasel, it is a menace to the poultry farm. It assists the farmer by destroying rats, but may kill the chickens as well. A mink on a rampage may kill dozens of "broilers" in one night.

The mink travels far and wide and has many affairs during the mating season. After two months of such living, he is ready to settle down for a while and be a devoted and hard-working husband and father. He and his last mate set up housekeeping.

Naturalists differ about the length of the gestation period. Most opinions agree that it is forty-two to forty-four days, but there is evidence that it may last as long as seventy-five days. Possibly the time may vary, due to delays in the attachment and growth of the embryos.

The four to eight or even more young are about as long as pea pods and covered with very fine, short, whitish hairs when born. Even before their eyes open at the age of five weeks, the little minks chew on meat brought by their mother and father to the den under the roots of a tree on the streamside. As soon as they can see, their mother no longer nurses them but puts them on a meat diet.

The parents carry the young by the scruff of their necks on land, and "pick-a-back" when in the water. A doting couple were once seen swimming with one little fellow across both backs.

Around home the young are very playful in a savage way. A favorite game is "stalk and pounce," a practice for hunting. The victim of the stalk turns on his back and tries to fend off the aggressor with all four feet. Throughout the struggle, both little minks squeal, hiss and growl ferociously. When they become adults, they quarrel violently to the accompaniment of almost continuous screeching.

When the youngsters are old enough to travel on their own legs, they accompany their mother and father on all their wanderings. Usually at night, but sometimes during the day, the family proceeds on its rounds to gather food. The year-round range is large, probably including several square miles. It is not covered systematically. Instead, a temporary headquarters is selected—a natural cavity in a bank, or perhaps a muskrat lodge or rabbit burrow is commandeered —and the minks work out from there. Then, in a week or two, they move along the circuit to the next stand. They frequently travel in a slow, lumbering walk, with arched backs, but their best gait is a bounding, graceful lope that can be kept up for miles, apparently with little effort.

At times a mink can be very nonchalant. It has been seen in the Adirondacks of New York, floating down streams on bright autumn days, curled up, apparently asleep.

A mink's hunting seldom takes it any distance from streams, lakes or tidal marshes. Occasionally minks have been known to live on the shore of the open ocean, miles from the wooded creeks of the typical mink territory.

In late summer the family breaks up, father, mother and children all going their separate ways. By the time the first snow falls, each of them has established its individual territory. In the case of a female, this is small, hardly ever exceeding twenty acres. She is smaller than the male but she too can kill a big muskrat unaided. After raising a strenuous family, she is glad to live alone until mating season comes again. This occurs from the end of January in the South to early April in the North.

The male mink wanders over much larger ranges. The territories of the different minks may overlap and the same den may be used by several animals successively. The hunting routes are irregular and indefinite but tend to follow streams or lake margins. During very cold weather following a snowfall, the animals generally stay at home and sleep curled up, with heads under their tails.

It is fortunate that the mink spends much of the time in water. That is all that keeps it from asphyxiating its neighbors. Although it cannot spray its enemies, like the skunk, it discharges acrid musk from similar glands. To most people it is more obnoxious than that of the weasel, and considerably worse than that of the skunk. The older the mink is, and the nearer it is to mating season, the more unbearable it is. Much less restrained than the skunk, the mink goes around issuing this stench on the slightest provocation. This discharge has little value as a defense weapon. Apparently its function is to attract the opposite sex.

The mink does have its lighter moments. They are infrequent, but definitely light. It has been seen to copy the otter and slide down hill on its belly just for fun. In at least one case on record, a mink made eight successive slides down a slope covered with a couple of inches of snow.

Mange, bot flies, lung flukes and tapeworms sometimes cause serious trouble to the mink. Few animals have the temerity to pick a fight with it. Only the lynx, bobcat and fox, among the mammals, and the great-horned and snowy owls, among the birds, are known to prey on it. When attacked by too formidable an enemy, it can dodge and slip into shelter like a flash. If cornered, it becomes a demon of fury. It tears at the enemy or a trap with vicious teeth and claws. Its face is contorted into horrible grimaces. It discharges enough musk to smell to high heaven. It spits, hisses, and squeals shrilly with rage. Sometimes it barks hoarsely. No animal goes more berserk in a trap. It may even bite off its caught foot beyond the steel trap, which does it no good, or may bury itself, trap and all.

Human trappers account for far more minks than all other factors combined, except perhaps shortages of food caused by epidemics among the rodents. Nevertheless, the species has held its own fairly well. Most wild minks are caught in steel traps. The Eskimos, however, use a funnel-shaped wicker basket, made on the principle of a fish trap, which is set in a narrow channel where the animals are likely to swim.

The mink has the most beautiful and costly coat of all the small mustelids. The value of a good, dark pelt from the northeastern part of the range is ordinarily about ten dollars. Louisiana produces more mink fur than any other state (168,600 pelts in the winter of 1945-6), but the quality of the fur is not as high. In the great boom of the late 1920's, a small lot of very choice dark skins sold in New York for one hundred and seventeen dollars apiece.

The mink was the first American furbearer to be "domesticated." The business of raising the animals for breeding stock or fur began on a very small scale shortly before the Civil War. In the early days, some minks were sold as ratters. With many ups and downs, the mink industry has expanded until each year many thousands of minks, about forty per cent of the total marketed, are raised in captivity and pelted. The high quality of these furs, which are unblemished by trap and other scars, make them worth twenty to twenty-five dollars under average market conditions. Good animals for breeding purposes bring seventy-five to one hundred dollars.

An extinct species, called the sea mink (*Mustela macrodon*), was a light-colored, reddish brown animal. Larger than the common mink, it lived along the coast of Maine and New Brunswick. It apparently vanished for good about 1860. A couple of faded mounted skins, and many bones in Indian village sites and shell heaps, are all that remain.

General description. A weasel-like animal about the size of a small house cat. Body and neck very long; legs short; tail long and rather bushy; head rather short with pointed muzzle. Fur soft and well covered with long, glistening guard hairs; color uniform russet brown to very dark chocolate brown with white chin and irregular white spots on throat and breast. Total length, 20 to 30 inches; height at shoulder, 5 inches; weight, about 2 pounds. Females are considerably smaller, sometimes only half as heavy as males.

Distinguishing characteristics. The mink is larger than the weasel, is generally darker in color than the weasel's summer coat and lacks the extensive white under parts of the weasel; also, does not turn white in the winter. The marten has a more bushy tail and *yellower* brown fur. The otter is much larger and has a heavy tapering tail, while that of the mink is not heavy and is more nearly cylindrical.

Range. All of North America north of Mexico, except Newfoundland, northern Ungava, northeastern Mackenzie, northern and extreme western Alaska, southern half of Florida, and southwestern United States, including the drier plains and deserts from southern Texas to the coast of southern California.

WOLVERINE

GULO SP.

The wolverine is a lonely, bad-tempered animal. It will brook no interference, even from a mountain lion or a grizzly. It can spit in anybody's eye. Its father might as well have been a bear, and its mother a skunk. It smells like one and looks like both of them. Some people call it Skunk-Bear.

The powerfully built body lumbers along on short squat legs. The dark brown hair is long, coarse, thick and shaggy. It has a bushy tail, hair-covered feet and bearlike claws. Three to four feet long, including the tail, it is the largest of all the weasel tribe.

The wolverine has been seen to drive bears, mountain lions and coyotes away from their own kill, and then nonchalantly eat it himself. Not only one bear or mountain lion at a time but sometimes two or three!

Apparently the wolverine just gets mad when it sees someone else eating a good dinner. The hair on the back and neck rises straight up, the tail is hoisted like that of an angry bison, and it advances to the attack.

Three large coyotes have been seen to leave their meal of dead horse when this happened. At least one pair of adult black bears are known to have beaten a hasty retreat when a wolverine demanded their dinner. Two mountain lions

WOLVERINE

relinquished a deer they had killed when a wolverine in California stalked toward them. One of the lions protested violently but even it was afraid of the little bow-legged robber.

The wolverine is said to have attacked and killed mountain lions, coyotes, bears, moose, caribou, sheep and deer. The short legs and bearlike gait prevent it from chasing these animals, which are so much larger. But it is a strategist. According to a number of hunters and trappers, it has leaped on elk and moose when they were bogged down in the deep snow. These animals have been found with a hole chewed or torn in the back, and their spinal cords cut or torn. Wolverine tracks pointed to the assassin.

A mountain lion was once found terribly chewed and lacerated, with one leg broken. In the deep snow, footprints of a wolverine, mixed with those of the lion, told the story.

Other large mammals seem to have been leaped upon from trees or overhanging rocks. Tracks of wolverines following Dall sheep in Alaska indicate that the wolverine hunts sheep. It is quite possible that it follows the sheep until they reach the corner of a cliff, where it makes a quick leap or two onto a sheep's back and cuts the jugular vein.

This short, bow-legged Napoleon is the strongest for its size of all North American mammals. A wolverine near Mount McKinley was known to drag a small Dall sheep down a mountain, across a river bar, and over a steep bank— a total distance of at least one and one-half miles. All this was done before it settled down for a feast. The ground was covered with snow but the carcass must have weighed three times as much as the bantam warrior.

The only creature not reported to have been attacked by the wolverine is man. On the Alaska Peninsula, I once scared off a flock of mallards that a wolverine had been trailing. It turned and faced me. For a long minute it stared vengefully, then its mouth opened in a snarl of rage but it didn't try to attack me. With a final glare, it turned and loped angrily off into the alders.

Apparently, only a porcupine can damage the wolverine. When very hungry, a wolverine will tackle a porcupine but does it so clumsily that it may pay with its life. Wolverines have been found dead with great numbers of quills sticking in their mouths and throats, their stomach walls covered with quills, many of which had worked through into the body cavity, and their intestines pierced.

The wolverine is supposed to be the glutton of all gluttons. For this reason it has been given the Latin name *Gulo,* meaning gullet. Its powerful digestive system disposes of food so efficiently and frequently that it can eat immense quantities of food. It cannot, however, live up to its backwoods reputation. It does not clean up a whole moose or caribou at a sitting. But it frequently camps by a kill until everything edible has been devoured. It sleeps off its gorges in a nearby rock-cranny or thicket and returns after each siesta. If it gets tired of the same food, it will carry away and store the remainder. It tears the pieces into chunks and caches each piece separately.

Meat of all kinds, ages and conditions makes up its diet. It has been seen eating snails and frogs. Probably it depends chiefly on mice, chipmunks, ground squirrels, ground-roosting grouse such as ptarmigans, and marmots. It does relatively little digging after small fry, for the front feet are not well equipped for the purpose. Its great strength, however, enables it to turn over slabs of rock, and to roll over logs or tear them apart to get at rodents that have taken refuge there.

If a wolverine finds and takes a notion to follow a trapline, it may drive the trapper to his wit's end and ultimately ruin him. With diabolical ingenuity, it will remove every bit of bait, every trapped animal, and often hide the traps or destroy them, but is usually too smart to get caught itself.

It can dig, climb or gnaw its way into almost any building. At times it has broken into cabins and eaten or destroyed a whole winter's supplies in one week. Flour and other food that it does not eat is spoiled by the vile-smelling secretion from the anal glands. Canned goods, pots, pans, dishes, cutlery, and stove lids are scattered through the woods as if out of sheer deviltry.

It enjoys eating and hunting too much to hibernate. When winter comes, it puts on its heaviest coat, stiff hair soles on its feet, and continues to eat and hunt, hunt and eat.

You can't find out much about the private life of the wolverine. It appears to be a solitary, grumpy animal that seldom teams up with any other animal. The only exception occurs in February or March, when it takes a mate. After a brief courtship, it goes back to its solitary ways.

The two or three young—rarely up to five—are born during June in a den, under an overhanging rock, in the shelter of dense coniferous foliage, or at the base of a hollow tree. From the beginning, they learn that life is hard and there are no downy comforters for them. The woolly newborn coats are very pale, light brown, buffy, or even nearly white, but they have the color pattern of their parents. Darker bands occur along the sides.

The mother is an unusually capable defender of her family. She is an absolutely fearless fighter. By late fall, the youngsters are two-thirds grown and ready to fight their own battles. The family usually breaks up completely by the time the ground is covered with snow, but sometimes a couple of the cubs may continue to hunt together.

Although the wolverines may defile man's possessions, or even their own food through carelessness, they keep an immaculate house. The mother housebreaks her children at an early age, and the toilet is outside.

In spite of its heavy body and short legs, the wolverine can climb a tree if necessary. Several wolverines have been known to climb to the very top when chased by a pack of hounds.

The wolverine ranges over a considerable area. A hunter in the Cascade Mountains of Washington once followed a wolverine's trail for two days, from the headwaters of Ashnola Creek to the Canadian boundary, but never overtook the animal. In central Alaska the wolverine is said to have regular routes or circuits, and to pass a given point every eight to ten days.

The wolverine's coat is too bulky, and too difficult to get, to be popular fur for garments in the United States. The total number of pelts sold annually is between one thousand and twelve hundred. Practically all of them come from northern and western Canada, Alaska, and the Soviet Republics. The value is not high, rarely over twenty-five dollars for an exceptionally fine skin, and the average is only six to eight dollars.

The native people of the Arctic, however, prize wolverine fur out of all proportion to its monetary value. It is used as trimming for garments. The best-dressed Eskimo is the one who has the most yards of wolverine skin. Eskimo hunters believe that a belt or hunting bag made of the skin of the legs and face will give them some of the physical strength and cunning of the redoubtable animal. Because the guard hairs of the wolverine will not accumulate frost, the pelt is a favorite trimming for parka hoods and cuffs.

Warm climates have no attractions for the wolverine. Its tribe is found all the way around the northern world, south of the Arctic Ocean, in Asia, Europe and North America. On our continent, the range extended from the southern polar islands to the southern boundary of Canada, and into the United States in the great mountain chains and around the northern part of the Great Lakes. Northern Pennsylvania, southern Colorado or northern New Mexico, and the southern end of the Sierra Nevada mark the farthest extensions of the aboriginal habitat.

Never numerous anywhere in this country, even before the coming of the whites, the wolverine is now extinct east of the Rocky Mountains. The last specimen had been trapped from the Wolverine State before any of the skins that passed through the trading posts was identified certainly as having originated in Michigan. Today wolverines are very rare in the few localities in the Rockies and Sierra Nevada where the race survives. The number of pairs living in the entire state of California has been estimated at not more than fifteen.

This small warrior with the big growl may soon become extinct unless given absolute protection.

General description. A thick-bodied, short-legged animal with a shaggy coat, looking not unlike a cross between a skunk and a bear. Head broad, with short ears, body sturdy with a high-arching back; tail fairly long and bushy; feet large, with large stout claws that are semi-retractile. Color dark brown to almost black, with a broad brownish white stripe running along each side from shoulder to rump and onto upper part of tail; head grizzled gray with black muzzle. Total length, 36 to 44 inches; height at shoulder, 15 inches; weight, 20 to 35 pounds, to a possible maximum of 50 pounds.

Distinguishing characteristics. The size and bearlike form and light-colored band on the dark brown, shaggy coat.

Range. From the southern islands of the Arctic Ocean south to central Quebec and Ontario in the East and to Colorado and southeastern California in the West. Very rare within the United States.

THE OTTER

LUTRA SP.

Otters have a delightful sense of frivolity. Young and old, they tumble and wrestle like high-spirited children. They love a good game of tag and follow-the-leader. Chasing each other, they roll gracefully through the water like small dolphins.

Even an old female otter can amuse herself for hours playing with a flat stone. She tosses it from paw to paw until she is bored, then throws it into the water and dives after it. The game is to catch it in her teeth before it strikes bottom.

The otter's favorite pastime is sliding. During the warm months a mother and her young or perhaps several adults select a smooth steep bank that drops into a stream or pond. Climbing to the top, they push off with all four feet turned backward. Head first, down they go on their bellies, and kerplunk into the water! In a few minutes the minor bumps are worn away and the wet bodies have made the slide as slick and smooth as any metal slide on a school playground.

In midwinter I have seen several slides on snow-covered slopes. The otters,

OTTER

with a run and a rush, do belly-whoppers like small boys on toboggans. The soft deep snow at the bottom acts like a featherbed in stopping the exuberant animals.

Like the sea otter, the river or land otter has the outline of a small seal or a very big weasel. From three and one-half to four and one-half feet long, the slim sleek body has a broad flat head and webbed feet for swimming.

The river otter is probably the best swimmer of all our "land" mammals. It can stay under the water for a quarter of a mile without coming up for air. To keep warm in the intensely cold waters of the north, it has two coats. Under the skin is a layer of fat that extends over its entire body and functions as insulation, just as does the thick blubber sheath of the whale. In addition, the otter wears a coat of short, remarkably thick underfur which is overlaid with long guard hairs. From the front, this coat glistens and shines; from the rear, it is just another fine fur coat.

Normally the otter's beautiful dark brown fur is the same color and texture throughout the seasons, and the hair is perfectly straight. Sometimes, however, the tips of the guard hairs are curled. Trappers imagine that these pelts are "singed" from too much sun-bathing.

Some naturalists have believed that the otter is monogamous, but as a matter of fact he may have a number of mates each season.

The one to five, usually two or three, pups are born in April. Home is usually in a bank burrow, perhaps a muskrat or beaver den that has been abandoned by its owner, or in the base of a hollow tree. The hollow trunk of a fallen tree also makes an acceptable nursery. In the flat marshes and the "tules" of California, where a suitable tree is not available, the mother makes a wigwam. Bending tall marsh plants together at the top, she encloses a small circular room. A clean animal, she arranges for one or more outside toilets.

When born, the young otters are about the size of small ground squirrels. Their eyes are closed and they are very dark, almost black. They develop rather slowly, and do not see until about five weeks of age. It is said that they must be taught to swim and to hunt for fish. The mother is a patient instructor and tends her brood carefully. In the water, she is said to carry them on her back until they can swim alone. They stay with her until they are almost a year old, when the next annual litter is due to arrive.

The fact that young otters, as many as five in number, have been seen accompanied by two adults may indicate that two mothers may join company, or an occasional and exceptional father may be allowed to share in bringing up his progeny.

Paddling about in a lake, or lying in the sun on the bank, the otter family present a picture of peace and affection. The mother and the young may take turns combing each other's fur, starting at the head and working back. They converse a great deal in low mumbling tones. Too rough play brings out a complaining whine or a sharp bark of protest. The approach of an enemy is signaled by a low warning cough or grunt.

For a carnivore, the otter has a varied diet. It eats snails and clams and other fresh-water shellfish occasionally, crushing the shells with its strong teeth. Crayfish is a favorite food, and otter droppings are frequently composed entirely of the broken "shells" or outer skeletons of this crustacean. Insects, mudpuppies, frogs and any snakes that happen along are also grist for its mill. Otters were once seen in Yellowstone eating stalks of waterplants for several hours.

Should all otters be killed as enemies of muskrats, beavers and ducks? Whether an otter will clean out a colony of muskrats in a short time seems to depend entirely on circumstances. On some national wildlife refuges the two species live in the same neighborhood without any bloodshed. Probably the otters much prefer more easily caught food, but will kill and eat muskrats rather than go hungry. The same seems to be true of birds. An otter in Yellowstone Park was once seen with a blackbird in its mouth, and another with a flicker. On several occasions, otters have been seen swimming or feeding within a few yards of ducks. The otters seemed completely indifferent to the potential value of a duck dinner, while the birds showed no alarm or tendency to move away from possible danger.

It cannot be denied that the otter competes with man for fish. This is the otter's favorite food. It loves a big salmon or trout, but probably takes the first or easiest-caught fish that comes along. In a stream containing trout, squawfish and suckers, with the squawfish predominating, an otter has been known to content itself entirely with squawfish.

A cunning and stealthy fisherman, the otter creeps up slowly through the water to surprise unwary fish. Some are cornered against the bottom in weeds, or in angles of banks. At least three otters in Yosemite National Park have learned the advantages of pooling their efforts. Diving in a circle, they seemed to be driving startled trout toward each other's waiting jaws.

The otter eats a fish head first and discards the tail fin. Usually, after each meal, it cleans its face and whiskers by wiping them on the grass or snow.

The search for food is aided by a keen sense of smell and a set of highly developed whiskers that may serve as sense organs when it is looking for food in muddy or roily water. Its eyesight is good but not outstanding, and its hearing is somewhat less reliable.

Whenever possible, the otter travels by water. Its legs are too short for easy hiking. However, when it wishes to move from one stream to another, it strikes off across country at an awkward but efficient lope. If necessary, it can run as fast as a man, and can outdistance a man on snowshoes. It probably has regularly used crossings between streams, and may even climb high ridges.

During the winter it may have to hike many miles to find holes in the ice for fishing. I once followed an otter's trail for several miles in the Upper Peninsula of Michigan. It had investigated all openings where the stream was swift enough to keep free of ice. Diving in, it had fished awhile and then returned to the snow-covered banks to resume its journey. The short legs acted merely as paddles in the deep soft snow, for it really traveled on its belly. Every two or three leaps it slid forward as far as possible, then made two or three more bounds and slid again.

One would think that a dripping wet otter would freeze after emerging from a swim into the icy air of a northern winter. In cold weather or hot, the otter's first thought after a swim is to dry its coat. Shaking itself vigorously to send the water flying, it then rolls over and over in the snow or on the grass until fairly dry.

Although rather solitary most of the time, land otters keep tab on each other by means of scent posts. At chosen spots on the shore, almost every passing otter leaves a sign consisting of a twisted tuft of grass on which a few drops of scent from the anal glands are deposited. These scent posts are a great convenience in mating time.

If captured when only a few weeks old, otters make affectionate and gentle pets. They are intelligent, easily trained and friendly. Older otters are too set in their ways.

A dark rich brown, appearing almost black when wet, the otter's coat is somewhat paler and grayer underneath than on the back, and changes to grayish on the throat and muzzle. It is one of the most durable and valuable of North American pelts and at the height of the market in 1946 brought as much as fifty dollars or more. Ordinarily, however, No. 1 skins bring between ten and twenty dollars, depending upon size and color. Those from eastern Canada and the northeastern United States are darkest and are valued at almost twice the price of paler pelts from the South and about thirty per cent more than the better grade of skins from Alaska and the Pacific Northwest.

In recent years, the states reporting the highest catch of otters have been: Louisiana, about two thousand per year; New York, four hundred; Wisconsin, three hundred; Washington, two hundred and fifty; Georgia, one hundred and seventy-five; and Maine and Oregon, about one hundred and fifty each. The take of land otters in Alaska has been about three thousand per year, with a value of more than fifty thousand dollars. In that Territory, the otters of the interior rivers have small silky pelts, while those living along the coast are larger and bluish brown in color.

Otters are found north of the Rio Grande except on the tundra of the far north and the deserts of western Texas, southeastern New Mexico, and California, Nevada and Utah. Even before white men came to America, these animals were scattered rather thinly. In order to secure sufficient food and, perhaps, because of an innate restlessness, they ranged widely in twos or in small families.

Trapping and the encroachment of man have thinned the sparse otter population over vast areas and have extirpated it from much of the eastern and central states wherever agriculture is intensive. Nevertheless, these animals survive in much settled country and surprisingly close to big cities, provided they are protected by enforced laws or natural barriers from human intrusion.

General description. A long-bodied animal formed like an over-sized weasel, with flattened head, slender body, and tapering tail; legs short; all four feet webbed. Fur very dense; underfur whitish gray at base, changing on upper parts to dull dark brown at tip; guard-hairs similar in color but glossy; under parts, throat, and muzzle grayish. Total length, $3\frac{1}{2}$ to $4\frac{1}{2}$ feet; height at shoulder, 9 to 10 inches; weight, 10 to 25 pounds. Females are definitely smaller.

Distinguishing characteristics. Weasellike form and aquatic habit. The large size distinguishes the otter from any other weasel, including the mink.

Range. Fresh-water streams and lakes of North America north of Mexico, except the treeless tundra of the Arctic slope and the deserts of western Texas, southeastern New Mexico, southern California, Nevada and western Utah .

SEA OTTER
ENHYDRA LUTRIS

If you are ever lucky enough to see a live sea otter, you will probably find several, all floating on their backs. Arms are crossed on their bosoms, their webbed toes are turned upward and their tails straight out. Unless you take a picture with a telephoto lens, you will miss the trustful expression of the friendly, white-whiskered face and big black eyes. Occasionally they put one or both paws over their eyes to shut out the light so that they can doze better.

It is amusing to see them stand straight up in the water and peer over the waves or seaweed to see what is going on. With their be-whiskered mouths half open, and apparently toothless, they look like quizzical old men.

They have the most exquisite fur in the world—the rarest and most costly. For two centuries this elegance has brought death and near extermination to the sea otters. Because of their great value, lands were explored, men eagerly braved the hardships of the most perilous waters, and hundreds lost their lives.

In 1737 the white man first learned of the beauty of these skins. For centuries before, the Chinese and west coast American Indians had been using them. Trust the avid white race to gobble up and destroy every valuable resource that could be assimilated.

In the first year after the discovery of the Pribilof Islands, two Russian sailors slaughtered five thousand otters at St. George Island. The following year they could secure only one thousand. During the next five years every last animal was killed. This stupid slaughter continued wherever sea otters were found.

SEA OTTER

The animals were hunted from small boats, pursued until they were exhausted. The desperate creatures became cunning, hid behind rocks, or made for tide rips or breakers. Sometimes they dove in the opposite direction and came up behind the pursuers. But the hunters were persistent and indefatigably spurred by greed.

The sea otter is four to five feet long, including its ten- or twelve-inch tail. An adult male weighs up to eighty pounds. An enlarged edition of his inland relative, he has a long supple body, small fore feet and large webbed hind feet. His head is broad and flat, with ears almost hidden in the fur. His hind feet are very large and powerful, and are haired on both surfaces. Reddish brown or dark brown, sometimes almost black, his beautiful body fur is frosted with white, while the head and neck are paler, frequently grayish or even cream-colored. The white hairs in the coat are not a sign of age. Adults may have none. Youngsters are definitely more grayish than any "grown-up."

Even matter-of-fact hunters have gone into rhapsodies over the otter's fur. The undercoat is unusually fine, soft and dense, about three-quarters of an inch long and overlain by sparse, long guard-hairs. Close to the roots, the fur is white or silvery, darkening progressively toward the outer tips. The whole effect is of luster and velvety grace. The fur is always prime, for the otter lives in a fairly uniform climate and doesn't need a summer and winter coat. It sheds its hair quite gradually, the largest quantities in May and June. It is so permeated with oil that it rarely, if ever, becomes water-soaked.

One remarkable feature is the looseness of the coat. It hangs on the otter's body like the slack skin on a puppy-dog's neck. One would think it was designed for an animal almost twice its size. When removed, it stretches to as much as ninety inches long and thirty-six inches wide.

A rocky, broken coast, plenty of food and an abundance of kelp are the requirements for the sea otters' home. A great bed of coarse "sea-weed" breaks the sweep of the waves and forms a protective screen against enemies.

The otter has three meals a day—an early breakfast, a noonday lunch, and an evening dinner between five and eight o'clock. In a herd of sea otters, there are always some that take a snack between meals. Others that have poorer appetites may skip some of their meals and remain indolently in the kelp beds.

In the north, the sea otter eats sea urchins (three-quarters of its food), crustaceans, mussels, clams, snails, crabs, fish roe, limpets, chitons, polyps, cuttlefish, occasional smelt and little sardinelike fish.

In the south (California) the diet is made up of red abalone, sea urchins, crabs, and mollusks with the exception of mussels. Occasionally it nibbles a kelp.

Pebbles or bits of coral rock are sometimes taken accidentally with shellfish and similar food.   •

The otter is an expert at diving for food. It dives without splashing, folding its arms on its chest and swimming obliquely downward with undulating body and powerful kicks of the huge hind-feet paddles. In the depths it must rely mostly on the senses of touch and smell. Even at bright noon, there is little light at a depth of one hundred feet or more. At the height of the foggy, Alaskan winter, there are only a few hours of dull daylight which never reaches much below the surface of the water. Even on the surface, the otter's sight and hearing are not good but its sense of smell is acute.

A man must use a tool, such as a leaf of an automobile spring sharpened at one end, to pry abalones from the ocean bottom at low tide. The powerful muscles of these great shellfish are a menace to any fisherman. A friend of mine once helped to retrieve the body of a Chinese who, at low tide near San Francisco, had tried to pull up an abalone with his hands. The abalone clamped the man's fingers fast between its shell and the rocky bottom. The tide swept in, no help came and the fisherman was drowned.

How does the sea otter detach these great shellfish with only teeth and paws for implements? Blithely it brings them up, apparently without casualty. It probably is able to catch them when relaxed and unaware. A large piece of shell is always broken out of one side. Perhaps the otter bites it out or possibly pounds it out with a stone. Returning to the surface, the adroit animal turns on its back. Holding the six- to nine-inch shell with its paws, it tears out a chunk of flesh from the abalone.

It habitually uses its chest or abdomen as a table, and its sense of balance is so fine that no meal goes overboard, even when rocked by the waves. The legs of a crab are eaten one by one, while the rest of the creature waits on the otter's belly. When a large purple sea urchin is captured, the otter bites a hole in the "shell" or test, or cracks it with thickly calloused paws. Then it sucks or licks out the soft interior parts with great gusto. It even licks its fingers thoroughly afterward and not a morsel is wasted. The smaller sea urchins which occur in Alaskan waters are eaten, shell, spines and all.

An efficient creature, when it brings up a bivalve, it also carries a flat stone about six or eight inches long and wide. Placing the stone on its chest, it crashes the mollusk down on the stone with a full-arm swing of both paws. Perhaps several blows are required to break the shell, but the otter is persistent and expert.

Sometimes, like a small boy, the sea otter becomes restless in the course of a meal. Clasping the uneaten food to its chest, it turns over and over in the water, chewing a mouthful as it goes, perfectly unconcerned about mixing sea-water with its dinner.

Once I saw an otter interrupted at dinner by an itching at the base of one ear. Setting the food down on its chest, it began to scratch vigorously with both hands. The thick fur seems to be a haven for fleas or lice. At times otters are driven to dashing about madly, frantically scratching and biting for three or four minutes, or even longer.

Usually, if not in a hurry, the sea otter swims on its back. It may merely scull with the tail, moving it from side to side or in a circle. A little more speed is gained by an undulating movement of the body. If that is not enough, it lowers one or both hind feet into the water and really strikes out.

When frightened or in a hurry, it turns over on the abdomen and makes off at a speed of about ten miles per hour. The feet may stroke in unison or alternately, or they may switch from one system to another. The otter swims in a graceful, undulating course, now on the surface, now below. It rides over swells as if they were not there, but it usually swims through, not over, the waves. If really hard-pressed, it can swim under water for four or five minutes.

A stormy period is a hard one for the sea otters. They must work all the time to prevent being blown away or dashed onto the rocky shore. When the wind dies down they are glad to rest. Wrapping themselves in strands of kelp to avoid drifting away, they yawn themselves to sleep.

Except on moonlight nights when they may swim about for a while, the sea otter herd goes to bed with the coming of darkness. A favorite dormitory of kelp is used night after night. Ribbonlike kelp is preferred to the tubular species because it is easier to wrap up in and is less likely to slip loose.

Sea otters growl, bark, squeal and spend a good deal of time squabbling. When one of them takes a nip at a passing herd-mate, it may be answered by a cuff and a protesting, drawn-out squeak that is almost a whistle. Not infrequently one of them will rob another of food. Only an easy-going creature will ignore this affront. When fighting, the otters leap clear of the water, dive and dash at each other with incredible swiftness and great splashings. The mother otters avoid much of this bickering and spend a great deal of time playing with their children.

Sea otters may mate in any month. The male courts his prospective mate by rubbing her cheek with his, or patting her fondly with his forepaws. After a gestation period of about nine months, the single pup is born on an isolated rocky islet or in a thick bed of kelp in a sheltered cove. The mother's faithfulness and affection for her youngster are infinite. She never deserts it. If chased by an enemy, she seizes it by the skin of its neck in her teeth, and makes a series of dives short and quick enough so that the little one will not drown. When diving for food or in play, she may carry it more casually in the crook of her arm. When it is tired of its swimming lessons or of being carried around, she brings it in her arms or on her chest back to their kelp bed.

Her love for her offspring, which is so great that it overcomes any fear, was often utilized by the hunters. Because she would not abandon her pup, she was handicapped. If the pup were captured, they would use it as a decoy. When the mother was killed and picked up first, the crying puppy would swim up to the boat and be taken alive.

The young sea otter is born with its eyes open and a full set of teeth, but grows up rather slowly. Not until it is about six months old does it eat solid food. At this time the mother removes bits of crabmeat and clams and other shellfish from the shells and feeds them to the pup. She continues to nurse it while floating on her back until it is at least a year old. It may not be weaned even then unless another brother or sister is born. Unlike most adolescent animals, it is not forced to shift for itself at that point. Mother sea otters are frequently accompanied by their young of two ages. The otter reaches its full growth when about four years old.

With the exception of man, enemies seem to be few. Only the killer whale is formidable. Seals and sea lions may compete for food but do not attack. Gulls sometimes annoy by swooping hungrily about, hoping to snatch up bits of food. The otters try to frighten them off by splashing water in their faces or to confuse them by diving and coming to the surface elsewhere. Storms sometimes kill old or weak otters by dashing them on jagged rocks. Once in a great while slides from cliffs may kill an animal. Female otters occasionally die in parturition, for the pup is comparatively large and mature when born. Many sea otters probably have toothaches, as cavities are frequent in their broad, flat teeth. Sometimes the decay results in abscesses. It is possible that part of their dental trouble may be due to breaking open the hard spiny shells of sea urchins.

We have seen how the sea otters were slaughtered ruthlessly by the Russians in the late eighteenth century. As a result, the government imposed rigorous restrictions. By the 1860's, the sea otter population had recovered sufficiently to furnish an annual crop of about five hundred pelts.

Then, by the Treaty of Sitka in 1867, Alaska was purchased by the United States and unlimited killing of the otters began again. The price of pelts went down to about fifty dollars and the sea otters quickly became almost extinct.

In 1910 a single skin brought one thousand seven hundred and three dollars and thirty-three cents on the London market. The following year the governments of Russia, Japan, Great Britain and the United States agreed to cease all killing of sea otters. Under the penalty of heavy fines and jail sentences, poaching is now slight and the otters are slowly increasing. About three thousand are estimated to be in the waters around the Aleutian Islands, and more than two hundred live along the California coast south to Monterey.

For years the U. S. Government pondered the possibility of experimenting with raising sea otters in captivity. It remained for the Russians to put the scheme into execution. On one of the Commander Islands, they have established the only sea-otter experimental station in the world. In large pens on a salt-water estuary, where the tide rises and falls, the captive sea otters breed and rear their young.

General description. A large, slender, marine mammal with broad flat head, small ears, short legs, webbed hind feet and thick short tail. Fur soft, short, brownish black, sometimes much grizzled. Total length, 4 to 5 feet; height at shoulder, 10 to 12 inches; weight, up to 80 pounds.

Distinguishing characteristics. Smaller than the seals; body more uniformly slender throughout its length. The small front feet of the otter distinguish it instantly from the flippers of the seals.

Range. Coast and offshore islands of western North America from southern California to central Bering Sea. Commander and Kurile Islands, and possibly other localities, off the northeastern coast of Asia.

STRIPED SKUNK
MEPHITIS SP.

A skunk is not just a skunk. It may be a striped, or a spotted, or a hog-nosed skunk. The striped skunk has two white stripes down its back that join over the shoulders. The hog-nosed has one broad white band from stem to stern. The little spotted skunk has many narrow white stripes that are so broken at times that they appear to be spots.

Everybody knows the striped skunk. It is a big fellow, as skunks go, and lives almost everywhere in the United States and most of the settled portions of Canada.

Each of the three skunks is famous for its remarkable aim. With one gland on each side of the anus, it seldom misses its target. Looking straight at the enemy, it can bring its back around and fire directly at him. Previously hidden, the vents of the glands are now protruding. One may go off separately; usually both discharge at the same time. They may send one stream or a blinding, stinging spray.

"Wait till you see the whites of their eyes!" all the little skunks are taught. They do and then shoot straight at the eyes.

Many people believe that this will cause blindness. This is not true. The discharge will cause an excruciating burning and a copious flow of tears, but no more. Wiping or washing the eyes with water will hasten recovery, which the stream of tears will accomplish anyhow within ten or fifteen minutes.

Although the skunk's defense is automatic, the quantiy of spray is limited to five or six shots. Perhaps for this reason, or because of a naturally amiable disposition, it shows some restraint.

It always gives warning. LOOK OUT! It stamps its displeasure, patting the ground alternately with stiffened front legs. It may click its teeth, growl or hiss. If the enemy continues to threaten, up goes the bushy tail. Every hair is

STRIPED SKUNK

erected at right angles to the axis so that the whole effect is that of a flaring plume. This is the moment for you to run for your life.

Like a flash the skunk whips into a U-shaped position, with head and rear toward the enemy. Swiftly it shoots to the right, to the left, in front or above, apparently without moving. The gorgeous tail is held carefully aloof. You may be sure the skunk is not soiling its own fur.

The powerful hip muscles contract and squeeze part of the contents of the glands through the ducts. The openings of these ducts are everted slightly past the anus like twin nozzles. The two fine streams of thick, oily, yellowish liquid unite about a foot away into one spray of increasingly fine droplets. This spray is astonishingly accurate up to about twelve feet from the animal. If the air is still or the wind is blowing directly toward the target, the stream may strike six or eight feet farther.

To some people the scent of skunks is extremely obnoxious, bringing on violent nausea and weakness, while others do not mind it much. To me, a little of the skunk scent is not unpleasant. The acrid odors of weasel and mink are far more repugnant.

Don't think you are safe if you grab the skunk by its tail and keep its feet off the ground. That theory has been exploded too many times. If you must hold a skunk, keep it belly up, grasping the head in one hand and the base of the tail with the other. Needless to say, keep the base of the tail pointed AWAY from you, and remember too that the skunk has a set of very sharp teeth!

It is possible sometimes to handle a skunk without being bitten or gassed. Of course the reactions vary with circumstances and the disposition of the individual animal. The skunk is not naturally belligerent and will often respond to gentle treatment and soft speaking. I once caught a female striped skunk, by accident, in a No. 4 steel trap that was intended for a bobcat. The powerful jaws had broken the poor animal's hind leg. Slowly I walked up to her, speaking gently as I approached. Working carefully, I simultaneously released the trap and worked her into a burlap sack. After carrying her a hundred yards to my car I drove several miles over a rough road to a stream, where I mercifully drowned her. Not once, in the trap or during my experience with her did she release her scent. On several other occasions I have also handled skunks with impunity.

A famous scientist says that running water will largely remove the skunk odor from pelts. My wife does not agree, at least about my pelt. The only time that I ever received a shot I landed in the dog house. Running water did nothing for me, nor did soap do any good.

A couple of washings with gasoline worked wonders however. If you can't spare the gasoline, wash your clothes in ammonia, chloride of lime or a dilute solution of sodium hypochlorite. A mixture of equal parts of oil of citronella and oil of bergamot will help to neutralize the odor on your person. Trappers sometimes smoke their clothing over burning juniper or cedar leaves.

A skunk hunts all night and sleeps most of the day. The striped skunk is apt to get up earlier and stay out longer than other skunks. It does not spend every day in the same bed. Because it travels so slowly it frequently does not have time to get home. When dawn comes, or soon thereafter, it picks out a likely abode. If other residents are already bedded down, it doesn't mind. Everybody curls up somehow and goes to sleep. In winter time, the more occupants in the nest, the warmer it is! Sometimes there are as many as fifteen skunks sleeping together.

The "V" striped skunk is one of the very few North American mammals of any economic value whose lot has been improved by the coming of Europeans. The near-destruction of the once-great forests of the eastern half of the continent and of the Pacific slope has been hard on most mammals, but not the skunk. It likes forest borders, brushy field corners, fence rows and open grassy fields broken by wooded ravines. A few wanderers select the deep forest for their homes, but the vast majority of skunks prefer the open places where insects abound.

Even in cold climates the skunk may winter above ground, under a building or in a pile of stumps or field stone. Usually, however, it picks out an earth den. This winter home is ordinarily deeper than the summer home. It may be an abandoned woodchuck or badger or fox den, or one dug by the skunk itself. The tunnel (frequently two) will run into the ground at a gentle angle for six to twelve feet. This terminates in a small room whose ceiling is about two feet below the ground level.

Into this chamber the owner lugs as much as a bushel of dry leaves and grass, scraping the material along the ground under its belly until reaching the front door. Then it pushes the load ahead of itself down the tunnel. This vegetation is used not only for bedding but to plug the doorway in very cold weather. The entrance to the tunnel is fairly well hidden in grass or under a brush pile or overhanging foliage.

Although scats are found in the nest, it is not as smelly as might be imagined. The skunk is a fairly clean animal and one can detect only a faint odor at the door, or about its person.

Skunks do not really hibernate. Low temperatures bring a drowsiness, especially to the females and the younger animals. If disturbed during such times the animals waken, and resist any attempt on the part of the intruder to drag them from the den. If prevented from returning they make the best of it, curling up and falling asleep in a few minutes.

The length of this winter's "sleep" varies greatly with locality and with sex and age. In the South the skunk is inactive rarely longer than a few days. In the North, young skunks retire with the first cold snap and don't poke out their noses until spring. Adult females sometimes stay inside for six to twelve weeks, although this is rather rare. The males, on the contrary, are out in every mild spell and, as the winter wears on, they may require temperatures well below zero to keep them underground.

Skunks may den alone or in almost any combination of ages and sexes. The combination may vary from day to day. There may be a pair of adults, a mother with her young of the past season, or several males exercising some sort of supervision over a batch of youngsters. As many as ten females and two or three males have been found together. Usually there is only one male with a group of adult females. He may very likely keep out the other males. Skunks sometimes winter in the same tunnels, but usually in different chambers, with opossums, woodchucks and cottontails. Probably these other animals prefer to ignore the intruders.

By February the older females are ready for mating and the males are out looking for them. This occurs even earlier in the South. Although the cold increases, the would-be fathers ramble oftener and farther. They may travel four or five miles in a single night on their quests. This is a long trek for a skunk but during this month, and in March when the younger females come in heat, they are out exploring every sleeping-quarter for possible mates. These quests and the communal life lead to numerous fights, and much squealing. Sometimes they get so excited that they waste their spray on each other.

The females who stay indoors during the cold weather are fortunate. It is trapping season of course. They may lose weight, but they save their skins. This is probably one of the reasons that the skunk race continues to increase.

After a gestation period of about eight weeks, the mother skunk brings forth a litter of from three to eight young. To some extent her age and size determine the number. A larger and older mother usually has more offspring than the younger ones.

The little fellows are wrinkled, blind, toothless and almost earless and hairless. Their black-and-white pattern is already evident on their pink skin, and their front claws are well developed. The mother with her six pairs of nipples nurses them by sprawling over them or later by lying on her side.

The young grow rapidly and soon have good coats of fur. Their eyes open at about three weeks of age. Two weeks later the little animals are walking about sturdily and rapidly. At two months of age they are weaned, and by fall, some or even all of them have wandered away from their mother to range on their own.

The striped skunk is a silent animal under most circumstances. Only when it loses its ordinarily equable temper, does it utter a single low hoarse bark, or a soft growl.

Beginning at about seven weeks of age, the mother takes her brood on hunting expeditions. The summer diets of all three species of skunks are much the same, depending on the region and kinds of food available. Insects are the most important, especially grasshoppers, beetles, crickets, and their larvae. A long list of fruits, both wild and cultivated, such as cherries, blackberries, raspberries, blueberries, strawberries, currants, apples, serviceberries, cactus fruits, persimmons and even the fruits of dogwood and viburnum are eaten.

Many kinds of small mammals are killed and devoured. Anyone who has watched a skunk hunting knows that it can be nimble and quick when a meal is in question. Its sense of smell and hearing are much better developed than its eyesight. Now and then it bats a few minnows out of a stream. It doesn't like to get wet but can swim if necessary.

In spring it depends on meadow mice for three-fourths of its living. Throughout the warmer months, it feeds on white-footed and jumping mice, pocket gophers, ground squirrels, shrews, moles, chipmunks and cottontails as well. Corn may be eaten while in the milk stage. Any kind of carrion, fish, flesh or fowl, is a mainstay in times of stress.

The skunk is often roundly denounced for destroying ground-nesting birds, their eggs and young, and domestic poultry. It is even on the "predatory animal list" in some places, to be killed on sight and perhaps for a reward. At times it destroys great numbers of honey bees, scratching on the front of the hives and then stamping on the angry insects when they emerge. How can it swallow them, as well as yellow jackets, without being stung? If apiaries and chicken houses are properly fenced, they will be safe from the striped skunk, for it cannot climb.

Hasn't the bird-killing propensities of the skunk been greatly exaggerated? Numbers of birds nest near skunk dens without ever being molested. As a matter of fact, the skunk probably saves the lives of many ducklings and other water birds by digging up and eating the eggs of the snapping turtle.

A live skunk is probably worth more to agriculture than a dead skunk to the fur trade. It removes vast hordes of cutworms, potato beetles, white grubs, May beetle grubs, army worms, tobacco worms and other larvae that would ruin our lawns, hay meadows, and crops. Because the skunk proved so efficient at destroying the hop grub, the first legislation enacted in New York to protect the skunk was due to the insistence of the hop growers.

The pelt of a skunk is worth only about one dollar and twenty-five cents under ordinary conditions, although occasionally it brings three times as much. A minimum of white in the pelt is most desired. Skunk fur is deep, rich, glossy, and very durable. Entire coats are frequently made of it, but most of the skins go into trimmings of cloth coats and for scarfs and muffs. Not until recently did the dealers come right out and call it SKUNK. It went under various trade aliases, but on wet nights its aroma shouted its true name.

Skunk oil was once highly esteemed for the treatment of rheumatism.

Because of its fairly effective defense, the skunk has never had to learn to be smart. It plods on its way without caution. Many animals get out of its way. Five bears have been seen to leave their dinner when one mild little skunk stopped by. Small skunks have been seen playing around a bobcat without being molested.

In hard times, however, it is different, for hungry mountain lions, coyotes, badgers, bobcats, foxes, horned owls and eagles will risk the stench for the sake of an easy dinner.

If you aren't squeamish, you may find out for yourself that skunk meat, when uncontaminated by musk, is delicious. Even an old skunk, when properly cooked, is tender and sweet.

The skunk, when young, can be relieved of the scent glands by a fairly simple operation. Separated from these glands its personality is delightful and it makes a charming pet. It is much more gentle and responsive than the domestic cat. Of course there are skunks and skunks. The females, like those of most species, are more gentle and affectionate. The young ones are easily trained, but the old ones, especially the males, are apt to be troublesome.

A beauteous blonde has been seen traipsing down Broadway with a skunk on a leash walking ahead of her. She and other skunk owners have found that skunks make charming pets.

Like all animals, the skunk is subject to disease. Its blood may be sucked by lice, fleas, ticks and mites. Its vitality may be sapped by such internal parasites as roundworms and flatworms. Even a skunk may have sinus trouble! A wireworm (*Filaria*) living in the nasal passages and frontal sinuses causes infections that are often fatal. Large numbers of skunks sometimes succumb to epidemics of distemper, rabies, and a variety of virus-caused diseases. Under domestic conditions, they are subject to pneumonia.

The Hooded Skunk belongs to a separate group or subgenus of the striped skunk. The hood or cape is formed by long white hairs of the neck and the back of the head. It may have much or little white on its back. Ranging from southwestern New Mexico and southeastern Arizona through most of Mexico and Guatemala, its habits are little known. They probably differ but slightly from those of the striped skunks proper in that part of the world. The mother has five pairs of nipples instead of six as in the striped skunk.

General description. A stout-bodied animal about the size of a house-cat, with small head, large bushy tail, and short legs. Underfur short and soft, overlaid with long heavy guard hairs. Color shiny black or brownish black with a band of white running from the back of head along each upper flank to the base of the tail which is black and white. In extreme cases the white stripes may be absent or they may be so broad as to merge on the skunk's back to form one very broad white stripe or "saddle." Total length, 24 to 30 inches; height at shoulder, 7 to 8 inches; weight, 3½ to 10 pounds.

Distinguishing characteristics. The bushy tail and double band of white running the length of the back.

Range. All of the United States except the southern tip of Florida; northern Mexico; Canada from Nova Scotia, James Bay and Great Slave Lake south to southwestern British Columbia.

HOG-NOSED SKUNK
CONOPATUS SP.

The hog-nosed is the only skunk that lives in South America.

Through the ages, the most venturesome individuals of this stolid, slow-moving species have wandered northward. By gradual progression they moved through Central America, until now, the race is established in our southwestern border country.

This skunk has a long bare flexible snout and goes around rooting for all the world like a hog. It is nearly as large as the striped skunk. Instead of the V stripe and white-tipped, bushy, black tail, it has one broad white stripe from crown of head to base of an all-white, comparatively scanty tail.

The hair is not thick and soft like the striped and spotted skunks, but is coarse, harsh, comparatively thin, and has little value in the fur market. The heavy shoulders and long heavy claws on the front feet cause some people to call it the "badger skunk."

The hog-nosed is more rare, more nocturnal and apparently more shy than the striped and spotted skunks. The mother skunk has only three pairs of nipples compared to the four to six pairs of her relatives. As far as is known, the litter may be one to four. This is one of the reasons for a smaller population of hog-nosed skunks. Another reason may be that they are even slower of body and perhaps of wits.

Naturalists still have much to learn about the hog-nose, but many of its habits seem to be like those of its striped cousin. Where the ranges of the two species overlap, they occupy the same habitats and use similar dens. Their food habits are much the same. They down everything edible, including meat both fresh and rank, prickly pear fruit, many kinds of small rodents, and small birds and their eggs if they stumble on to them.

The hog-nose concentrates more on insects than the striped skunk. Long nose to the ground, it sniffs around until it locates beetles, crickets or grubs. Then it roots, turning up the soil over many square yards. This dual use makes it an unusually valuable nose!

In Mexico the hog-nose has gone into the mountains where it may live as

HOG-NOSED SKUNK

high up as ten thousand feet. Here it puts on a longer and thicker coat and dozes through the winter storms like its more rugged relative of the north. The fur of the mountain dweller is comparatively long and soft. The hog-noses that live on the desert have no use for a thick, warm coat.

Like other skunks, the hog-nose sometimes kills poultry or makes a nuisance of itself by taking up quarters under dwellings. A good way to discourage it is to put mothballs in the nest. A more polite method is to close all means of entrance with wire netting or boards. If these measures fail, it can be trapped easily. When caught in a box trap, it may be deported and released, drowned, or killed with carbon bisulphide or the exhaust from an automobile engine.

General description. A large, stocky skunk about the size of the striped skunk, with a long naked muzzle and small poorly haired tail. Color rusty black to black, with a wide band of white or faintly yellowish white running along the upper surface from forehead to end of tail. Total length, 25 to 33 inches; height at shoulder, 7 inches; weight, 4 to 10 pounds. Females are smaller.

Distinguishing characteristics. The skunklike form and single, very broad back stripe.

Range. Southeastern Arizona, southern Colorado, and southwestern Texas south through most of South America.

SPOTTED SKUNK
SPILOGALE SP.

Who likes a skunk? If more of us could get acquainted with the little spotted skunk, we might rid ourselves of some of our prejudices. The spotted skunk is smaller, prettier and more lively than other skunks. Its eyes are larger and more appealing and it seems to be more intelligent. The narrow white stripes on the black coat are broken many times into spots.

It is true that it carries the same scent glands as the rest of the family, and is perfectly capable of using them if it must. Experienced victims tell us that its discharge is stronger than that of other skunks, but there isn't as much of it.

Anybody who has watched it daintily running about on noiseless feet like a small canyon sprite will almost fall in love with it. Gaily and nimbly the spotted skunks play together in a woods clearing. They seem to get a lot of fun out of life. Hunting a daily meal of crickets is an exciting game full of zest and merriment.

Fences, walls and partitions are not likely to keep out the spotted skunk, for it is a good climber, and a persistent little rascal. One spotted skunk reportedly crawled into a comfortable barrel from which it could not escape. At last the owner up-ended the barrel for the skunk's convenience. It was too good a mouser to be refused hospitality, for any skunk will catch more mice than a cat.

SPOTTED SKUNK

The spotted skunk has a unique habit of standing on its hands when excited. Up go the body and hind feet into the air for perhaps five seconds at a time. This is repeated again and again. Sometimes it does this in play or exuberance; at other times it is a bluffing attitude when threatened by a possible enemy. If it is necessary to aim high, it is apt to take this "hand stand." Most of its spraying, however, is done with all fours on the ground.

The spotted skunk is less likely to be routed than its larger cousins. When necessary it is quite as likely to ascend a tree as to take to a den in the ground.

The little fellow seems to be much more nervous than its larger, stolid relatives. Those that I have caught in steel traps frequently died within a few hours, even in warm weather.

In the southeastern United States, this little animal lives in hedgerows and waste areas such as gullies. In the West it seems to look for rock slides and outcrops and broken ledges. However, it never has an aversion to farms and the shelter of buildings. Generally speaking, the spotted skunk is partial to brushy places, while the larger striped skunk can be perfectly at home in open fields. The spotted skunk doesn't need as much food as its larger cousin, and is more often found in desert country than its cousin, which might go hungry there.

Any kind of a home will do. On the southwestern deserts it has been known to live inside the hollow, mummified carcass of a cow! Now and then it has taken up residence in an attic. It loves cast-off toys, especially a rubber ball to bat around.

Ordinarily it picks out a rocky crevice, a corner of a shed foundation, an abandoned woodchuck or badger burrow, a hollow log or stump, or a brush pile.

Like other members of the tribe, the spotted skunk eats almost anything available wherever it may be. In summer and fall, insects are its principal foods including grasshoppers, crickets, carabid and May beetles, and their larvae. At all seasons, and particularly in winter and spring, it preys on mice, woodrats, young cottontails, jack rabbits and hares. Carrion comes in handy then, too. Chipmunks and smaller ground squirrels make fine juicy prizes when they are available. Other flesh foods are lizards, salamanders, crayfish, and snakes.

We cannot approve when the spotted skunk snaps up ground-dwelling birds —quail, doves, meadowlarks, and their nestlings and eggs. The poultryman must keep it and all other skunks away from chickens and eggs. Still the little fellow does many good deeds around buildings by destroying scorpions, cockroaches, mice and rats. Everyone knows that rats are hard on young poultry.

The spotted skunk is fond of fruits of many kinds, and eats them in quantities when they are ripe. They vary in kind with the region—persimmons and mulberries in the South, cactus fruits in the desert, and grapes and cherries everywhere. Late in the autumn, when other vegetable foods become scarce, it eats a great deal of corn, and roots up peanuts. Mushrooms are welcome treats throughout the summer and fall. Most of the tree-growing fruits eaten by the spotted skunk are picked up from the ground after they ripen and fall. Frequently, it goes into bushes and lower trees and into massed grapevines after delicacies.

Very little is known about the breeding habits of the spotted skunk. He selects his mates in late winter and the progeny are born in early spring. The number of young is usually limited to four. At birth they weigh almost one-third of an ounce and are four inches long. Although so finely haired as to appear almost naked, the black and white pattern can be seen plainly. Their eyes and ears are closed and they are toothless, but they squeal shrilly when disturbed. At five weeks the young skunks are walking clumsily, and their eyes have been open for three or four days. Their weight has increased to five ounces and they measure almost ten inches from nose to tip of bushy tail. By the time they are five months old they are as big as their parents, weighing one and one-half pounds.

When hungry, the young skunks chirp or cry continuously like a nestful of little birds, but as they grow up they lose such youthful habits and endure discomforts in silence.

One name very often used for the little spilogale is "civet cat." It is not a cat. Neither is it related to the civets of the Old World. This name, however, is frequently used in fur-trade literature and price lists.

"Phoby Cat" and "Hydrophobia Cat" are names used in the South and especially in the Southwest. The spotted skunk is much more bold and fearless than its big relatives, and at times it even bites people sleeping on the ground. However, it is no more apt to carry rabies infection than the striped or hog-nosed skunks, or any other susceptible animal.

During mating time, the male may go a bit wild in his actions. One such skunk is reported to have scented straight into a bull's face and driven him out of his bed in a dusty road. Another invaded a wolf's nursery and shook the young wolves by their ears. This "mating madness" has led to many false stories of hydrophobia.

The spotted skunk is prey to the same animals and the same diseases as its cousins. Fifty per cent of one collection of spotted skunk skulls showed sinus infection.

The spotted skunk is not nearly as widespread as the striped skunk. Although its fur is prettier, it has considerably less value. The skins seldom bring more than twenty-five cents apiece to the trapper. They are popular, however, for inexpensive trimmings and jackets. Many thousands are used in the fur trade each year.

General description. A small, slender skunk about half as large as a house-cat, with small head, short legs, and bushy tail. Fur rather long, soft, and black with a number of long narrow white stripes which tend to break up, thus often resulting in spots. Tail black with a white end. Total length, 14 to 22 inches; height at shoulder, 6 inches; weight, 1 to 2 pounds, averaging about 1½ pounds. Females weigh 1 to 1½ pounds.

Distinguishing characteristics. The several parallel white stripes or lines of spots on the black coat, together with the *slender* skunk form.

Range. Mountainous parts of the southeastern United States from West Virginia and Kentucky to southern Alabama; southern Florida; southern Illinois, central Minnesota and southern Idaho to extreme southwestern British Columbia, thence south through Mexico to eastern Guatemala.

BADGER
TAXIDEA TAXUS

Have you ever seen a badger do its "disappearing act?" Using all four feet and its mouth, it digs into the ground in a few seconds. The dirt flies for yards around. The tail vanishes into the churning earth and the badger plugs up the hole behind it, almost before you can say "Jack Robinson." Only a patch of fresh soil marks the spot!

Because of its disappearing act, and its fierceness when cornered, few animals ever attack it.

It is tough, chunky, low-slung, bow-legged, and pigeon-toed. The powerful jaws and physique are backed up by extraordinary courage. Few dogs can whip a badger; most of them know better than to try. Rash or foolhardy ones, two or three times its size, have been killed or fearfully slashed by its sharp teeth and long, strong claws. The heavy hair and loose skin prevent a dog's teeth from getting a firm grip on its body. The thick shoulder and neck muscles further protect the arteries and nerves.

Usually the badger can stand off a whole pack of dogs until it reaches a safe den or "digs itself in" on the spot. An unarmed man may have to hop like a jack-in-the-box when a cornered badger snaps at his legs.

In Yellowstone, an avocet, two long-billed curlews and a number of crows got together and went after a badger. Probably it had been robbing a nest. Since it couldn't go up in the air after its attackers, it prudently retired into the ground.

When angry, it hisses and does a ridiculous imitation of its cousin, the skunk. Up goes the stubby little tail and out comes an odoriferous secretion. Like the tail, it is a weak imitation and it probably occurs only during mating season.

Now and then a coyote kills a badger. One badger is reported to have been rescued from an eagle. Perhaps these were weaker members of the species.

The badger's long claws are its most important means of defense and of securing food. Perhaps for this reason it often gives itself a manicure and pedicure. No dirt is left under the nails or between the toes when it gets through.

If you are foolish enough to insist on getting a badger to come out of its den, there is only one way. Flood the tunnel. It must come up for air, but you would be smarter to leave it in. Be prepared to meet your match!

BADGER

Naturalists have not been able to find out very much about the badger's private life. After long argument, it has been decided that badgers mate in autumn or early winter, depending upon the location. Cold weather stops the growth of the embryos for at least two months. After development is resumed the young require about five weeks to reach the proper stage for birth.

The mother badger has only one litter a year, usually in May or June, or earlier in the south. Her brood is quite variable in number, from one to seven young. The average is probably three. Their home is a chamber, two to six feet deep in the ground, at the end of a tunnel that may be six to thirty feet long. A nest of dry grass keeps the youngsters off the chill earth. Now and then careless mothers in the South provide no bedding for their children, but they seem to thrive.

The young badgers' eyes open when they are a month to six weeks old. By the time they are half grown, they are weaned, and from then on their mother brings them food until they are two-thirds grown. Then they are old enough to go with her on hunting trips.

With some possible exceptions, father badgers assume no responsibilities for their offspring. Their help is unnecessary since the mother badgers are perhaps even fiercer and more able fighters. One mother badger, escorting her brood, was seen to take issue with a moving automobile. She stood her ground, and retreated slowly only when her young were safely in the clear and the whirring monster but three feet away. Under such circumstances, the badger can travel backward almost as easily as she can run forward.

Rather an unsocial creature, the badger usually hunts alone. In captivity, however, it is apt to be quite light-hearted. If not too old, it will dance and skip about with great abandon.

In the wild, it makes its living by digging faster than the moles, the marmots, the pocket gophers and other earth-dwellers. It goes down after them and gobbles them up in no time at all.

Anything in the meat and egg lines, fresh or carrion, appeals to this miner. Rodents make up by far the largest item; but ground squirrels, field mice and deer mice, rabbits, insects, and ground-nesting birds and their eggs are included in the northern and eastern parts of the United States. In the Southwest, the badger eats ground squirrels, prairie dogs, pocket gophers, kangaroo rats, woodrats, mice, insects and lizards. It picks up birds' eggs as it chances on them, not by systematic search.

The badger is very thorough in its business. It usually comes back periodically to its diggings to re-examine them for surviving prey, or for new occupants. Since jackrabbits and cottontails use old shallow diggings as "forms," a return trip is always worth making on the chance of surprising a fine meal of rabbit. Incidentally, the badger also helps the rabbit, except when cashing it in as a meal, by providing many shelters against a host of other enemies.

Not all of the badger's meals are dug out of burrows. Badgers have been seen to run down ground squirrels. Usually these swift little rodents can scamper to safety if they have a head start. Eventually some unlucky squirrel is cornered or caught when it trips over a root and then is snatched up and killed with a few shakes.

The badger sometimes eats snakes. A California badger was seen to dig up and eat a rattlesnake that had been killed days before. It ate all except the head.

By autumn the young badgers are nearly full-grown and can forage very well for themselves. The family breaks up, for animals with such big appetites as badgers need considerable range. If they remained in groups, they would have to travel even farther to gather enough food for all mouths.

Except in the extreme north, badgers do not hibernate in the true sense. Winter food is scarce since ground squirrels, marmots and some of the other rodents are safely asleep under several feet of frozen earth. Nature helps the badger to bear up by cutting down its appetite a little and making it drowsy. It also goes into the winter rolling in fat. A cottontail rabbit or a skunk that has the misfortune to wander forth during a mild spell will satisfy the badger and send it back into its den for a little while. From below frost line it pushes loose dirt back up the tunnel to keep out draughts. As soon as it is hungry again, it starts out, whether it is thirty degrees below zero or thawing. Where the ground is not frozen hard all winter, the badger is as active as in summer.

A batch of sleepy skunks which often den together in groups of half a dozen during winter offers several weeks' supply of food. Their den entrance may require only a little enlarging to enable the badger to reach and kill them. Being a prudent creature, it puts the surplus carcasses in storage. Burying them in the ground, it digs them up as it needs them. Even in late spring it may be provident, doubtless having the memory of a long, hard winter fresh in mind. In Yellowstone Park one summer, a badger that unearthed numerous ground squirrels ate only the small ones and buried the large ones after killing them.

Although the badger ordinarily lives on the plains and deserts, it can swim rapidly and easily when it wishes. One badger was seen in the middle of Devils Lake, North Dakota, a half-mile from shore.

In country districts of northern Ohio, badgers have been accused of robbing graves. Many ghoulish stories have been told of their activities. One animal was trapped in a cemetery back in the early eighties and exhibited from town to town as the "Wood County Grave Robber." The title probably was not justified. The animal simply prefers to live on sandy knolls or ridges where rodents are concentrated and digging is easy. These are just the places selected by the early settlers for their burial grounds. The skulls and bones are kicked out by the badgers only incidentally when they go after their prey.

In their eagerness to capture deep-digging rodents, the badgers sometimes throw out great heaps of earth. When they are in traps, they do the same to escape. An Arizona badger that I once caught in a No. 1 steel trap, instead of pulling free, dug a hole about four feet deep and four feet across at the top.

The frequency of "prospect holes" wherever the badger has been hunting has caused a good deal of swearing by cowboys and other horseback riders. One of these holes may cause a hard fall and a broken leg for a horse. Whether the hole be that of a badger or another animal, the badger is blamed. For this reason the little miner is shot on sight, or roped and dragged. As a matter of fact, a bad accident caused by a badger's hole is extremely rare.

In irrigated valleys, the badger sometimes damages the ditch banks while digging out pocket gophers and ground squirrels. Nevertheless, the badger's score is heavily on the credit side. It is an important check on the larger rodents which consume enormous quantities of grains and forage.

The badger has turned many ordinary, long-haired pelts into silver fox imitations. Clusters of the badger's white-tipped hairs are glued by the furriers throughout the plain black hairs of other animal pelts. This "pointing" attempts to give the effect of the more luxurious silver fox fur for the woman with a lean or frugal pocketbook.

The coarse but striking fur of the badger is very serviceable and is made into collars and cuffs for cloth coats. Formerly used in making the best shaving brushes, the hair once sold for eighty-five dollars a pound. Synthetic bristles have now taken its place. Ordinarily an average badger pelt brings five or seven dollars, but choice ones in boom times have sold for as high as twenty-five dollars. The demand for the fur has encouraged attempts to raise the animals in captivity, but they do not stand restricted conditions well. With their voracious appetites, they eat up all the profits! Badgers caught when young make affectionate pets.

General description. A stocky, flat-bodied animal with broad, flattened head and short legs and tail; ears short and rounded; neck short; feet, especially the forefeet, equipped with large heavy claws. Fur long and shaggy, silvery gray grizzled with brownish and black; blackish face definitely marked with a white stripe over the forehead and a white crescent behind and around each eye.

Total length, 25 to 30 inches; height at shoulder, 9 inches; weight, 12 to 24 pounds.

Distinguishing characteristics. The stocky, flattened body and distinctively marked head.

Range. Northern and north-central North America from the Great Lakes (Michigan and northwestern Ohio), eastern Nebraska and northeastern Tamaulipas, Mexico, northwest to the Pacific Coast of Baja California; thence north to San Francisco Bay, southern British Columbia, southern Idaho, and central Saskatchewan and Alberta. Absent from western Washington and Oregon.

11. The Wild Dogs

RED FOX—*VULPES* SP.

All its life the red fox has a struggle to keep its glossy, golden-red, fur coat on its back. Some one is always trying to snatch it. The trapper is after the fox with a bundle of clanking steel traps and stock of tricks. The angry farmer is out with a shotgun to avenge some missing poultry. Finally there comes the dog, to which the scent of fox is both tantalizing and maddening, a perpetual challenge to speed and intelligence.

Instead of giving up a struggle for existence that seems impossibly difficult, and withdrawing into the wilderness, the red fox continues to live on right under the noses of the trapper, the farmer and the hound. It merely takes more precautions.

It seems to enjoy matching wits against a pack of hounds. It walks logs, stone walls and fence rails, to make its trail difficult to follow. It back-tracks up brooks and streams, sets up a criss-cross of tracks, or circles and comes in behind the pack. Then it laughs from a safe distance as the dogs yelp and flounder in confusion. Anyone who has seen the fleeing fox deliberately pass by dens or other places of safety, sometimes several times, and only finally take refuge there, must conclude that the fox plays the game of hide-and-seek with enjoyment.

The chase requires skill and not brute strength. The fox is not an extremely swift runner and its endurance is not remarkable. In a show-down fight with hounds, it doesn't stand a chance. It is not much stronger nor more dangerous than a big alley cat.

Sportsmen regard fox-hunting as grand fun, whether they sit on sunny porches and listen to the baying hounds or risk their necks in dashing madly on horseback after the pack.

Unlike the gray fox, the red fox prefers mixed farm lands and woodlots. It will live in the deep forests, but the brushy fringe, bordering on marshes or tilled fields or pastures, is much more to its liking. Although the dangers are greater, this sharp-faced little native dog is keen enough to survive and to take advantage of the many choices of food.

It is an opportunist. From month to month, its diet varies, consisting of many easily procured foods, both meat and vegetable, alive and dead. Small mammals, especially meadow mice but also including other kinds of mice, and cottontails are staples throughout the year.

Ordinarily, unless it is made desperate by hunger, the fox does not care to tackle anything more formidable than a rooster, a cock pheasant, or a jack-rabbit. If you find the remains of anything larger at a den, you may assume that the creature was probably already carrion when the fox found it. Exceptionally husky dog foxes (males), however, sometimes prey on young deer fawns, lambs, and even grown turkeys.

The red fox kills many shrews and weasels and some moles, especially the

RED FOX

surface-living star-nosed variety, but few are eaten. They are left lying around, often at the den. Usually they are not even cached. Apparently these musky little animals challenge the fox's hunting instincts, but do not appeal to its palate. In summer, it takes advantage of such rodents "in season" as chipmunks, ground squirrels and woodchucks that hibernate and are safe in cold weather.

Small ground-nesting birds are sometimes captured and the eggs or fledglings gulped down. Studies show that ruffed grouse and quail as a rule are rather seldom killed. The red fox likes turtles and their eggs. Insects, especially grasshoppers, crickets and beetles, are important and are eaten more and more as the warm days pass. At times they may be eaten to the exclusion of other things.

The fox eats small amounts of grass quite regularly. It is fond of fruits—blackberries, raspberries, strawberries, blueberries, partridgeberries, serviceberries, grapes, wild cherries, apples, persimmons, and the fruits of wintergreen. Virginia creeper and wild sarsaparilla. It gets some of its needed minerals by eating quantities of clay and gravel. It likes to hunt house rats out of their field burrows. Sometimes it catches tadpoles and frogs, which are real treats, and after heavy rains picks up fat earthworms as they crawl over the ground.

Winter food must be more strictly carnivorous, especially in the north, but frequently includes dried fruits. The fox digs through the snow in orchards to get at frozen apples. Occasionally hunger drives it to attack a porcupine. Naturalists have sometimes found its scats made up mostly of porcupine hair and quills, the latter pointing in all directions. Quills have also been seen in its nose and face, some of them embedded in the bone. These wounds may eventually prove fatal.

As it goes about the daily hunting, Reynard slow-trots with a light airy grace. Its sharp face and squinting eyes are alert for anything that moves, and the triangular ears are erect and listening. Perhaps it sees the gray flash of a mouse scooting between grass clumps. Again, there may be the faintest rustle as the tiny animal brushes past a blade of dry sedge that has fallen across the runway. The fox turns and approaches the spot, stepping high and cautiously like a small shepherd dog or wriggling low and tense as a stalking cat. Then comes a pause, and if the prey is located the fox closes with a rush or with a long, stiff-legged leap and pounce. A snap of the lightning-quick jaws and the mouse is limp in death.

Like other wild dogs, foxes cache much of their food that is not needed for immediate consumption. Sometimes edibles are left lying beside the trail just as they are carelessly dropped, but usually they are tucked away neatly under snow, among dry leaves, or with some grass drawn carefully over them. The red fox likes to revisit these hidden treasures even when not hungry and when it doesn't intend to draw on the stores. It may nibble a bit, or may only pick up the mouse or squirrel or woodchuck head, toss it, mouth it, and then replace it under cover. Perhaps it enjoys looking over its souvenirs, as an old soldier likes the touch and feel of his medals.

In the great marshes of the Eastern Shore of Maryland, where muskrats are extremely abundant, the fox lives on the islands and preys on these big rodents. One more chalk mark against the red fox! The trappers who derive a large share of their income from gathering muskrat pelts resent this competition.

There is no doubt that the red fox may raid poultry yards at times. Single fox families have been known to kill as many as one hundred and sixty chickens from a flock in two days. These exceptional instances of guerilla warfare have given the fox a bad name. Much of the damage attributed to the species is undeserved. Many of the poultry remains, leg bones of partly-grown lambs and calves, and young pigs found at dens are carrion salvaged from farmers' fields or dumps. Chickens can usually be protected by fencing, by a good watch dog, and by cutting down rank weeds or other growth through which the foxes might approach under cover. Under ordinary circumstances the red fox is a useful friend of the farmer.

Although red foxes probably do not mate for life, they remain faithful for most of the year. The male stays with his current spouse from mating time in February until the young are able to shift for themselves at the beginning of the next winter. The expectant parents select a den used year after year by one fox family or another. Or it may be an old woodchuck or porcupine burrow, which is cleaned out and remodeled to suit the ideas of the new tenants. In forested country, the den site is usually concealed in woods or a thicket, but it is sometimes in an open field. Well-beaten trails lead to the entrances, of which there may be four or five facing in as many directions. The doorways vary in size; an old den is likely to have entrances seventeen or twenty inches across, while that of a new burrow would be less than half as large. Some fox homes are complicated, with numerous chambers opening off a tunnel that may be up to fifty feet long.

Since the fox is not well equipped for digging, it likes soil that is loose and sandy, and easily scratched away. Old sawdust piles are frequently used, and in time may be honeycombed with tunnels. Once in a while a den is located in a broken rock ledge or, rarely, in a hollow tree or fallen log. On the treeless barrens of the far north, the dens are located near the top of a ridge or bank and the entrances are well concealed in rank grass.

Young foxes, which vary in number from four to nine, require fifty-one days development before birth in March or April. When they appear outdoors at about five weeks of age, they are chubby, short-legged little bundles of fluff, with sharp eyes that seem to take in everything that moves. They are as playful as puppies, but much more agile and lively.

I spent a number of hours one August in Mount McKinley National Park watching and photographing a family of young red foxes at the entrance to their den. There was something doing every minute. The little animals developed their muscles with wrestling bouts, rolling and tumbling like boys on the sandy platform in front of the den. Except in unusual excitement, they did not bark or whine, but too-vigorous use of teeth brought sharp squeaks of protest.

Those young Alaskan foxes were surprisingly unafraid, perhaps because they had seen people passing on the park road about one hundred feet from their den and had never been harmed. A glance in my direction about every ten minutes seemed to be enough. I noticed, however, that at least one of the brood scanned the sky every two or three minutes. Had they been taught by their parents that the screaming golden eagle might plunge from the clean blue vault overhead? That great dark brown bird with the cruel yellow talons is thought to kill foxes, although it probably catches only the young or careless. Perhaps it swoops at many animals that it doesn't really expect to catch, but takes a chance.

The male or dog fox brings food to his family until the late summer when the young can be taught to hunt. At this warmer season food is plentiful and he doesn't need to travel farther than a couple of miles from the den. In winter, when he needs to hunt only for himself, he may have to cover much greater distances.

The red fox would like to be a hail-fellow-well-met. It has been known to try to make friends of domestic dogs, and to play with them. In Newfoundland and Alaska, it has been seen leaping around caribou and bighorn, rubbing against them, gently biting at their faces, and then leaping away as if it wanted them to play tag. Sometimes the bighorn would bunt it playfully, but the caribou were less responsive.

Swimming is easy for this wild dog. It floats high in the water, for the long furry coat holds considerable air and is buoyant.

I have noticed that many foxes, while crossing the open grassy valleys of central Alaska, carry their bushy tails turned up at an angle of about fifty degrees. Whether this is a possible shield against attack from the air, or a kind of lure to cause a swooping eagle to aim too high, is only a guess. Perhaps it is to keep the gorgeous brush dry and unsoiled.

In the serious business of hunting ground squirrels or mice, the big tail serves as a balance. As the fox twists and leaps at sharp angles to block its dodging prey, it whips its tail dextrously to save itself from tumbling end over end. In cold weather it curls up on a hummock, folds the tail over its feet and nose and goes to sleep. This fur quilt comes in handy, for the fox sleeps out in the open except during breeding season.

While resting, it likes to sit up to see what is going on. As a result the fur on the haunches is sometimes badly worn. The white Arctic fox does this less often and does not get threadbare.

The red fox must look out for coyotes, wolves, bobcats and lynxes, as well as eagles. As a rule, these hunters can kill few adult foxes in good health. Only the sick or young and foolish fox may be caught napping.

Probably three-quarters of the red fox population carries parasitic roundworms and a smaller number harbor tapeworms. At times epidemics of rabies occur. Numbers of "mad" foxes have been seen during recent years especially in parts of Georgia, Alabama, Kentucky, and other southeastern states, and in central Alaska. A rabid fox loses all sense of fear, and in the last stages of the disease the unfortunate animal may race about the country, half-blind, drooling saliva, and snapping at dogs, cattle, persons, or inanimate objects. This is one of Nature's most violent and spectacular means of correcting overpopulations of foxes, for when the animals become scarce the disease apparently disappears.

A red fox is often not red. There are four distinct color phases. Besides the normal red-coated fox, the melanistic red fox is completely black except for the inevitable white tail-tip. Another red fox may be "silver." It is black with a liberal sprinkling of white-banded guard-hairs. The "cross" fox is largely brownish yellow and has the conventional black stockings. However, it has considerable black underfur and a broad black band down the back and across the shoulders. The resulting cross gives this red fox its name.

A mother fox may have any combination or all four colors in one litter. One or more of these phases may be common or rare in various sections of the country. In the eastern United States, for example, practically all red foxes are really "red." In the Sierra Nevada, "cross" foxes are very common. In Alaska it seems that nearly half the animals are black, silver or cross.

Two other variations of the red fox offspring are less common but have been given names. A "samson" fox, being without guard-hairs, has a wooly pelt which is almost worthless in the market. A fox with a dark, smoky coat, midway between the normal red and black is called a "bastard" fox. These may occur in any of the best regulated families.

Everyone knows the red fox pelt when made up into ladies' coats, jackets, and scarfs. It is a beautiful, dense, soft and fairly durable fur. A good pelt, when prime, is worth ten to fifteen dollars in an average year, but in 1928–29 the same grade of skin brought fifty dollars.

Silver fox fur is more fashionable and therefore more costly. Most of that sold comes from fur farms in the northern United States and southern Canada, and from "fox islands" in Alaska. More silver foxes are raised in captivity each year than any other furbearer except possibly mink. While extraordinarily fine skins sold about thirty years ago for as much as one thousand five hundred dollars, quantity production has brought the price down to one hundred to one hundred twenty-five dollars for the same quality. You can now get two ordinary silver fox pelts, already tanned, lined and ready to wear about your neck for one hundred and fifteen dollars the pair.

Now the breeders have developed unusual strains such as the "platinum" fox, which has a pale, smoky fur. When new and rare, "platinum" fox pelts sold at auction in New York for five hundred and fifty to eleven thousand dollars apiece. The latter is the highest price ever obtained in this country for the skin of any animal.

General description. A doglike animal, about the size of a small collie, with sharp nose, large triangular ears, and long, bushy tail. Fur long, full, and very soft, rich golden reddish yellow with black feet and legs; chest, under parts and tip of tail white. Color phases are pure black, silver, and cross (brownish yellow with a dark band across shoulders intersecting a similar band down the back). Regardless of color phase, tip of tail is always white. Total length, 3 to 3½ feet; height at shoulder, 16 inches; weight, 5 to 10 pounds.

Distinguishing characteristics. The golden reddish coat, white-tipped tail which is circular in cross section, black feet and back of ears, and large size separate the red fox from the smaller gray fox. The latter is gray, not reddish, on the back, has a triangular tail which is black on the upper surface along its entire length, and backs of ears and legs reddish gray. The still smaller kit fox is more slender than either of the above; it varies in color from gray to pale buffy, has very large, tall ears, and a black-tipped cylindrical tail.

Range. All of United States, Canada, and Alaska except the southern Atlantic coastal region, lower Mississippi Valley, south-central Great Plains, southwestern desert, and Pacific coast region.

KIT FOX

VULPES VELOX AND V. MACROTIS

The kit fox is smaller than the other foxes. It is also much shyer and more retiring. Avoiding the haunts of men, it knows little about their wiles. Without guile itself, and without suspicion, it walks into the simplest traps. It gulps down poisoned bait that the canny coyote wouldn't dream of touching. Due to trapping for its inexpensive fur, and poisoning to destroy predators, the kit fox has been extirpated from large sections of its natural range. Nowhere does it seem to be abundant.

The kit fox has one superiority over the other foxes. It can run faster. For perhaps one hundred yards it is one of the fastest of mammals. This ability has been responsible for one of its common names,—"swift fox," or, frequently, just "swift."

This burst of speed does not last long. The little kit fox either pops down a burrow, to hide out from trouble, or begins to dodge. This in itself is an efficient defense against a pursuing eagle, dog, or coyote. The fleeing "swift" zigzags sharply, with great speed, and so suddenly that the human eye cannot see just how it is done. One instant the fox may be racing north. The next moment it is traveling west or east at undiminished speed. Meanwhile the baffled pursuer is slowing down, and violently trying to turn. All the time the kit fox runs low, hugging the ground, with its tail straight to the rear. The chances are that the kit fox will be able to find an old badger hole or similar shelter before tiring out.

The name kit fox refers to the small size of the animal. Because of the large, prominent ears, it once in a while is called the big-eared fox. These organs are very efficient in spite of the dense screen of long, fine hairs with which they are almost filled. Possibly this unusual web of hair is intended to prevent the choking dust of plains and desert storms from reaching the auditory opening and the delicate apparatus inside.

The kit fox travels mostly at night and spends the daylight hours underground or resting on its den mound. At least one good home burrow and a number of well distributed emergency shelters are essential.

Like other wild dogs, the kit fox is poorly equipped for digging. Therefore the den must be located on loose, sandy soil. Usually it is found on flat ground on a sand dune, or near the crest of a little bank or arroyo wall, and must have two to five exits to provide ample means of refuge and escape. The walls of the burrow are circular, about nine or ten inches in diameter. You won't mistake it for a badger's home. The badger's walls are oval and usually larger. Sometimes the kit fox takes over an abandoned burrow, such as the badger's, and remodels it as necessary.

The kit fox seldom digs its burrow more than five feet deep into the ground, or more than ten feet long. Even if twice that length, as has been recorded, the course of the burrow is so twisting that the den chamber, near the deepest point, is seldom far from the entrance. The den, which is austerely bare of bedding, measures from twelve to eighteen inches wide and is about twelve inches high. The fox takes no precaution to hide its home. The excavated dirt is just scooped out of the burrow and allowed to lie where it falls.

The fox chooses the sandy plains for a home, not only because they make easy digging, but because they are attractive to rodents. These little mammals are the favorite food of the kit fox, and their shallow burrows are everywhere. The kangaroo rat is the most frequent victim. The kit fox is rarely or never found outside the range of this grotesque, long-legged creature. Other succulent mouthfuls are pocket mice, ground squirrels of various species, jack rabbits, cottontails, and smaller rodents. A few ground-dwelling birds may be picked up, as well as snakes and lizards. Beetles, grasshoppers, and other insects are staple diet when available. Kit foxes also eat grass, and when more is known about their lives I believe we will find that they like fruits and seeds such as pulpy cactus fruits and mesquite and catclaw beans.

On the hunt, the kit fox moves with wonderful grace, gliding silently along on padded feet. When a prospective victim is sighted, heard or smelled, it makes a stealthy stalk . . . then rushes. If the rabbit or kangaroo rat dodges and races off, the kit fox wastes little effort in trying to follow. It shrugs off its misses and looks for other less wary prey.

Unless very hungry, the kit fox does not devour its victims on the spot, but carries them home and eats them there. Soon the ground around the den is littered with bones, fur and other discards. As far as we know, the kit fox does not cache its food.

The mother kit fox usually has four or five young, but the number may be as low as two or as great as seven. Those on the southern deserts are born in February. In the north the birth date is a little later. The mother nurses her young for about ten weeks, and then the father helps by bringing meat to feed his offspring.

At times fashion has forced the small value of the kit fox pelt up to two, three or even five dollars. At present, the fur is considered dull and nondescript. A good, prime skin brings only one dollar. To the naturalist this is a poor scale of values. Alive, this little nocturnal prowler of the plains may plunder a poultry roost once in a while, but month in and month out it is a destroyer of hordes of rodents. The kit fox is one of the rarest, least known, and most fascinating of our mammals.

General description. Smallest of the foxes; slender, with large ears and cylindrical bushy tail. Color gray, buffy gray, or buffy yellow (depending on the species); backs of ears and outside of legs yellowish brown; tip of tail black; under parts white or pale buff. Total length, 2 to 3 feet; height at shoulders, 12 inches; weight, 4 to 5 pounds.

Distinguishing characteristics. See this section under "Red Fox" (page 234).

Range. Western North America, from southern Baja California and south-central Chihuahua north through the San Joaquin Valley, northern Nevada and Great Salt Lake, and through central Colorado and western Kansas to east-central Alberta, central Saskatchewan, and southwestern Manitoba.

GRAY FOX
UROCYON CINEREOARGENTEUS AND *U. LITTORALIS*

The gray fox is the only fox that is apt to climb trees. It may go up just to look around. When pursued by dogs, it sometimes leaps into the branches, bounces from limb to limb and then hides quietly in the thick foliage. If the lowest branch is ten feet above the ground, it may "shin" itself up the trunk like a bear until it can hook a front foot over the first limb. Sometimes it uses a convenient fork just to rest and soak up the sunshine.

A little smaller than the red fox, this graceful animal has a black stripe from neck to tail-tip on its soft gray coat. It likes warm climates and is much more abundant in the South, Southwest and the Pacific slope region than the red fox. Nevertheless, it has been increasing in the North during the last twenty years. This is one more animal that is extending its range into new regions in the North.

Few people are aware that the gray fox is in the neighborhood unless they recognize its yapping bark, repeated four or five times. It is louder and harsher than the red fox's exclamation. Probably not as crafty as the red fox, it prefers the comparative safety of the swamps, woodland, chaparral, or the cactus and mesquite thickets of the arid deserts. Shy and retiring, it leaves the dangerous open farm land to its bolder cousin the red fox.

When disturbed on a hunting trip, the gray fox seldom races off. It often merely steps aside and fades into a dense patch of brush waiting for the intruder to go on about his business. If hounds take up its trail, the gray fox usually runs but a short distance. By actual test, its top speed has been found to be only about twenty-six miles per hour, and that for but the first one hundred yards. At the end of a half-mile run, the speed has dropped to about twenty miles an hour. Lacking the stock of tricks of the red fox, it drops into a den in the ground, or takes to a tree.

Although much less suspicious than the red fox under ordinary conditions, the gray fox can learn by sad experience. Survivors of intensive trapping are as wary as the most careful wolf.

January, February and March is mating time. Male foxes may stage vicious fights over a favorite female. On one occasion, in eastern New York, two battling rivals slid over the brink of a cliff. In a shower of snow and leaf litter they dropped ninety feet to the rocks below and were killed. Tracks in the snow indicated that a third fox, presumably the "femme fatale," had looked on.

GRAY FOX

About sixty-three days after mating the young foxes are born. Blackish, blind, and almost hairless, they may number from two to five, but the average is nearer five. Home may be any one of a great variety of places: a hollow ledge, a pile of rocks, an earthen den, a cavity in the base of a tree, or a hollow log.

One gray fox mother near the western base of the Sierra Nevada in California made her nest of leaves and shredded bark in the large hollow limb of an oak, about twenty-five feet above the ground. Another, in western Pennsylvania, picked a discarded ten-gallon milk can that had been thrown on a dump in a brushy ravine. The can was padded with a little grass and leaves.

The father gray fox helps his mate in caring for the young. Their family record is similar to that of the red fox, with the young animals gradually learning the business of earning a living, and drifting away from parental supervision by late summer.

Their enemies are the same as those of other smaller and weaker wild dogs; coyotes, bobcats, golden eagles, parasites, and rabies and other diseases. The life expectancy of a gray fox is probably relatively short, perhaps about five years. Few meat-eaters survive so successfully in the wild after reaching old age as did a gray fox in central Massachusetts. Practically toothless, he was able to pick up enough food in such small pieces that they could be swallowed whole. This aged animal kept himself in fine, fat condition, but eventually fell to a hunter.

The gray fox eats meat, fruit, and vegetables. The most important food is the rodents and near relatives: the cottontail, marsh rabbit, cotton and wood rats, ground squirrel, rock squirrel, meadow mouse, white-footed mouse, pocket gopher, once in a while a field-dwelling house mouse, an unlucky tree squirrel, or a varying hare. Birds, ranging from small ground-nesting birds to pheasants, are captured occasionally. The belief of many sportsmen that the gray fox customarily kills five or six pheasants a night is absolutely unfounded. It does prey on poultry at times. Other animal foods are turtles and their eggs, snakes, lizards, insects, and carrion of all sorts.

Even more than its red cousin, the gray fox steals eggs. If it finds a quail's nest it may take the entire clutch, up to fourteen eggs. It gobbles them down, shells and all. If it has already dined heartily, it may leave part of the set and return later for the rest.

Vegetables and fruits round out the diet of the gray fox: grass, nuts of beech, oak, hazel and hickory, peanuts, peaches, apples, grapes, wild cherries, coffee berries, juniper berries, cactus fruits and persimmons.

It does not store food. Usually living in a warm climate, it has never needed to develop thrifty habits. The bulk of its diet is meat, which would soon disintegrate if put away.

The gray fox sometimes attacks the porcupine in a foolhardy manner. In New Hampshire a gray fox was found in such a weakened condition that she was caught by hand. Despite bountiful gifts of food, she died. Then it was discovered that her chest, forelegs and mouth were full of fresh porcupine quills so that she was unable to swallow food that was set before her. Other quills had worked into the body cavity where they had punctured her stomach, intestines and other organs many times.

The pelt of the gray fox is used for collars and other trimmings of ladies' cloth coats of the cheaper grades. Although fairly colorful, the fur is rather coarse and thin. The best hides sold in 1946, a year of high prices, for three dollars. Ordinarily they are worth between one and two dollars.

Two distinct species of the gray fox are known. The foxes on the Pacific islands off southern California have shorter tails and are fully twenty per cent smaller than the species (*O. cinereoargenteus*) on the mainland. The island foxes have been given the scientific species name *littoralis*, from their habit of patrolling the beaches for food cast up by the waves. These little foxes nearly always have many spines embedded in their hides as a result of using the dense beds of cactus for shelter.

General description. A slender, medium-sized fox with long, slender tail that is triangular in cross section. General color grizzled gray and blackish, sometimes with much yellowish and rusty red; reddish brown on backs of ears and sides of neck and legs; face and muzzle blackish; dark streak down back to tip of tail; cheek, inner ear, and under parts white. Total length, 40 inches; height at shoulder, 15 inches; weight, 7½ to 11 pounds.

Distinguishing characteristics. See this section under "Red Fox" (page 234).

Range. Southern and eastern North America, from northern New Hampshire and northeastern North Dakota south to the Florida Keys and entire Gulf coast; also south from northwestern Colorado, northeastern Utah, and southwestern Washington to southern Baja California, Mexico and northern South America.

ARCTIC FOX
ALOPEX LAGOPUS

It is a February noon on the Arctic coast. In the dull light from a sun that is still far below the horizon, the earth merges into the sea in one monotonous white and gray expanse, broken here and there by piles of pressure ice or wind-drifted snow. Against the uniform, shadowless white of a fresh snowfall, move three little black disks. Arranged in a small triangle, with two uppermost and the third midway below, the dots move erratically, silently along the beach. They are the dark eyes and the black nose of the white Arctic fox.

Moving without a sound on its fur-soled feet, it must be very close before the pure white uniform can be picked out against the winter background. It carefully examines the shore for any bit of food, living or dead. Gifts from the sea are welcomed, whether fish, flesh or fowl. Shellfish, spiny echinoderms, and crustaceans are gathered at low tide.

The carcass of a whale is a real windfall, enough for many animals for an entire winter. Nearly one hundred white foxes have been counted at one time feeding on the mountainous hulk of a stranded whale. Like small white dogs, they gather for the feast from many miles, along with the great white polar bears. When the wind blows hard and the temperature drops to fifty degrees or more below zero, each fox burrows alone into a snow drift and ignores the cold.

Many Arctic foxes travel out to sea on icebergs and floes, and live there through the winter months. Unlike the bears, they do not swim unless forced by a crisis. Life becomes almost subsidized if a polar bear decides to stay on the floe. The respectful foxes follow the bear everywhere, at a discreet distance. Unless extraordinarily hungry, the bear leaves behind about half of its seal kill and frequently as much as three-quarters. When it abandons the kill to sleep, the foxes glut themselves on the remainder.—The wild animal that kills more than it eats is not wasteful, but is providing, not purposely of course, for others. Unsubsidized, these sea-going Arctic foxes must stalk and kill the birds such as gulls and auklets that come to rest on the ice.

Although the usual home of the white fox is the Arctic coast and islands, every fourth winter sees a migration southward. Occasionally, wandering animals may reach northern Saskatchewan and Manitoba. Thousands of white foxes appeared in the spring of 1922, in southern Labrador, far south of their normal range. A year later, one was shot on Cape Breton Island, Nova Scotia. These wanderers are leaving their overpopulated home territory where food has become short. It is said that a winter of light snowfall is apt to induce more traveling than winters of deep snow.

The chunky lemming, looking like an over-sized meadow mouse, is the main cause of these wanderings. It is the most important item in the diet of the Arctic fox. Therefore, as the lemmings increase in numbers up to the four-year peak, the foxes live high and multiply accordingly. When the lemming hordes begin to die, they do so with devastating swiftness. The foxes become desperate for food. Many of them that try to stay home starve to death. Few of those that wander to the southward ever return or are able to survive there for long. Every fifth year, then, is a winter of few foxes, and the Eskimo must use his credit at the trading post to buy his simple necessities.

While many sea-going foxes scavenge on the leavings of the polar bears, some foxes that stay ashore follow the great Arctic wolves. Even the most thoroughly cleaned-up carcass of a caribou or muskox will have something of value. Foxes have even been known to follow the trail of wounded animals to lick up every spatter of frozen blood from the snow. They are careful, however, not to trail the wolves too closely. Those marauders are much more agile than

ARCTIC FOX

the bear and can catch the most madly-twisting fox. The summer sun often reveals on the greening tundra little clumps of matted white fur, grim relics of foxes that were overtaken and killed during the previous winter.

February is an important month for the polar foxes. The molt begins, not to be completed until late spring. The white foxes gradually lose their beautiful white coats as the brown hair comes in. The slowness of the change is often amusing. I have seen a white fox running around with a brown tail that certainly looked as if it belonged to someone else.

Blue foxes undergo a less radical change. They are "brunette" Arctic foxes that correspond to the black phase of the red fox. Their bluish gray winter coats gradually turn dull and brownish. Beginning on the head and shoulders, these coats are finally replaced by sooty-gray summer coats. As with the other Arctic foxes, the reverse change to winter dress occurs in August and September.

When the Arctic foxes start getting new summer coats, they also start looking around for their mates. The weak, high-pitched, husky barking is often heard through the gloom. Even when you are close to the animals, their yapping seems curiously far away and according to one great naturalist "much like a bantam hen that has just laid an egg."

Some naturalists think that Arctic foxes are monogamous. Against this is the fact that the males fight savagely at this time. However these may be only the young animals, about ten months old, that are settling their first courtship problems. Of course there are foxes and foxes. There is no doubt but that some may have more mates than others.

Once the foxes have paired off, the male is a constant husband and good provider, at least until the new pups can make their own living. Throughout the long summer days he hunts lemmings, ground squirrels and other rodents, birds and their eggs and young, and similar delicacies, to feed his mate and young.

The young are born in May, fifty-two days after actual mating. The average number in a litter is six or seven, but there may be as many as twelve.

Many pairs are forehanded and look up a den ahead of time. However, an occasional female is careless and waits until the last minute. After the complete litter is born just anywhere out on the open tundra, she scrambles madly around to get her lemming-size youngsters, weighing about two ounces each, under cover. Although they are clothed in short, fine, dark brown fuzz, they cannot stand much exposure. Frantically she runs here and there on her wild house-hunt, usually carrying one or two of the shivering youngsters in her mouth. At last she gets settled in a burrow which ordinarily is in a hillside near a source of food, and is fairly deep. It is much branched and has several exits,

When about a month old, the young offspring toddle out of the den to look around. They and their parents like sunshine and spend hours in the middle of the day lolling around and absorbing it. When the pups are able to walk about, they may be moved by their parents to temporary shallow holes near the hunting ground along the beach. The family breaks up by September or October.

Visitors to fox islands are always astonished at the curiosity and tameness of Arctic foxes. These little wild dogs come out of their burrows to stare, and yap half-heartedly like terriers. Where human visitors are rare, they will gather around a campfire at night and sit for hours in wonder. They are the easiest of all the larger northern mammals to trap.

Bears and wolves are constant hazards and they may try to dig the foxes out of their dens. The great gray owl, the snowy or Arctic owl, and perhaps the raven, may prey on the pups. Internal parasites—roundworms and flatworms— at times have very serious effects. Skin mites also cause mange. Cannibalism may occur when there is a lack of balanced diet or scarcity of food.

Although we have previously discussed the Arctic fox's natural diet, we might go into a little further detail. At fur-seal and sea-lion rookeries, it has a constant source of food in the carcasses of those animals that die or are killed by man for their skins.

Young gulls, ducks, and turnstones, sandpipers and many other kinds of shore birds may be captured. Inland, there are ptarmigans, and their eggs and young, and smaller birds such as finches. On the Pribilof Islands, the numerous blue foxes feed in summer largely on birds and their eggs, especially the least auklets and murres. Since the murres live on the cliffs, the foxes climb about on almost sheer walls, hundreds of feet above the breakers, where it would seem that the nests would be safe from any enemy except the ravens and jaegers.

The foxes extract the auklets from their shallow burrows in the ground and eat them in enormous numbers. They frequently carry away both dead birds and their eggs and cache them here and there in the spongy tundra for future use or for feeding the growing pups. Despite this toll, the bird colonies are so huge that the foxes do not seem to have affected the hordes that depart each autumn.

The foxes also prey on the spawning salmon when the fish come into the smaller streams. Later in the season they look for blueberries, huckleberries, squawberries, and other fruits on the hillsides.

They hunt their animal prey against the wind. In their environment, where the winter night is several months long and the summer sun does not set for many weeks, they do not have a regular hunting schedule. Weather, and especially the emptiness of the stomach, regulate the fox's working hours.

Trapping foxes for their silky pelts has become a principal winter activity of the Eskimo, and is the source of most of his worldly wealth. He traps the foxes on the tundra, or around stranded carcasses on the ocean beach. Formerly, baited pitfalls covered with thin strips of whalebone were used. Steel traps have largely replaced the old-time devices.

"Blue" foxes may occur anywhere, but they are much more rare in the central Arctic than along the eastern and western corners of the continent. On the Pribilofs and on other Alaskan islands devoted to natural "ranching" of foxes, white animals are rigorously culled out. In time, a nearly pure strain of "blue" fox is developed. Because of its beauty and its comparative scarcity, the blue fox is worth almost three times as much as a white pelt of similar quality, or fifty to seventy-five dollars. An exceptional blue fox skin has sold for as much as one hundred and fifty dollars.

General description. A small fox with short face, low ears, very long, dense fur and bushy tail. Color in summer deep brown to dark gray above, whitish to yellowish white or buffy on chest, flanks and belly; in winter, pure white. In the blue phase, the sooty gray summer fur becomes a bluish gray in winter. Total length, 2½ feet; height at shoulder, 9½ to 12 inches; weight, 6 to 12 pounds, occasionally as much as 21 pounds.

Distinguishing characteristics. Within its range, can be confused only with the red fox and coyote. The Arctic fox is smaller than either; it is the only one of the trio that is white in winter. Its ears are much shorter than those of the red fox.

Range. Circumpolar. Arctic America, the islands of the polar sea, and coastal areas of Greenland. On the American continent, from northeastern Quebec and James Bay north of the tree limit to northwestern Alaska; thence south along the Bering Sea slope to the Alaska Peninsula, the Aleutian Islands; and the islands of Bering Sea.

COYOTE
CANIS SP.

A coyote creeps across the meadow. It is almost hidden in the deep grass. Ahead on the river bank is a flock of Canada geese. The big birds are resting

COYOTE

and picking at the new grass shoots. Their black, gray and white uniforms are bright in the morning sun. Suddenly a goose on watch stiffens. Its snaky head is thrust forward. It stares at the gray furry back moving through the golden-rod. "Look out!" it clarions the single warning. Instantly the flock is alert, staring, ready to leap into the air or take to the water.

The coyote straightens up. With an embarrassed look, it tries to shrug off its failure. Ostentatiously, it picks up a grasshopper and crunches it. It sniffs at a mouse burrow, surveys the horizon, and gazes into the skies. In its rough, brownish gray coat, it looks rather like a sharp-faced collie dog. The mouth is open in a toothsome grin, the bushy tail almost wags, then it turns and wanders away.

Frequently the coyote hunts with his mate and one or more friends. He is satisfied with only one mate for at least a year and probably for a lifetime, or until she is killed. In the latter case, when mating season comes again, he sets out to acquire another mate. If two or more males decide to court the same female, bloody fights may occur. When the fur has finally settled, it is likely to be she who does the choosing. Capriciously, she may pick the bloodiest and most thoroughly defeated candidate in the lot, if she can get away with it!

The usual breeding time is late January through February, although climatic disturbances, altitude and latitude may cause it to be a little earlier or later. The season is very definitely limited to less than two months for the female and under four months for the male. With rare exceptions, if they do not find mates during that one period, the animals are unable to breed until the following year.

Now and then there may be an irate and brutal husband as is found in the human world. Perhaps it was such a scoundrel, or a rejected suitor, that was once seen chasing a terrified female. Obviously she had young and had been nursing them. The male was wild-eyed, his mouth was open and the hair on his neck stood straight up. She was a little thing and ran desperately. But he caught her, grabbed her by a hind foot, and threw her five or six feet. Then he seized her by the neck and shook her so violently that a mouthful of hair came loose. She managed to escape the next attack and began to run again. Unfortunately the observer lost sight of them both at this moment.

Ordinarily the male is a devoted husband. He has been caught in the same trap-set with his mate. He brings her food when she is pregnant, and works hard to help feed and bring up their young. If dogs or men come near their home, he or his mate will try to decoy them away.

When the pair first set up housekeeping, they occupy one or the other's den, cr find or build another for the coming family. One unusual female chose the hollow of a tree five feet above ground. Usually they settle in the hollow base of a tree in a forest, a hollow log, a cave in a cliff or mountainside, a space in a pile of rocks in the open, or a burrow on the prairie or under the rim of an arroyo.

The animals dig readily with their clawed feet if the soil is fairly loose. They excavate a tunnel between one and two feet in diameter and five to thirty feet long. Labor is often conserved by enlarging or remodeling the burrow of a badger, skunk or fox. Generally there are several branches. The dirt is pushed back to the entrance and tossed out in a low, fan-shaped heap. At the end of the burrow is the den, a chamber a little larger than the passageways, whose roof may be anywhere from one to six feet below the ground surface. No grass, leaves or other bedding is used. The entire burrow is kept clean. It is sometimes ventilated by a hole in the ceiling of the den, and droppings are always deposited outside.

The mother may have three to nineteen young. All in only sixty to sixty-three days after mating. The average litter numbers five or six. Shortly before the pups are born, the father is requested to establish a separate domicile somewhere in the neighborhood. Here he lives for the next couple of months. Instead of leading a gay dog's life, he works hard to make a living for himself, his mate and family. He brings rabbits and small rodents, and carrion from larger animals, and solicitously deposits them at the den entrance. The mother does some hunting for herself when she can spare time from nursing all of her brood. She weans them with partly digested food regurgitated from her stomach or sometimes the father's.

Once in a while two adult females den together during this period. The extra female may be a peg-legged spinster who helps out with the young, or she may be an older mother with lots of advice and a litter of her own. Very rarely, two females of the same age, both with litters, are in the same den. Perhaps they are widows, or deserted by their mates, or just plain congenial.

When the pups are five or six weeks old, they spend most of the sunny hours in rest or play around the entrance to the den. They look like plain-colored gray or grayish buffy puppy-dogs, but with bigger, upstanding ears and smaller eyes. From constant playing and association together, they develop a strong fraternal feeling. If one happens to wander off a little way, it quickly becomes uneasy and returns by back-tracking with its nose.

About the time that the young are two months old, the mother permits her mate to return to the family den and make the acquaintance of his progeny. Hunting lessons follow. Both parents take the brood out in the fields and show them how to hunt for mice and rabbits. Wild with excitement, the youngsters rush about, yapping, puffing and getting under foot at critical moments, but eventually learn the business of making a living.

Because the parents have established their hunting preserve years before, which can yield only a certain amount of food, the young coyotes must eventually find unstaked territory elsewhere. By autumn the young of the year are wandering about uncertainly, meeting with rebuffs. Many of these inexperienced and less clever youngsters die of hunger or are killed by other animals or by man. In this search for a place to make their living, grown pups have been known to wander an airline distance up to one hundred and twenty miles from their birthplace.

If taken from the den at a very early age and reared by hand, the coyote is as tame as a dog and makes an intelligent and interesting companion. It is inclined to be less reliable than a dog, however. When protected in the wild state, it quickly comprehends that man is harmless. In a number of the western national parks, where predators as well as other animals find refuge, the coyotes greatly intrigue the visitors. For hours the tourists watch the little wolves hunting, resting or sunning.

In a few cases here, the animals have learned that food can be begged, so they come into the headquarters communities and make the round of kitchen doors. Several minor arguments over food have occurred and women and children have surrendered packages of groceries to insistent coyotes. I have never heard of a normal coyote biting a human, unless it did so incidentally when reaching for food. It seems safe to say that a normal wild coyote will not attack a person. (A coyote infected with rabies is not itself, of course.) Even when caught in a trap, the coyote cowers and cringes and seldom makes the least pretense of self-defense. In very rare instances coyotes have followed humans at dusk or in darkness, apparently out of curiosity. One coyote followed a ranger in Yellowstone for a mile and a half about noontime.

It is not always a grim, serious killer. It has been seen playing with a raven, rushing, jumping and rolling over with amusement, and waving its legs in the air while the bird evaded or swooped threateningly. After watching many coyotes, I really believe that they have a sense of humor at times. On one occasion a coyote played with a live field mouse, letting the little animal run toward a waiting raven, then leaped just in time to snatch it from the bird's talons. Grisly humor this time! When two coyotes meet, they sometimes touch noses, a friendly inquisitive salutation.

The coyote eats everything that is edible, and numerous other objects. Leather—straps, bits of harness and dried cowhide—is chewed down although the animal may not be particularly hungry. Even a lady's powder puff with the right scented powder is irresistible. When a trapper north of Reno, Nevada, found that coyotes had pawed and scratched over a place about twelve feet in diameter, he investigated more closely. In the middle was a scented powder puff. Using this puff as bait for a trap again and again, he caught nine coyotes one after the other.

Because of the coyote's toll of sheep and other domestic stock, many studies have been made of coyote food habits. Its diet is better known, probably, than that of almost any other wild animal. Data on the stomach contents of three coyotes in Yellowstone during October showed that they had dined as follows:

mice	hair of brown bear (obviously carrion)
squirrels	
birds	feathers
fish, chicken and pork bones	rubber from a hot-water bottle
pine needles	miscellaneous bits of garbage

Although it eats a little of nearly everything, including a great variety of fruit and a little grass, the coyote is usually an almost one hundred per cent carnivore. Throughout the year, rabbits and many rodents make up about half of all the food eaten. Anything it can catch by speed or stealth, from jackrabbits, marmots and prairie dogs to ground squirrels and all varieties of mice, are devoured.

It is seldom able to down a healthy adult deer. However, I once saw a coyote team up with two companions and kill a yearling. One coyote chased the deer to the top of the ridge where I stood, and then turned it back to the two accomplices that waited below. The deer screamed with terror again and again. As all three coyotes, barking furiously, joined in a deadly assault, it stumbled and fell. In a few moments they had severed the muscle that operated the main tendon of a rear leg. The deer continued to bleat hoarsely as they bit at its hip and groin. But it never rose again.

The coyote goes into the water after fish, crayfish, frogs and tadpoles. In winter, it hunts through holes in the ice for trout and perhaps tries to get them away from the otters at times. It also goes down in the warm, ice-free water below hot springs for crayfish. Sometimes it catches beavers when they are wandering away from water. One coyote was seen to kill and eat a bull snake four and one-half feet long. Quite frequently it eats porcupines in spite of the quill menace. Seventy-five per cent of the coyotes killed in Yellowstone during the late twenties (before predators were protected) carried porcupine quills.

Carrion is an important source of nourishment at all seasons and it is most abundant and also most useful during winter when other food is scarce and hard to get. Winter-killed livestock or game animals, remains of fish, slaughterhouse offal, and carcasses of its own race are all eagerly devoured.

At times, however, this confirmed meat-eater lapses into a fruit diet. I have found droppings composed entirely of undigested juniper berries, and others made up of the remains of chokecherries. Coyotes in the desert frequently dine on the fruits of prickly pear, and on mesquite beans. Persimmons and all sorts of cultivated fruits are favorites. Coyotes like watermelons, and are expert at picking out the ripe from the green ones.

Once, near Cook City, Montana, I found a fresh coyote dropping composed entirely of green sedge. It was January, and last season's sedges were dead and brown and buried under four feet of snow. Down in the valley was a warm spring; here this canny coyote must have come for greens when its less enterprising kin were living monotonously on stale, winter-killed elk.

The coyote often tags along close behind other hunters to pick up their leavings or grab scraps that escape more clumsy paws. I have seen it sauntering behind a bear that was after mice or ground squirrels. The bumbling bear knew it was being imposed upon, but only grumbled testily. Sometimes the coyote has the temerity to nip a bear; when the bear drops its food to turn around and charge, the coyote speedily makes a grab and runs.

Like most dogs, the coyote frequently stores surplus food. The ravens, which feed on the same carcasses, may follow to spy out the cache. When even one of them succeeds, the entire supply is likely to be gone when the coyote returns.

If there is one single animal sound that typifies the West, it is the frequent song of the coyote. The little wolf has a varied repertoire. It barks, a low, yapping sound, and sometimes sets up an amazing chorus of whines, barks, howls and wails that range across at least two full octaves. One animal, in the darkness, may sound like three or four choristers. But when a lone coyote sits down on a knoll and really sings, it is as thrilling a solo as ever I have heard. One low bark begins the mournful music and it swings slowly into a long-drawn-out, quavering wail that seems to rise all the way to the stars and beyond. To some people it is distressingly human. Several coyotes often sing together, each on its own orchestration.

Wolves, coyotes and domestic dogs all belong to the closely related group *Canis,* the Roman's word for "dog." Occasionally, during the mating season, a coyote will make advances to a dog and a number of hybrid families have been produced. The offspring are more nervous and untamable than the wild parent. Although extra-large coyotes sometimes are supposed to be the results of crossing with wolves, this seems doubtful. Even the largest coyote is much smaller than a wolf, and the two species are antagonistic and fundamentally different in temperament. Wolves seem to regard coyotes as poachers and kill them when possible.

The first white men to see this wild American dog, so like the Old World jackal, were the Spaniards. They adopted his Aztec name, *coyotl*. The Castilian pronunciation of "koi-oothay" has been sharpened by Mexicans to "ki-ō-tee," which is the preferable American usage. In parts of our West, this is frequently corrupted to "ki-ōt." Sometimes, particularly in forested regions, the name "brush wolf" is used to indicate that the coyote can be found frequently in the cutover country close to man's habitations, while the more intolerant true wolf keeps to the heavy timber. Similarly, the term "prairie wolf" has been applied on the plains. "Little wolf," which is seldom used, accurately describes the difference in the sizes of the two animals. The wolf is about twice as large.

Although typically a resident of the open plains and the shrubby deserts, the coyote often makes a living in the mountains as high as timber line or even beyond. It does not mind snow if compact or crusted, but it does have to eat. Therefore it usually follows the game or livestock herds, descending to the canyons or foothills in late fall and returning to the high meadows and peaks in spring.

Unlike many animals, the coyote doesn't sleep through the winters. After two or three days it is so hungry and nervous that it leaves the winter den or open bed under a tree or bush and strikes out through the snow. If there is plenty of time, it walks or jog-trots, stopping frequently to investigate possible food supplies or indications of the passing of its fellows. At these slower gaits, the tail droops or is even tucked between its legs. On more urgent business, it lopes, taking an easy swinging gallop that covers ground rapidly and with apparently little effort. When pursued closely or frightened, it really digs in its toes and fairly flies. With legs working like short pistons, the ears laid back on outstretched head, and tail streaming behind, the coyote's body skims the ground. There is no lost or bounding motion.

Several coyotes have been clocked by automobiles going at twenty-nine to thirty-one miles per hour. In one instance, a coyote ran in a straight line for several hundred yards and attained a top speed of forty-three miles per hour. Finding that it was becoming tired without throwing off its pursuer, the coyote twisted and dodged for a total of forty-seven minutes before being run down and killed.

The coyote has several enemies besides man. Wolves sometimes surprise and kill it, very easily too, for they are much larger and far more powerful. Members of the prey species, like deer and elk, occasionally turn and beat off attackers. On a number of occasions, coyotes have been found beaten and trampled into bloody pulp by an infuriated band, or by a mother deer or elk. I once watched a doe mule deer dash at a coyote and drive it from the dead body of a recently killed member of her band. With ears laid back and eyes blazing, the doe struck repeatedly with her sharp front hoofs. The coyote cringed and fled before her righteous rage. Her swift thrusts might have mashed its ribs or even broken its back.

Starvation is not an infrequent cause of death. During winters when there is much soft, deep snow, many coyotes die even in the presence of deer. The long-legged deer are not so greatly hampered by soft snow, but coyotes flounder about and cannot catch anything. Since it is a good winter for the big game, there is comparatively little carrion. The coyotes get weaker and thinner until they are too weak to kill even a sick deer.

Lack of food does not always kill. But it may have far-reaching effects on the coyote race. In June, 1945, after an open winter with little loss of game, seven coyote dens in Yellowstone Park were dug open. The seven dens contained a total of only twenty-five pups. The mothers, who had been undernourished all winter, had produced scarcely more than three pups apiece. This was far below the normal average of five or six.

Coyotes are supposed to avoid cougar kills. In one instance, a cougar was feeding on a deer carcass when a coyote rashly approached. With a couple of springs, the big cat was on the intruder. One snap of the great jaws and the tusks penetrated the coyote's brain, killing it instantly. Even the golden eagle has been known to swoop down and cripple or kill it by tearing at the throat or back. Coyotes have died from the results of encounters with porcupines, but generally the quills do not cause any great trouble.

All the diseases of the dog family, including distemper and rabies, plague the coyote. These two diseases can be communicated between it and our domestic dog. On the cattle and sheep ranges of the West, the rabid coyote, or the anticipation of one, is a fearsome spectre. In the "mad" stage, the sick animal is devoid of fear and may bite stock or the herders' dogs, and come into a camp to attack humans. Fortunately this happens very seldom. Coyotes are also hosts to internal and external parasites. Sometimes mange mites almost denude an animal of hair. Paralysis, deafness, and blindness are other afflictions.

During one winter trip on snowshoes in Yellowstone Park, I came across evidence of an epidemic among the coyotes. The first animal encountered had worn a circular trail under a big fir tree. It hated to leave the trail, and although it did so when I approached closely, I easily caught up with it in the deep snow. Farther down the valley I came upon the carcasses of two dead coyotes together, while a third, very sick animal limped away through the sage.

Coyotes have been found with undershot jaws, resulting from failure of the facial bones to develop normally. Other curiously abnormal animals were an earless pup, and a California coyote whose legs were only about two-thirds the usual length.

In spite of all these trials and tribulations, the coyote continues to increase and spread over the country and in many ways to be helpful to man. The coyote is the garbage man, the health officer, the sanitary engineer and the exterminator. All this it does with no pay except bed and board. It prevents the pollution of streams in many cases by cleaning up the carcasses of animals that die of injuries or disease. It puts a quick end to senile, wounded or starving creatures. One of the most potent checks on the rodent host, it keeps down crop and range damage and lessens the danger of epizootics. Throughout the ages it has helped to weed out the unfit and keep survivors alert. Largely due to it and other predators, the deer, the antelope and other hoofed mammals have evolved into swift, graceful, efficient animals. Were it not for the coyote, they would not only overpopulate and overeat their ranges, but would doubtless become lazy, fat and have cirrhosis of the liver.

Even when dead, the coyote may continue to do service. Its pelt is a good-looking, durable fur that brought five dollars for average No. 1 skins during the worst depressions of the market, and twelve dollars to a top of sixteen dollars in 1943.

Balanced against these assets are its liabilities. The super-smart coyote who has lived near domestic herds has discovered the easy way to make a living. It causes a serious annual loss to the sheep industry, kills a considerable number of turkeys and other poultry, and on rather rare occasions pulls down calves. An unusually bloodthirsty coyote killed twenty-six ewe lambs in three days. Having lost two toes in a trap several months before, its tracks and method of killing identified it. The handicapped animal, which has to find an easy way, kills one-third more sheep and goats than the normal one does. This is the peg-leg who has lost all or the greater part of one or more feet in traps, or an old coyote whose teeth are worn and whose joints are stiff.

Only a minority of coyotes should be blamed for these depredations. But the whole race is condemned for the deeds of some, and is subject to incessant warfare. An estimated total of one hundred and twenty-five thousand coyotes are shot, trapped or poisoned each year in the United States, Canada and Alaska.

Nevertheless, due to their large and frequent litters, their cleverness and adaptability, they have spread and increased greatly in spite of such wide persecution. Fifty years ago they were almost unknown east of a line running from east-central Texas to eastern Wisconsin and thence to Great Slave Lake, and west of a line drawn from Great Slave Lake to northwestern California. Now they live in abundance, in places as far as western Ohio, eastern Ontario and

Keewatin. They have spread to the shore of the Arctic Ocean near the Mackenzie River, and to the Pacific in our Northwest and British Columbia. They have come to occupy all of the vast territory of Alaska that they can reach without crossing the glaciers.

Even localities as remote from their natural range as Maine and Florida are occasionally visited by coyotes. Periodically, "strange doglike animals" are killed or trapped in the East, to become two- or three-week sensations in country newspapers. They are finally identified at museums as "brush wolves" (coyotes). Sometimes these animals have been shipped from the West while young and palmed off on fox-hunting associations as red fox puppies. More often they have come East via automobiles as family pets, only to escape or to be turned loose.

In spite of the coyote's shortcomings, it is a clever little pilferer at worst and often a useful, interesting member of the society of mammals. The West would not be the same without it. The plains and deserts would seem mute without its plaintive song. For better or for worse, I hope that the little wolf and its descendants will be with us always.

General description. Resembling a dog of the collie type, but with shorter body and rough, grizzled coat. Fur thick, fairly long and coarse. Upper parts grizzled grayish or tawny, black and yellowish, under parts whitish, tail tipped with black. Total length, 42 to 50 inches; height at shoulder, 18 to 21 inches; weight, 20 to 30 pounds, and rarely to 60 pounds.

Distinguishing characteristics. Much larger than the foxes, whose coats are smooth as compared with the rough, grizzled fur of the coyote. About half the size of the wolf. Also of more slender build and face, and much smaller ears and feet. Compared to a domestic dog of the mongrel collie type, the coyote is more slender, with longer and thinner face, slenderer legs and smaller feet. Its ears are never "lopped" at the tips like those of most dogs.

Range. Western and central North America; from Costa Rica north throughout Alaska and the lower Mackenzie, and from the Pacific Ocean eastward to eastern Texas, Arkansas, Missouri, western Ohio, Michigan, eastern Ontario and Keewatin. Sporadic in every eastern state and Quebec.

WOLF
CANIS SP.

The wolf is a savage, powerful killer. It has been one of the most feared and hated animals in the white man's world.

Yet there is no kinder and more devoted mate in the wild fauna of North America. A tender, conscientious father, he labors long hours to care for his offspring. Usually a sociable fellow, he prefers to hunt with his relatives and friends than to go alone. The bloodthirsty mother is affectionate and big-hearted and has been said to have added wolf orphans to her own brood. The hero and heroine, the villain and villainess of folklore that has come down through the centuries in many languages—this is the wolf.

Man's hand has been against the wolf for centuries. The species has been eliminated from all settled regions of North America. No wolf which escaped being killed could exist after the wilderness was destroyed. It was the only animal that years ago was extirpated by hunting from every national park in the United States. But it has flourished and become more numerous in Alaska and vast stretches of Canadian forest and tundra. Small numbers of wolves have managed to persist in a number of our western states and in the northern Lake States. Mexico still is the home of a sizable wolf population, although the original range has been somewhat restricted. During the past ten or fifteen years the wolf has been given at least partial protection in the Alaskan and Canadian national parks where the species still survives.

In the wolf world, the family is the social unit. The pack is usually made up of the mother and father, their growing pups and perhaps several aunts and uncles. This is an efficient group. There are enough members to cooperate in relaying and running down game without being so numerous as to deplete the food supply. Tradition says that packs of "fifty to one hundred" or even more wolves once ranged the eastern forests. At times two or possibly three family packs may join forces temporarily, especially in winter, but herds of fifty to one hundred would quickly exterminate prey species in these days and be forced to break up from sheer scarcity of food.

In January, February and March, shortly before the youngest wolves are three years old, a restlessness seizes the pack. The long, low, wolf howl is heard far more frequently. Deep, throaty, but clear, it carries remarkably far without being loud. It is the most melancholy sound I have ever heard in the wilderness.

The two- and perhaps some three-year-olds are now ready to mate for the first time. Even with full stomachs, these young animals travel farther than ever.

WOLF

They carefully examine and follow the tracks of other bands. All along the way are scent stations—trees, bushes, or clumps of grass. Here each traveler deposits some scent that to any other wolf tells age, sex, and many further personal details. It sniffs excitedly at every station and adds more messages. One by one every young and some older unattached males slip off to follow the females that, according to the scent stations, have appealing characteristics. The parent pairs, which often stay together for a lifetime, also mate.

Sometimes a lone stranger seeks out and joins a pack, attracted by one of the unattached aunts or uncles, or a younger wolf. As the newcomer arrives, it comes up slowly with many protestations of friendship. With sociable motions of tail and body, the newcomer disavows any hostile intent. Warily, the pack receives it with suspicion. They examine it carefully with many sniffs. Perhaps they will accept it at once, but the chances are that they will gang up on it, roll it in the snow to the accompaniment of growls and barks, and perhaps a few bites to see if the newcomer can take it. Or they may take an immediate dislike to the stranger, in which case they drive it away ferociously or kill it. Wolves are particular about their associates.

Early in the gestation period of sixty-three days, the female picks a suitable den. If she chooses an old badger or coyote burrow she will need to enlarge and renovate the interior. She may find a good place in the base of a hollow tree, a fallen snag, a rocky cavern or under a tumbled pile of rocks. She has even been known to commandeer an abandoned beaver dam! If nothing appeals to her, she scratches into a steep bank covered with brush or grass and digs out a tunnel herself.

A wolf den that I saw in central Alaska was a remodelled fox burrow. The entrance was about two feet in diameter. It was located just under the crest of a bluff. From the threshold, the wolves could look across a wide shallow river to a great expanse of open tundra, beyond which rose the majestic glacier-covered mountains of the Alaska Range. Undoubtedly this site was picked for its commanding view over the caribou range, rather than for scenic inspiration. Many dens are located in woodland where the view is limited but the homesite is better protected from the observation of a casual passer-by.

The mother wolf bears her litter of four to fourteen pups on the bare earth floor of her den—even in the Arctic. Most little wolves arrive in April or May, but there may be some as early as March and as late as early June. They are fuzzy, grayish brown, gray or blackish little fellows. Their faces are blunt, their legs short, and their tails pointed and skinny. Their eyes open when they are five to nine days old.

During the first three weeks, the pups are fed only their mother's milk. Gradually she weans them. At first she gives them partly digested meat that she disgorges from her stomach. By the time they are eight or ten weeks old they are gulping down choice bits of meat and are developing their teeth and jaws on bones. This sort of exercise makes them capable later on of slashing through tough hide and tendons and breaking the heavy leg-bones of deer and caribou.

The weight and massiveness of the wolf's head and jaws are astonishing. It was striking even in a young captive wolf, only three months old, with which I once played in Alaska. She was careful not to bite, but when she took my hand in her mouth, I could sense the solid grip and the bones and muscles behind it.

Wolves grow with great rapidity. Five months after birth they stand about twenty-four inches high at the shoulder. Before they are a year old they look practically as large as their parents.

While the pups are still nursing every hour or two, the mother must spend most of the time in the den with them. She comes out only to feed on the meat which her mate and others of the pack carry to her den or cache in the neighborhood. Sometimes the hunting grounds are fifteen to twenty miles away, a long distance to carry a caribou leg or mountain-sheep head. The wolves may cram the meat into their stomachs and disgorge it at home, which seems a convenient way to carry it. Occasionally a sympathetic female takes over the night shift and the mother relaxes by going off to hunt.

Father wolves have been seen to enter the den when their offspring were only a couple of weeks old. This care and solicitude shown by the males and by the other adult wolves of the pack continue until the pups are adolescent. Even when they tumble and play roughly and persistently around an aunt or uncle, there is no snapping or peevish display of temper. If the big wolf is tired from a long hunt, it merely gets up and picks another bed where it can find peace.

When the pups are eight or nine weeks old, and fairly strong, the family moves away from the den. If disturbed and feeling insecure, the mother wolf will sometimes move her brood to a new den earlier. Usually the one home serves for a nursery until the young can stand exposure to the summer winds and rains, day and night. The pack moves about slowly, and for short distances, until the pups can make long journeys. Food is easy to find, and training the young to hunt is the most serious occupation of the fond parents.

Most wolf education is acquired by watching the parents or other adults of the pack, and then imitating their actions. In addition there is some positive training. Late one afternoon I was watching a wolf family moving through Polychrome Pass northeast of Mount McKinley in central Alaska. The father, a big gray fellow, jog-trotted steadily westward across the open tundra. About a quarter of a mile in the rear two half-grown pups followed. Like human children, they traveled by fits and starts, now stopping to paw at a ground-squirrel's den or to chase a mouse. Then they would dash ahead to make up for lost time.

Suddenly the big wolf stopped and looked backward over his shoulder. I could hear no sound. Through my binoculars, I saw that he did not open his mouth to call. Far in the rear, the two pups dropped to the ground. Perhaps the father suspected that there might be game or danger in the next few hundred yards, and did not want to be hampered by juvenile carelessness. He resumed his slow trot toward the distant divide. Nearly ten minutes later he stopped and looked back again. At once the two pups leaped to their feet and pattered along once more.

As the pups go into their first autumn, they acquire their adult, rough, heavy winter coats. In northwestern Canada and Alaska the colors seem to vary much more than in the United States and Mexico. Here the prevailing tone is gray or brownish gray, with some black individuals. On the Arctic coast, wolves are likely to be very pale, sometimes almost white.

Inland, however, dark colors predominate. Many grays are very deep in tone. Blacks are common, and often they are grizzled with buffy or reddish guard hairs. Sometimes one sees duo-colored animals with contrasting silvery or bluish mane, black face mask, or other odd pattern. In Arkansas, Louisiana and eastern Texas the prevailing color is rusty or reddish, so the name "Red Wolf" is used. Numerous individuals of this small race are black or gray, however.

Many wolves, especially those without family responsibilities that tie them down to one locality, have a hunting route that they cover several times each month. This runway, often more than a hundred miles long, is not a well-defined path except at certain lookout points that the animals visit on almost every trip.

Elsewhere they improvise, swinging out one to several miles from the course, as scent, sound or fancy indicate. For reasons perhaps unknown even to themselves, wolves generally travel their circuitous routes in a counter-clockwise direction. The "home-range" is thus very large. A wolf family in the Upper Peninsula of Michigan was believed to hunt over an area of two hundred and sixty square miles.

The wolf seldom eats fruit or vegetables as the coyote does, but may nibble at grass occasionally. In general, the diet consists of the fauna of the home region. The wolf can kill the largest mammals, even the great muskox and bison if desperate from hunger, but is often forced to content itself with smaller creatures. The majority of food in a wolf's stomach consists of mice, ground squirrels, rabbits or pocket gophers. What big game he catches usually consists of young animals, sick or injured. Many strong healthy animals are run down and killed by him and his cohorts, however.

Occasionally the wolf stalks or ambushes large prey, but it runs down most deer, caribou, bighorn, elk, moose and antelope in open chase. It is easier if members of a pack can work in relays, but a lone wolf is not hopelessly handicapped. In central Alaska, single wolves have been watched while hunting caribou. The wolf selects a band and chases it for a mile or two. If a weakling does not drop behind, the wolf turns away and tests another group. Sometimes many miles are run before a crippled caribou, or one somehow below par, cannot keep up with its companions. Swinging along at a swift gallop, the wolf slowly closes the gap between him and his prey. With a final spurt he is alongside. Then a sideways lunge against the gasping, fear-stricken victim causes it to stumble and the wolf is upon it for the kill.

The highest speed that a wolf has been known to run is only twenty-eight miles per hour and that for but a couple of hundred yards. On a long chase the top speed probably would be about twenty miles an hour. This is much slower than most big game animals, but the wolf is persistent and has remarkable endurance. Mile after mile, for many hours, it maintains that implacable steady lope, and wears down the fastest deer and even the moose.

The wolf has been accused of going berserk on occasions and killing beyond its requirements. At times it does keep on after a band of prey animals, such as deer that are handicapped by deep snow, and kills one after another. This is a sort of food storage, the wolf taking advantage of an unusual opportunity to bring down enough food to last for a while. It will return to unused carcasses later, a fact that is well known and used by trappers and poisoners. Preferring fresh meat, it eats much carrion, some of which is exceptionally rank. It also (like the coyote) has a fondness for leather!

If food is abundant, surplus kills are left uncovered and much of the meat is eaten by foxes, bears, eagles, and other scavengers. (Numbers of ravens have been seen flying along, chattering and squawking, accompanying a wolf pack on the hunt.) When food is scarcer, parts of a kill may be carefully buried in snow, under a windfall or other debris, or in the ground. After digging a hole with its paws, the wolf deposits its food and pushes the earth or snow back in with its nose.

Like most other carnivores, the wolf can eat an enormous amount of food when hungry. By actual test, a medium-sized wolf has been known to eat almost one-fifth of its own weight.

These animals are efficient, powerful brutes. Why have they not overpopulated the northern world and exterminated such "helpless" pray as the antelope and deer? Disease is an important check. When wolves become abundant, an epizootic of rabies or distemper can spread like wildfire and decimate the population. Mange at times may also denude animals and make them a prey to cold. Food shortages also occur and are just as hard on wolves as on primitive man.

Under ideal conditions, wolves are relatively long-lived. A wolf born in the National Zoological Park, Washington, D. C., lived to a ripe old age of more than sixteen years. Under natural conditions, probably not more than one wolf in a thousand will live that long. For an animal that pulls down prey weighing five times as much as itself, or more, life is one hazard after another. A moment's carelessness may allow a threshing hoof to lame or break its leg, shoulder, hip, or even its back.

Mankind is a mortal foe of the wolf because it is sometimes a serious menace to livestock. When a wolf learns that man's animals provide an easy and sumptuous living, it may develop an uncanny skill in avoiding traps, poison, dogs and guns.

The wolf is not generally as prolific as that other wild dog, the coyote. Although the mother wolf has a large family, an average of seven puppies and as many as a record of fourteen, some females do not breed every year. Apparently these breed only once every second or third spring season.

To maintain itself the wolf must be more cautious. It tries to keep out of man's way, while the coyote boldly moves in next door. The wolf makes forays against livestock from the deep woods or the mountains and returns there with its booty. When it fails to avoid man, it learns quickly. After strychnine has been used for a short time in wolf control projects, the surviving adults learn to shun it. Apparently they recognize that the sweetish smell around a carcass means danger. From then on, only an occasional, young, uneducated wolf will eat it. The poisoners must try a different formula. The wolf is believed by many trappers to be America's smartest mammal.

One of the most famous wolves, the "Custer Wolf," lived for years in the southern Black Hills of South Dakota, "boarding" on unwilling stockmen. Year after year they failed to catch him. Then there was "Three Toes," named for his maimed foot. He levied toll in northwestern South Dakota for at least fourteen years before he could be trapped. Irate ranchers claim that he destroyed fifty thousand dollars' worth of stock, including full-grown cattle and horses. He is said to have killed as many as thirty-four ram sheep in a single night. "Gray Ghost," another elusive killer, was trailed by dogs and hunted by an airplane before he was finally caught.

It seems doubtful that wild, normal wolves in North America ever venture to attack persons. Perhaps our species is less savage than the European animal that, according to newspaper stories, is the terror of French, Rumanian and Russian peasants. Our backwoodsmen apparently must freeze or starve to death before the American wolf will consider them safely palatable.

The pelt of the timber wolf makes a rather coarse but very beautiful fur. In the trade, dark gray pelts are most desirable, and those with the greatest contrast of dark back and pale belly fur bring the highest price. An "average" good skin in the 1943–44 market was valued at thirty-five to fifty dollars. The catch varies from year to year, but in 1941 the fur markets of Canada handled five thousand seven hundred and thirty pelts; those of the United States, nine thousand three hundred and thirty, and about five hundred were sold from Alaska.

The Arctic dog teams that have wolf blood are highly prized. Captive and semi-domesticated wolves are often mated with sled-dogs in order to "build up the breed." One-quarter wolves are judged to have the best combination of rugged strength and endurance, ease of handling, and ability to withstand hardships. These crossbloods are large, powerful beasts that strongly resemble their wolf grandparent. The prehistoric American Indians almost certainly kept domesticated wolves which they used for hunting and for hauling loads, and very likely for crossing with their savage dogs whose ancestors came from Asia.

General description. A wild "dog" similar in appearance and size to a very large police or German shepherd dog. Frame (especially skull and fore legs) heavy; head broad, fore feet large; fur thick and heavy. Color very variable with the species and individual, gray, grayish brown, black, reddish brown, or grayish white, darkest on back and palest under body and lower half of legs. Size varies with the species: total length, 4 to 7 feet; height at shoulder, 19 to 38 inches; weight, 30 to 100 pounds and, in the Arctic, to extremes of 175 pounds. Female about 20 per cent smaller than the male.

Distinguishing characteristics. The generally larger size and heavier frame, broad, blunt head with heavy muzzle, and large long forelegs and feet, set the wolf apart from the coyote. When compared with dogs of similar type (such as sled dogs) the wolf is more slender and rangy, has longer legs, and due to a narrower chest the front legs are set closer together.

Range. Originally all of Alaska, Canada, and the United States (except western Nevada and southern California); and south in Mexico to the region of Mexico City. Now exterminated from the St. Lawrence watershed, Newfoundland, all of the eastern states (except northern parts of Michigan, Wisconsin and Minnesota) and the tall-grass prairie states; exterminated or uncommon in most of the remainder of the United States and the extreme eastern and prairie provinces of Canada.

12. The Cats

THE COUGAR—*FELIS CONCOLOR*

Purple dusk deepens in the canyon shadows and the last color fades from the wispy clouds far overhead. The sun has gone down behind the distant rim of the desert. On the rocky ridge the mule deer are stirring as they gather their evening meal. They are nervous, looking up quickly and often. They stare this way and that. Their great ears swivel and twitch. Earlier, a gentle breeze had carried a hint of a musky odor from across the canyon.

They pay too much attention to the brushy slope below and the opposite canyon wall. Behind them and across the ridge along which they feed, just under the sky line, a huge cat slinks between the pillarlike trunks of the yellow pines. Her eyes are intent and unblinking as her head swings in a semicircle. Her nose wrinkles as she scents the deer. She guides her course by the lightly moving air that comes up and across the ridge. Each step forward is a slow, imperceptible movement. When the weight of her great crouched body settles on a broad paw, the sound is like the bending of a single pine needle. Finally, behind a patch of oak, she creeps silently onto the ridge top.

Only sixty feet away a buck picks at a seedling manzanita. Immediately the cougar's muscles, like taut steel springs, release the pent-up energy. A swift, cold fury, she makes two tremendous leaps, then a final short one. The victim has only time to hear a rushing sound and to throw up his head. Then he is struck by the avalanche. With more than one hundred pounds of weight behind them, the great forepaws strike the deer's shoulder. They drive the front quarters violently away. The head and neck snap around against the cougar's body. Like a sack of bones and flesh the deer crashes to earth fully twenty feet off. He is dead, the neck broken.

As the clattering hoof-beats of the terrified survivors fade away in the distance, the cougar drags the dead deer to the edge of the brush. Here she rips open the belly with a single stroke of her powerful, extensile claws. One swift movement disembowels it. Sometimes she leaves the entrails in their unbroken sac. Tonight she devours some of the hot smaller intestines, then turns to the ribs and loin. Gradually her gaunt flanks round a little as she gulps down six or seven pounds of meat and fragments of bone that she chops off with her

COUGAR

serrated cheek teeth. Satisfied and replete, she takes a final look about, covers the torn remains of her feast with leaf litter and dead sticks, and pads softly away in the darkness.

Under ordinary circumstances, the cougar (or panther, puma, or mountain lion as she is variously named) would have selected a smooth spot on the forest floor and gone to sleep within a short distance of the kill. With the return of consciousness and appetite, another big meal, a cold one this time, would be made from the remains. However, in this case three small kittens are waiting at the open cave under a ledge about three or four miles away. The mother must return to nurse them.

The family is the result of a brief mating several months earlier with a big grayish male. He had lived and hunted the range for a couple of years. At times, as he sauntered along the ridges, he had left "scratchings" of bare earth from which the grass or litter was flung. These billets gave notice that he was in a courting mood.

The female cougar ignored him until one night a "scratching" awakened a new emotion. Several days later the two cats met. For two weeks they lived together. During this time any other male that tried to interfere would have had a battle on his hands. ("Tom" cougars are notoriously jealous and have been known to maul fatally an interloper.) The mating period was short, however, and the two big cats separated to meet again only by chance, and then probably with a tinge of hostility.

Now and then there may be exceptions to these short-lived unions. Several years ago in Colorado, cougar tracks indicated that a male and female were together and had kittens less than a month old. After the female was killed, the United States Forest Service hunter found that the male had returned and eaten the kittens. Time and again the male returned to the cave, apparently looking for his mate. In a terrific battle with the hunter's dogs, he killed the lead dog and escaped. He was finally caught in one of two traps covered with leaf litter, and close to lion scratchings anointed with catnip oil.

This father lion may have eaten his children in anguish at losing his mate. However, almost any American cat father is likely to do this if he gets a chance. For this reason, most cougar mothers probably never let a male come anywhere around her litter.

Three kittens were born to our female cougar about three months after mating. She was an average mother; other litters might contain one or even up to five. The little kittens were about twelve inches long, and weighed around one pound. Although blind, they were fully furred. They did not at all resemble their parents at birth. Instead of long, round tails, they had short ones. Instead of plain colored coats, they had many distinct brownish black spots on their pale fawn suits, and rings of the same color on their tails. It happened that this litter of little kittens entered the world in spring, when most cougars are born. However, the adults do not follow a rigid schedule in their mating, and the young may be born in any month of the year. August seems to be a rather popular birth month, next to springtime. The climate, of course, may affect the date.

On this particular night, our lion kittens are nine or ten days old and their eyes are just opening. They are playful little animals, beginning to roll about and wrestle with each other in typical cat fashion. Their claws are like steel needles, and too rough play is punctuated by shrieks of rage and pain from the underdog of the moment. After a couple of weeks the kittens spend the sunny hours outside the den, where, as their eyes strengthen, they begin to see across the mountains of their future hunting grounds.

What the mother lacks in size, as compared with male cougars, she makes up in determination to keep her kittens fed. She has to hunt hard to maintain her milk supply and later to bring meat, perhaps from long distances. Even though deer may be abundant, they are wild and wary. They know that, next to man, the great dun-colored cat is their worst enemy. Lying in wait on a ledge or tree limb overhanging a trail seldom brings results, for the deer are careful about such traps and avoid them. The cougar's habitual method is still-hunting. There are many slips, and an average of two out of three deer manage to avoid the final spring of the enemy and get clear away. If the cougar misses and the quarry runs, she makes no more than a few jumps in pursuit. She knows that in a footrace she has no chance to overtake a deer.

Sometimes luck runs against the mother cat for days together. Then she must depend on picking up smaller mammals, such as raccoons, foxes, rabbits, or, at the expense of some painful quills, a porcupine or two. At such times, skunks are not refused, even at the price of a vile atomizing. In extremity she may also eat the leavings of a bear or another mountain lion, but cold, left-over meat from another animal's kill is not appetizing. Of course, if man's domestic stock are in the mountains and not well guarded, our cougar has little to worry about. She could knock over a sheep, a hog, a goat or colt without any difficulty, or even a full-grown steer or horse if necessary. If food were plentiful, she might make a fresh kill every night, and leave the uneaten portions for those less fastidious scavengers, the bears and coyotes.

By the time the kittens are six or seven weeks old, they are chewing bones and eating some meat. They are almost two and one-half feet long and weigh a little less than ten pounds. If the mother makes a kill in the vicinity, she will lead them to it and stand watch while they chew at bits of meat and wrestle with lengths of intestines. As long as they are hungry, they tear at the carcass and growl fiercely, but as the meal progresses the growling dies away and is gradually succeeded by loud, hoarse purrs of contentment.

When they are about two months old the kittens commence going on nightly hunting trips with their mother. By this time their black markings on body and tail have faded, although once in a while a young cougar will show a few indistinct spots, especially on the hindquarters, until it is as much as ten months old.

It takes a good many trials to learn to kill a grown deer quickly and without a struggle, during which the prey may escape. The young cougars slowly acquire skill and strength. At eight months of age they weigh fifty pounds, are between four and five feet long, and look like very competent hunters. Their mother realizes their shortcomings, however, and instead of deserting them so that she can mate again, waits until they are able to take care of themselves, which may be as much as another year. By that time they are nearly two years old and hunt alone.

Barring the natural vicissitudes of a hunter's life, the cougar may live to the age of a dozen years. It seems to have no important enemies among the mammals, although accidents may happen in meeting an ugly bear or jaguar or even by being too careless with a little porcupine. The only other cat of equal strength is the jaguar. The mountain lion is longer, if you count the tail, but the jaguar is heavier. The lion is supposed to be victorious in any combat between the two because it is more agile.

Does the mountain lion scream like a woman being murdered? It is supposed to be the strong silent member of the cat family. Certainly it doesn't go around yowling its head off the way some lesser cats do. Because it has been known to fight silently, and to suffer great agony in traps without uttering a sound, many naturalists have insisted that it did not have a cry. The famous and meticulously honest lion hunter, Jay Bruce, who has killed or captured more than six hundred and sixty-eight lions, has never heard a mountain lion scream.

Several times in the Washington Zoo, I have stood within three feet of a female mountain lion and heard her shriek repeatedly. I never heard a woman being murdered, but I think it is likely that she might be a whole lot more quiet about it. Robert Bean, Director of the Chicago Zoo, has heard mountain lions scream many times, but they were always females, and it was always mating time. It seems that the males respond with that universal masculine expression of admiration, a whistle. It is not as loud as that of the red-tailed hawk or blue jay.

Most of the screams attributed to the mountain lion prove, on investigation, to come from a lovelorn bobcat or from various species of owls. In the lonely darkness the weird sounds echo from the canyon walls and are fearsomely distorted. Only rarely can they be traced and the quaking listeners naturally think of the mountain lion as the only creature capable of such yells. A number of times in the Chiricahua Mountains of Arizona, I have heard screams that seemed to sound exactiy like those of the lion in the zoo. But not being face to face with the animal at the time, I suppose I should not swear that they were mountain lion screams.

During forty thousand miles of foot travel, chasing these cats, Jay Bruce has never seen but one that was not treed by dogs. Few people have seen them at all. Perhaps that is one reason for the tales about enormous cougars. According to hearsay, they sometimes grow to a length of a dozen feet and a weight of three hundred pounds. Possibly some of these fables arise from seeing skins which, when stretched, may be as much as two feet longer than the owners while alive. A cougar that is more than nine feet four inches long and weighs more than two hundred and twenty-seven pounds would be a breaker of all authentic records. The biggest cougars live toward the extremities of the long range, in southern South America and in our own Rocky Mountains and the Pacific coast region from Oregon to southwestern British Columbia. The animals of the tropics are considerably smaller but more brightly colored in shades of reddish brown.

Cougars have a wider distribution than any other American mammal. They are found on plains near sea level, on high mountains, in the foggy, chilly rainbelt of the forested Northwest, on the burning sands, and deep in the dense growth of the tropics.

The home range of a cougar depends on the abundance of food. If this is scarce, it may be obliged to hunt over a great circle before killing a deer, elk, bighorn, or other animal. Under average conditions, the range may be about a dozen miles across. A male cougar looking for a mate, or with wanderlust in his blood, may travel far. A hunter in New Mexico once followed such an animal for two full days during which the lion covered thirty miles without eating or stopping for any length of time. The man then abandoned the chase.

Apparently even the mountain lion plays capers now and then. In May, 1945, Charles D. Campbell of the National Park Service staff heard a series of growls when he was hiking through the oak brush and juniper wilderness on the east rim of Zion Canyon. As he proceeded, they grew much louder. Alarmed, but curious, Mr. Campbell continued on his way. Suddenly, just fifty yards away, he saw the animal that was making all the noise. It was a mountain lion! "Rolling over and over in the shade of a tree, it was scratching itself against the trunk, curling its tail and acting like an overgrown tom-cat." On realizing that it had a human audience, the cougar abruptly ceased its antics and disappeared.

If we can believe Latin American legend, *el leone* is sometimes friendly to man. According to one account, it attacks the jaguar at every opportunity when the ranges of the two species overlap, and even defends man against attack by the big spotted cat!

Personally, I should hate to depend upon the lion to get me out of trouble. Certainly the North American lion preserves a most uniform reluctance to have anything to do with people. Considering the tremendous strength of the animal, I feel that this is fortunate for us. Any creature that can kill an elk or a large horse and drag it about could make short work of an unarmed person. Very few cases of undoubted attack on humans are recorded. Most of these were committed by animals that were very old and unable to kill their usual prey. In one or two instances, the cougars were probably suffering from rabies, perhaps indirectly acquired from man's dogs, in which event they were hardly responsible for their action. A few attacks on men who were wearing fur coats may have been the result of mistaken identity.

A fourteen-year-old boy was attacked and killed by a cougar near Brewster, Okanogan County, Washington, on December 17, 1924. The lion had devoured all the boy's hair, large pieces of skin, flesh and bone, and had departed by the time the body was found that night. The two searchers covered what was left of the boy's face with his coat and went for assistance. When they returned an hour later, the coat was gone, but was found, covered with blood and torn to shreds, the next morning in a lion's den about two hundred feet away. Like most mountain lions, this one had returned to its kill!

On January 20, 1925, a lioness was trapped and killed about four miles from where the boy had been attacked. Her stomach and its contents were sent to the U. S. Biological Survey for laboratory examination. In the stomach were found a solid mass of human hair containing bits of blue denim, a piece of coarse white cloth material with a seam, a discharged cartridge marked "U. S. C. Co., 38—S. W.—center fire." The latter had been partly flattened, probably by the cougar's teeth. Digestive juices had apparently snarled, matted and felted the hair together into such a hard compact mass that it could not pass out of the stomach during the five weeks that it had been there. (Stomach obstructions by balls of hair are not uncommon with hoofed animals, and are often found in long-haired domestic cats.) Microscopic examination of the hair proved that it was of human origin. Total evidence indicated that it, as well as the blue denim, other material and empty cartridge shell belonged to the boy. There was little doubt that this young, healthy mountain lion was the killer.

It must be reiterated that an attack on a human by a mountain lion is extremely rare. Most stories of such attacks are only yarns. Almost every mountain lion can be depended upon to mind its own business.

Young cougars vary greatly in temperament. Some are peevish, short-tempered and wild; others may be gentle and tractable. If taken captive while still a kitten, one of the latter sort may remain easy to handle throughout life. I knew a female mountain lion in the Washington Zoo that delighted in the company of a mysterious woman visitor who scratched her under the chin and about the ears. By some strange sense, this lion knew when the woman was coming, before she appeared. The lion might be sullen and bored. Nothing seemed to arouse her out of her apathy. Suddenly she would leap about the cage in great excitement. In a few moments, her favorite visitor would arrive, and the lion could barely contain herself. Edmund Kean, the famous actor, had a pet mountain lion that followed him about like a well-trained dog.

Some Indians regarded the cougar with reverence. To the tribes of Baja California, the animal was a god who provided them with much of their food, while the vultures and condors showed them the way to these cougar kills. When the whites came and kept domestic livestock, they did not acknowledge the divinity of the cougar, nor did they appreciate its "help" in slaughtering. Consequently, the big cat was the object of some of the earliest bounties. Massachusetts offered as much as four pounds for a "panther" scalp in 1764. Four pounds was a lot of money at that time. In Centre County, Pennsylvania, six hundred "panthers" were killed between 1820 and 1845. The last of the species in that state was recorded in 1891. It is doubtful if a single animal now lives in the entire region of eastern Canada and United States, except in a couple of wilderness areas in Florida and perhaps on the Blue Ridge in Shenandoah National Park, Virginia.

Extravagant claims are made that a grown cougar will kill about three hundred of its favorite prey each year. Careful estimates by naturalists run from thirty-five to one hundred. The chances are that the annual kill of deer by the average cougar is closer to the lower number. This toll is frequently more beneficial than harmful. In numerous isolated regions of our western mountains, deer populations have outrun both food supply and hunting pressure. Deer, when overpopulated, have injured whole forests and "have eaten themselves out of house and home." Cougars become more abundant where there is plenty of food, and they help to hold down these wild "hoofed locusts." Furthermore, one naturalist who carefully studied the carcasses of eleven deer killed in New Mexico found that all of these animals had been abnormal. Some had prenatal injuries, others had hoof deformities or a heavy infestation of ticks or bots. A number showed malproportions of leg bones or body length. The biologist concluded that the mountain lion may be an important factor in weeding out subnormal deer and in keeping the species normal in size and body proportions.

Unfortunately many cougars learn to make an easier living by preying on domestic stock. Where horses are numerous the colts seem to be a favorite prey, and the largest race of mountain lions has been given the scientific name *hippolestes* (horse killer). The crimes of the few have brought down the wrath of the stockmen on the entire species. At every opportunity, therefore, the animals are trailed, brought to bay by dogs, and then shot.

Melanistic or black cougars are known; cougars of Florida seem to run strongly to that "freak" color. The pelt of any cougar may be prized as a trophy, and made into a rug or a wall hanging. It has little value as fur for the guard-hairs are rather stiff and the underfur is short and thin. The skin makes a strong, durable leather: in the Brazilian Matto Grosso *el leone's* hide brings two to three dollars and is used for making sandal soles. I have never eaten cougar flesh, but I know residents of the Olympic Mountains who always save the meat to be used fresh or canned.

General description. A very large, slender cat with small head and long, heavy, cylindrical tail; rounded ears which are not tufted. Fur soft, uniformly dull yellowish brown, reddish brown, or gray, paler on the flanks and shoulders and merging into dull whitish on the under parts; tail tipped with dark brown to blackish. Total length, 6 to 8½ feet, or more; height at shoulder, 26 to 30 inches; weight, generally 100 to 175 pounds. Females weigh about 40 per cent less than males. Animals at northern end of the range and in southern South America are much larger than those of the tropics.

Distinguishing characteristics. Great size and unspotted fur; the only other North American cat of comparable size, the jaguar, has a heavily-spotted leopardlike coat.

Range. Wilderness areas of western America, from southern Alberta and British Columbia, eastern New Mexico and Louisiana to the Pacific coast, and south to the Strait of Magellan; also several areas in Florida.

JAGUAR
FELIS ONCA

The jaguar is the largest and most powerful cat in America. Sometimes, but very rarely, it is as big as an ordinary tiger. It can easily break the neck of an ox, a mule, or a horse. Its gorgeous tight-fitting coat is bright yellow, splashed by large black rosettes with yellow centers.

"Leopard! Leopard!" exclaim nine out of ten persons on seeing a jaguar in the zoo. Some skins are matched so closely that not even an expert can tell from the color pattern which is the leopard and which is the jaguar.

As a general rule, close inspection reveals that the hides of most jaguars have larger and somewhat fewer rosettes. In the yellow centers are usually one or two black dots. On the jaguar's chest, the rosettes tend to elongate into solid black bars. However, some leopards also have short bars on their chests and center spots in a few rosettes.

A reasonably observant person should have no difficulty in distinguishing the two animals when they are alive. The jaguar is built more heavily than the leopard. Its shoulders, chest and barrel are thicker, its head is larger and appears more blunted, and the lower jaw is heavier.

Of course, the jaguar lives in the Americas while the leopard lives in Africa and Asia.

The color of a jaguar's coat varies in tone from a clear yellow to a distinctly tawny tinge. It depends on whether he lives in open arid country or in the shade of hot steaming jungles.

The wickedest and most sophisticated-looking jaguar is the melanistic or black phase. The fancy rosettes are almost lost in the deep darkness. Against the glistening black coat, the yellow eyes glare out balefully. Lithe muscles ripple threateningly under the sleek "velvet." It is popularly supposed to be fiercer than its more gaudy brother.

Unfortunately the biggest specimens seem to have gone unweighed and unmeasured while in the flesh, but it is possible that they may have approached three hundred pounds. The largest skull on record is that of an animal killed near San Andres, Mexico, in 1894 by E. W. Nelson and E. A. Goldman. The skull measured eleven inches in length and six and seven-eighths inches across at the widest point. Farther south, jaguars grow even larger. The champions of the family are said to live in southern Brazil, where jaguars occur in comparatively large numbers. An average male there will be nearly nine feet long and weigh two hundred and fifty pounds. The female weighs only fifty pounds

JAGUAR

less. One peculiarity of the family is that a race of big jaguars may live close to a race of small jaguars. Unlike most mammals, these cats do not grow progressively larger or smaller according to geography. Some other unknown factor determines their size.

Endowed with tremendous strength and the cat family's agility, the jaguar's list of prey includes almost any bird or mammal that comes within reach: peccaries (probably their most important food), deer, turkeys, and even fish. The old people of the California Indian tribes are said to have followed the jaguar's trail to dig up its buried kills. (The jaguar no longer exists in California.) It may even kill and eat the redoubtable alligator and crocodile if it can catch one napping in the sunshine. It captures turtles while they are ashore to lay their eggs. It also patrols beaches at the proper season looking for the wide trails that may lead the way to the sand nests where the clutches of leather-skinned eggs can be uncovered.

Most of the hunting trips are confined to the ground. Occasionally, however, it may go into trees if it spots a flock of parrots or band of monkeys that seems to be asleep and offers a chance for a meal. Although it carries its bulk with typical catlike silence, it often goes through the forests talking to itself. The deep, throaty grunts, "uh—uh—uh—uh," carry far in the night air, and to the deer and peccaries, must sound like the voice of doom.

Folk tales say that the jaguar attracts fish by drooling saliva over a pool. Then, from its position on the bank or an overhanging log, it scoops out the striking fish, flipping them onto dry land where it can easily eat them. If it drops saliva in the water it is probably just drooling with anticipation. It actually does go after the slower warm-water fish under favorable circumstances such as when they may be frightened into shallows by crocodiles or predators of their own kind. Quite at home in the water, these big cats do not hesitate to cross wide streams, not because they are pursued, but simply to reach the other side where hunting may be better.

Jaguars may be very destructive to livestock. Being fond of peccary flesh, they also take readily to a diet of domestic swine. Many large ranches in the tropics maintain hunters whose duty is to track down stock-killing jaguars.

Even where the jungle floor is littered with tracks, the great spotted cat is so sly that dogs must be used to track it down. It may take many days for the hunter and his pack of noisy mongrels to come up with quarry which covers such a wide territory. Once it is surrounded, it prefers to retreat into a thicket or to seek safety in a tree. Then it may be shot from a distance with little risk.

At close quarters, the jaguar does not behave as meekly as the treed mountain lion. It fights back at any enemy within reach. The white fangs and sharp claws, powered by great cheek, neck and shoulder muscles, can tear dog or man to pieces.

Perhaps the acme of skilled sport has been worked out by a few sportsmen, notably Sascha Siemel, who has often lectured in the United States. When the jaguar is finally brought to bay by the dogs, the hunter advances, armed only with a spear ten or twelve feet long. As the distance slowly narrows to about thirty feet, the exasperated cat charges and makes a terrific leap for its tormentor's throat. Instantly the hunter plants the base of his spear against the ground and the cat impales itself on the forward-pointing spear.

That, at least, is the theory of the game. The jaguar may introduce many uncertainties in the speed of its charge, length and angle of leap. Or it may prefer not to leap at all. The hunter must be prepared to meet attack anywhere between the ground and head-height. In case of an error, an expert rifleman should be stationed at one side and to the rear. It is possible that a hospital might be able to patch up the remains.

The jaguar is not an aggressive beast if left alone. Authentic cases of attack are almost unknown, although there are numerous "reports" of fatalities. A guidebook issued about ten years ago for Nahuel Huapi National Park in western Argentina states that the jaguar is "very bold in its desire to feed on human flesh, as it has done innumerable times, circling villages during entire nights in hope of waylaying human beings."

Tradition states that the American "leopard" may invade isolated villages when floods cut it off from its usual food supply. However, since the jaguar is a strong and willing swimmer, this belief seems shaky.

Perhaps more than most cats, the jaguar is curious about matters it does not understand. Numerous people have been followed by jaguars without any harm resulting.

The great naturalist, Humbolt, has checked and accepted as true a story of "Ferdinand, the Jaguar."—One day in a small clearing of a great forest, two Indian children were at play. Suddenly a jaguar ran out of the woods and began to leap around them playfully. Closer and closer it bounded. Fascinated, and too young to know fear, the children watched this beautiful and graceful creature. Its yellow-and-black satin skin gleamed and rippled in the sunlight. Apparently it wanted the children to gambol too. It drew closer and closer. Finally it brushed against the younger child and made playful blows. Accidentally, perhaps, it scratched the child's forehead with its claws. *That* hurt! The older child picked up a stick, and struck the jaguar on the head. Startled and offended, the jaguar ran away into the forest and was seen no more.

There are few Ferdinands in captivity. Most caged jaguars are considered highly dangerous and unreliable. Trainers rate them as more difficult than leopards.

Many natives of Central America and northern South America believe the cougar and jaguar are mortal enemies and fight to the finish whenever they meet. (In spite of the fact that it is lighter in weight, the cougar's superior agility is supposed usually to bring it out on top.) Although the two cats might quarrel over food, there seems little to substantiate this belief. Yet these country people term the cougar "the friend of man," and the jaguar "the enemy of man."

The name jaguar comes from the South American Indian *jaguara,* which is said to mean "carnivore that overcomes its prey at a single bound." This succinctly and accurately describes the big cat's method of hunting. Most Latin Americans call it *el tigre.* Many English-speaking people use the term "spotted king cat."

Gestation requires one hundred days. Then the mother gives birth to two young, as a rule, although the number may be three or even four. In the tropics they may arrive at almost any time of year, but toward the extremes of the range the birthdate is in spring. They are browner than the adults. Their hair is longer and finer. Instead of fancy rosettes, they have only spots. Young jaguars grow up rather slowly. They require considerable training and experience before they are able to make a successful living, so the mother probably spaces her broods about two years apart.

The jaguar is adaptable. It may live in the deserts of northern Mexico and southwestern United States, on grassy plains, or in torrid, wet jungle. It does not seem to like very high elevations and even near the equator is not found above eight thousand feet.

Most of the flashy, rosetted skins are made into wall and table decorations, or coats. In 1942 a good pelt brought about thirty dollars in the raw-fur market. Constant hunting has decimated the jaguars in the northern and southern parts of their range. As the jungle is opened up and exploited, the species will become more rare there also.

Within the United States the jaguar probably was never a common animal. It seems to have been rare in southern California and has been extinct there since about 1860. It once traveled as far north as the Grand Canyon in Arizona. Most of our present-day records come from the southeastern quarter of that state. Few of these animals seem to be residents. They wander north from Mexico, most of them to meet the fate of one whose end was described to me by a friend, the late John Hands of Portal, Arizona.

The jaguar had killed a cow and her calf as they were grazing peacefully at the forks of Bonita Canyon. The ranchers set traps around the remains, and a week or ten days later the cat, returning for a meal of well-ripened steaks, stepped into one of the snares. Pulling and jerking furiously, the jaguar broke the drag chain. Its foot still in the trap, it made off for the high mountains.

The three Hands brothers trailed it to a small cave. They could not see it, but could hear it growling threats. There was only one way to get it, they thought. Feeling extremely leery, John (with a knife in his belt and a rifle in his hand) crept into the darkness on hands and knees. It was a mad thing to do, but just the sort of thing that a Hands boy couldn't resist. Almost before he knew it, he faced two gleaming eyes only four feet away, and too close to risk shooting. The knife wasn't such a good idea, either. He backed out in a hurry. Taking a deep breath, he cocked his gun, and looked into the cave again. Just then the jaguar decided to look out. John fired instantly and fortunately shot the cat through the head. The skin of this jaguar is at the University of Arizona. It was seven feet and four inches long from nose to the end of its rather short tail. That is a good-sized cat for this northern extreme of its range.

General description. A very large, heavy cat with large head, short muscular legs and long heavy tail. Coat deep yellow to tawny, thickly marked with black or brownish black spots or rosettes. (The rosettes on the back and flanks are frequently rings that enclose one or two small black spots.) Under parts much paler; tail heavily marked and tipped with black. Total length, 6 to 7 feet; height at shoulder, 28 to 30 inches; weight, 175 to 250 pounds. Females are 20 per cent smaller than males.

Distinguishing characteristics. A leopardlike animal with spotted coat. The only similar native animal, the ocelot, is considerably smaller and its flank markings usually take the form of broken lines.

Range. Southern border regions of Texas, New Mexico and Arizona, south to about 40° latitude in south-central Argentina. Specimens have been taken as far north as the Grand Canyon and in northern New Mexico.

OCELOT
FELIS PARDALIS

The ocelot is one of the handsomest of all the cats. Its light-colored, short-haired, sleek coat is gaily splashed with black spots, blotches, rings and stripes. For this reason it is often called the tiger cat and the leopard cat. Its scientific name means leopardlike.

It has a far better disposition than most cats. Few people would ever think of petting a bobcat or a lynx. The cougar and jaguar are much too big for general fondling. But the ocelot has a placid, satisfied face that reflects its amiable personality. Even when trapped and faced with death, it does not spit and plunge in angry terror. It is neither belligerent nor cowering. Sitting quietly, it awaits its fate with philosophical indifference.

Numbers of ocelots have been kept together in a single cage with very little quarreling, and none of it bloody. Such crowding would not be tolerated by any other American wild feline.

Ocelots have been partly domesticated many times. Poultry, lambs and young pigs must still be carefully protected from them. At least one ocelot has been known to romp on the floor with a four-year-old child, rolling him over and over with its paws. It was always careful to keep its sharp claws sheathed. A few years ago, a group of Mexican Army fliers, visiting Washington, D. C., on a good-will tour, brought along a pleasant-mannered ocelot for a traveling companion.

OCELOT

Few North Americans have ever heard of, much less seen, this animal. The species was once fairly numerous in southern Texas. It ranged as far north and east as the Red River (which includes a bit of southwestern Arkansas and Louisiana) and west beyond the Big Bend. Bone carvings, believed to be of this animal, have been found in Mound Builders' mounds in Ross County of southern Ohio. This *may* indicate that in prehistoric times the species lived even farther north.

Now ocelots are scarce north of the Rio Grande, and most of them persist only because they have thick shelter along the lower part of the river and adjacent sections of Texas. Farther south, through Central America and the South American tropics, ocelots are common.

No ocelot is exactly like another. The color of different individuals of one species, even in the same neighborhood, varies greatly, all the way from ruddy yellow to grayish. No two coat patterns are exactly alike. One side of an ocelot doesn't match its other side. The lines, spots and rings run in a crazy pattern.

Ocelots range in size from that of a large house cat to a Canada lynx. All the ocelots that occur north of the Rio Grande are of one species. They tend to be more on the grayish side, with the black markings reduced in extent so that the spaces between them are wide. They are about ten per cent smaller than the largest species, the Costa Rican ocelot. The latter is unnecessarily but greatly feared by the natives.

The ocelot's only offense to man is its depredation on small domestic animals. Being smart as well as beautiful, this spotted cat does not hesitate to pick up a juicy fowl whenever it gets a chance. This becomes a habit, and before long a whole village may experience a shortage of chickens and guinea fowls. The larger species can kill bigger game: young calves, pigs and lambs, and even small mongrel dogs.

The most practical means of controlling these raids is by use of steel traps. Hunting is apt to get nowhere, for the ocelot is too well concealed in dense thickets and brushy arroyos and ravines. It is sometimes found asleep on the limb of a tall tree. Then it tries to hide by crawling slowly and stealthily into dense foliage. However, as soon as the men begin to shout and the dogs to bark, it runs quickly to the ground and races off.

The ocelot hunts day and night, providing there are no humans around. It does most of its work on the ground, stealing about without a sound from its big paws.

It has a gentle disposition, and mates live together for years. When they hunt, they signal back and forth with soft "mews," or louder calls if they don't get an answer. Within the United States, their home range is said to be much larger than in the Central American jungles, probably because food is less plentiful. Our ocelots are very fond of snakes. They also like rabbits, mice, woodrats and other rodents, ground-dwelling and perching birds and occasionally are able to get a deer fawn. In the tropics, agoutis are a favorite prey. If the cats feel in the mood, they can hunt in the trees as well as on the ground and sometimes catch unwary monkeys and tree lizards as well as nesting birds.

Porcupine quills have been found imbedded in the neck and shoulders of these cats. Their toe pads have been filled with long spines of chonta palm, but there was no infection.

In Texas the young ocelots, usually twins, are born during September or October. The nursery is a den in the rocks, or sometimes a hollow log. The mother pads their bed with whatever soft material she can find.

Although the adult cat is quiet when trapped, and rarely pulls out even if caught only by a slight hold, it is said that it gets up its dander when cornered by dogs. A Texas hunter claimed that his hounds, which always made short work of a bobcat, found the ocelot "a tough proposition."

Handsome and unusual, the pelt of the ocelot is small and the fur is short and thin. The average price for a good raw skin in 1942 was about six dollars.

The margay (pronounced mar-guy'), or *Felis wiedii*, is closely related to the ocelot. Gaudily spotted, be-ringed and striped like the ocelot, it is more slender and the tail is longer. Probably its name is derived from a South American term meaning "little ocelot" or "small cat." It is found from northern Mexico to Bolivia and southern Brazil. Although said to range into Texas, only one specimen has been taken and that at Eagle Pass on the Mexican boundary. Apparently it does not find the United States hospitable.

General description. A medium-sized, slender cat with small head. Tail about one-half as long as head and body. Color extremely variable even in the same locality, from deep tawny to pale gray. Heavily marked from nose to tail-tip with black spots, streaks, and chains of dots which on the back and flanks are elongated horizontally. Ground color and markings become much paler on under parts. Total length, 42 to 48 inches; height at shoulder, 16 to 18 inches; weight, 25 to 35 pounds. Females are about 20 per cent smaller.

Distinguishing characteristics. General form of a house cat, with marbled coat. Very much smaller than the jaguar and has stripes and streaks instead of spots on its neck. The only American cats of similar size (lynx and bobcat) have stub tails and comparatively drab, grizzled coats. The lynx occurs far to the north of the ocelot's range.

Range. Southern Texas from the region of Matagorda west to the Big Bend, and from Kerrville and Rock Springs southward through the tropical zone of Mexico; also (rarely) from southern Arizona southward in western Mexico. South of the Mexican Plateau the range extends throughout Central America to Ecuador, the Amazon, and northeastern Argentina.

JAGUARUNDI

FELIS CACOMITLI

The jaguarundi's name is more formidable than the animal. It seems more like an otter or big weasel than the cat that it really is. Its body is long and unspotted. It has a small head, short legs and a long, slender tail. The natives of southwestern Mexico call it "otter-cat," because of its appearance and because it shows such readiness to take to water when it wants to cross rivers.

A strange and little-known tropical animal, the jaguarundi or eyra is found north of the Rio Grande only in extreme southern Texas. Along the lower Rio Grande, the mesquite, ironwood and catclaw grow densely under the hot sun. In this almost impenetrable thicket the jaguarundi lives, threading its way over the narrow twisting paths. Being extremely agile, it can climb easily through the thorny tangled shrubs, looking for careless sleepy birds or eggs and fledglings in their nests. Most of the time it stays on the ground where travel is easier and faster. There it preys on ground-nesting birds, cottontails, jackrabbits, mice, woodrats and cottonrats.

Farther south, the jaguarundi frequents the high tropical jungle where the floor is almost always sunk in gloom even at bright midday. Here it hunts chiefly at night, but if the cover is good, as in the south Texas thickets, it may be abroad at any hour. This habitat is also the home of our few ocelots. Because of its smaller size and more furtive ways, the jaguarundi is sighted even less often. Trapping indicates, however, that jaguarundis are somewhat more numerous than the few sight records would indicate.

The jaguarundi (frequently spelled "yagouaroundi") is found from the southernmost tip of the United States south to Paraguay. There is little reason or cause to exterminate these animals, aside from their use of a few small game animals and birds for food. The skins are practically valueless.

Unfortunately, steady progress has been made in recent decades to burn and root out the dense thickets of the Rio Grande delta and convert the land to citrus groves and cotton fields. This means that a number of interesting animals,

birds as well as mammals, are deprived of the most essential of all requirements:
a place to live.

For many years it was believed that this region sheltered two species of small,
plain-coated cats. One was smoky gray, sprinkled in a pepper-and-salt effect
with black, whitish, and buff. It was christened "jaguarundi." The other
"species" came in several shades of rusty brown, with black hairs scattered over
the back and grading into near-white on its lips and throat. It was called the
"eyra." But the form and skeletal structure of these animals turned out to be
identical, and they were found together in the same thickets. Actually, there was
only one species. It was merely dichromatic or two-color phased, like black and
cinnamon bears, and red and gray screech owls. One mother might have both
colors in a litter. This made another name appropriate for the jaguarundi, "red-
and-gray cat."

So secretive is this animal that almost nothing is known of its home life.
Young jaguarundis have been seen in summer and winter, appearing to have
been born in March and August. It is probable that, in the warm even climate

JAGUARUNDI

of most of the habitat, breeding might take place at any time during the year.

General description. A small cat with long, lithe body, small head, short legs, and long tail. Color fairly uniform except paler on under parts; two phases: a grizzled, salt-and-pepper gray which is darker in winter; and a brownish red with blackish on back and whitish on lips and throat. Total length, 3 to 4 feet; height at shoulder, 9 to 12 inches; weight, 10 to 20 pounds. Female smaller.

Distinguishing characteristics. The unspotted coat is the criterion for separating the jaguarundi from the ocelot; this also, with the long tail, differentiates the species from the lynx and bobcat.

Range. Southern Texas, thence east of the Mexican Plateau to the region of Puebla; also western Mexico from central Sinaloa and joining the eastern range in Puebla; thence south through South America east of the Andes to Paraguay.

LYNX
LYNX CANADENSIS

The lynx is usually a silent animal. Even when caught in a trap and clubbed to death, except for possible hissing and spitting, it may remain stoical to the end. Occasionally it and its companions will call back and forth while hunting together. But many naturalists and hunters with years of experience in the woods have heard the low catlike "me-eow" only once or twice.

At mating time, late in winter, the lynx may let loose a series of yells that compensate for a whole year of restraint. Two males will shout at each other in tones that probably cause the mice and other small animals to shudder in their snow-bound burrows! Their passionate cries to the females have different arias, but do not diminish in volume. Human females in extreme agony can scream no louder nor longer. French-Canadians, who call the lynx *loup-cervier*, have built up a folk-lore concerning this caterwauling that out-banshees the banshee stories of Ireland.

The lynx looks like an over-grown tabby cat with high-tufted ears and a dignified ruff. It has long legs, very big feet, and a ridiculously short tail. It lives only in the northern coniferous forests and adjacent tundra where the winter cold is long and intense. The soft winter coat of pastel-shaded gray fur sprinkled with faint brownish keeps it warm on long hunting trips. In some lights it has a lavender tint. More than an inch thick, the coat is made of hair

LYNX

up to four inches long. In summer it is more brownish and of course is lighter weight.

Because the lynx is shy and essentially a night-prowler, few persons ever see it. Those so fortunate are most impressed by its penetrating eyes, which have given rise to the expression "lynx-eyed." In daylight the pupils of the lynx's eyes are reduced to the tightest slits; the yellow irises seem to cover the entire eyeballs.

In far northern America, where the forest is squeezed down to patches in sheltered valleys and along streams, the lynx must hunt in the open as well as in the woods. It prefers the rough mountains, however, and is not found far out on the level tundra.

Throughout most of its range, it is able to stay in the deep woods. There on the log-littered forest floor, it hunts as silently as a shadow. Unless very hungry, when it may venture forth in late afternoon, it waits for darkness. Then the great light-absorbing eyes give it an advantage over many of the animals on which it preys. The lynx's name comes from a Greek term for "one who can see well in a dim light."

Depending on circumstances, the lynx may still-hunt or lie in wait for a passing victim. If game is abundant, it may climb on a ledge, a fallen log, or an overhanging tree from which it can leap down on its prey. Usually it walks about slowly, crouching down to be as inconspicuous as possible. From time to time, as it reaches a down log or just below a ridge crest, it gradually straightens up to full height for a long, careful scrutiny of the terrain ahead.

If a prospective meal is in sight, it commences a careful stalk. Crouching down until hips and shoulder blades protrude above the backbone, it makes an approach from the rear. Taking advantage of any shelter such as windfalls, rocks, or tree trunks, it gets into position. Its nose twitches, muscles tighten, ears are laid back, and the hard yellow eyes measure the distance and actions of the prey. Then, like steel springs, its muscles send it flying through the air. If the victim is small, such as a rabbit, mouse, squirrel, or skunk, it is crushed down by the impact of the lynx's heavy body, and a quick bite through the neck vertebrae or brain brings the end.

Although the snowshoe hare is the lynx's staff of life, ground-nesting birds, such as grouse and ptarmigan, and their eggs provide many calories. The lynx even kills foxes, especially when they are floundering about in deep soft snow. The lynx wears snowshoes that enable it to walk like a feather on a slight crust, and to stay well up in newly fallen snow. The snowshoes are formed by a thick growth of hair on the sides and soles of the large feet which greatly increase their size.

If the lynx's usual fare of small creatures becomes scarce, or if an exceptional opportunity is offered to bring down several meals at once, it may attack and kill deer. It knows that young fawns of any of the hoofed animals are likely game, if it can find them while their mother is away.

The adult deer are not easy for a predator as small as the lynx to kill. It rarely weighs more than thirty pounds, and usually much less. A grown deer is at least five times as large. The cat must approach by stealth or leap from a tree and land securely on the victim's shoulders. Then while the terrified animal bucks and dashes off, the lynx must bite through the tough hide and muscle into the neck to cut the jugular vein. If not quick enough, the lynx may be dashed against a tree or rolled upon as the deer plunges frantically.

Near the north base of Mount McKinley, Charles Sheldon once surprised a lynx in the act of killing a young Dall sheep ram nearly two years old and weighing one hundred and fifteen pounds. In the snow he was able to trace out and reconstruct the whole story.

The lynx had stalked the sheep from the mountainside above and finally lay in wait on a ledge. Unconscious of danger, the ram fed along on his way. As he passed almost directly under the ledge, the cat leaped on the middle of the ram's back. With one forefoot gripping each side of the ram's neck, it reached forward and tried to bite out the left eye. The sharp fangs dug well into the bone. The ram struggled down the ravine, falling several times. Finally the lynx lost its hold on the left eye, but changed to the right eye and gouged it out. The struggle had now been fought over three hundred feet of trampled, bloody snow. Exhausted by loss of blood and terribly shocked, the ram sank down, dying. Arriving on the tragic scene at this point, Sheldon shot the lynx as it fled, and then killed the sheep. Even without Sheldon's interruption, the lynx would not have gotten off without damage. In the fight to down the sheep, it had suffered a bad bruise on one hip and a fracture of the bony arch protecting the right eye. Perhaps the cat had attacked the victim's eyes because the sheep's dense winter coat of four-inch hair prevented it from getting the usual hold on the throat.

Most adult lynxes, but not all, hunt alone. Family groups, mother and young, usually remain together through the youngsters' first winter. On their excursions they spread out in a line across the woods, instead of stringing back in single file. In this way a much larger area is examined for signs of game. It is possible that two or more families may join forces, for hunters have told of seeing signs of as many as eleven lynxes traveling together.

Because the lynx digs into a carcass that is buried in snow and therefore invisible, it seems likely that it depends upon its sense of smell as well as its eyes in locating food. It is particular about what it eats. It wants meat reasonably fresh, and prefers it hot and quivering. Only extreme hunger will force the lynx to accept carrion. Although it lives in some western regions where spawning salmon die in great numbers on the stream banks, it is not fond of fish.

It can swim very easily and for considerable distances if it wishes. Some lynxes float low in the water, with only nose, ears and stubby tail above the surface. Others have been seen gliding along with their entire back fully three or four inches out of water. I assume that the latter animals may have been fatter and therefore more buoyant than the former.

The mother lynx gives birth to her brood after a gestation period of about two months. The kittens number around three, although there may be as many as five, or only a single one. They are similar to newly-born house cats, although a little larger. Their eyes are closed until they are ten days old. They are warmly wrapped in pretty fur coats that are reddish or buffy and decorated with many stripes and rows of blotches. Do these ornate young lynxes "take after" their ancestors of some remote period in the history of the race? If this is so, they may stem from the same group of cats as the ocelot. By the time they are about four months old, they acquire the less-variegated coats of their parents.

The young lynxes spend their first couple of months in or close to their birthplace—a rock den, a hollow tree, a prone log, or a dense windfall. Then they start on short trips with their mother. They have been eating meat and chewing on bones for some time, and shortly afterward are completely weaned. When a year old they may be expected to produce offspring of their own. Their normal life-expectancy is unknown, but in the sheltered existence of zoos, lynxes often live to be ten or twelve years old. This is probably longer than they live in the hard, precarious life of the wilds.

Few four-footed animals care to bother an adult lynx. Nevertheless, at least one lynx has hastily abandoned its meal and fled in evident fright when a wolverine approached.

The lynx is a smart hunter but, unlike its close relatives, does not learn to avoid traps. This trait and the destruction of much of its habitat has resulted in general reduction, and even extirpation, of the race, especially along the southeastern boundary of its former range.

Once found as far south as Indiana and Pennsylvania, the lynx has been pushed back to northern New England, the Adirondacks, and the northern side of the Great Lakes. It is only barely possible that a few animals may remain in the Upper Peninsula of Michigan.

Trapping is carried on relentlessly, for lynx fur is dense, soft and beautiful in its pastel colors. In good years many thousands of pelts are taken. Most come from Canada, but in normal years about two thousand are trapped in Alaska. The United States accounts for only a couple of hundred. In 1942 a good Canadian skin brought about thirty-five dollars. Lynx pelts are used mostly for trimming coats, and as scarfs, but many jackets and short coats are made entirely from the fur.

A blue or "dilute" mutation occurs once or twice in about every thousand skins. This abnormal pelt is bluish gray, including the usually black portions. The nearest approach to this in the domestic cat is the Maltese shade.

Although most men, even Indians, now recoil at the idea of eating lynx or bobcat, our pioneer ancestors were not so finicky. In good times as well as bad they ate the wild cats and liked them. About a century ago in the Canadian Rockies, during a hard winter when the mountain sheep were very lean, the traders stuffed fat lynx carcasses with chopped sheep meat and roasted them whole. The result was said to be delicious.

It was once believed that lynxes made periodical migrations, thus emptying a region in a few months. Now it is known that the fluctuations of hares or snowshoe rabbits often determine the abundance or scarcity of the lynxes as well as some other carnivores. So dependent is the lynx on the hares for food that a great die-off of these big rodents is followed, perhaps the following winter, by starvation among lynxes. Most of the survivors are unable to breed as usual, and the race does not recover until the hares increase once more.

The lynx seems to be generally unable to adapt itself to a substitute diet. When the snowshoe hares died off in the Mount McKinley region in 1907, practically all the lynxes preferred to starve rather than to live on the mice which were abundant. The naturalist, Charles Sheldon, found only one fat lynx all winter. She had lived comfortably and well on the little rodents.

A careful study of the fur sales records of the Hudson's Bay Company for the past two hundred years has been made by Dr. Charles Elton of Oxford, England. The number of lynx pelts sold at the London auctions has fluctuated violently from year to year. Sometimes it has fallen from thirty-six thousand to as low as two thousand only two years later. The interval between peak sales is uniform, averaging nine and six-tenths years. By comparing these fur sale records with old diaries, reports and other evidence left by trappers and traders, Dr. Elton has proven that these cycles of fur sales correlate with the cycles of lynx populations. The variations in the number of lynxes all the way across the continent also occur at intervals of approximately ten years.

Toward man, the lynx is absolutely inoffensive. Only in a trap will it fight back, and even then it may not. Hunters sometimes condemn it because it kills grouse and some of the game animals. Considering our surpluses of deer, and the fact that natural causes, such as weather, disease, and food, control grouse and game-animal numbers, it is regrettable that the lynx cannot be allowed its small share of food.

General description. A medium-sized, rather chunky cat with tall, usually tufted ears, long legs, large feet, very short tail, and rather fluffy fur. Color variable—very pale to medium grizzled gray and brownish, lightly streaked and spotted with blackish on neck ruff, forehead, back, and legs; ears and tail tipped with black. Total length, 30 to 39 inches; height at shoulder, about 24 inches; weight, 15 to 40 pounds.

Distinguishing characteristics. Usually paler than the bobcat, which it closely resembles, and generally larger, with longer legs, larger feet, and longer ear tufts. The end of its tail is *completely circled* with black. The end of the bobcat's tail is black above, white below.

Range. Northern North America, generally south of the tree limit, from Newfoundland and Nova Scotia to western Alaska and Puget Sound; south to northern New England and New York, possibly the Michigan Upper Peninsula, and northern Wisconsin and southern Saskatchewan; in the Rockies, to Colorado and in the Cascades to central Oregon. Not found in northern Ungava, northern Keewatin and Mackenzie.

BOBCAT
LYNX RUFUS

The bobcat is named for its impudent and abbreviated tail. The lynx is the only other North American cat that has a similar appendage. But it has much larger ear tufts. It is also a forest-dwelling animal of the North and is found only occasionally within the northern United States. The bobcat, which is smaller, lives in middle North America from coast to coast, in all kinds of habitats.

"Wildcat" is another name for this American kitty. It is a wild and ferocious warrior. Few of its kind ever become friendly or tolerant of their human captors. Even when captured as an impressionable, still-blind kitten, it is likely to be resentful and sullen.

A friend of mine, Lowell Sumner of Menlo Park, California, found one temporary exception. He boarded a wildcat whose mother had been killed by a hunter. For a time the kitten was fairly amenable and friendly, but when it was about six months of age, its tree-climbing and warlike propensities became dominant. Since it had to be kept indoors, safe from the ranch dogs, window curtains and draperies were pinned up out of reach. Only a stout pair of doorway portieres were left available. The cat delighted in climbing these and waiting on the rod over the doorway for passing game below. The sudden impact of its weight, and the scratches of the sharp clinging claws were very unpleasant. Friends began to show reluctance to accept invitations to the Sumner home. At the least sign of discipline, the bobcat would retire beneath a bed. Spitting, growling and making horrible grimaces, it defied all efforts to dislodge it. Several sub-bed battles took place between the cat and its owner. When it was less than a year old, the wildcat had to be returned to the wilds.

I have kept several bobcats and never found them friendly. Some were coldly aloof, and others plainly disagreeable. Some became contemptuously tolerant, while others remained openly resentful.

In the wilds, the bobcat at first seems a timid animal that runs at the slightest

BOBCAT

provocation. Almost invariably it will detect the approach of any invader, quietly leave its resting place, and silently retreat without ever being seen. It is so successful at keeping out of sight that few persons are ever aware of its presence. When cornered or attacked by enemies, it becomes a different creature, a wild demon with unlimited courage. It screams, growls, spits, hisses, makes horrible faces and tries to scratch out the eyes and every other part of the enemy's anatomy.

The bobcat is most active at night, although restlessness or hunger may send it out during the day. In settled country, it seldom takes a chance in broad daylight. This caution and a tendency to mind its own business often has enabled it to persist in agricultural regions as long as any bits of woodland remain.

It is not particular about its home, but is found in the cold woodlands of the northern states and in the hot humid swamps of the South. I have seen tracks on the desert sands in southern Arizona and in the mountain ranges far above. It is perfectly at home on the central plains provided there are rocky "breaks" or canyons, or a good fringe of trees along a water course. Cut-over lands are quite acceptable. In fact, it prefers variegated country with plenty of openings and brushy patches to solid primeval forest, because the small animals which form the bulk of its diet are more plentiful there. During the last thirty or forty years, the Minnesota bobcat has extended its range one hundred to two hundred miles north as lumbering opened up the country. Extreme cold is the only climate that it will not take, and it is not found far north of the southern boundary of Canada. The boreal forests are left to the lynx.

The color and weight of the bobcat's coat depends a great deal upon its home. In the East, North and Northwest, the coat of the forest dweller is apt to be dark, while on the sandy deserts of the Southwest it is protectively pale. There is much variation even in the same locality. The winter pelage is grayer and less spotted and barred. An old animal, particularly, tends to be plainer than the much-spotted young. The larger, grayer individuals are sometimes called "lynx cats," an allusion to the backwoods fancy that they are crosses between lynxes and bobcats. An almost-black (melanistic) bobcat was once captured in Florida and exhibited at the Philadelphia Zoo. In the warm climates, the coat, of course, is light in weight, and in cold climates it is comfortably heavy.

Although a good climber, the bobcat is not an arboreal animal by any means. It goes up trees after occasional tempting food, such as a brood of young flickers, woodpeckers or other high-nesting birds that advertise their presence by noisy squabbles. Most food is gleaned from the ground, and the trees are used only occasionally, for resting and for refuge.

On snow-covered ground the bobcat's track looks like that of a greatly over-sized house cat. The impression of one foot is about two inches long and one and three-quarters inches wide, up to a maximum of two and one-quarter by two inches. The footprints are rounded and placed nearly in a straight line, one ahead of the other. When the animal is walking, its stride is irregular and less than about ten inches in length. At a trot it is very even and ten to thirteen inches long.

In deep snow the bobcat sinks down until it must force its body through by sheer strength. Under these circumstances in the West, its trail may be confused with that of a coyote. The latter, however, travels more directly and avoids thick undergrowth. The bobcat zigzags about and is very likely to investigate the possibilities in any tangle, down log, or thicket. It has a strong curiosity about anything unusual, and will follow a snowshoe trail even when it leads away from the course. Discarded articles such as paper bags or candy-bar wrappings are irresistible.

Like the domestic cat, it occasionally limbers up its muscles and sharpens its claws by digging the latter into a tree trunk. Selecting a dead tree without bark, it rears on its hind legs, gets a good grip with its extended fore claws, and pulls downward.

The bobcat's enemies are relatively few. Other carnivores and the great horned owl may feint at a bobcat just from force of habit. (Animal hunters overlook few opportunities for a meal.) The attack may be perfunctory and quickly abandoned. When the object is a bobcat, the latter course is especially likely.

In farming country, dogs are likely to be the greatest annoyance to the bobcat. When not necessary to make a stand, it expediently takes to its heels. It runs only a short distance, bobbing much like a fleeing rabbit, then dives into a rock den, or takes to a large tree. It has plenty of courage, when necessary, and can seldom be overpowered by a single dog.

Potential enemies which cannot be fought off with teeth and claws live in the bobcat's internal organs. When devouring its prey, it takes in a variety of flatworms and roundworms. These adapt themselves readily to their new environment. The cat tapeworm (*Taxocara cati*) has been found in Minnesota bobcats more often than other species of parasites. As many as forty-four such worms have been counted in one animal. Apparently these and other worms ordinarily do little harm.

Like other fluffy-haired cats, the bobcat is not fond of water. Melting snow, which fills the northern swamps with spring run-off, drives it to the ridges and hills. To cross a stream, it will go out of its way to find a log "bridge" rather than wade through a few inches of water. It has been known to swim at times, however, quite voluntarily, as well as to escape from trailing dogs.

Any meat-eater as large and well-armed as the wildcat may offend mankind, at least occasionally, by killing domestic or wild game creatures. Sometimes, it has been known to kill domestic sheep and even calves. During two evenings, one wildcat killed three ewes and nine lambs. Chickens and turkeys are easy game if it wishes to take the risk of entering poultry yards.

Bounties for the wildcat's scalp were offered as early as 1727 by Massachusetts, where the reward was thirty shillings for each adult. Much later, in 1903, the state reestablished the bounty at five dollars which was raised to ten dollars in 1925. Many other states offer smaller amounts.

Bobcats are often trapped for the pelt alone, which produces strong leather but rather brittle, perishable fur. A good skin is worth only about seven dollars in a boom market such as that of 1946. The fur is used for trimming coats of cloth or of other animals' fur, and for women's jackets. While most persons consider that the flesh of any cat is not fit for consumption, some hunters have tried bobcat meat and recommend it with enthusiasm. They claim that it is sweet and tender.

The wildcats that escape these various hazards mate in January to late February. At this time, the animals out-scream themselves. They squall and yowl like over-grown alley cats. They have a varied repertoire, with astounding range and volume. As soon as a male has achieved results from a successful serenade, he goes on his solitary way to further vocal and amorous triumph, that is, if he can find another female that is free or can be taken away from her current mate. As a rule, the bobcat is a rather silent animal. When approached in a trap it first growls, then, baring its teeth, spits and hisses ferociously.

After a gestation period of about fifty days, one to four (usually two or three) kittens are born. Their birthplace is most likely to be in a rock ledge or cliff, but occasionally it is in a hollow stump or fallen log, or in a standing tree at almost any height above ground.

Although they are warmly wrapped in spotted fur, their eyes do not open until they are nine days old. The mother weans them in June but keeps them with her, educating them in the art of making a living until early autumn. At that time they weigh about five or six pounds. According to some investigators, the bobcat may have a second litter of kittens in August. Young bobcats usually stay together as a brood through their first winter, but older cats live alone.

The individual's range will vary in size with the abundance of food. As an average, it covers at least four or five square miles. When food is scarce the winter range may expand to an area ten or fifteen miles square. Of course the bobcat does not cover this territory in a single night. It hunts a given area thoroughly, wandering here and there, crisscrossing its own trail, even back-tracking, and always keeping a sharp lookout to avoid missing anything edible.

Depending on the abundance of prey, it will walk or trot two to seven miles in a night. Morning finds it rarely as far as four miles in a direct line from the starting point. Sometimes it is only three-quarters of a mile away. Instead of returning to the previously used shelter, it may pick out the nearest likely spot and "hole up" for the day. This may be under a windfall, in a hollow log or a hollow standing tree, or even in a thicket. Any place where it will be concealed from view is satisfactory, for it cannot afford to be too particular. A nomadic hunter, it must range haphazardly to be reasonably sure of finding food. It would go hungry if it hunted out of one camp for long.

When looking for a mate, the bobcat may have to travel a whole lot farther than its hunting range, perhaps over a circle twenty to twenty-five miles in diameter.

The size of area necessary to support a bobcat indicates that the animals cannot become abundant as the vegetarian species do. The population of bobcats in the entire state of Minnesota has been estimated at one thousand eight hundred to four thousand. This figure is based on average conditions. Bobcat popu-lations shrink and expand markedly, probably due to fluctuations in the numbers of rodents and members of the rabbit tribe.

Cottontails and snowshoe hares are stalked through the thickets and swamps. Moving slowly, the bobcat hunts by sight rather than scent. Tracks are followed only incidentally, and then for but a short distance. Carefully it searches through thickets and similar hiding places, creeping up to logs and the crest of knolls, and looking over the area ahead before proceeding. Its keen eyes examine every detail of the woods and catch the slightest movement. Sometimes it steals close to its prey and leaps upon them while they are asleep or resting in their forms. At other times it watches patiently for hours from the vantage of a hummock, a stump, or a prostrate log. When game approaches, it flattens, then rushes sud-denly forward. At other times it ambushes the animal on its trail. Leaps of seven or eight feet are not at all extraordinary. It is said that the bobcat can cover ten feet at a single bound. If it cannot leap upon or overtake its intended prey after a brief chase, it gives up and resumes the search elsewhere.

In the desert, it catches woodrats while they are away from the safety of their houses. Unlike the wild dogs, the bobcat does not break into dwellings of its prey. Its closest attempt to house-breaking is on the very rare occasions that it claws (ineffectually) at the rotten logs where its nose determines that small rodents have been hiding. Other foods are mice, tree squirrels, chipmunks, ground squirrels, marmots or woodchucks, shrews and muskrats. Although commonly accused of killing birds, as stated before, the bobcat seldom goes into the trees to hunt. Ground-nesting birds such as grouse are avidly seized at every opportunity. Carrion is eaten, and sometimes green grass and foliage of trees and shrubs are taken as a tonic. Miscellaneous appetizers, including turtles, dead fish and insects are picked up here and there.

Bobcats kill and eat porcupines. It has been assumed that only foolhardy youngsters that are hard pressed for food will attack this quill-coated prey. However, a study of bobcat diet in Minnesota revealed that porcupine flesh was the third most numerous food and was present in ten out of fifty stomachs. The quills do not seem to cause any great injury once they are swallowed, even though they work through the walls of the intestines. However, some cats die from the effects of too many quills in the mouth, face and neck. Bobcats have been seen to meet skunks and pay little attention to them, but they have also been known to eat them occasionally.

For many years naturalists believed that only a very exceptional bobcat would be able to kill a grown deer, and then largely by accident. The declarations of old woodsmen that it did so were disregarded.

It now seems certain that, in some regions, many bobcats make such kills. They steal up, leap on the deer, and bite into the jugular vein high on the throat. Frequently the stricken animal drops within a couple of leaps, and the cat proceeds to feed on the warm flesh. In one instance a struggle between a buck deer and a bobcat was waged for between three and five hours. A human interloper then frightened away the bobcat. Deep snow handicaps the cat as much as it does the deer. The cat must make its assault in about two jumps with such speed that the deer is caught by surprise. A successful hunt seems to depend more on the approach and efficiency of attack than on the condition of the victim, although, of course, a sick deer would be less wary than one in good health.

Wildcats vary greatly in size and weight, from fifteen to a possible forty pounds. Even a medium-sized animal, weighing only twenty pounds, has been known to kill a two-hundred-pound deer. The very large, and therefore old, bobcats are likely to be less successful because their teeth are frequently broken and are worn and blunt. Bobcats are also believed to kill bighorns and young elk on some occasions, but the toll is not known. Most of the big game eaten is carrion. Depending largely on smaller creatures, the cats help to keep down excessive numbers of snowshoe hares, cottontails, porcupines and some of the smaller rodents.

General description. Similar to the lynx, but smaller. Feet considerably smaller; ear tufts are small and sparse or even absent. Upper parts pale yellowish brown to reddish brown mixed with gray and brownish or black, becoming whitish spotted with black on the under parts; under side of tail-tip white. Total length, 32 to 42 inches; height at shoulder, 14 to 15 inches; usual weight, 15 to 25 pounds, up to 39¾ as a known maximum.

Distinguishing characteristics. The bobcat and lynx are our only bobtailed native cats. The bobcat is smaller, brownish (rather than gray), and its shorter fur is much more spotted. It has smaller feet and shorter legs. The ear tufts are rarely more than one inch tall, while those of the lynx are usually much longer. The bobcat's tail is white on the lower surface at the tip, instead of being completely ringed with black like that of the lynx.

Range. The entire United States, extreme southern Canada including Nova Scotia, and Mexico south to southern Puebla (exclusive of the central plateau).

13. The Finfeet

FUR SEAL—*CALLORHINUS* SP.

Asleep on shore, or awkwardly worming their painfully slow way over a rocky coast, the seal family seems to be hopelessly handicapped. With feet and legs modified into fins, they must move with waddling or caterpillar motions. Big liquid eyes seem to entreat pity from the men who hunt them with clubs.

Once in the water, they become amazingly skillful. Pursuing and feeding on fish, or gracefully playing, they shoot through the water or dive instantly without causing a ripple. Their paddle feet and webbed toes serve them well. Unfortunately their fatty bulk, which is a protection against the icy waters, also spells their doom. As producers of animal oil, they are second only to the whales.

Fine swimmers though they are, the Finfeet are not independent of land as are the whales. They spend considerable time on shore, although they rarely wander far beyond the fresh-water lakes. The walrus and the Arctic-dwelling seals often rest and soak up the ephemeral summer sun on the edges of ice floes.

Most of the family are gregarious. The eared seals establish harems and the earless seals are promiscuous during the mating season. Single young are the rule. Most of the little fellows miraculously escape being trampled to death in the closely packed summer colonies. They are fed and taught to swim by their mothers' example.

Seals must have strong stomachs. Since their teeth are not fitted for chewing, they must bolt their food whole and alive. Fish is the steady diet of the seal tribe. Depending on the species, varying reliance is placed on crustaceans, and squids and other mollusks. The bones and beaks of large cuttlefish have been found in stomachs of the hooded seals.

The most astonishing item on their diet is stones! Seals have been found with rocks as large as hen's eggs and weighing as much as three pounds in their stomachs. Possibly the stones and sand are swallowed for "roughage" or for grinding food, as birds eat gravel, and as humans eat bran. I do not believe, as sailors suggest, that they take the stones for ballast! Perhaps the stones are picked up with the cuttlefish which, when grabbed, try vainly to cling to the ocean floor.

The Finfeet are highly important to the human race. The fur seal has been killed in millions for its dense soft fur. The "true" or earless seals and the walrus are vital to the Eskimos clear across the top of North America. They depend on these animals for practically all the necessities of life, including food, clothing and equipment. Before petroleum came into general use for lighting and for lubricating purposes, great numbers of sea lions, sea elephants and harp seals were killed for their oil.

Divided into two families, the seals are known as the Eared Seals and the Earless or "true" Seals. There are only two Eared Seals, the fur seal and the sea lion, and the next pages are devoted to them.

The fur seal has larger harems than any other mammal in the world. Forty to sixty mates are his average, but now and then a strong old bull will have more than a hundred. It is not surprising that the little seventy-five- to one-hundred-pound females are docile, for their masters weigh up to seven hundred pounds.

Each spring the northern bulls push lustily ahead to the ancestral rookeries on the Pribilof Islands in Bering Sea. By late April or early May, they have hauled out on the rocky beaches. Although thousands of bulls may be crowded on one island, each harem bull picks out a likely part of the beach for his own, perhaps seventy-five to one hundred feet in extent, and fiercely drives off all intruders. Those that get there first get the best positions, centrally located, and nearest the water's edge. Here they can intercept the cows when they come ashore a month or more later.

The late-arriving bulls must take second and third choice, farther back from the beach. Those behind the first rows of harem bulls are called idle bulls because they cannot hope to establish a harem until the harem masters become weary and relinquish some of their mates. Behind the idle bulls are surplus bulls and bachelors. The surplus bulls move into idle-bull positions when opportunity offers, but the bachelors are too young to mate.

The harem bulls do not risk losing their choice positions by leaving, even to get food. They have a long wait. Most of the cows arrive between the fifteenth of June and fifteenth of July.

Heavy with pup, the females give birth to their single offspring within a few hours or days after their arrival. They are welcomed with great flurry and bustle. Each bull tries to collect as many mates as possible. The cows seem to believe in safety of numbers and prefer to enter large harems. Occasionally they try to escape from one bull to another and are jabbed in the flanks and shoulders for their efforts. Sometimes one is killed. However, a bull seldom leaves his harem to go into the water after an escaping cow. As long as the cows stay within the harem boundaries, he treats them well. He does not demand their attentions until they come in heat after the pups are born.

With rumbling roars and deafening bellows, each harem master warns one and all against any movement toward his packed harem. But time and again a rival waddles ponderously over the invisible line that marks the limits of each little domain. Like boxers, the bulls move sluggishly for position, their thick necks are raised and heads pointed skyward. They sway, roaring, as if in a mad, fantastic dance. Suddenly one grabs like a flash and seizes the muzzle of the other. The long sharp canines dig deep into the flesh. Blood streaming, the injured bull may tear loose and rip a mighty gash in his rival's neck. Sometimes a flipper is torn off or paralyzed.

The fight seldom lasts long. Usually a gash or two will drive the intruder away. Occasionally the harem master is dispossessed. The beaten one either goes out to sea, back to the rear of the beach to die, or to nurse his wounds and speculate on his chances to steal another bull's harem. Sometimes he retreats so far that a sympathetic cow joins him and a new rookery is started.

The victor does not swagger; he strokes his neck with his hind flipper non-chalantly, but keeps his big eyes open for the next male intruder.

It is a harrowing season. No bull with a harem dares to leave his quarters even to eat. He can't trust his wives nor his closest associates and goes without food for two to three months.

At six years of age a precocious bull may hold as many as four cows if he stays on the fringe of the rookery and no more-mature bull goes after them. It usually takes a ten-year-old to hold over a hundred.

Harem masters who last until August are thin, worn out and hungry, and are ready to retire. Just about this time, thousands of two-year-old virgins arrive ready to be mated. The exhausted old sultans are not interested in them, and the idle and surplus bulls that have been biding their time are fresh and rested and come forth eagerly to meet the newcomers.

The female fur seal has her first blue-eyed pup at the age of three, after nearly a year of pregnancy. She is a fairly devoted mother at first. Going out to feed, she always returns to nurse her pup, pulls it out of rock holes, and endeavors to save it from the path of the trampling harem master.

Each cow is believed to recognize her own little black pup out of the thousands of squealing, darting youngsters that look as alike as beans in a peck measure. Ordinarily she will not nurse any other pup, and during the days of pelagic sealing, the beaches were littered with the bodies of pups that had died of starvation.

Once, however, two mothers were seen wrangling over one pup. Apparently one of the mothers had lost hers, and each thought this pup belonged to her. Both had a strong grip on the poor little squirming creature and were pulling in opposite directions.

The pups learn to swim in about six weeks or two months and from then on take care of themselves except for nursing. By the end of September, they have brown eyes and new silvery gray coats, and go on trips around the island by themselves.

They are weaned the hard way. At the tender age of three or four months, they are driven by the approach of winter into the open sea for the annual migration. Separated from their mothers, they must find their own food and escape from their enemies. Fifty per cent of the male pups and forty per cent of the females die before they are three years old.

Like the female of the human species, the fur seal cow often lives longer than the bull. Apparently her life is easier. Female seals, twenty-one years old, have been seen with healthy pups. Males have been known to live to twenty-two but they are usually worn out long before then.

The females of the restless northern race may travel as much as six thousand miles each year, two thousand of which are over the open North Pacific Ocean. How they find their way across this trackless foggy expanse, between their wintering waters off California and the passes to the Pribilof Islands in the Bering Sea, is one of the most remarkable feats in mammal migration.

The old bulls stay in the north, wintering south of the Aleutians and in the Gulf of Alaska. The younger bulls go a little farther south. Spending their winters in the killer-whale waters may partly explain the great mortality of the male seals. A killer may swallow as many as twenty-four seals, whole and struggling, for one meal—a twelve-hundred-dollar meal, by the way.

The fur seal is the only seal that has a fur coat. It has caused the race no end of trouble. The durable, soft, silky furs, overlaid with longer glistening crisp guard-hairs, have been taken in millions by the fur trade.

Pribilof Islands in Bering Sea are the only places where the northern fur seals come on land. Here they return each summer to bear their young and to breed. The rest of the year they spend in the sea.

Discovered in 1786 by the Russian, Pribylov, the islands became the scene of terrific slaughter. In a frenzy of profit-taking, the fur traders slaughtered millions of seals, leaving most of them to rot. This waste was stopped by the Russian government and the number of seals restored to perhaps four millions. In 1867, after the purchase of Alaska by the United States, sealing privileges were leased. By 1911, the seals had been reduced to one hundred and twenty-four thousand.

Drastic steps had to be taken. Through treaties between the United States, Great Britain and Japan, all killing of seals at sea was prohibited. Killing on land (except for necessary native food) was suspended for five years.

In 1918, the annual kill of three-year-old bulls, under the direction of the United States Bureau of Fisheries (now a part of the Fish and Wildlife Service), began. Since the three-year-old bachelors are relegated to the rear of the rookery, they can easily be driven like sheep to killing fields before the mating season breaks up, without disturbing the breeding grounds. Of course some of the older bulls that arrive late and a few stray females are caught in the drives. They are not killed, but are the worse for wear and tear on flippers and dispositions. A percentage of the three-year-old males is reserved for breeding.

Fifteen per cent of the skins have gone annually to Canada and fifteen per cent of the receipts from remaining pelts to Japan. In 1941, however, the Seal Treaty was abrogated by Japan. She claimed that the seals damaged her fishing industry. By this action, she forfeited her share which had amounted to approximately one million five hundred thousand dollars annually. Twenty per cent of the skins now go to Canada and eighty per cent to the United States.

The skins are salted and cured for ten days and are then rolled singly with a liberal amount of salt on the flesh side which is turned inside. These are shipped in barrels. The United States Government has a contract with the Fouke Fur Company at St. Louis for dressing, dyeing and selling the skins at auction. The record for gross receipts was established at the sale on April 29, 1946, when 28,032 pelts brought $2,453,156. The average price, therefore, was $87.51. Oil and meal are rendered from the blubber and carcasses in a by-products plant on St. Paul, one of the Pribilof Islands.

Seal meat is the beefsteak of the natives. Served at meals for white employees on the island, it is quite palatable when cooked in piquant sauces or stewed with onions. Cooks in the United States who have experimented with it find that the strong "fishy" odor, while cooking, spoils their appetite for it.

Under the conservation management of the Fish and Wildlife Service, the fur-seal herd has been restored to over three million, and more than a million bachelor seals have surrendered their coats to the females of the human species. Pups have been branded from time to time to secure scientific information, and various studies have been carried out.

Light yellowish albino seals with pink to brown flippers and pink-iris eyes occasionally grow to the age of five years. Usually the eyesight is defective and they die much younger.

Fishermen have accused the more than two million fur seals of eating enormous quantities of salmon and halibut, but it has been proven scientifically that salmon is eaten only incidentally. Hundreds of seal stomachs were opened to determine their eating habits. Herring was always found to be their mainstay. Very little salmon and no halibut was present.

A southern race, the Guadalupe fur seal, lives along the coast of California and Baja California. Slaughtered unmercifully in the early days, for years they were thought to be extinct. A few have been seen in recent years, however. They are of little economic importance, compared to the Alaskan fur seals.

General description. A medium-sized seal, more active on land than any other seal, often assuming an upright position. Webbed feet turn forward. Fur thick and silky with coarse guard-hairs, black on the upper parts changing to gray on the shoulders and neck and reddish brown underneath. Size of males: total length, about 6 feet; height of head when animal is standing, about 4 feet; weight, 300 to 500 pounds and very rarely as much as 700 pounds. Females are much smaller, and their fur is gray over the back.

Distinguishing characteristics. Among the other seals, the fur seal resembles only the sea lion which is larger and has a coarse hairy coat.

Range. The coast of Baja California north to Alaska and the Pribilof Islands. Other fur seals occur along the Asiatic, South American and Australian coasts, South Africa, and in the Indian and Antarctic Oceans.

SEA LION
EUMETOPIAS JUBATA AND *ZALOPHUS CALIFORNIANUS*

Although larger than the fur seal, the Steller sea lion does not have as many mates. An average of ten to fifteen are enough for him to keep in order. He does not take them as seriously. Food is more important to him than to the fur seal, and he does not fast as long. Exacting a certain amount of fidelity, he is not as jealous nor does he get as irritable if one of his cows goes off to an idle bull.

Ten to twelve feet long, he may weigh a ton or even more. Because of this greater weight, it is more difficult for him to get over the ground. Perhaps this is one reason that he is content not to chase down as many females! Although fur seals can be driven several miles to slaughter, the northern or Steller sea

SEA LION

lions are worn out after two miles. Nevertheless they spend much more time on land than the fur seal, that never goes ashore except during the breeding season.

The fur seal and the sea lion are the only representatives of the Eared Seal family. Lacking the fur seal's beautiful fur coat, the sea lion has short, thin, coarse hair. His mates are less than half as big and more slender.

For a sea-going flesh eater with a swollen neck, a terrific clamor, a light brown hide (when dry), lion-shaped eyes with white iris and golden pupil, the northern species' original name of *Leo marinus*, meaning "lion of the sea," seemed to be appropriate. Steller, the naturalist who named it, chose an obvious title. (Most scientists name their discoveries for some inconspicuous feature, such as a long toe-nail or under-sized whiskers.)

Unfortunately Steller's appellation did not stick. "Leo" had been given already to the King of Beasts of the dry African veldt. Quite plainly, the two animals were not closely related. For almost two centuries, mammalogists wrangled over a suitable name. At last they compromised on *Eumetopias jubata*. But the animal is still popularly known as the Steller sea lion. (The much smaller sea lion in California waters is technically named *Zalophus californianus*. This species has a very faintly leonine "mane," a crest that runs from between the eyes over the back of the head. Its habits are much the same as those of the Steller sea lion.)

Although less tempestuous, the domestic life of the sea lions is very similar to the fur seals. When they are spread out in the sun on the breeding and hauling grounds, and are dry, they look like great tan blanket rolls. Rising to swash around with their clumsy-looking bodies, they become grotesque dancers in a street fête. It is astonishing to see how nimbly their great bulks can clamber up steep pinnacles of a craggy island. Only when they are driven to slaughter do they become ferocious and dangerous.

An island shore is the hereditary breeding ground and nursery. Here the cows arrive, one by one, sometime between the middle of May and early June. Within a few days of their coming ashore, the pups are born. As mammals go, the little sea lion pup is precocious. In this trampling mob, it must develop mobility quickly or be crushed to death. Its great blue eyes are open wide immediately after birth. Already it has ten or twelve teeth. In a few days its dark little body is romping in and out among the vast light-colored hulks of the elders. Soon it can dodge all except the swiftest rushes of its battling uncles.

The mother nurses her single youngster on thick rich milk and it grows rapidly. Weighing thirty-five to fifty pounds at birth and measuring thirty-eight to forty inches long, the Steller sea-lion pup may be as big as a three-year-old one-hundred-pound fur seal by the end of its second month. The California pup is smaller. As it grows older, the shoulders of the young sea lion develop while its middle shrinks. Instead of being pot-bellied, as at first, the weight is centered in the shoulders and neck. The weights of young males and females differ little, but later in life the bulls are several times heavier than the cows.

It is popularly believed that the sea lion's mother picks it up by the scruff of the neck and carries it to the water for swimming lessons. Like all mammal children, except the whales and the manatee, the sea lion must learn to swim. Probably it finds out by struggling as it follows its mother into the sea. By the time it is two months old it can tumble over the sand and boulders to paddle through the surf by itself. The dark brown coat lightens, and its blue eyes turn deep brown. Soon it can ride in on a wave, take an expert foothold on the steep slippery rocks and waddle high for a sun bath.

The summer days are soon passed. The masters of the harems are exhausted as a result of their exertions in June, the mating month; their huge bulks are shrunken, their hides are scarred and torn. Wearily, one by one, they slip down the sloping beach to the sea as the cows and young also leave. A few months of fat living on fish and crustaceans will fill out the emaciated forms, but will not completely mend the rents in their skins.

At sea, the killer whale and the shark are their only serious enemies. Man has been the worst hazard. For untold centuries the American natives killed the northern species for the flesh, the hide and the oil. The hide is still preferred by Alaskan natives to canvas for covering such boats as kayaks and bidarkas. Much tougher than canvas, it is safer in the rock-infested waters. The oil was stored in pouches made from sea lion stomachs by the natives. When sea lions were still numerous enough to make their hunting profitable, their oil was used commercially for oiling machinery. The animal's intestines, cut into ribbons and sewed together, made excellent transparent tough raincoats long before the Duponts started the demand for fancy slickers.

Until a few years ago, old sea lion bulls were especially valuable. Their gall bladders, lips with whiskers attached, and genitalia were shipped to China. The whiskers were used for ornaments and for cleaning out the long stems of opium pipes, the gall-sacs for medicinal purposes, and the genitals were ground up and sold as "rejuvenators."

Because the sea lion was cautious, rarely going ashore farther than a hundred feet from the breakers, and wary of danger from the land, it was able to exist in many thousands under primitive hunting methods. Today, persistent persecution has made the surviving lions more wary than ever. They usually shun the mainland shore, preferring rocky islands. The Steller sea lions breed on Bogoslof Island in the Aleutians and the Pribilof Islands in Bering Sea.

During winter, they leave the clammy cold of their Alaskan home, and go south as far as California. Even the California sea lions probably move southward a little way at this time. These southern sea lions range in summer from north of San Francisco to southern Mexico. This is the species whose breeding colonies are so noticeable on the "Seal Rocks" of San Francisco and the rocky islands off Point Lobos near Monterey.

Fishermen have accused the sea lion of destroying great numbers of food fishes, and of ruining nets when attracted to gilled or trapped fish. Several scientific investigations have demonstrated that the first charge is largely unjustified. While the northern or Steller sea lion depends heavily on fish for food, they are mostly species that man does not use. The southern or California sea lion lives chiefly on squids.

The "trained seals" you see in the circuses are really sea lions. They are the much smaller California species. The male weighs only about five hundred pounds and the female a great deal less. They are more adaptable and much more lively than the Steller sea lions and the "true" seals. Given an opportunity, they enjoy the company of human beings if they keep their proper distance, and occasionally will stay at a private beach all summer. Now and then one has become an affectionate pet. Fun-loving creatures, they seem to enjoy their stunts in the circus as much for the exercise and showing off, as for the fish that reward a good performance. Intelligent, they can meet a new situation so well that when someone muffs a cue, the whole act will not break down. Their long necks, flexible as human arms, are just the equipment for passing a big rubber ball. If their legs were more useful, they would be the answer to a baseball club manager's prayer.

Sea lions are divided into two genera or groups which externally are quite similar except in size.

1. The Steller or northern sea lion (*Eumetopias*) is the larger, a big male weighing fifteen hundred to eighteen hundred pounds, and even more. The crest is not pronounced. The range extends from Bering Strait to the neighborhood of San Francisco.

2. The California sea lion (*Zalophus*) is much smaller—about five hundred pounds for the male. Adults have a crest which runs from between the eyes to the lower back of the head. The species ranges along the coast from northern California to southern Mexico.

General description. A very large eared seal; heavy body graceful in water, long neck and pointed head; hind limbs capable of forward motion, and fore limbs almost as long as hind limbs, enabling comparatively active movement on land; feet webbed; ears small. Hair coarse, yellowish brown to black. Total length, up to 13 feet; height of head when animal is walking, 5 feet; weight, recorded as high as 1810 pounds and 2179 pounds. Females are much smaller: up to 9 feet in length, and 400 to 500 pounds.

Distinguishing characteristics. A large marine mammal which on land carries the neck nearly upright and is capable of a lumbering gallop for very short distances. Distinguished from the fur seal by larger size and hairy coat instead of thick fine fur; from the "true" seals by much larger size and more upright carriage and hind feet turning forward; from the elephant seal by more slender, graceful body and sharply pointed nose; and from the walrus by the same characteristics and by lack of long tusks.

Range. The Pacific coast of North America from southern Mexico to Bering Strait, and southwest to Japan. Other sea lions live along the coasts of South America and in the Antarctic.

THE EARLESS SEALS
FAMILY *PHOCIDAE*

The earless or "true" seals have no external ears. But they can hear perfectly well. Tiny channels to their inner ears open when they are out of water, and close tight when they go under. These valves operate automatically like the valves at the back of their nostrils.

Unlike the eared seals (sea lion and fur seal), their legs turn backward and are of no use for locomotion on land. Even with heads in the air, they must walk on their bellies, humping themselves along like caterpillars, and proceeding by fore-and-aft expansions and contractions of their bodies. Apparently this procedure is not as uncomfortable as it looks.

Extremely polygamous, the earless seals do not bother to establish harems as the eared seals do. The males mate indiscriminately and incur no domestic responsibilities. Possibly this is due to the fact that it is even more difficult for them to move about on land than it is for the eared seals.

All northern seals, except the harbor seal (and very rarely the hooded seal), prefer the colder waters of Canada and Alaska. They swim as far south as the northern boundaries of the United States. The ringed, harp, and bearded seals inhabit the Arctic Ocean and the Atlantic south to the region of the Gulf of

St. Lawrence. The ribbon seal is limited to the Bering Sea coast of Alaska and the Aleutian Islands, while the gray and hooded seals live along the Atlantic coast from Greenland to Newfoundland or Nova Scotia.

The very rare West Indian seal once lived on the coast of Florida, but now is probably restricted to a few isolated islands near Yucatan.

The following seals are the more important of the earless seal family.

HARBOR OR HAIR SEAL—*Phoca vitulina*

The most numerous seal, and the species most likely to be seen by us, is the harbor seal. It is practically the only seal that lives along the inhabited coast of North America. Frequenting both the Atlantic and Pacific shores, many thousands of these mammals may be found north from southern New England (rarely from as far south as North Carolina) to the Arctic Ocean and from Baja California to the Pribilof Islands.

Usually known in Alaska and western Canada as the hair seal, the harbor or common seal is also called at times the leopard seal because of the spots on its coat. The rather coarse hair varies from yellowish gray with dark brown spots, to nearly black with yellowish markings. (It looks much darker when wet.) Albinos are rarely found.

Each fall the "hair seal" puts on a new hair coat. About five feet long, the male may weigh as much as two hundred and fifty-six pounds, but probably averages around one hundred and sixty. The female seems to be about twenty-five per cent lighter. No great seafarer, the harbor seal sticks closely to the coastline and prefers sheltered bays and river estuaries. In fact, it sometimes ascends rivers for hundreds of miles and has been found in fresh-water lakes. It is not known to migrate.

Apparently it cannot sleep in the water as some of the eared seals do, but must come ashore to rest, day or night, according to its mood. Although it can stand up briefly on its hips when on land, like all eared seals, it cannot lift its belly from the ground when traveling. The five claws on each flipper are a help in getting a hold on sloping or rocky terrain, but all progress is slow and laborious.

The harbor seals usually like to hunt alone, but gather in rather large herds when they come ashore to rest or when they find a situation of common interest. A sunny sand bar at the mouth of a river may be a favorite spot. One morning I counted well over a hundred harbor seals enjoying the warmth of an unusually bright autumn sun on a small bar in Katmai Bay in southwestern Alaska. When disturbed, they bounced into the water with a loud chorus of short, sharp barks.

On numerous occasions, I have seen dozens of them bobbing in the water in front of Alaskan glaciers. Apparently fish had gathered to feed on the swarming shrimp there, and many birds, as well as mammals, had come to prey on both.

When born, the single harbor-seal pup may still be wearing its soft, white, woolly, fetal coat. If it has not shed this shortly before birth (as is often the case), it exchanges it for the adult spotted "leopard" coat a few days afterward. At birth the pup weighs twenty-five to thirty pounds, and its sharp claws are all ready for use. The mother nurses it for perhaps four to six weeks. It cries "M-a-a-a" rather like a sheep, or a much more desperate "Kroo-roo-uh" if it is lost.

Taught to swim in shallow water, it does not have much endurance at first. When it gets tired, the mother gives it a lift on her back. If chased, an adult seal in top form can swim twelve to fifteen miles an hour for a half-mile, but then it has to slow down considerably.

An amiable creature, the harbor seal seldom fights except perhaps at mating time. During this period there may be a good deal of bawling and rival mates will grab each other by the neck, sway back and forth, claw and bite. No doubt some of the scarred hides that have been taken have resulted from these contests. A single snort from one of the animals at any time of year is said to have been heard for a mile or more away.

Man has many cruel devices for killing the harbor seal: shooting at them from power boats, harpooning, trapping, tangling in hooks, beating, dynamiting. Pups are destroyed so that their nursing mothers may be killed easily when looking for them.

The harbor seal's two greatest natural enemies are the shark and the killer whale. Either one can easily swallow a small seal whole and without a struggle. Any of forty-eight external and internal parasites may bother the seals. Those in the stomach, intestines and nasal passages are perhaps better known. Probably only a captive seal will live as long as seventeen years.

An outstanding trait of the harbor seal (in fact all of its tribe) is curiosity. They will gather around a boat, bobbing and staring, until they are satisfied or frightened away. Usually wary, they are careful not to rise too high in the water or to stay too long in one spot. They disappear so quickly that only an expert can shoot them in the water. On the North Pacific coast their caution is founded on bitter experience. Fishermen detest the "hair seals" as destroyers of food-fish and nets, and shoot at them whenever they are seen.

Much of this prejudice seems to be based on casual observations. Analysis of the contents of the stomachs of one hundred and fourteen harbor seals killed along the Washington coast revealed that the animals fed on the most readily available food: tom-cod, flounders, Pacific herring, hake, sculpins, cod, blue-cod, pollack and shiners. Squids were eaten in winter, and octopuses in summer. Salmon (the fishermen's catch) was found in only four stomachs.

When a seal does steal a netted fish, it is likely to eat only the soft central and lower portion, but the remainder is unsalable. This is a serious matter to the fisherman who may have succeeded in catching only one or two salmon in a night.

Indians of the northwestern coast sometimes boil and eat the dark-red flesh of the harbor seal. The Thlingits and Aleuts of Alaska use the skins for making moccasins and other articles. Furriers of the white race sometimes use the leather, dyed black or brown, for jackets. Skiers often fasten strips of sealskin to the bottom of the skiis so that the backward-pointing stiff hair will prevent them from slipping back while climbing slopes.

HARBOR SEAL

HOODED SEAL—*Cystophora cristata*

When the hooded seal is angry, he blows up his hood and lumbers in full sail at the source of his displeasure. The hood is an inflatable sac cf muscular tissue on top of his head. Only the male has it, and he uses it often to vent his rage. Because of this appendage, sealers have given him another name, "bladder-nose seal." His slate black coat has brownish spots on the flanks. He averages seven to nine feet long, but an old male will grow to enormous size, quite often up to eleven and one-half feet.

Accompanying this great physique and irascible disposition is tremendous strength. The hooded seal has the reputation of being able to leap farther out of the water than any other seal. He has been known to flip himself into a boat from his reclining position on an ice floe. At least once he has been known to leap out of the water, across a dory, and land on an iceberg nearly six feet above the water. With his enormous teeth, he can crunch to bits the thick oak gun-wale of a small boat.

The range of the hooded seal extends from Greenland as far south as New-foundland and, rarely, New England. Westward in the Arctic, this species is one of the most abundant of the several kinds of seals in Lancaster Sound, west of Baffin Bay.

Lacking sharp claws on its flippers, the hooded seal is not able to keep breathing holes open through the ice. It lives, therefore, in broken ice or along the edge of the pack. Sometimes it is necessary to make long journeys over the ice to find open water, but the hooded seal does not stay on or near land for any long period.

On the northeastern coast of North America, it travels with the harp seal during migration. However, it prefers its own heavier ice floes to the east and northeast for the whelping and mating season in March.

The single pup weighs eight to twelve pounds at birth and has a gray back, fading into white on the belly. Although supposed to be much less quarrelsome than the male, the female is said to fight fiercely for her youngster and to die rather than run off and leave it. Soon after the young are born, the mother seals mate again. At this time the males battle so noisily that the racket can be heard for miles. For a few weeks the males remain in the sea near the mothers and their pups, ready to defend them against interference of any kind. Then the adult sexes part company and live in small, separate bands for the remainder of the year.

The flesh of the hooded seal is excellent, more like that of land game than the fat meat of other sea-dwelling mammals. The hide, however, is so porous, thin, and lacking in strength that it is useless for making lines, boat coverings or boots.

HARP OR GREENLAND SEAL—*Phoca grœnlandica*

The harp or Greenland seal is also called the saddleback, because of the brown band across the shoulders of the male. The general color is dark gray, with deep brown on the head and spots on the hind legs. Old males may be seven feet in length and weigh six hundred to eight hundred pounds. The females are smaller.

This seal is remarkably abundant. Even now, when their numbers have been much reduced by sealing for oil, vast herds winter in the Gulf of St. Lawrence and in the Strait of Belle Isle between Newfoundland and Labrador.

Unlike most other seals of the far north, the harp seal does not make breathing holes in the ice. Consequently, the herds are obliged to move south in autumn. In early days this migration must have been spectacular. Seen from the Labrador shore, vast numbers of seal heads dotted the ocean to the horizon, every nose pointed south.

Off Newfoundland, the young seals, weighing seven to nine pounds, are born on the big ice fields during March. Twins have been seen, but are rare. Sometimes spring storms break up the floes, grinding the ice to splinters and the helpless young seals to pulp. But if all goes well, the mother harps go off each day to fish, and return to nurse their offspring at night.

The seemingly impossible task of finding the right baby among thousands of exactly similar babies, thickly sprinkled over flat ice sheets that may circle and drift miles in a day, seems to be simple for the unerring harp mother. In twenty-five to twenty-seven days, the stiff, white, woolly birthcoat is shed. Gaining weight at the rate of three pounds a day, the youngsters are soon nearly half grown (although much of this bulk is fat) and can swim readily. The great assemblage of harp seals then starts back on the thousand-mile trip to the summer feeding grounds on the coast of Greenland.

They can swim at a speed of twenty miles an hour for a short time, if necessary, and are said to stay under water as long as twenty minutes. Harp seals have been seen eating fish whose habitat is two hundred feet down in the ocean.

RINGED SEAL—*Phoca hispida*

Small, yellowish rings, or blotches, on the ringed seal's coat are responsible for its name. The dark brownish hair pales into yellowish under parts. Quite like the harbor seal in build and size, the ringed seal is the common seal of the Arctic. It lives on the ice of quiet bays and inlets. This preference for quiet waters instead of the turbulence of the open sea has given it the additional title of fjord seal.

Here the white woolly pup (sometimes a twin) is born during February, March or April in a burrow in the hard snow dug out by the mother's heavy claws. The tunnel, from six to ten feet long, runs from the breathing hole in the ice and ends in a little igloo about four feet in diameter. It makes a safe retreat from most enemies.

The Eskimo locates the nest by following fox tracks or by means of his dog, and attempts to capture the pup by crashing in the snow roof. Keeping out of sight, sometimes for hours at a time in temperatures of thirty to forty degrees below zero, he tries to harpoon the mother when she returns home. She is a timorous creature and will leave at the first sign of danger.

In the routine of everyday food gathering, the ringed seal remains under water seven to nine minutes, then comes up for about forty-five seconds to breathe. In a desperate attempt to escape after being harpooned, one animal stayed down for twenty-one minutes.

The standard summer food is cod, but before the runs start, the seals feed heavily on salmon. Scorpions, gammarids, cuttlefish and all kinds of shellfish are staple articles of diet.

RIBBON SEAL—*Phoca fasciata*

The ribbon seal wears "ribbons" of yellow around its neck, forelegs and rump which decorate the dark brown coat. It is about the same size and build as the harbor seal. Even to the people who inhabit the shores of its Bering Sea home, it is a rare species. Almost nothing is known of its habits except that it is found singly or at most in very small groups.

When the ribbon seal can get no food because of a solid freeze, it has been known to travel south, on land and over mountains, to reach open water. It is hard going for these marine mammals. Their almost useless legs are turned backward and they must laboriously hump along on their bellies. They can travel only a few miles each day by this slow motion and without food. Their fur becomes worn and thin.

The Eskimos and the early fur traders of the Alaskan coast valued the skin because of its striking pattern of yellow and brown. Slit along the belly, the skin was removed entire. Properly prepared and fitted with eyelets and draw string, it made a highly prized clothes bag.

BEARDED SEAL—*Erignathus barbatus*

A dignified tuft of stout white bristles growing down on each side of its muzzle gives the bearded seal its name. One of the largest of the family, the grayish to yellowish male is eight to ten feet long and weighs up to eight hundred pounds. He and his brothers are not very numerous. Except during mating season, he lives alone on the ice floes not far from land. Not too energetic, he uses the natural openings in the ice instead of breaking holes to reach the shallow water.

The bearded seal, like the other species, is very curious when not frightened. Swimming up to a vessel, it will examine the boat first on one side, then on the other. Diving noisily, it comes up again for a different view. But once it learns that mankind is dangerous, it takes every precaution to preserve its skin. Immediately upon sighting human approach, it dives, whether it is on ice or already afloat. Making a great splash with its rear flippers as it strikes the water, it departs for safer regions.

Eskimo hunters learned a peculiarity of this mammal that they used against it when circumstances required. Several hunters would surround and creep toward a bearded seal asleep on the ice. If the animal showed signs of waking, the men would burst into a horrible chorus of screams and yells. Paralyzed with fear at the uproar, the seal would lie still and could be harpooned before it recovered enough to dive into the water.

The single youngster of the bearded seal is born in late March. It is grayish black, with curlier hair than that of the ringed seal pup. The mother is an affectionate parent, and cares for her adolescent child over a long period.

If a young seal becomes separated from its mother while swimming, she will whistle to it—a very high-pitched sound which becomes deeper and deeper, finally ending in a prolonged sigh as the whistling note dies out. A deep "whistle" or dull sound is also given by the diving seal, supposedly by expelling air from the lungs as it reaches the sea bottom.

Bearded seals live in the Arctic across the entire top of North America from western Alaska to Labrador. Occasionally one will wander as far south as Newfoundland. They seek their food on the bottom of the sea, much like the walrus. Diving to great depths, they scrape with their claws for crustaceans and mollusks, including big clams. Scorpions, salmon trout, and even cuttlefish are eaten in emergencies, although they are not as palatable to the seals.

The flesh of the bearded seal is said to be coarse and tasteless to man. Some of the Eskimos of the eastern Arctic enjoy the hind flippers when boiled, but dislike the flesh unless it is well decomposed and then frozen. The liver is alleged to be poisonous, like that of the polar bear. However, these seals are hunted for their very thick skins. These are prized for heavy-duty articles, such as harpoon lines, which must be strong and elastic. The hides are also good for sole leather and for covering tents and skin boats (umiaks). They are too thick and heavy for use in making clothing.

Man is not their only enemy. A large bearded seal was killed at Cape Prince of Wales, Bering Strait, whose back and belly showed great scars where the claws of a polar bear had cut through the skin.

GRAY SEAL—*Halichœrus grypus*

The gray seal is soberly cloaked in ashy to dusky gray, with faint blackish spots on the upper surface and flanks. A large seal, it is ten to twelve feet long. The species lives on both sides of the North Atlantic, from Great Britain to Iceland and Greenland, thence south to Nova Scotia.

On the United States coast the gray seal is uncommon. Almost the only information on the private affairs of the species comes from the British Isles, but the habits of the animals are probably quite similar on both sides of the ocean.

For the first seven months of each year the seal remains at sea or pokes about in rocky channels where the swirling tides carry plenty of food. It is not overly anxious for company, but may hunt around with a few others of its kind. In late August or early September, instinct urges the bull ashore on a rocky beach. He does not know it, but his ancestors for centuries have been coming each summer to this very place, or to one of a few others like it. More bulls arrive, until hundreds are lying side by side, or even sprawled across each other. Drowsing in the sunshine, they scarcely move for hours at a time. A few more enterprising ones creep inland, sometimes as much as a quarter of a mile. They pick out choice patches of ground, perhaps by a rivulet or a tidal pool.

Somewhat later the cows begin to drift ashore. Each one settles down and gives birth to a single pup. Every bull immediately wants to attract one or more females into the few square yards that he manages to clear around him. He menaces any competitor by displaying white fangs. Rolling from side to side, he arches his neck and head far back, and throws up his fore flippers. If the rival does not retire, a fight ensues and the winner takes all.

In its long coat of fine white hair, the new-born seal pup is an appealing little animal. Big dark eyes stare out of a wondering face, and the white fur dress, rumpled from lying on the rocks, reminds one of a child's teddy bear. For two to three weeks, or rarely for as long as a month, the young seal is carefully tended by the mother. She feeds it on milk which is more than one-third butterfat. It grows amazingly fast, but she loses weight correspondingly. She is likely not to eat at all during this period, and may not even go into the water.

The little seal is much like a human baby its in cries and reactions. After feeding, in utter contentment, it puts its "thumb" in its mouth and murmurs happily. The mother may add to its pleasure by scratching it gently as it lies on its side.

The youngster's white coat commences to fall when it is about two weeks old. This hair is pushed out by a short blue-gray growth. Two weeks later the beautiful new juvenile coat is complete. When only two to three weeks of age, the young seal is abandoned by its mother. Terribly shrunken, for she has lived and nursed her young on her stored blubber, she must go out to sea to feed and recuperate. Her youngster and all the other offspring are left to make their way in life without any instruction. Instinct alone must guide them to food in the ocean. This may take anywhere from a week to a month. They lose a good deal of weight before they have learned to find a meal. Going down steep, high cliffs to the sea, some fall to death or fatal injury, but the majority make their way safely.

Maiden cows and the younger bulls meet and mate on reefs entirely separate from the colonies of their elders. All the racket and excitement of mating season ends in November. Leaving their breeding grounds, the adults congregate sedately on other reefs, where they rest, scratch and rub off their old coats on the rocks, and grow sleek new robes. Then they are off to sea again until another autumn.

Dr. F. Fraser Darling, who has studied the gray seals on Roma Island off the west coast of Scotland, has pointed out that these animals must always be given protection during the breeding season. About fifty years ago, high prices for pelts in England made it profitable to slaughter the seals in great numbers on their rookeries. Almost helpless ashore, the mothers would not abandon their young at this early stage. Their destruction was a simple matter. The species was almost wiped out at that time in the eastern Atlantic, but, under protection, has since recovered.

General description. Thinly-furred animals with hind legs turned backward. Size generally small to medium as compared with relatives such as the sea lion. No external ears. Neck short. Color varies with the species, as does size: 5 to 12 feet long and up to 800 pounds in weight.

Distinguishing characteristics. The backward-turned hind legs, prone posture when on land or ice, smaller size and lack of external ears separate· the true seals from their two close relatives, the sea lion and the fur seal.

Range. The coasts of North America and the lower parts of larger rivers from southern New England (rarely North Carolina), north to the Arctic, then west and south along the Pacific coast to Mexico. Seals inhabit the coasts of all the other continents as well.

SEA ELEPHANT
MIROUNGA ANGUSTIROSTRIS

The largest of all the seals is the sea elephant or elephant seal. The northern elephant seal, which lives in the southern part of North America, may be as much as fifteen feet long and weigh over five thousand pounds. The southern elephant seal, that lives in the Antarctic, is even larger, its waistline being some fifteen to eighteen feet around.

The snout, which gives the elephant seal his name, usually hangs limply over his muzzle. It almost falls into his mouth when he yawns or barks. But when he becomes excited, he blows up the two large internal chambers at the end of his twelve-inch nose. This inflation of his "trunk" is supposed to remind you of an elephant. The female elephant seals have only an ordinary snout and must express their anger in a less spectacular manner.

When a young male elephant seal dives for food, he closes his nostrils at their outer ends in order to keep water out of his lungs. As he grows older and his snout develops, the nostrils enlarge until they can close no longer. Luckily, he has a spare set of valves back in the nasal passages. These keep out the water and, incidentally, cause those heavy snoring sounds. Elephant seals are known to stay under water for a period of at least three to seven minutes.

Like all other "true" or earless seals, the hind legs of the elephant seal turn backward. It swims with fair speed by means of these propellers, the front feet being held against its sides. If it wishes to stop and look around, it stands upright in the water, using its front flippers to balance itself. It can stabilize itself high in the water with the waves lapping around its shoulders, or can float with only its eyes and nostrils showing. It can also rest on its back with head and hind flippers out of water.

The hind legs, which serve so well in the sea, are of little use on land. When worming itself onto a sandy beach, it spreads them apart, trying to get a lift from the breakers. Using all the push possible, it laboriously hauls its huge bulk beyond tide mark. It stays here inertly all day, for it feeds mostly at night.

The hot sun seems to bother these dark, yellowish-brown seals, as do the

SEA ELEPHANT

buzzing flies which are always swarming. After getting settled in a soft sandy spot, the sea elephant sprinkles its back with sand as a protection from the heat, crosses its hind flippers, and goes to sleep. It awakes often, however, to fling more sand over its back.

A highly uncomfortable custom is the semi-annual shedding of the old coat. Most animals shed only their hairy coat, but the sea elephant loses its skin as well. Young animals begin to shed in April, while the older ones are in the throes during July, when the weather is much more unpleasant. The old skin peels in shreds and tatters until it is scratched off, littering the beach in pieces as big as a man's hand. The sun seems to scorch the new tender skin into a raw pink, and a sand blanket is not much protection against sunburn.

If the sun becomes too hot to endure, the seals may retire to the shade of a rocky cavern that has been formed by the wash of the waves. Probably this habit helped to save the species from extinction by the sealers. On several occasions, crews from sealing ships heard the roaring of sea elephants in caves, but were unable to reach them through the surf-torn tunnels.

As the bulls grow older, the skin of the neck becomes thick and rough. Although this shield is a valuable protection in the combats that occur during the mating season, they are often badly scarred. Rearing high, the bulls slash at each other with their long canines. Like other fighting males of the seal tribe, they try to grab the most vulnerable spot of their opponents—the nose. No holds are barred and no quarter is given.

Even now, little is known about the sea elephant's early life. The mother has but one fat, sleek pup, which is born between February and June. It appears that the birthplace is on a beach quite apart from the father's rookery. Bull elephant seals are as careless and rough as sea lions and fur seals, and weigh many more pounds. Infant sea elephants would not live long if their first days were spent in the colony of their jostling, fighting fathers.

For countless centuries, until about a hundred years ago, generations of sea elephants led lazy uneventful lives. Scattered in great colonies, they once inhabited the Pacific coast from Point Reyes, north of San Francisco Bay, to the region of Cape Lazaro in Baja California.

Then appeared the universal enemy, the white man. The blubber of a sea elephant was almost pure oil and a big bull might yield more than two hundred gallons of oil, which was considered superior even to that of the sperm whale for lubricating machinery.

Unwary of man, sea elephants were easily butchered. Rushing ashore on the breakers, the hunters endeavored to frighten the huge animals into retreating to higher ground. Stragglers, or those that showed spirit enough to fight, were shot, clubbed or speared to death. Then, running into the compact herd, the sealers killed as many as possible before the remnants could get back to the water and safety. The fat was cut off the carcasses and towed out in long strips to the ship.

Between 1855 and 1870 the great elephant seals were slaughtered by thousands. Finally the survivors were so scarce that their pursuit became unprofitable as a specialized form of sealing. Occasional vessels passing by the sole remaining colony (on Guadalupe Island off Baja California) did not neglect any opportunities to pick up a few barrels of oil in the form of individual seals. By 1892 only nine animals remained on the island, and seven of these were killed by visiting scientists, to preserve them from the oil-rendering vats!

Fortunately, other elephant seals were at sea or had taken refuge in caves. Even at the slow seal-family rate of reproduction of one pup per cow each year, the sea elephants kept ahead of their enemies. Apparently they do not suffer as many casualties from their one known mammal enemy, the killer whale, as do the rest of the seals.

By 1930 about five hundred were counted. The main colony was believed to contain about fifteen hundred animals, and wanderers began to swim north into United States waters. In the past few years, groups of sea elephants have returned to the Channel Islands off Santa Barbara.

The sea elephants owe their lives to the Mexican government. In 1911, killing of the animals was strictly prohibited. For the past twenty years, a garrison of soldiers has been stationed on Guadalupe Island and no one is allowed even to come ashore without proper authorization from Mexico City. The guards are ordered to shoot first and discuss the amenities later.

A few suggestions for official visitors are in order. Very often the whole rookery may be asleep or dozing and will ignore you. Occasionally, however, a panicky elephant seal will try to escape to the sea. Backing away, with its eyes steadily on your advance, it may bump into its closely packed companions, which in turn will start retreating and bumping into others. Fights will start and become furious, while the helpless pups may be piled up in "pods" and smothered or trodden to death.

Sometimes an elephant seal may become sufficiently annoyed to scoop up a couple of pounds of sand and gravel with a backward motion of its front flipper, which it will hurl at you with great force and accuracy. This, almost its only defense, is likely to be effective. Remember that it weighs over a ton and don't let it fall on you! Watch its lumbering, caterpillar motions, the hind feet trailing uselessly.

Its stubby front flippers are not only very powerful, but remarkably flexible.

With the flat heavy claws, the animal can scratch itself dexterously, bending its "finger" joints as readily as a person.

The sea elephant dines mostly on slow-swimming fish. One known meal consisted of seven ratfish, four squids, three skates, a dogfish shark and a swell or puffer shark. A few mouthfuls of seaweed are occasionally eaten. The ability of the seal to dive is shown by some of the food items found in its stomach. Ratfish, for example, never live in less than three hundred feet of water, and some of the other food items live as deep as seven hundred feet. All of the sea elephant's food is small, for its teeth are not fitted for chewing. Spikelike, without grinding surfaces, they are set far apart, so the animal must bolt its food whole and struggling.

General description. Largest of all the seals; earless; hind feet turning backward. Males are much larger than females and have a long snout capable of inflation. Adults are yellowish brown to slate gray, immature animals gray. Total length of northern male, about 15 feet; weight, up to 5000 pounds. Female is about 10 feet long.

Distinguishing characteristics. Large size; the long snout and thickened, scaled skin on chest and neck of the mature males. Because of their elongated necks, both elephant seals and sea lions seem to have the fore flippers placed farther back on the body than do other members of the family. The eyes of the elephant seal, however, are located noticeably higher on the head than are those of the sea lion.

Range. Coastal islands of Baja California and of southern California, from Cedros Island north to the Channel Islands.

WALRUS
ODOBENUS SP.

> *"Oh, Oysters, come and walk with us!"*
> *The Walrus did beseech.*
> *"A pleasant walk, a pleasant talk,*
> *Along the briny beach."*

Only blind, dumb oysters could be lured by the invitation of a walrus. It is one of the ugliest creatures in the world. Small eyes and nostrils are pushed up on the top of its earless head. Its almost hairless, wrinkled body is huge and

WALRUS

ungainly. Ten to twelve feet long, the male weighs two thousand to three thousand pounds.

Well, the oysters went walking with the walrus, the poem tells us. And it wept, how it wept, as it ate them one by one.

The walrus is a kindly, inoffensive creature, until annoyed or threatened. Then a swift Dr. Jekyl and Mr. Hyde change may transform it into a ferocious, dangerous enemy. Often its many associates will come to its aid, and the whole herd will attack.

The long, yellowish-white tusks, dropping from the corners of the walrus's mouth, give it an air of respectability. The female's tusks are more slender than the male's, and are curved in the middle.

The tusks run fourteen to twenty-six inches long, sometimes even thirty-nine inches outside of the jaw bone. They weigh six to nine pounds. The walrus uses these weapons not only for fighting, but for a much more utilitarian purpose, that of digging clams. When it is hungry, it takes a deep breath and sinks slantingly to the bottom of the sea, which may be anywhere from sixty to three hundred feet below the surface. Turning over until it stands practically on its head, the walrus moves backward, grubbing as it goes with its long tusks. Up come the great clams, sea snails and other mollusks, shrimps and starfish that live on the ocean floor.

Protruding pads on each side of the walrus's muzzle force the food into its mouth. These pads, which are fitted with short bristles as large in diameter as a crow's quill, serve as lips and hands. The real lips are relatively weak and the flippers (if it is an adult) are not long enough to reach its mouth. One can almost say that the walrus's mouth stands on its side in the animal's face.

The walrus cannot tear off chunks of solid food with its front teeth, as do wolves, cougars and other land animals. The great tusks prevent this by protruding ahead of the other front teeth. The space between these tusks also limits the size of every piece of food that it takes into its mouth. Nevertheless, the bristly pads are highly efficient forks and knives. An occasional lone walrus takes to eating seals, which it seems to have no difficulty in tearing to pieces with these mouth pads and bristle spikes.

Some authorities say that the walrus swallows clams and other mollusks whole, shells and all. The powerful stomach juices would digest the meat, leaving the whole shells to pass down through the intestines. Other hunters state that the stomachs of dead walruses contain few or no shells, and that the bivalves are chewed in the mouth and most of the shells ejected. In either case, a walrus eats heartily. When satisfied, its stomach is distended to a length of three feet and contains enough clams to fill a washtub.

Eskimo hunters consider the half-digested clams from a walrus's stomach a great delicacy. A big chowder, prepared right on the ice floe over a seal-oil stove, is one of the immediate rewards of a successful hunt.

The walrus is an indolent creature, and spends much time sprawled out on the ice. If the floe drifts fifty miles while the animal sleeps off a clam feast, it doesn't matter. The sea bottom is still within reach, probably, and it can dive for another meal. If the water is too deep, it leaves the ice pan and strikes off nonchalantly for the horizon.

Using both fore and hind flippers, the walrus is a strong and fairly rapid swimmer. Even though perfectly at home in the water, however, it cannot swim indefinitely. When a walrus gets tired it must find ice or land—or drown. In one instance a herd got too far from the rapidly drifting ice to catch up again, and were so desperate that they hauled out on the nearest shore. A native village was situated on the point of land and the Eskimos killed almost a hundred of the huge animals right on "Main Street."

The old Norse sailors called the walrus a "valross," meaning whale horse. Many fables grew up around the creature, and in early drawings it was pictured as an enormous beast with an evil human face and hands.

If undisturbed, the walrus actually is easy-going to the point of stupidity. It is highly gregarious and likes nothing better than to climb onto an ice floe already crowded with hundreds of others. For such a huge, low-slung beast, this would seem to be no easy feat. Raising its head, it hoists its chest onto the ice, then gets a front flipper "aboard" and with a mighty scramble hauls itself out of the water.

Sometimes the earlier occupants of the ice move toward the center to make room. If they are too sleepy to make way, the newcomer is not abashed. It waddles and slides over the prostrate hulks and finally come to rest, perhaps in an open space or perhaps with its rear high in the air on top of one of the sleepers. This may cause objections, and is sure to start a fight if the breeding season is on. Tusks may be splintered or broken, and the necks, shoulders and flanks of the bulls are battered and bruised.

Occasionally the sprawling heavyweights may crowd too far to one side of a small ice floe or may make it top-heavy. Then, with a swish, it turns over and dumps the entire herd into the icy ocean. One can only imagine the blistering comments that are made in walrus talk!

Not that these animals are silent. They are the most vociferous mammal inhabitants of the Arctic. When excited—as in quarrels, when danger threatens, or at times while migrating—they roar and bellow. At such periods, the clamor, like the baying of a pack of hounds, can be heard for several miles. They also try to frighten an enemy by blowing loudly through their nostrils.

Drifting with the ice, the walruses come south into Bering Sea in autumn and return to the Arctic Ocean in spring. During the latter migration in May or early June, the mother walrus gives birth to her single pup. She is a devoted parent. In fact, most walruses think a good deal of the young, whether related or not, and show much bravery in defending them against enemies.

The baby walrus rides on its mother's neck while she travels in the water. As she swims or dives, it holds fast with its front flippers. When about three months old it is some four feet long and weighs around one hundred and twenty-five pounds. According to a famous British naturalist, the young walrus nurses until it is two years old. At this age its tusks are three to four inches long.

Until they have developed to this extent, it lacks tools for digging adult food and is entirely dependent upon the mother's milk.

Because of its size, the walrus has comparatively few enemies. It has its share of little annoyances, however. On "warm" days (above freezing) it is kept busy trying to scratch the lice that live around the scattered hairs and in the numerous folds of its skin. Of much more serious concern is the polar bear, which may kill a young walrus, and that universal marine terror, the killer whale.

About 1936, a large herd of walrus is said to have been driven ashore on St. Lawrence Island by a school of killers. They were so badly frightened that, while making their way up the beach in the surf, a pile-up occurred and over two hundred walruses were smothered and crushed to death. The Eskimos had an unexpected feast.

Man is even more rapacious than the killer whales. In the old days, the Eskimos hunted the walrus with harpoons in the water and with lances on the ice. It was a risky game and the men frequently went hungry if indeed they were not drowned, lost in the ever-present fog, or crushed by the moving ice.

Now the rifle has provided the Eskimos with an all-powerful weapon. Their caves are filled with a one- or two-year supply of meat, fat, and oil. They have plenty of ivory for tools and carving. The hides, from one-half inch to three inches thick, make covers for houses and boats, as well as ropes, dog harness, and all other leather articles.

Walrus hunting for oil was, for a short time, a lucrative trade for the white man. The ships frequented the west or Asiatic side of Bering Sea, as the prey was more numerous there than on the Alaska shore. Like Arctic-dwelling whales and seals, the walrus is extremely fat as a protection against the cold. So efficient is this blubber coat that even if submerged in the icy water for twelve hours after death the carcass is still very warm.

The Eskimos usually shoot the walruses on the ice, where they seem more stupid and allow a close approach, provided they do not smell the hunters. If the herd does not contain pups, there is little real danger to the men.

Hunting in the water, however, is more hazardous. The animals are much more wary. Because they sink or escape quickly if not instantly killed, the hunters take many chances in coming close to wounded animals.

Charles Madsen of Kodiak once told me of a narrow escape under such conditions. He had shot and wounded a bull. Paddling rapidly to the spot in his skin boat, he tried to lasso the animal before it sank. Suddenly, to his dismay, a tusk of the walrus pierced his frail boat, then withdrew. The Arctic Ocean started to pour in. Pulling off his fur cap, Madsen stuffed it in the tear and thus saved his life. The walrus, he thought, had not attacked, but had accidentally struck the boat in its dying struggles.

Two kinds of walruses live in the waters adjacent to northern North Amer-ica—the Pacific walrus and the Atlantic walrus. The two species are much alike, except that the Pacific walrus has shorter and smaller whiskers. Fully adult bulls also have longer, stouter and more diverging tusks than the Atlantic walrus, so the mammalogists have named the western species *divergens*.

In Pleistocene time, when a spreading ice cap drove the Arctic fauna south-ward, the Atlantic walrus came as far south as Georgia. Paleontologists have found its bones in gravel beds and clay banks along the entire coast. When the Puritans founded Bay Colony, they saw walruses once in a great while in Massa-chusetts Bay. These were stragglers, for the southernmost breeding ground was on Sable Island off Nova Scotia. The colonists sent ships to this island several times to secure oil and tusks. In 1641 an expedition returned with "four hundred pair of sea horse teeth, which were estimated worth three hundred pounds ster-ling." That was a great deal of money in the Bay Colony in those days. The Atlantic walrus was exterminated from Sable Island about 1650, and the breed-ing range was steadily pushed back to the Arctic Circle.

Once every five years or so, the Labrador Current brings a lone walrus as far south as the Strait of Belle Isle, at the head of the Gulf of St. Lawrence. The species is still abundant in some parts of the far north, but the Canadian gov-ernment has found it necessary to regulate the killing of these animals and to put a strict limit upon the export of the tusks except as they are manufactured into articles by the Eskimos.

General description. A very large marine mammal with massive body, especially shoulders and neck. Head small, with wide muzzle showing short, very coarse bristles; canine tusks up to 39 inches long, pointing downward from each corner of the mouth; tail very short. Hide thick, wrinkled and "warty," yellowish brown in color. Dark brown hair very sparse, sometimes practically absent in patches. Total length, 10 to 12 feet; head height when animal is standing, about 5 feet; weight, up to 2000 or even 3000 pounds. Female is about one-third smaller.

Distinguishing characteristics. The long tusks are sufficient to distinguish the walrus from any of its seal relatives.

Range. The Arctic Ocean from the neighborhood of Spitsbergen west to Cape Shelagskii in eastern Asia; south on our Atlantic coast to Newfoundland (very rarely), and in Bering Sea to the Pribilof Islands and the Amur River. Now practically absent from Point Barrow east to Bellot Strait.

14. The 'Chucks and Ground Squirrels

WOODCHUCK—*MARMOTA MONAX*

The woodchuck is not big or powerful. It cannot run fast or far. It is not good-looking. In fact, it isn't even smart. But it has a day to itself on the calendar. February 2 is Groundhog Day. According to legend, the woodchuck stretches, yawns, and lumbers slowly to the mouth of its den. It looks at the earth near its feet. If it sees its shadow, it turns around, returns to the nest chamber and goes to sleep for six weeks longer while blizzards rage and the thermometer stays down. But if the sky is cloudy when the woodchuck makes its first appearance, and if its body casts no shadow, it knows that winter is over and its long sleep is at an end. This folk tale was accepted as the gospel truth during colonial times. Even today many people take it seriously. Of course, there is not a grain of truth in it.

The woodchuck is a dignified, deliberate animal. It looks as if it might have a lot of knowledge stored in that small head, but it knows just about enough to keep alive. Sometimes three-quarters of its life is spent asleep. In the North its winter slumber is very long and deep. It begins while the noons are still warm and sunny. This may be the middle of October in Maryland, October 1 in southern New England, September 15 in Quebec.

It goes below for the last time, to the grass bed at the end of the tunnel or into a side chamber that may have only a bare earth floor. Sometimes skunks, opossums, or even rattlesnakes wander in for bed and board. To ensure privacy as well as an even temperature, the woodchuck may wall itself off from the main hallway by scraping dirt from the end of its room and packing it tightly in front.

Then it rolls up in a ball, its head between its hind legs and the front paws together and around its shoulders, which are now against the floor. Breathing slows down until it practically ceases. Just the barest trickle of air moves into its lungs, then out. The pulse becomes very faint and the animal grows cold, down to forty-three to fifty-seven degrees Fahrenheit. It is in a profound sleep, insensible to touch or sound. Awakening would require several hours, even if it were taken to a warm place.

As spring approaches, the groundhog stirs in its sleep, and eventually gets up and stays up. The time varies with the severity of the season. In Missouri it is out of its den in early February, but in northern New York it does not emerge until more than a month later. Although it was "hog fat" the fall before, with as much as one-half to three-fourths of an inch of white fat over the hips, it is now lean. It has "lived slowly" during the winter, but, because it has eaten nothing all that time, it has subsisted on and used up the body fat. During a four- or five-month fast, it loses from one-third to one-half of its total weight.

Spring does not offer much food at first. Sometimes the woodchuck emerges into a world that is still covered with snow two or three feet deep. When no green grass has started, it eats very little for a couple of weeks. No matter how hungry or how little there is to eat, the male almost immediately sets forth to find a mate. Sometimes the quest is long and beset with perils in the form of hungry foxes, coyotes, or dogs, intolerant farmers, or some of the larger and more vicious hawks and owls. Nevertheless, he wanders along determinedly, poking into brushy fence corners and sniffing at every trail and occupied burrow.

WOODCHUCK

Other males with the same objective may resent his intrusion on their territorial rights, and offer fight. Tumbling and squealing, the woodchucks snap with their white incisor teeth. They breathe furiously, growl, and grind their cheek teeth in rage. Ferociously they chew their opponent's ears and tail. Hides are scarred and as much as half of the tail may be bitten off. But eventually the roving male usually finds what he is looking for.

After mating, the male may seek further conquests. Or he may be quite satisfied and remain with the female of his first choice, at least for some time. Not much is known about the woodchuck's marital affairs, but there is some evidence that the male is not always thrown out before the young arrive. Sometimes, when he refuses to leave, his mate seeks out another den for privacy. While it is true that woodchucks are usually solitary outside of mating season, there are some exceptions. In several instances two adults, perhaps mothers, have been seen feeding with youngsters. On numerous occasions two or even three adults have been found occupying the same den. At other times two woodchucks have been known to hibernate together.

About four weeks after the mother mates, between April 1 and May 15 in the latitude of New York, she gives birth to from two to six young, and rarely seven, eight, or nine. The average number, as well as the most usual size of brood, is four. Newborn woodchucks are naked, pink, wrinkled little beings, less than four inches long and weighing one to one and one-half ounces. They are blind and quite helpless. If the mother moves them, she picks them up with her teeth, grasping the loose skin over the neck or shoulders. With the opening of their eyes at four weeks of age, they commence to take an interest in the world above ground. Walking unsteadily to the entrance of the den, they nibble at green food.

Up to this time the little woodchucks, like other young mammals, have been nourished on milk. The mother stands on all fours, or sits up on her haunches like a miniature bear, while the brood nurses. Just before the babies are able to walk she brings a few tender green plants to them in the den and thus the process of weaning is begun.

Young woodchucks have to be house-broken like human children. Until she gets them trained, the mother is kept busy changing the bedding. Repeatedly she brings in soft dry grass and throws out the soiled material.

By the middle of summer the nursery-den has become overcrowded, especially if the brood is large. Some of the young woodchucks, or all of them, are driven out by the mother to take up separate residences in nearby dens. There they can be under her experienced guidance until they wander off in the fall to find territories of their own. This annual shifting, as well as the widespread search of mating males in spring, serves to scatter the blood strains far and wide.

At two months of age an average woodchuck is about fifteen inches long and weighs one and one-half pounds. By early August it measures about twenty inches in length and weighs approximately four pounds. At a distance it appears to be almost as large as the mother, but it will not attain full growth and weight until the end of the second year. Possibly twenty-five per cent of the woodchucks mate when only a year old. The young females are likely to produce fewer than the average number of offspring. Woodchucks are old—and presumably hoary— at the age of five or six years. Individual young animals may have much white "frosting," however.

Young groundhogs are playful animals, but soon settle down to the task of making a living. There seems to be only one observation of adult sportiveness. In that lone instance two woodchucks engaged in a brief and amiable wrestling match in which the object seemed to be to throw the other on a fixed spot on the ground.

Once in a while a woodchuck's home is in a natural cave in a bluff or rock ledge. A few animals have been known to use hollow logs or even trees that had a cavity at the butt. Most of them live in a ground tunnel which they dig for themselves.

They may excavate in a meadow, on a hillside, in a gully, or in a forest. The entrance may be hidden in shrubbery or under a pile of rocks or a stone wall, or may be completely exposed in a grassy field. Because of less likelihood of disturbance, a brushy wood border, hedgerow or gully is the best choice. There a site can be picked between the roots of a tree or stump which will prevent would-be diggers, such as foxes or boys, from enlarging the doorway and reaching the occupant.

The lumbering woodchuck likes to have two or three, sometimes four and even more emergency exits. The main door is about twelve inches in diameter. Inside, the shaft narrows sharply to about four or five inches in width and height. In its total length, which may vary from ten to forty-five feet, the space may be enlarged in places to permit the woodchuck to turn around easily. Rocks in the ground and other obstructions, as well as the fancy of the digger, will determine the course of the tunnel. In soft, friable soil, the tunnel may be as much as six and one-half feet below the surface. In hard, stony ground it may be three or four feet deep or even less.

A woodchuck burrow is rarely a single tunnel. Usually it is forked, with several side passages or rooms that may be from one to twelve feet long. One to three rooms, usually located at the ends of the principal tunnels, are the sleeping chambers. They are about fifteen to eighteen inches in diameter and seven to ten inches high. In most cases a nest or mattress of dry grass, or grass and leaves, is provided, but many rugged woodchucks disdain such softness and sleep on the earth floor.

The bedrooms are usually located higher than the middle portion of the tunnel as a precaution against floods. The woodchuck can put up with water in its corridor if the bed remains dry. Sometimes a burrow is found that shows lack of planning and an upward extension of the sleeping chamber that had to be made when the original room was inundated. The roof of the bedroom is often within two feet of the surface of the ground.

The short, blind tunnels that run off from the main shafts are either hibernating rooms or toilets. The woodchuck is a clean animal. If it cannot go outdoors, it deposits its feces in one of the special rooms and covers them with earth. In good weather, if an enemy is not lurking about, it uses the mound of loose soil outside the main doorway.

This mound is a characteristic of all woodchuck homes, and consists of the excavated soil from the tunnel. The one or more other entrances, which do not have earthen mounds, show that the animal dug the openings from within. These side doors are generally small, about four or five inches in diameter, just large enough to admit the owner, and are well concealed in grass or brush. Inside these smaller openings the tunnel usually dips steeply, often going almost straight down. The tunnel inside the front door slopes much more gradually.

Equipped with strong muscles and heavy, sharp claws, the woodchuck is an efficient miner. It uses its strong, chisellike teeth to loosen small stones and to cut through any roots that it may encounter. Propelling itself by its hind legs, it shoves the excavated material ahead of its chest and out of the tunnel.

Some remodeling goes on as long as a den is occupied. Toilets are cleaned out periodically and the contents buried in the entrance mound. One can usually determine that a den is in use, during the season when woodchucks are active, by the fresh earth on the doorstep.

Woodchucks generally appear only in the daytime, but sometimes go abroad on moonlit nights, especially during early spring. That, of course, is the mating season.

They eat three times a day and nap the rest of the time. Early morning, late afternoon and evening are meal times. They follow a set routine on arising. Each woodchuck walks to a point about three feet inside the doorway and listens. Frequently it whistles a low, abrupt note, often followed by a tremulous, wavering call that dies slowly away. This has earned for it the name of "whistle-pig" or, as the French called it, *siffleur*.

If everything is quiet, the woodchuck advances slowly, cautiously raising its head until it can see the surroundings. Then it moves to the top of the entrance mound, rears to its full height and makes another long survey. At last satisfied, it drops to all fours and slowly waddles down one of the numerous radiating trails to a feeding place. Once there, however, it dares not relax, but every few minutes stands upright and takes a good look around. About half of the feeding time is spent thus in watching. Any sight or sound of an enemy sends it galloping heavily back to the burrow. Although awkward-looking, this gait will keep it ahead of a man running at top speed over uneven ground for the short distance that is necessary.

Once safe in the hole, the animal is apt to whistle several times. Lethargic as it is, it has a great curiosity and sometimes, even after whistling, will stick its head out and may stop a bullet. It has tremendous vitality and, unless instantly killed by a slug through the brain, is usually able to scramble so far down the tunnel that the hunter cannot easily recover the body.

After establishing its home, the groundhog rarely goes farther than about one hundred yards away, except in spring when on the mating trek. Ordinarily, if food is plentiful, it prefers to stay much closer to refuge. Quite often it has a series of burrows scattered across a field or along a fence line. Connecting them is a network of trails which enables the woodchuck to cover all of its territory without getting far from a doorway to safety. The trails are narrow, about two to four inches wide, and are well hidden when the vegetation is tall.

Woodchucks usually pay little attention to each other and, except during mating season, do not seem to be jealous over their home ranges. Where they are numerous, they may be seen foraging within a few feet of each other and certainly overlap each other's feeding ground. The den, however, is a strictly personal possession and stoutly guarded. Sometimes, when a sudden alarm throws a field full of feeding woodchucks into confusion, one of them may disappear down the burrow that is closest, although it belongs to another. The rightful owner, even though smaller, will immediately chase out the intruder. Whether the ejected woodchuck gets home safely or not is no concern of its inhospitable neighbor.

In an emergency, the tubby, clumsy-looking woodchuck can go up a tree trunk in a rush. Usually it climbs no farther than necessary, eight or ten feet. However, it has been seen as high up as fifty feet. It goes into trees and shrubs for fruits, and at least one woodchuck has been seen stripping and eating quantities of aromatic leaves from a sassafras tree.

Water is no barrier to a woodchuck. Perhaps it doesn't like the effort, but if it wants to cross a stream it just wades in and dog-paddles. Probably depending on its physical condition (fat or lean), it rides high with shoulders and upper back out of water, or sinks so low that only the upturned face and tip of tail are visible.

Once in many years one may see an albino woodchuck. Melanistic animals are more common. One that I collected in Lyndon, Vermont, had a typical blackish body sprinkled with white hairs and here and there a brownish cast. The head was little darker than that of a normal woodchuck.

It takes a long time for a woodchuck to get its one annual new coat. In the North, the process lasts from the end of May until early in September. The frayed, faded coat falls out gradually, commencing on the tail, and each hair is replaced immediately by a new hair. The shedding moves slowly ahead until it reaches the animal's nose, and at last the woodchuck is ready for another winter. Young woodchucks often delay replacing their juvenile dress and winter catches them only about half changed.

In spite of its apparent lethargy, the woodchuck is so alert and quick to dive into its safe den that few other animals are dangerous foes. The tiny pests, roundworms and flatworms that live in the intestinal tract, and protozoans that get into the bloodstream, are much more likely to be fatal. Ticks and many fleas live in its fur, and warbles burrow into the skin or infest nasal and ear passages.

Man is its worst enemy. Without good sense, the groundhog may stick its nose into a convenient garden and eventually pay with its life. It is easily caught in steel, leg-gripping traps or in box traps of wire mesh. Thousands of ground-hogs are poisoned, or gassed by dropping carbon bisulfide or calcium cyanide down the tunnels and sealing all entrances with earth.

Except in the garden or grain field, the woodchuck is actually a useful animal. Farmer boys in the Northeast once used the tanned, tough hide for patching leatherwork and making straps, ball covers and catchers' mitts. The flesh of all except old woodchucks is excellent eating and is relished even now in country districts. After removing the pair of small red musk glands from the inner sides of the upper front legs, and then excess fat, the meat is soaked for several hours in soda water. Then it may be parboiled and either roasted, fried, or made into a stew.

There is no better small-game animal for the sportsman who cannot travel far from home. The woodchuck is in the fields right on the edge of town, a wary target that is a test for the best marksman. Several eastern states recognize this fact and enforce a closed season during the spring and early summer, except for those individuals that are damaging crops. This ensures a good number of woodchucks for a later hunting period.

Another benefit that the woodchuck unwittingly confers on its enemy, the human hunter and trapper, is that the extra dens frequently attract game and fur animals for shelter. Skunks, foxes, weasels, opossums and rabbits use them, either for temporary shelter or permanent homes.

Despite its faults and the fact that it is not overly bright, this roly-poly fellow is likable. In our highly cultivated, perhaps too regimented farming country, it is an interesting inhabitant. It is almost the sole survivor of our once abundant mammals that can be seen readily in daytime. I hope that no super-efficient poison or trap will ever be found to exterminate its race.

After all, it is pretty much of a vegetarian—about ninety-nine per cent! It dines heartily on leaves, flowers and soft stems of green forage plants, such as grasses, alfalfa, clover, and such herbs as wild lettuce, dandelion, buttercup, white daisy, coltsfoot, thistle, and paintbrush. The bark of young maples, hickories, wild cherries and sumacs is scratched or nibbled loose and eaten, especially in spring. It is fond of fruits, particularly wild cherries, blackberries and raspberries, and has been known to travel far to feed on them.

Its most costly appetite is for quantities of grain and truck crops: oats, barley, corn, wheat, and almost any kind of garden produce. Unfortunately, not only does its stomach hold one and one-half pounds of greens at a time, but it tramples down much that it does not eat, and the diggings are hazardous to the mowing machine and horses. It is especially fond of entire bean plants, and cantaloupes and other melons. In autumn it gorges on fallen apples, and sometimes even goes up into the trees after them.

The final one per cent of the woodchuck's ration is made up of animal food. Grasshoppers and June bugs are occasionally eaten, as well as other insects at special times. It is sometimes accused of killing and eating young poultry, as well as robbing the nests of wild ground-nesting birds of eggs and fledglings. Since many rodents are highly carnivorous at times, it is not unreasonable to suppose that the woodchuck eats birds too. However, there is little evidence on this point.

General description. A large ground-dwelling rodent with broad head, low ears, heavy body, short legs and short, flattened tail. Fur medium long, coarse. General color brown, washed with grayish or reddish and frequently "frosted" with white, shading to whitish or paler brown on belly; head and tail dark brown to black. Total length, 18 to 25 inches; height at shoulder, 6 to 7 inches; weight, very variable, from 5 to 10 pounds up to an extreme of about 13 pounds.

Distinguishing characteristics. Combination of stocky build, short tail, and large size distinguish the woodchuck from all ground squirrels that dwell in fields, rockpiles, or sometimes in woods or wood borders. The yellow-bellied marmot is more brownish, and has yellowish or reddish legs and feet, while those of the woodchuck are nearly black. The hoary marmots are larger and are mixed black and white (except for the species on the Olympic Peninsula and Vancouver Island, which are completely brown).

Range. Extreme northeastern Quebec and Nova Scotia to southeastern Virginia and northern Alabama; west to Great Slave Lake, southwestern Yukon, northwestern Montana, central Saskatchewan, eastern South Dakota, and northeastern Oklahoma.

MARMOT
MARMOTA FLAVIVENTRIS AND
M. CALIGATA GROUP

All three American members of the woodchuck tribe whistle, but the hoary marmot is the champion. If an avian dive-bomber such as the golden eagle appears overhead, this western woodchuck lets loose a shrill blast that sets the echoes ringing. Every inhabitant of the high places is alerted. Underground dwellers pop into their shelters, bigger mammals throw up their heads and prepare for trouble and the birds cease singing. There is no sound on the rocky, flower-strewn slopes except the irrepressible hum of insects and the repeated, almost human whistles of marmots as they spread the alarm. On a windless day, the racket may be heard for a mile.

Late one summer afternoon I was hiking up the canyon of Savage River, northeast of Mount McKinley, in Alaska. My companions had gone on while I examined some especially interesting bighorn range, with the understanding that we would rendezvous before nightfall at the head of the canyon. The sky clouded over and the canyon filled with gloom. Suddenly I was jerked out of my abstraction by a whistle from the cliff above. My first thought was of my companions, that they had made a side trip across the mountain and had signalled for me to join or wait for them. So I whistled back. Another shrill sound returned from the crags. I replied and tried to sight my friends. Then whistling broke out all along the mountainside. I realized that I had been fooled. Far above, the head and shoulders of a marmot projected from the point of a rock spur. "Phooey!" he shrieked at me in marmot whistle-language.

In late summer, colonies of hoary marmots are especially clamorous. On sunny days the animals seem to be staging whistling matches. As Fred Overly

MARMOT

once described it: "Those marmots sit up on the rocks and whistle till their eyes pop out!"

The sharp, penetrating signal is not made by the marmot's lips. Apparently it is formed in the throat, for the mouth is neither open nor pursed as the sound issues. The marmot does not limit itself to whistles, but when excited may burst forth with a variety of barks, yips and yells. If angry and frightened, it grinds its teeth.

The smaller, yellow-bellied marmot that also lives in the western mountains, but at lower elevations than the sky-high hoary marmot, is less accomplished. It is still a fairly powerful whistler, but its note is more like a shrill "chirp." The weakest whistler of the three is the woodchuck in the East. Oddly enough, this was the one that was originally named *le siffleur* (meaning whistler) by the French Baron La Hontan in 1703. The name was carried westward by the French fur traders. It is rarely used now for the woodchuck, except by country people in eastern Quebec.

The three kinds of woodchucks are the eastern woodchuck and the two western marmots. They occupy enormous ranges in North America. Only in northern Idaho and southeastern British Columbia are all three found in the same region. Here they do not live together, but occupy different zones of altitude. The woodchuck is sandwiched between the two exclusively western cousins.

The marmots of the West are divided into two groups, the hoary and the yellow-bellied (see p. 341). Both are hoary, that is to say, frosted with white-tipped hairs. The yellow-bellied is more yellowish than gray, as in the true hoary species.

The hoary marmot usually lives near or even considerably above timber line, except in Alaska where the forest belt is not wide anyhow. There it may leave its usually beloved rocks and make its home on open, grassy hillsides or even far out on the flats.

Yellow-bellied marmots are occasionally called rockchucks, because they locate their burrows under ledges or broken slide rock. Sometimes a crack in a cliff runs back far enough to make a suitable cave dwelling. Since the chief object in having a tunnel reinforced with rock is to keep out bears or other hungry enemies, the cliff apartment is a prize and is occupied by many generations of marmots.

No naturalist has ever taken the trouble to trace out a marmot burrow and den, except where it has already been opened and largely destroyed by bears. We know only that the marmot gathers and carries dry grass in its mouth into the cave for a bed. During prolonged spells of wet weather, it may be seen removing damp bedding and searching diligently for dry material to replace it. Ordinarily it is a glossy, rippling, carefully groomed creature, but at such a time it may be as bedraggled as a wet alley-cat.

The marmot may be conscious during only three months of the year, while the other nine are spent in a deathlike sleep. It retires as early as the middle of June in the low, arid valleys of the Northwest, but not until late August on the high mountains of Glacier National Park. It has eaten nothing for two weeks and the intestinal tract is then empty. It rolls up into a coil, puts its hands over its eyes, and becomes dead to the world until the next year. It misses the beautiful autumn weather, sometimes even part of the summer, but it is not aware of any loss. Unlike many other animals, perhaps it is lucky not to have to fight the cold and search, often vainly, for food in winter.

Coming out of hibernation early, the exact time depending on the altitude and latitude, the marmot frequently finds nothing to eat. It may be early April or even March, south of the Canadian boundary, and the marmot may have to dig through several feet of snow to get out. For a couple of weeks it has little appetite and does not seem to mind fasting.

As the snow melts and the green growth starts with a rush, it makes up for lost time. During early morning and late afternoon it may be seen grazing near its den, eating all kinds of grasses and other succulent plants. Its lean form fills out, begins and continues to bulge until it is much wider than high. Its short legs cannot prevent the stomach from rubbing on the ground. Then the marmot becomes a little more particular about what it eats. Sitting up in the meadow, it pulls over the nodding stalks of wild lettuce and knotweed, and expertly bites off the white flowers.

At this stage you could run down the fat marmot on level ground. But don't do it unless you are prepared for a tough fight. All members of the woodchuck tribe are lumpy and lethargic-looking, but are brave and able fighters. Not even when cornered by a man with a club will they cower. Of course, a marmot would prefer to run, and if it can reach a cliff or talus slide will rush up it almost as easily as a rock squirrel.

Like the woodchuck, the marmot is almost entirely a daytime animal. It may not even go below for the midday rest period. If the sun is shining, it prefers to spend this time stretched out on a rocky point or on the earthen platform before the den, soaking up the ultraviolet rays. It stays inside most of the time during cloudy and stormy weather.

Enemies are always prowling about, looking for a meal. When the marmot is above ground, eagles may swoop from the blue sky, and hawks are well able to seize and kill the younger animals. Coyotes, bobcats, lynxes, foxes, cougars and wolves make careful stalks or lie in ambush for it behind rocks or bushes in pastures. A grizzly or black bear would be only too glad to smack down a carelessly dozing marmot and thus save the effort of digging it out of the stony ground.

Smaller predators, like the mink, may attack a marmot and sometimes be routed. A marmot in Yellowstone Park was once seen to chase off a mink which had caught a ground squirrel. Philosophically, the rescuer then sat down and washed its face while the rescued squirrel, fatally injured, breathed its last.

Marmots are always community-spirited with their own kind. Whistlers are especially sociable and live in villages. Yellow-bellied marmots are less gregarious, but live in groups. Both species seem to post sentinels that are keen-eyed and vigilant and usually succeed in warning everyone of danger. But perhaps these "watchmen" are only self-appointed worriers. Most members of the community are alert, curious and ready to whistle at the first sight of trouble anyway.

An outline of the marmot's early life is much like that of the woodchuck.

The parents mate during early spring. The young, three to eight but usually four or five in number, are born from about March 15 on the lower Columbia River to about the middle of May in the mountains of Colorado. Hoary marmots may be a little later, but for both species the season varies with location. Young yellow-bellied marmots appear above ground when they are about the size of grown Columbian ground squirrels. The mother sends her young out into the world before their first autumn because she is getting ready to retire. They develop more slowly than woodchucks and few of them mate before they are two years old.

Albino marmots are rare, but melanistic animals are common in some localities. The Teton Mountains of northwestern Wyoming is one of these. The dark animals may be as black as coal, with perhaps a few white hairs or a patch of reddish brown surviving from the normal coat. Some strange dwarf marmots, adults but no larger than two-month-old youngsters, have been reported in northwestern Colorado.

The two marmots and the woodchuck all share in the rodent characteristic of having front teeth which grow rapidly and continuously. Usually these are kept ground down to proper length by use. Sometimes, by accident or in prenatal growth, one or more incisors are thrown out of line. Unopposed, they grow out of the animal's mouth in a great spiral. (Eastern woodchucks have been found with teeth as much as three and one-half inches long.) Sometimes the erratic tooth enters and destroys an eye, or wraps itself around the opposing jaw, thus locking the mouth of the unfortunate animal so that it starves to death. In many less severe cases, both the eastern and western woodchucks have managed to maintain themselves in good condition despite the handicap.

Many Indian tribes of our northwestern states, western Canada and Alaska value the marmot for food. A Colville Indian of northern Washington once said that he would rather have a good marmot pasture than a fine cornfield. Europeans, especially Swiss, who have settled in western Washington, are said to make hunting trips to the mountains just for rockchucks, the meat of which reminds them of the marmots they enjoyed in the Old Country. The pelts are beautifully colored and the fur warm, as it is provided with a thick undercoat. (The fur of the eastern woodchuck is coarser and lacks this important feature.) The Eskimos of northern Alaska prize the skins for making robes and parkas, which must be warm, light, and durable under hard usage. In fact, our marmot furs are just as satisfactory as those of European and Asiatic species, which are used in great quantities in the fur trade.

When they get the opportunity, marmots are as destructive to crops as woodchucks. Fortunately, most of the western animals live in rough, infertile places where man does not try to raise crops. The worst charge ever brought against marmots is that of harboring some dreaded diseases, including sylvatic plague and tularemia. They have been known also, in Montana, like many other animals, to serve as hosts to the tick that carries spotted fever.

The marmots are divided into two groups:

1. The yellow-bellied marmot (*Marmota flaviventris*), which is small to medium-sized, with buffy patches on the sides of the neck, usually a band of white across the face between the eyes, and light buffy to dark brown (never black) feet. It is found in hilly or rocky areas from southern British Columbia to Owens Lake, California, and eastward to the Black Hills and north central New Mexico.

2. The hoary marmot (*Marmota caligata*) is large, chiefly black and white, frequently tinged with rusty, with buffy red on the hind quarters, and blackish brown feet (therefore the name *caligata,* meaning "boots"). Found in mountains (except in the far north) from northwestern Alaska and the Alaska Peninsula to central Washington and Idaho.

General description. A western woodchuck. Color and size variable, but rarely as red as the eastern animal; under parts generally yellowish or reddish. (The hoary marmot is almost whitish underneath, rich buffy red on the rump and lower back and grayish elsewhere.) Total length, 15 to 30 inches; height at shoulder, about 7 inches; weight, 4½ to 20 pounds. Females are about 20 per cent smaller.

Distinguishing characteristics. Typically woodchucklike. Generally associated with rocky places such as talus slopes. Larger and more stocky than ground squirrels. The prairie dog is smaller, chunkier, paler in color, and lives in colonies on the plains. Distinguished from eastern woodchuck by generally less reddish color and by geographic location.

Range. Western North America from central New Mexico and the southern Sierra Nevada of California north to the Black Hills, central Montana, northwestern Alaska and the Alaska Peninsula.

COLUMBIAN GROUND SQUIRREL
CITELLUS COLUMBIANUS

Ground squirrels are well named, for they seldom leave the ground. Some of them spend as much as three-fourths of their lives under it, asleep.

When awake and above ground, they spend a great deal of their time sitting straight up on their haunches, their backs and necks as straight as ramrods. For this reason they are often called "picket pins." Depending upon the species, they are some nine to nineteen inches long, two and one-quarter to three and one-half inches high at the shoulders, and weigh from four ounces to two pounds.

They can be found in almost every part of North America except the East. From extreme northern Canada and Alaska south to Guerro and the Valley of Mexico, from the Pacific Ocean and Bering Sea to Hudson Bay, Lake Michigan, Indiana and eastern Texas (except coastal Washington and much of British Columbia), they become tremendously abundant under favorable conditions.

They raise large families. Each female of many species produces eight to ten or even twelve offspring in a litter. In about a month the youngsters are well grown and eating large amounts of vegetation.

Because of their fondness for grains and alfalfa, ground squirrels levy an enormous toll on the farmer. Their extensive burrows sometimes channel rainwater into underground streams that erode the soil and cause landslides. Their tunnels in the banks of irrigation ditches may cause washouts and loss of water and crops. They carry and spread diseases that often are fatal to man: tularemia,

COLUMBIAN GROUND SQUIRREL

spotted fever, relapsing fever and the dreaded bubonic plague (the Black Death of mediaeval Europe).

For these reasons, many thousands of dollars have been spent in learning the details of ground squirrel existence in order to guide the expenditure of millions of dollars for control of the animals.

All ground squirrels are not equally destructive. The mantled ground squirrel lives in the mountains, while the round-tailed, the spotted and the antelope ground squirrels reside on deserts. Man rarely tries to grow crops on such land. Many individuals, as well as entire geographic races of the "pest" species, moreover, live out their existence in northern regions where they seldom or never conflict with man's interests.

Every ground burrower aids in working and reworking the soil, aerating and mixing it. Even the destructive squirrels accomplish some further benefit to agriculture by destroying harmful insects.

Living under varied conditions, from the Arctic tundra to the deserts of Mexico, the tribe has become greatly diversified. Zoologists recognize thirty-one distinct species, which are further divided into about one hundred geographic races. The habits of the animals vary accordingly. Obviously it would require about one-third of this book to even sketch the life histories and descriptions of all these ground squirrels. We have room for but one example of each of the outstanding types (see pp. 348–349).

Eleven to fifteen inches long, the Columbian ground squirrel is one of the largest and most populous of this tribe of rodents. The range of the species and its close relatives, covering a vast expanse of northwestern America, includes some of the most important areas of the continent for growing fruits, forage and grain crops.

Experiments have determined that a female that is nursing fairly well-developed young will eat more than seventeen per cent of her weight every day, or about one-seventh of a pound of clover. As many as twelve hundred Columbian squirrels have been trapped from two hundred acres of land, an average of six squirrels an acre. Probably a considerable number survived the trapping. The twelve hundred were consuming enough food to support three cows or twelve sheep.

In one experiment, two equal-sized plots of growing wheat were surrounded with squirrel-proof fences. An adult Columbian ground squirrel was released in one of the enclosures. For two months the animal fed to its heart's content on the juicy leaves and stems. Then, as these parts became woody, it switched to the fast-developing grain. When the remaining ripe wheat was harvested, it was found that this one squirrel had destroyed forty-four pounds of kernels. An area of five hundred square feet surrounding the animal's den (the region of greatest damage) yielded only four pounds of grain and one sheaf of straw. A comparable portion of the other plot, which was protected, produced forty-one pounds of wheat and nine bundles of straw.

Columbian ground squirrels prefer rocky slopes with scattered trees. However, they frequently move far out onto open valleys, where they become abundant in grain and hay fields. Lowlands, and mountain parks up to eight thousand feet elevation in the Cascade Mountains are equally enjoyed. The northern members of this group must get along without trees. I have seen great grassy slopes in southwestern Alaska pocked by open pits where the brown bears had been digging out Aleutian ground squirrels (close relatives of the Columbian) from their dens. There the rodents were living far from any timber. Almost the only rigid requirement of the Columbian squirrel group is green vegetation, and plenty of it. They are hearty eaters and must have enough to fill their stomachs.

The Columbian ground squirrel is a nervous, active, sociable creature. It lives in a colony which may extend almost without interruption for miles. Nevertheless, it wants privacy in the underground home, which it occupies from sunset to an hour or so after sunrise, and again during the heat of the day. It dislikes being out in cold, windy, or rainy weather. Whenever the sun shines, however, it is in the open, gathering food and chattering in low chirps with the neighbors.

This animal does not require water and may never take a drink in its life. How does it manage?

A number of other inhabitants of the desert satisfy their thirst by eating succulent cactus or by converting the starch of grains in their stomachs into water. The Columbian ground squirrel does not live in a desert, but a part of its range is in an important agricultural district where almost all the precipitation comes in winter. Crops and other vegetation grow rapidly in spring and early summer. Each plant must drink fast to get its share of the moisture which is stored in the ground.

When the available supply is depleted, the plants stop growing and mature. They become dry and woody and, to the ground squirrel, distasteful. Day after day the summer sun glares down from a hot metallic sky, shriveling the leaves, baking the ground. A most unhealthy situation for a little animal that does not know any world more than a quarter-mile distant from its birthplace.

Long ago the whole ground squirrel tribe worked out an answer to this problem of how to subsist without water to drink. They go to sleep and sleep so soundly that their heart and breathing almost stop. Their cells require practically no moisture at all.

As early as July, or even earlier, the ground squirrel may acquire its winter coat and retire to its den for seven or eight months. If it does not live in the parched lowlands, it can stay out longer. The herbs of the uplands hold their juices and the seeds are not forced to early maturity. Some of the more restless young squirrels may be seen outdoors as late as the first week of October.

The squirrel must make preparations for its long sleep. During the few months of the year that it is awake, it stores up a great deal of food in its body in the form of fat. It must have enough to live on not only for seven or eight months but for the lean two or three weeks after it emerges in spring, before green food is plentiful again. By the time it retires it may be so fat that the belly seems to drag on the ground.

A special sleeping den has to be tunneled. This hibernating room is a perfectly round cell about nine or ten inches in diameter and lined with grasses. It is located at the end of a short slope running out from the summer burrow. Usually it is two to three feet below ground, but may be as shallow as six inches or as deep as five feet. When the den is not on a steep hillside, the one or more drain tunnels, about two feet long below the bedroom at an angle of about forty-five degrees, draw off any moisture that might seep down from above. Then a shaft may be dug upward toward the surface, so that that much work on the exit will be finished when the animal wakes up and wants to leave the following spring. To leave as it entered, through the summer burrow, would be contrary to the family custom.

As its world dries out it becomes increasingly sleepy. It eats practically nothing, and finds the heat more and more oppressive. In fact, it is so sensitive to sunshine that lengthy exposure would kill it. Then it goes into its round cell and plugs the entrance. Tamping loose earth together solidly with its nose, it cuts itself off from the world.

In a daze, the little animal sits back on its hips and curls its head and body forward and back until its nose is against its abdomen. So tight is this vertical loop that nearly all air is pressed out of the lungs. In a few hours the breathing and heart action have nearly ceased. The body temperature drops from the normal ninety-eight degrees Fahrenheit to only forty. Gradually it passes into an almost deathlike trance. For the ground squirrel, three to five feet below the sun-parched countryside, time rolls to a stop.

The end of February arrives and many a squirrel begins to stir. In as short a time as it passed from life to near-death, each squirrel is alive again. Digging to the surface, it surveys a cold spring landscape. In a few days it will probably abandon its hibernating den forever. It is partly filled already with the soil carelessly thrown behind as the occupant claws its way out.

Old males appear a week to ten days ahead of the adult females. They are naturally more interested in food than anything else in life. Unlike the females and younger fry, they frequently have packed away some food before going to sleep. Stores of seeds and bulbs are sorted and placed in separate bins beneath their nests. These cupboards are not touched until spring. Then, when the weather is bad and food hard to find, these provident old fellows dine sumptuously and continuously—in bed.

Very likely the entrance of the Columbian ground squirrel's old summer burrow is filled with wind-blown soil and rubbish. It may even be obliterated by fall plowing. However, the owner seems to have a good sense of orientation. It just digs a new shaft down until it breaks into the tunnel.

This summer home consists of several dens in various states of repair and use. They are lined with the finest grasses and are connected by tunnels about three and one-half inches in diameter. Additional blind shafts radiate from the dens. In an emergency they can be extended to the surface in a hurry. This ground squirrel wants no back doors left open for prowling enemies to enter. The burrow system is generally about two feet below the surface, but, depending on the type of soil and the slope, may be as much as five feet deep or as shallow as twelve inches. It may be rather extensive; an average system contains about sixty-five feet of tunnels, but many are longer.

Each squirrel follows its own ideas and no two burrow systems are alike. In firm soil the tunnels may last for many years and be occupied at various intervals by different animals, each of which makes improvements and additions. All of the earth removed from the summer den, as well as successive hibernating cells, is pushed laboriously out through the single doorway. The dump may soon contain four or five bushels of soil and stones, which provide a convenient guide post to the hungry bear that doesn't see very well!

A week or ten days after coming out of hibernation the mature squirrels mate. This is a period of great activity. The animals rush about nervously and are almost indifferent to possible danger, though they ordinarily show considerable caution.

After a development period of twenty-four days, the young are born in a special nursery den. This is larger than the ordinary room and is more carefully lined with soft grasses. The litter contains two to seven naked, pink little creatures. Although they are blind and toothless, and weigh only one-quarter to one-third of an ounce at birth, they develop rapidly. In two weeks their weight increases fivefold. (A human child requires at least three years to make a comparable increase in weight.) Although still sightless, the baby squirrels can chirp like their mother. Their fused eyelids part when they are three weeks old, and nursing continues for about thirty days. Some observers believe that the transition to a solid food diet may be assisted by their mother feeding them for a few days on partly digested food regurgitated from her stomach.

Timidly and unsteadily, the little squirrels venture to the entrance of the den a few days after their eyes open. They are able to dig at the age of four weeks, and a week or ten days afterward they leave the home den to set up their own establishments. Each youngster finds an abandoned burrow (of which there are usually a number) somewhere in the neighborhood, cleans out the essential tunnels, replaces the old nest with fresh material, and begins its independent life. At two months of age the first coat is shed. The squirrel now weighs between five and nine ounces, and it busily puts on more fat in preparation for going into aestivation and hibernation. It does not complete its full growth, however, until the second year.

It seems extraordinary that infancy and youth can be so telescoped. In the short space of ninety days the ground squirrel "grows up," accumulates enough fat to last for more than seven months, and manages to construct a winter home. It must be admitted that this first hibernating den excavated off from the summer tunnel is poorly prepared. It is small, only about six inches in diameter and only six inches to a foot below the surface. The drain is reduced to one ditch, instead of three or four that often radiate below the den of an old, experienced squirrel. The youngster may not even provide itself with bedding. Like a human baby, it may not need as much covering as its elders and is probably more hardy. Anyhow, many young squirrels manage to survive the long winter in poor quarters.

Immature ground squirrels sleep a little later in spring than adults. When they awake, they go out to find mates among their own generation, for the older squirrels have already finished this business.

The food of the Columbian ground squirrel is more than ninety-five per cent vegetable, of a great many varieties. The bulk consists of the leaves and stems of herbs and grasses. Bulbs of wild onions, glacier lilies and camas are dug up and devoured. Flowers of such plants as lupines, buttercups and dandelions, and fruits such as currants, gooseberries, serviceberries and strawberries are eagerly eaten in season.

The squirrel's appetite for cultivated crops attracts its most deadly enemy—man. While not endowed with much intelligence, the little animal is quick to learn that a rifle or shotgun must be avoided at all costs. Only during the mating craze does it forget caution. At this time it may blunder into any trap or snare.

no matter how obvious. It has never learned to pass by poisoned grain. Whole-sale slaughter is achieved by the use of carbon bisulphide. When a little of the liquid is poured on a bit of waste and thrown into the hibernating burrow as soon as it is opened in spring, the heavy gas spreads and kills the occupant. This is usually done during early morning or evening in order to find the animals at home.

Besides these dangers, the ground squirrel is sought for food by every sizable flesh eater that walks, flies and crawls. A few of the most persistent are hawks, coyotes, bears, wolves, foxes, badgers, and rattlesnakes.

Not as fussy as the white man, most Indians ate all species of ground squir-rels. The Piutes regularly captured those in their region (Nevada) by filling their dens with water and grabbing the half-drowned rodents by the necks as they emerged. Thin squirrels were turned loose; fat animals were killed, eviscerated, and then buried in hot coals until the hair was completely burned away. The charred skin was then peeled off and the fat flesh eaten. Even today, most of the older Piutes still use this age-old recipe. Enterprising individuals capture and sell live squirrels for ten cents each or three for "two bits," to "be kept on the hoof" until needed for a meal.

The ground squirrels of the genus *Citellus* are divided into eleven distinctive groups with easily recognized coats. Each group includes two or more species and a number of geographic races.

1. Townsend's ground squirrel and relatives are small and plainly colored—gray with a pinkish cast and cinnamon-tinted tail. Range: south central Wash-ington and eastern Idaho south to southern Nevada and southeastern Utah.

2. Washington ground squirrel and relatives are small. Color gray, spotted with whitish, and the tail is mixed brown and grayish white with black tip. Range: eastern Washington, northeastern Oregon, and western Idaho.

3. Richardson's ground squirrel and relatives are medium to large. They are colored brownish or grayish above, dappled with cinnamon; under parts pale buffy, with the under side of tail gray, buffy, or brownish. Range: south central Alberta to eastern Manitoba, south to central Oregon and the southern Sierra Nevada of California, central Utah, north central Colorado, and southwestern Minnesota.

4. Columbian ground squirrel and relatives—see page 341.

5. The striped ground squirrel and relatives—see page 349.

6. Spotted ground squirrel and relatives are small to medium in size. Upper parts are various shades of brownish or grayish, marked with squarish white spots; tail ends in a black tip and is pinkish on the under surface. Range: south-

western North Dakota to southeastern Texas and central Mexico; west to the Colorado River in northern Arizona, and south-central Arizona.

7. Franklin's ground squirrel is large and grayish, with a blackish tail frosted with white. Range: east-central Alberta to northwestern Indiana, westward to south central Kansas and western North Dakota.

8. The rock squirrel and relatives—see page 355.

9. The antelope squirrel—see page 359.

10. Round-tailed ground squirrel and relatives are small and gray, with a distinct pinkish or cinnamon cast. Range: southern California and southern Nevada, south to northern Baja California, south-central Arizona, and south-western Sonora.

11. The mantled ground squirrel—see page 363.

General description. A fairly large ground-dwelling, burrowing rodent. Squirrel-like in general form, with low, rounded ears and short tail. Upper parts rusty grayish, mottled with blending narrow bands of rusty yellowish; under parts pale buffy or tawny; the head, legs and feet, and tail, tawny or grayish. Total length, 11 to 15 inches; height at shoulder, 3½ inches; weight, 1 to 2 pounds.

Distinguishing characteristics. See page 343. Compared with others of the group, the Columbian ground squirrel is large.

Range. Animals of this group are found from Kodiak Island, some of the Aleutian Islands, and the Bering Sea coast of Alaska east to northeastern Hudson Bay; the Arctic coast south to southern Keewatin, Great Slave Lake, and, in the mountains, to western Montana, south-central Idaho, and eastern Oregon.

STRIPED GROUND SQUIRREL
CITELLUS TRIDECEMLINEATUS

The "thirteen-lined ground squirrel" is supposed to have thirteen stars and stripes. For this reason it is sometimes called the federation squirrel. The scientific name also means "thirteen lines," but the animal may have a few more or a few less. The stars are much more numerous, and are only squarish spots.

This ground squirrel is a hearty meateater. Fully half of its diet is meat, more than that of any other ground squirrel. It pounces on grasshoppers and other insects and can catch even deer mice and meadow mice. Sometimes it sits

STRIPED GROUND SQUIRREL

up on a dangerous highway, nibbling away quickly at the crushed body of one of its own family.

It is not unusual for this squirrel to steal eggs or fledglings from the nests of ground-dwelling birds. It must be cautious, of course, and not go blundering into the home of a sizable bird, for it is a small mammal and rarely weighs as much as half a pound. A good-sized nester, such as a meadow lark or killdeer, can often put up a stout defense against the striped neighbor and send it off scratched, battered and wiser. Smaller birds occasionally lose their families, and an adult would be quickly killed if the striper found it napping or crippled. It has been seen to kill a seventeen-day-old domestic chicken by biting through its side under the wing.

With these murderous proclivities, it gives one an eerie feeling when the striper calls. The high-pitched, quavering whistle is so birdlike that it sounds almost like the voice of its most recent victim.

It is interesting to watch this little rodent hunting live prey. It stalks and pounces on grasshoppers, leaping swiftly and pinning them down with its front paws. Then it starts to feed immediately, beginning with the head. Caterpillars are killed by striking them rapidly and repeatedly with the claws of its front feet.

In addition to grasshoppers, crickets, cutworms, webworms, beetles, and ants, and the eggs of all kinds of insects, the striped ground squirrel eats almost any variety of seed that it can stuff into its cheeks. This includes all kinds of cultivated grains, goosefoot, wild sunflower, knotweed, gromwell, ragweed, black locust, cotton, dandelion, buffalo-bur, domestic flax, wild beans and many kinds of grasses and legumes. Also on the list are cactus fruits, acorns, roots, the foliage of tender grasses, and nightshade berries.

Whether it eats its finds on the spot or carries them home for storage, this ground squirrel is likely to fill its cheek pockets first. It does not do this with the paws, but, lowering the head, forces the food in by swelling the neck muscles. Then it can let the grains slip, a few at a time, out of its cheeks and onto the grinding molars. Discarded husks are spit out, while the masticated food slides backward down its throat. The capacity of the cheek pockets is considerable. One squirrel was found to be carrying no less than one hundred and ninety-six seeds of the catchfly (*Silene*).

The species' preference for insects more than balances in value its destruction of birds and agricultural crops. This is especially true in meadows and pastures where insects often eat a considerable amount of forage and multiply into hordes that devastate crops on cultivated lands.

The striped ground squirrel goes out for breakfast as soon as the sun comes up. Heat doesn't seem to bother it. On the midwestern prairies the summer sun at noon may drive a shaded thermometer over one hundred degrees, but the striper skips about, the only zestful creature in a broiling, wilted world. Of course, it goes into the underground den for a nap now and then, but it doesn't retire for long, not until sunset. Then it presumably sleeps soundly all night.

The elevation where this squirrel is found may be anywhere from sea level to ten thousand feet in the Rockies. Living entirely in dry, open fields where the grass is somewhat sparse and short, and only occasionally in brushy fence rows or wood borders, it must keep a sharp watch for enemies. It has a great many, from hawks to coyotes, weasels, badgers, foxes, house cats, and such crawlers as the fox snake and black snake. To see around the flat domain, and to listen for hostile footsteps, the ground squirrel, like its many relatives, stands bolt upright on its haunches. Propped on its legs and tail as a flat tripod, the back is a straight rigid line from base of tail to back of head. Turning its head from side to side, it makes a careful scrutiny of the surroundings. If a predator is near, the little rodent scurries for home, its short legs blurred with motion.

The alternating pale and dark stripes running the full length of the back are conspicuous on a dead squirrel that is examined closely. On a live animal, they serve as excellent camouflage by breaking up its outline and making the squirrel seem a part of the field with the seed stalks, crisscrossing weed stems, bits of exposed earth, and tiny shadows. Its buffy brown colors blend perfectly with the yellows and browns of curing grasses. It is a "successful" species. As land has been cleared for agriculture, striped ground squirrels have multiplied and spread, especially in the eastern portion of their range north of the Ohio River and east of the Mississippi.

Great numbers of striped ground squirrels or "striped gophers," as they are erroneously called, are killed by automobiles as they hurry across the highways. One hundred and seven dead were once counted on eleven miles of highway in Iowa by Dr. W. J. Hamilton. Other thousands are destroyed by farmers to protect their crops. On the whole, however, civilization has helped this ground squirrel more than it has hindered it, by creating a vast acreage of suitable food and environment.

To keep ahead of their losses, striped ground squirrels have big families— from five to thirteen at a birth. The adult males wake from their winter sleep between March fifteenth and April twentieth, the time depending mostly on the season and latitude. Two or three weeks later the females appear. While waiting for mating time, about three or four weeks after the first animals emerge, the squirrels eat enormously. The females make necessary repairs to the burrows, clear out old nesting material, and build new nests.

Female stripers are willing to mate over a period of a month, but individual males are so inclined for only about two weeks. However, because all males are not sexually active simultaneously, the actual mating season extends from early April until well along in May.

An average litter contains eight to ten young. They are born after gestating twenty-seven to twenty-eight days, and are blind, pink little beings that weigh only one-tenth of an ounce or less. By the time they are twelve days old they are so well-haired on the back that their stripes are distinct. Soon their protesting squeaks begin to change to the tremulous whistle of the adult voice. At twenty-three to twenty-six days of age the front end of each sealed eyelid begins to separate. Between twenty-four and thirty-six hours later the eyes open completely. At this time the little animals weigh about three-fourths of an ounce apiece and are nibbling solid food.

When they are only about six weeks old the young ground squirrels are ready to leave home and go on their own. Possibly they get restless and leave of their own accord; more likely the mother begins to lose interest and even treat them with hostility. Like all normal ground squirrels, she enjoys neighbors but not household companions.

So the youngsters, perhaps a little more than half grown, look for new home sites. They may settle close around the mother's den, or may move some distance away. Although each one digs a separate burrow, the fraternal tie seems to be strong enough to keep all members of the brood in the same area. For some time, on sunny days, they can be seen playing together like the youngsters they are.

The homes of these juvenile squirrels are amateurish affairs. The tunnel is as short as six feet and usually close to the surface. In keeping with size requirements, the single entrance is only about one inch in diameter. Later in life each ground squirrel will build a more elaborate home. The entrance of this will dip almost straight down from one to nearly four feet, depending on the hardness of the soil. It then turns at right angles and follows an erratic course for as much as twenty feet. Side passages, some of them leading to the surface, will be numerous. A large den, from one to two and one-half feet below the ground surface, will be filled with a nest of fine grasses and rootlets, and several storehouses will be kept filled through most of the year with seeds or grains. Although the ground squirrel apparently eats little or nothing through the winter, it providently keeps plenty of food on hand for springtime and emergencies. Occasionally a lazy striped ground squirrel will move into an abandoned burrow of a kangaroo rat, prairie dog, pocket gopher, or other rodent. In one extraordinary case, a mother resorted to a mattress in an unoccupied house. It made a nest de luxe for herself and eight small young.

The side entrances of the striper's home are usually kept plugged with earth. When inside for the winter, or even overnight, it closes the front door also in this way. Perhaps it has a fear of awaking to find a snake in its burrow. Unlike the Columbian ground squirrel, the striped squirrel does not dump excavated soil just outside the door, but takes it out in its cheek pouches and scatters it at a distance. In the grass its doorway is hard to see.

Often it will dig several short tunnels as emergency shelters. Located at strategic spots on the foraging grounds, they are connected with each other and with the home den by little inconspicuous trails through the grass. They permit the owner to extend its feeding radius over a greater area without too much risk of being overtaken by enemies.

As the sun gradually moves southward in its daily course across the sky, the ground squirrels grow exceedingly fat. They shed their faded, worn summer suits for fresh, bright winter ones. No longer do they take pleasure in chattering back and forth across the grass stems. In fact, they become very peevish and irritable toward each other. Finally, about the last of August, the fattest squirrels lapse into drowsiness and retire to their nests. One by one the rest follow, until by late November the last of the juveniles and the few lean, restless adults are asleep too. In the typical coiled-up position, their temperature drops from a normal eighty-six to one hundred and six degrees Fahrenheit to only thirty-seven degrees. The heart beat is reduced from two hundred to three hundred and fifty per minute to a mere five. Oxygen consumption is only seven per cent of the amount used by active squirrels.

Although most of them awaken every couple of weeks, only a few animals in the southern regions go outdoors during the winter. During this six or seven months' fast, they lose flesh gradually, until, when they come out in the spring, they may have lost one-third to even half of their autumn weight. The best temperature in a den for safe hibernation is forty-one to fifty-four degrees Fahrenheit. A sudden fall to five or six degrees below freezing usually rouses the sleeper, whose body temperature then rises. If it does not awaken, it freezes to death.

General description. A small to medium-sized ground squirrel with a rather long, slender head and small, short-haired tail. General color cinnamon or buffy; upper parts marked by about five blackish or dark brown stripes extending the length of the body from neck to tail; each stripe carries a series of squarish white or yellowish white spots; alternating with the dark stripes are about six narrower whitish bands; below these stripes, on the flanks, are several more indefinite stripes or rows of spots; under parts pale buffy, pinkish, or yellowish white. Total length, 9 to 11 inches; height at shoulder, 3 inches; weight, 4 to 5 ounces, up to 8 or 9 ounces just before hibernation.

Distinguishing characteristics. The lengthwise series of distinct stripes, some of them with a row of white dots, set this ground squirrel apart from all other burrowing animals.

Range. Great Plains and prairie regions of central United States and southern Canada. Lower Peninsula of Michigan, western Ohio, western Missouri, and east-central Texas to the Gulf coast; north to north-central Minnesota, Lake Winnipeg, and central Alberta; west to northwestern Montana, western Wyoming, and eastern Arizona.

ROCK SQUIRREL
CITELLUS VARIEGATUS

The rock squirrel looks like a gray squirrel (*Sciurus*), although its tail is not as bushy. Much the same size, it is seventeen to nineteen inches long and may weigh two pounds. However, it is a ground squirrel, not a tree squirrel. At times, it may climb trees, but not far. I have never seen it higher than thirty or thirty-five feet, and it is not very sure of itself there. If frightened, it may stay

ROCK SQUIRREL

in the tree to hide, but is more likely to rush down to its burrow under the ground.

This squirrel is found only in the Southwest and far into Mexico, usually among the broken rock for which it is named. It is wary, unfriendly and suspicious. Even back in the remote canyons where human visitors are rare, I have seen it flee from a sunning spot while I was still some distance away. With a short, sharp whistle, it spreads the alarm to the neighbors and scurries to shelter. Just before it ducks into a rock slide or under a ledge it gives a final "whicker" or brief low-pitched trill. When the situation is not so critical, its loud whistle is more prolonged and sometimes quavers a little with emotion.

Most of these ground squirrels live in wild regions where they do not clash with man. Although not communal, like the Columbian ground squirrels, they may be numerous on a small talus slope if the food is abundant. Each adult pops into a different opening when an alarm is given. Apparently the grown squirrels do not live together outside of the mating season, and perhaps not even at that time.

Although the rock squirrel likes meat and eats it regularly, flesh is only a minor part of its year-round food. When available, grasshoppers, crickets, beetles, caterpillars and other insects are avidly devoured. In its eagerness, it apparently swallows earthworms whole. Eggs and fledglings of birds such as quail and pheasants provide banquets, and it has been known to carry off an adult robin while the bird's mate frantically but vainly tried to stop the predator. The ground squirrel had killed the bird by biting deeply into the upper chest region.

I have caught numerous rock squirrels in traps, baited with meat, that were set for foxes and skunks. Many other times I found that they had eaten animals already caught in the traps. One squirrel got into my kangaroo rat's cage, killed the occupant and ate its head.

During the early days in the Southwest, when prospectors, miners and other travelers died in isolated places they were customarily buried on the spot. Piles of stones heaped over the shallow graves to foil hungry coyotes were conspicuous attractions to the rock squirrel, which is always looking for shelter. As a result, it acquired a ghoulish reputation for robbing graves.

Most of the rock squirrel's food is vegetable. During spring, its diet consists of roots and tubers; blossoms such as willow catkins, rabbitbrush, mescal bean (*Sophora*), and agave; the pulp of cactus plants, and foliage. In the warmer localities many seed-bearing plants begin to bear fruit as early as the end of May, and rock squirrels can settle down to this preferred diet. They eat the berries of juniper, currant, wild cherry, hackberry and grape, and seeds of mesquite, saltbush, sumac, serviceberry, wild gourd and cultivated melons, false gromwell (*Onosmodium*), and screw bean. Naturalist Vernon Bailey once shot a rock squirrel in the Organ Mountains of New Mexico while it was loading its cheek pouches with seeds of prickly pear. The animal's stomach was full of the ripe, purplish pulp. Its face and hands were stained with the juice and even the flesh was tinted purple.

In the Chiricahua Mountains of Arizona I once saw a rock squirrel who hadn't waited for the seeds of the tall century plant to fall. Seed pods and shells littered the ground and scratches showed where it had scaled the giant flower stalk, ten feet high, and cut down the seeds. Otherwise, the birds or the little western chipmunks probably would have gathered them first.

Late in the season, nuts are an eagerly sought food, both for storage and for immediate consumption. They include piñons, walnuts, and all kinds of acorns.

Most rock squirrels put aside acorns, seeds or grain each fall. These stores are hidden, not only in rooms of their burrows, but in a number of other caches under rocks and logs and in crannies in ledges and slides. They carry this food in their capacious cheek pockets to their storage bins. Once I trapped a rock squirrel which was carrying home no less than one hundred and four seeds of the wild lupine, with broken fragments of quite a few more. The cheek pouches were distended almost to their full capacity.

Occasionally an especially lavish display of food may tempt the rock squirrels to desert their normal habitat for the open fields where they can still den in stone walls or under the protection of thorny hedgerows. Orchards of apricots, pears, peaches, plums, cherries and apples offer endless banquets. The squirrels will also feed on garden produce such as melons, squash, peas and beans and all kinds of grain.

Ordinarily rock squirrels do not range far beyond the Oak Zone along the mountain sides, although they have been recorded near the summit of the San Francisco Peaks, far above timber line. A few may live in the hot desert but only along the stream courses in the foothills. The lower edge of the Pine Zone, just above the oaks, seems to be more popular. I have seen many of them in this sort of habitat in southern Arizona. At that elevation (over eight thousand feet above sea level) snow becomes two or three feet deep and stays on the ground all winter. The squirrels that live there apparently sleep away the cold months from the middle or end of October until sometime in March.

Down in the lower canyons, during mild winters, rock squirrels are active practically all the year 'round. They love the sun and are outdoors whenever it shines and the air is still. Except during the heat of summer between mid-morning and midafternoon, they are out whenever the weather is pleasant. Strictly daytime animals, they stay in their beds at night.

The ground squirrel has been able to keep its family life pretty much to itself. It is probable that many mothers have two litters of young each year. Five to seven young arrive at a birth. In New Mexico they have been seen out of the den around the first of June, and very young animals have been recorded again in August.

Although the rock squirrel prefers to live in a rock slide, the broken debris at the foot of a canyon wall or a mountain side where the ledges crop out, it sometimes has to dig a burrow. One squirrel tunneled out a home in the matted roof of an abandoned beaver lodge that had been built in the bank of a stream. Ordinarily if a rock squirrel has to tunnel, it at least tries to locate the entrance between rocks so that the burrow cannot be enlarged by an enemy. With this reinforcement, it is not necessary to make the doorway inconspicuous. The rodent just pushes the excavated earth, sometimes as much as a barrelful, outside and lets it lie there. From time to time, it totes out a little more when it cleans the bedroom and food bins, or extends a tunnel.

The color of individual rock squirrels may be anywhere from pale to dark, even in the same species. Some are almost melanistic. True albinos are rare but have been recorded. Molting takes place in midsummer and progresses from the nose backward to the tail, very distinctly and evenly. As the fur ages, it takes on a brownish-yellow tint. Wear makes it a little finer and less harsh-textured than the fresh new hair. It is not known whether there is a second annual molt.

The subgenus *Otospermophilus* contains two highly important species, which resemble each other fairly closely in appearance.

1. The rock squirrel (*Citellus variegatus*), described below.
2. The California ground squirrel (*C. beecheyi*) which is small and less dependent on rocky areas for its home. A white patch on each shoulder extends backward as two indistinct stripes that fade out near the middle of the back and merge into a blackish triangular patch. The various races of this species occupy practically all of California, and extend south to central Baja California and north in eastern Oregon to the Columbia River.

General description. A large, rather slender ground squirrel with moderately large ears and bushy tail that is about two-thirds the length of head and body. Color varies with the species and individual: upper parts from grayish white and buffy to very dark brown or blackish, banded with brownish; head from yellowish or brownish pink to brownish black; tail is mixed black or brown and yellowish white. Total length, 17 to 19 inches; height at shoulder, 4 inches; weight, 1 to 2 pounds.

Distinguishing characteristics. Similar to the true gray squirrel, but the tail is much less bushy and the back and sides are stippled or mottled. Sometimes rock squirrels are seen in low trees, but, if danger threatens, they usually take refuge in the ground (not treetops). Distinguished from the chipmunk and mantled ground squirrel by much larger size and absence of longitudinal striping.

Range. Southwestern United States and northern and central Mexico; northern Utah and north-central Colorado, south through southern Nevada and central Texas and entire northern Mexico to Michoacan and northeastern Puebla.

ANTELOPE SQUIRREL
CITELLUS LEUCURUS AND RELATIVES

Scooting across the desert, dodging from creosote bush, to rock, to mesquite clump, the little antelope squirrel keeps its tail flattened protectively over its rump and back. As the tail twitches convulsively and rapidly, the exposed white undersurface reflects the sunlight. The dun-colored body blends into the sand and gravel. Like a ghost with the heebie-jeebies, the white tail seems to flee erratically all by itself. One is faintly reminded of the antelope and its going-away signal, which has given this ground squirrel its name.

The chunky build, lateral white stripe and nervous actions are also suggestive of the chipmunk. For this reason it is often called the "antelope chipmunk." Certainly it is the liveliest and most restless of the ground squirrels although it lives in the hottest, driest part of our country, the Southwest. It dashes about below sea level in Death Valley, or at three thousand to four thousand feet on the higher deserts and low foothills. The heat may be one hundred and thirty-four degrees in the shade! Occasionally it is found even higher, as far as the open cedar forests at six thousand five hundred feet. But if a human being finds the midday summer sun bearable, it will be entirely too cool for the antelope squirrel.

The squirrel is rarely up before seven or eight o'clock, and by that time the sun is so hot that the landscape is wavering. Enough is enough, however, so it retires about noon for a two- or three-hour nap and then goes out for an early supper. Sunset finds it back in the den for a solid twelve-hour rest.

Although it loves the heat, it does not hibernate, even for a short period. (The only possible exception is an individual that lives at the highest elevation.) During winter, when even the desert practically ceases to flower, the antelope squirrel remains fat by using its underground stores of seeds. It keeps warm by exchanging the close, short, warm-weather hair for a long, soft winter coat with a full lining of underfur. When the sun is shining, it has been seen out on snow a foot deep. Bad weather, however, is something that no antelope squirrel will tolerate. Rain, snow or cloudy skies and wind send it underground in a hurry. There it stays as long as the "weather" lasts, perhaps for weeks. But it does not go into a round-the-clock, round-the-month coma like many other ground squirrels.

A suspicious, super-cautious nature helps the antelope squirrel to avoid its many enemies. It runs at the first indication of trouble. In fact, the usual gait is a gallop of rapid leaps six to twelve inches long. It slows down only when it nears home or a tempting meal. Just a slight vibration of the ground from a footstep will send it off. At short intervals it pauses momentarily under a bush to glance back over its shoulder. All the time the tail twitches fore and aft and vibrates rapidly. Sometimes the squirrel climbs a bush to try to sight the cause of its fear; more frequently it does not take the time. At its doorstep it will stop

ANTELOPE SQUIRREL

for one final look, then plunges below. It is much too wary to stick its head out again for some time.

Even where these ground squirrels are abundant, as indicated by many tracks, it is usually very difficult to catch sight of one among the desert shrubs. They are never as numerous as many of their plains-dwelling relatives. A population of five or six to an acre is unusually high. These rodents do not seem to be hostile to each other; they are merely indifferent except at mating time.

Antelope squirrels pair between the middle of February and the end of May, early in the season on the warmest deserts, and toward the end of that period on the plateaus. The one annual litter may be enormous for a tiny creature that weighs only four or five ounces. As many as fourteen embryos have been counted, and as few as four. The usual number of young is eight or nine. Most of the litters arrive in late April or early May. The youngsters are able to find their own food when they are half grown. This is necessary, for the nervous mother seems to pay no attention to them after their weaning. Lacking education, many of the offspring fall prey to predatory birds, mammals and snakes before they can get experience.

Provided protection can be found for their burrows, antelope squirrels will live in quite a variety of places. Best of all are rocky foothills on the edge of a valley where seed-bearing shrubs and herbs abound. There the squirrels burrow in the gravel that the flash floods have swept out of the mountains and spread in great fans on the lower slopes. This debris is so compact that, once the burrows have been excavated, the occupants are fairly safe from any enemy less industrious and well-equipped than the badger. On other, less rugged ground, the squirrels dig under the protecting roots of a stout shrub or clump of bushes, or at the edge of a boulder. Thus they may be found living on the edge of a rockslide, a boulder-strewn slope, a lower canyon bottom, an old sand dune that has been stabilized by scrub growth or Joshua trees, or on sagebrush covered flats. Rarely do they settle on open sandy plains. Those that make this mistake may soon be routed out and eaten by even such poor diggers as coyotes and kit foxes.

The antelope squirrel has inefficient digging tools and it seems to lack the patience to keep at any hard chore for very long. The mouth of the burrow is oval rather than round, and two to three inches is the greatest diameter. The rodent does take the pains, ordinarily, to carry away and scatter the excavated soil. Since there is no mound or ditch, the doorway is flush with the ground surface. On level ground the tunnel drops steeply, and then levels off at a comparatively shallow depth and is quite short. A nest burrow and one or more granaries complete the establishment.

Sometimes the antelope squirrel takes over an abandoned den of a wood rat or a large kangaroo rat to save the despised labor of digging its own. It has even been known to move into an old badger hole.

It also uses wayside burrows. Several that were explored in California were less than twelve feet long and two inches in diameter. They were all within three feet of the surface and were not provided with sleeping rooms. Apparently they were built only for emergency use when it was impossible for the owner to get back to the safety of its home. There must be many times when it finds that these dugouts mean the difference between life and death.

The antelope squirrel has a large individual range and often makes trips that, for an animal of its size, are surprising. In one instance it was found carrying a load of wheat grains, although the nearest wheat field was a quarter of a mile away.

The antelope squirrel sometimes nibbles at tender green leaves of many shrubs and developing twigs and buds. It eats quantities of cactus fruits until its flesh turns purple from their juices. A certain amount of meat in the form of insects or other flesh is required. Late-rising human collectors have often found their catches of small, trapped rodents ruined by the tiny antelope squirrel. It had feasted on the corpses of mice and even members of its own clan. Caged antelope squirrels eagerly eat grasshoppers, grubs, and meat bones from the camper's table.

The main diet of this ground squirrel, however, is seeds. The more important kinds are those of many species of cacti, yuccas, ocotillo, sotol, palo verde, mesquite, the various acacias, saltbush, sumac, Russian thistle, alfilaria, wild plum, and piñon.

Grains, such as wheat, barley and oats, are eaten with gusto. Cultivated fruits —apricots, prunes, almonds and peaches, are special treats. Sometimes the depredations are of serious importance to small farmers. However, the antelope squirrel lives in arid regions where crops can be grown only by irrigating. Apparently it does not like the feeling of damp soil and the unaccustomed moisture in the rank vegetation. At any rate, it usually moves out or pines away when its valley home is "improved." Antelope squirrels that remain on the borders of the fields ordinarily continue to subsist mainly on their accustomed desert foods.

Most antelope squirrels live where rains are infrequent and streams flow only a few weeks each year, if at all. Unlike several of their desert companions that have practically lost their desire for water, antelope squirrels will run long distances to drink. Sipping daintily and rapidly, they will drink eight or ten times at a visit before rushing off again. Between such opportunities (which may be months apart), they get along on the moisture that their stomachs convert from the starch of seeds. This is supplemented by some green vegetation such as leaves and stems of Mormon tea and greasewood, and the pulp of cactus stems and fruits. These ground squirrels climb readily, and sometimes ascend shrubs just to see more of the world or to take a sunbath. They come down long straight trunks, such as agave stems, head first. Cactus thorns do not seem to bother them.

I have kept several antelope squirrels in large cages with sand floors. Proffers of friendship in the form of choice nuts and grains never availed. The little animals remained as wild and suspicious as the day I caught them in the San Simon Valley of Arizona. Whenever I appeared they uttered a shrill, rapid chitter that died weakly away as they dove for their nest boxes. In a few instances, however, some other naturalists have had better success.

General description. A small, rather chunky ground squirrel with short, wide, rounded ears, short legs, and tail about half as long as body. Body color uniform, varying from pinkish buffy to brown or gray becoming whitish underneath; one narrow white stripe extends along side of back from shoulder to hip; tail flattened, whitish underneath and mixed blackish and white above. Total length, about 9 inches; height at shoulders, 2 to 2½ inches; weight, 4 to 5 ounces.

Distinguishing characteristics. The single longitudinal white stripe serves to distinguish this animal from the mantled ground squirrel and chipmunk, both of which have a number of stripes.

Range. Western United States and northern Mexico; from southeastern Oregon and northwestern Colorado to southern Baja California, south-central Texas and southern Coahuila.

GOLDEN-MANTLED GROUND SQUIRREL
CITELLUS LATERALIS AND RELATIVES

This little ground squirrel with the brightly colored mantle sometimes forages in low bushes, and on rare occasions climbs trees as high as twenty or thirty feet. Its real preference is for solid earth; in fact, like other ground squirrels, it spends most of its life asleep underground.

Usually it has little to say to anyone but its own kind. You can walk through the yellow pines and aspens of the western mountainsides where it lives, and only the red squirrel and chipmunk will announce you. If you watch very carefully, you will see a golden-mantled ground squirrel here, another there, each sitting up on its haunches with hands folded primly across its plump belly. This

GOLDEN-MANTLED GROUND SQUIRREL

habit of keeping still is its best protection. The bold stripes seem to break into flecks of sun and shadow. The chestnut color, almost golden when viewed closely, blends with the brown forest floor.

When with relatives, it is quite talkative, especially when angry. It chirps, buzzes and grunts, and when actually quarreling, sometimes screams. A low "ticking," accompanied by flicks of the tail, may express nervousness or dislike. When angry or scared, it humps its back and fluffs up its tail. While fighting, mantled squirrels roll over and over, biting when they get a chance. Occasionally they stand up on their hind feet and hit at each other with their forepaws. Their quarrels are frequent but very brief, and seldom result in injury. They have no real valor. If a little western chipmunk looks mad enough and comes fast enough, the mantled ground squirrel, which is twice as large, will "run for its life."

Fastidious in some ways, it spends a good deal of time washing its face and brushing its handsome coat. In spite of this care, it is often troubled with fleas and has to stop what it is doing and scratch with its paws or hind feet.

In a number of national parks, these beautiful little ground squirrels are the tourists' favorites. Sitting up, they eat swiftly and continuously, using their paws. Only the bears are more voracious. The little squirrels become so fat on public generosity that they can scarcely waddle, yet still they beg for more, stuffing into their cheek pouches what their stomachs cannot hold. One pair of these pockets can carry as many as twenty-seven scrub-oak acorns. Few people can resist a group of these little beggars as they stretch up full length on their hind legs.

"Me! Me! Me!" they whimper. I have often seen golden-mantled ground squirrels and western chipmunks on the rim of Crater Lake steal an audience away from one of the world's greatest spectacles.

By the middle of September, as a rule, the golden-mantled squirrel is coiled up in true ground squirrel fashion, to sleep until early April. Restless individuals and the youngest generations may stay out through October. Those that live in warmer climates also stay out much later and emerge earlier in the spring.

These ground squirrels seldom go into such a profound sleep as other species, such as the Columbian. Restless hibernators, they wake up often and sometimes are alert for a day or two before resuming their slumber. However, when sleeping most soundly, they will not wake up although handled and exposed to strong light.

Even after seven months sleep, the typical golden-mantled squirrel continues to sleep every night and may not get up for breakfast until well after sunrise. By the time the sun touches the western horizon it is back indoors. It despises rain. Even cold, cloudy weather is enough to keep it inside, except for brief foraging trips when hunger becomes overpowering.

The much used shelter is a burrow, which is located among scattered trees. The entrance may be under or between rocks or stumps, or on open ground where a carpet of grass or herbs gives some concealment. Inside the doorway, which is about three inches in diameter, the tunnel tapers quickly to two inches. The shaft slopes down steeply at about forty-five degrees until about eight inches below the ground and then levels off.

In its irregular course the tunnel may vary in length between ten and fifteen feet, when it rises abruptly again to the surface. This doorway is usually well hidden in foliage, and seems to be used merely as an emergency exit or entrance. In a straight line, the distance between the front and back doors is only eight to twelve feet. About midway between them is the den, a circular chamber about eight inches across and four or five inches deep. The nest, which is made of dry leaves, shredded grass, bark, small rootlets or any similar material that may be available, is a thin mattress for summer use. In fall the material is increased until it serves both as bed and bedding to keep the sleeper from freezing.

Although the golden-mantled squirrel is exceptionally trim and neat in appearance, it is an abominable housekeeper. While careful not to scatter refuse near the doorways, which might attract the attention of enemies, it keeps a very untidy den. Consequently, the nest is often "inhabited." One that was excavated contained camel crickets, millipeds, thousands of mites, great numbers of fleas, some book scorpions and small ants.

Several pockets or blind tunnels up to two feet long are dug on either side of the main passageway. These may be filled with seeds and acorns in the fall harvest season, perhaps for use during the lean springtime when food may be needed badly. One mantled ground squirrel near Crested Butte, Colorado, had to tunnel through three feet of snow to reach the surface in spring.

Sometimes several of these side tunnels may be packed with discarded nest material. Perhaps this method of disposing of it is safer than strewing it on the ground outdoors, where a hungry fox, weasel or other carnivore might see or smell it and be led to look for the den. One more underground corridor, a circular tunnel that by-passes the nest chamber, is a safety measure that completes the entire burrow system. If a snake or weasel enters, or a coyote starts to dig, the owner has a better chance to escape than in a simple, unbranched shaft.

Golden-mantled ground squirrels are sociable to the extent that they like to talk and argue outdoors, but they have separate dwellings and usually prefer to be alone. Two adults were once seen entering one burrow in August, presumably not during the mating season, but this does not seem to be a common occurrence.

Two sets of glands may serve for leaving messages. An elongated area on the back, just behind the shoulder blades, contains a number of small glands which secrete a clear, light, oily fluid that has a musky or slightly rancid odor. Left on overhanging twigs or grasses, this may tell other ground squirrels the age, sex and perhaps some special news of the animal that has rubbed its back in passing. Each animal also has a set of three anal glands like those of other ground squirrels, the marmots, and a number of other rodents.

Albinos have been seen rarely. They are ghostly little creatures, with their lateral stripes showing very faintly.

Golden-mantled squirrels are believed to mate in early spring following their awakening from the winter sleep. The young are born comparatively late— between the end of June and the first week of August in the high Sierra Nevada. Even at the lowest altitudes near the southern deserts, they are rarely seen above ground before the first or even middle of July. At this first appearance, they are more than one-quarter grown.

There is only one litter a season, of four to seven young, the average being five. With this late start, they must eat heartily to put on enough fat to carry them through the winter. Consequently, they stay up about a month after their elders have retired in the fall, and by that time they have almost attained adult size.

Like other ground squirrels, this is a vegetarian that occasionally eats flesh. The bulk of the diet is made up of a vast assortment of fruits: those of piñon and yellow pine, cherry, Douglas fir, silver pine (*P. monticola*), all kinds of oaks, serviceberry, gooseberry and currant, thimbleberry, rose, lupine, puccoon, alfileria, bitterbrush (*Purshia*), clover, grasses, shepherd's purse, kinnikinnik, Oregon grape, dandelion, pentstemon, stickleaf, violet, and willow-weed.

The golden-mantled squirrel is fond of mushrooms, and often preys on insects such as grasshoppers, caterpillars, beetles, ants and flies. Many mammal collectors have learned to their inconvenience of its fondness for meat baits, from which one might assume that it will also eat carrion whenever it finds it. A western chipmunk was once placed in a cage with two mantled squirrels. They killed and almost entirely devoured it within a few hours. Other ground squirrels of this species in the wild been known to kill young mountain bluebirds in the nest. In Yellowstone Park one was observed eating a young meadow mouse. When water is handy, mantled ground squirrels drink it; otherwise they go without.

Soaking up the sunshine on a log or stump, the golden-mantled ground squirrel watches for its numerous enemies that crawl, walk or fly. When a human being approaches the imaginary safety line that each squirrel draws around itself, it will leap to the ground and, with tail twitching forward and back or defiantly held straight up, scurry to its burrow. At the threshold it pauses for a final look. Then, with a clear, explosive whistle, "Tsp!" it dives down the tunnel and out of sight until the intruder is at a safe distance.

This squirrel lives in our western mountains. Altitudinally it has a wide range, from the low foothills at six thousand feet above sea level to heights as great as thirteen thousand feet. Only a few of the hardier individuals live above timber line, perhaps because the growing season is so short and seeds are not plentiful. The vast majority live in open places in the forest.

The best place to look for a mantled ground squirrel is on a dry, gravelly slope in open woods. Dense stands of conifers offer no attraction, except when seed crops are maturing. Margins of rockslides offer many refuges, and numbers of squirrels are frequently found there. Man's summer-home colonies are especially alluring, for food is usually plentiful, both natural and artificial, and enemies seldom dare to hunt there. Logged off areas, where cull trees offer shade and shrubs are beginning to hide the stumps, half-rotten logs and slash, also offer good living places. Generally, however, it prefers that the ground be clear of undergrowth.

Golden-mantled ground squirrels are among our most handsome small mammals. Fortunately, they generally live in non-agricultural sections where they have no opportunity to damage crops. While they eat many tree seeds, they probably help the forest more than harm it, by planting (caching) numerous others and failing to eat them. If humans do not handle these ground squirrels, because of fleas and possible disease, and take reasonable precautions to protect food stores, they find the little animals are pleasant neighbors to have around mountain camps.

General description. A small ground squirrel much like a chipmunk, with stout body, short legs, and large rounded ears. Tail about half of total length of animal. Fur thick and soft. Grizzled dark gray or buffy above with a bright "mantle" of cinnamon-buff to russet over the head and shoulders. A pair of narrow white stripes from shoulder to hip is usually bordered on each side and between the two by a black stripe. Under parts yellowish. Tail mixed black and buffy above, buffy beneath. Total length, 9 to 12 inches; height at shoulder about 3 to 3½ inches; weight, 6 to 10 ounces.

Distinguishing characteristics. The bright chestnut "mantle" is usually apparent. If it is grayish, as in some individuals, the absence of a dark stripe down the back and of lateral body stripes that extend ahead of the eyes will determine that the animal is of this species and not a chipmunk.

Range. Western North America, almost entirely west of the 100th meridian (east central Colorado) to the Pacific coast; from northern British Columbia and Alberta to southern California and west central New Mexico; also an isolated species in the Sierra Madre, Mexico, from southern Chihuahua to northwestern Durango.

PRAIRIE DOG
CYNOMYS SP.

Cities of underground dwellings once stretched for hundreds of miles across the short-grass plains. The homes had guard rooms, bed chambers and toilets. Little circular dikes protected the doorways so that flood waters would not run

PRAIRIE DOG

down the hallways. The sociable inhabitants looked like plump oversized ground squirrels. Probably more than four hundred millions lived in a city that was one thousand miles wide and two hundred and fifty miles long. They chattered a great deal and barked furiously whenever an intruder appeared.

Because seventy-five to eighty per cent of their food was forage, they were persecuted by cattlemen. Many thousand pounds of strychnine were used to poison them, and they died by the millions.

Today prairie dogs are almost as rare on the Great Plains as buffaloes. Only in odd corners of the higher and rougher ranges do they still chatter and grow fat on the grass. Except in a few national parks, even these survivors live in daily danger of a visit from exterminators.

Outside of a couple of hours in the hottest part of the day, there is always something going on in a prairie-dog town. Within a few minutes after sunrise the animals are up, and more than likely will spend a little while on their dike mounds, just drinking in the sunshine. As hunger gets the better of them, each "dog" moves off to eat its breakfast. This, like the afternoon dinner, is a leisurely meal that is likely to last for two or three hours. In fact, in a large town a few prairie dogs will be found eating at almost any time. Nursing mothers and fast-growing young always seem to be hungry.

Prairie dogs never forget to watch for their enemies as they feed. After five to ten seconds of eating or searching for edible plants, each prairie dog rears on its haunches, or even climbs on a mound or grass clump. It takes a careful look around that may last three to five seconds or more. Rarely do any of them dare to forage more than one hundred feet from their home.

Enemies are never very far away. Golden eagles and red-tailed and rough-legged hawks swoop from the air. On the ground, coyotes, badgers, foxes and even bobcats may be lurking behind any hummock or clump of grass. Wolves still-hunt in places and badgers are even more dreaded. Old "Pick and Shovel" can dig out a shallow burrow in fifteen or twenty minutes. Finally, the black-footed ferret, although extremely rare, is an arch enemy that lives right in town with its prey and it always has fresh meat.

Rattlesnakes and the solemn little burrowing owls are frequently seen in prairie-dog towns, living in apparent harmony and good fellowship with the rodent inhabitants. Appearances never were more deceiving, for these meat-eaters seize any opportunity to eat each other's offspring and those of the prairie dogs.

The mother prairie dog would be furious enough to kill a feathered inter-loper if she caught it in her home, but she does not dare to attack the slithering monster with the death-dealing fangs. It is said that instead, with the help of eager neighbors, she plugs the burrow and seals it in to die a lingering death. However, snakes placed experimentally in prairie dogs' burrows for several days were not bothered by the owners. They merely left at the first opportunity and did not return until several days after the snakes had been removed. The "buried alive" theory may be a myth, or it may be true of only a few prairie dogs with exceptional intelligence.

When one of the prairie dogs sees something suspicious, it sounds a shrill alarm. Immediately all the other citizens sit up and take notice. If the danger is confirmed, there is a general dash for home. Except where a few dwellings are connected by underground tunnels, each inhabitant tries to reach its own doorway. Regardless of the urgency, anyone who confusedly enters the wrong hallway is ejected by the indignant owner. There is a rising chorus of shrill nasal yips as the prairie dogs stand up on their mounds and sound their fury and alarm. At last, just as each prairie dog seems about to explode, it drops to all fours, gives a final flicker of the short tail, and dives down the hallways and out of sight. About a minute later, it very cautiously and silently lifts an eye barely above the mound top to see if the enemy is still about. Then it goes below to stay until another sortie is unquestionably safe.

Prairie dogs seem community-minded about their feeding grounds. It is not often that an old, crotchety male chases a neighbor away from a bunch of choice herbage. Sometimes their homes are only a few feet apart, although thirty to fifty feet is more usual. After the mating season the mature males are likely to take up residence in a special sector of the town, away from the garrulous females and their noisy offspring. This seems to be the only evidence of "class distinction."

Depending upon the day's heat, ticks and fleas may become active on the prairie dog's thinly-haired skin. Dust baths are in order, and the rodents roll and squirm until they are well dusted. Conversation in low yips, "chir-r-r-rs" and chirps continues back and forth. As the sun slides to the top of its arc, the prairie dogs grow drowsy and one by one go below to sleep. This nap may last two to three hours, after which there is another feeding period. Finally, by sundown they are all inside for the night.

This is the schedule of a prairie-dog town on a pleasant day. A shower will send the whole town indoors, and cold, windy weather may keep them below for the duration. At such times they fast, for no stores have ever been found in a prairie dog's burrow. In winter, northern prairie dogs may not venture out-doors for long periods. Apparently they do not hibernate, for a fine day will quickly bring them out in full force. I have seen many prairie dogs abroad and lively in western South Dakota during January and February when the sun warmed their sheltered canyon well above the freezing point. White-tailed prairie dogs in Wyoming have been seen out on a foot of snow, following a night when the thermometer dropped to twenty-two degrees below zero. These northern animals grow so fat in autumn that they can hardly run, and they "live on themselves" until spring.

The prairie dog spends a great deal of time and effort on its dwelling, which is one of the most elaborate homes devised by any American mammal. The crater-shaped dike around the entrance may be as much as two feet high and four feet in diameter. Made of earth heaped up and tamped solid by repeated blows of the prairie dog's paws and blunt nose, it keeps the home snug and dry. Otherwise the water from summer cloudbursts, sometimes standing two or three inches deep on the flat, hard ground, would pour down the hole and flood out the owner. Inundation or drowning out was the method often employed by Indians to capture prairie dogs for food. Many tribes regularly ate prairie dogs, but white men dislike the peculiar "earthy" taste of the flesh.

Young animals often make low, slipshod dikes. Possibly they learn the necessity for good, careful work by getting wet a few times. Or perhaps they drown, and only the efficient builders survive to carry on the race. Prairie dogs that make their homes on sloping ground (mostly the white-tailed prairie dogs of the Rocky Mountain region) have little need for dams or dikes because the natural drainage is usually sufficient. Such animals just heap their bushels of waste earth on one side of the doorway, like the marmot. But prairie dogs that live on flat ground, including practically all of the black-tailed species of the Great Plains, must have these small circular dams around their doorways. They spend much time repairing, molding and pounding their dikes, which indicates that at least the adult prairie dogs know how important the dikes are to their safety.

The entrance of the burrow is about six to eight inches in diameter. Inside, the hallway narrows abruptly to four or five inches. It drops almost straight down, to a depth of three to sixteen feet, depending on circumstances such as the compactness of the soil, location of the water table, and determination and energy of the miner.

Almost invariably there is a guard room or listening post located three to six feet below the entrance. Frequently this is a mere shelf or niche on the side of the tunnel; sometimes it is a three-quarters room. Here the prairie dog stands watch and listens carefully to determine if it is safe to go out to sun itself or to feed. When it has been chased indoors it generally pauses at this foyer to completely satisfy its curiosity and figuratively thumb its nose at the enemy, before going on down to bed.

At the guard room the hallway turns horizontally, or perhaps a little upward. From this point, its course is seldom the same as in any other house. The tunnel may fork into blind passages or loop hallways. It may meander about or run nearly straight. Most dens have only one entrance, but sometimes the tunnel is extended to the ground level where it is left open as a back door. Often, however, this is used only temporarily for the removal of earth dug from the burrow, and later is plugged with soil. In many cases, one or more of the side passages are plugged with discarded nest material and with soil resulting from repairing or enlarging rooms and halls.

The sharp, rather long claws on the prairie dog's front feet are its digging tools. Instead of carrying earth out of the tunnel in its arms, it kicks it out by backward strokes of the hind feet.

The round bedroom, eight to ten inches in diameter, is dug at some point off the tunnel or at the blind end. This is lined with mats of dried grass, shredded stems of larger plants, or other similar material. The bedding is gathered and carried in a bundle between the animal's jaws.

Not all prairie-dog homes are equipped with a toilet. Although the bedrooms are kept clean, many residents may be very careless and unsystematic about such matters.

Male prairie dogs appear to enter the mating season about two weeks ahead of the females. The first unions occur around the last of March. There is no mistaking the season, for the animals do a great deal of running about and advertise their intentions with much loud talk. A little over half of the yearling females mate, while the rest wait until they are two years old. There is only one mating season a year.

No one has determined exactly the length of time that the mothers carry the young, except that it is between twenty-seven and thirty-three days. Mature animals may have large litters; as many as ten embryos have been counted, although the young actually produced average four to six. Young females ordinarily give birth to two or three young.

Sometime between June 15 and July 15, when the youngsters are about seven weeks old, they begin to spend the pleasant hours above ground. Weaning starts at once. Sitting upright, the mother still nurses several pups at a time. Although the young may nurse for as long as three weeks after making their first trip out of the den, they continue to get less and less nourishment from her and more and more from green plants. On this new diet they grow rapidly, and almost double their weight between early July and the middle of September. By this time, or earlier, they are completely weaned.

Although prairie dogs born at high elevations, or in the north, arrive as much as several weeks later than those in warmer localities, autumn finds them all of about the same size in comparison with their parents. Nature compensates for the apparent handicap of late arrivals by pushing their rate of growth.

Young prairie dogs are appealing little creatures. Their coats are soft and fine, paler than the coarse coats that, through July and early August, gradually grow in. The little prairie dogs are intensely curious but rather shy. If anything unusual occurs, they are all eyes and ears. Huddling together for mutual confidence, a family of young prairie dogs will stare and crane their necks. Even when they flee into the doorway, they flutter there with excitement until a stern command from their mother sends them downstairs to safety.

Soon after weaning her litter, the mother departs. She leaves the home to the youngsters and moves into a vacant burrow or digs a new one. Several weeks after this first break in the family circle, the youngsters begin to drift apart. They move singly into nearby empty burrows, of which there are always a considerable number in the town at this season. Their life expectancy may be about eight years. One prairie dog in captivity reached the astonishing old age of ten or eleven years. At this time its teeth, instead of being worn to the gums, were so long that it could hardly use them.

About ninety-eight per cent of the prairie dog's food is vegetation. Studies have shown that some forty-five per cent consists of wheat-grasses, and twenty-five per cent members of the goosefoot family. The entire plants may be eaten; stems, leaves, roots, and seeds. The rest of the diet is made up of insects, chiefly cutworms, beetles, and grasshoppers. Prairie dogs are often seen hopping vigorously about as they pursue and leap upon these long-legged, buzzing creatures. Numerous other species are found in the stomachs of prairie dogs examined but most of these miscellaneous small insects are swallowed by accident with leaves or stems of plants.

Prairie dogs are hearty eaters. It has been estimated that thirty-two of them will consume enough forage to support a sheep, and two hundred and fifty-six will eat the "keep" of a cow. Frequently, in a long-established town, the ground will be almost bare. Naturalists marvel at the ability of these big rodents to keep sleek, fat and cheerful, even when the favorite grasses have been almost completely eradicated and the ground is baked and cracked with drought. Cattlemen swear, and again place strychnine-coated grain in the burrows.

Black-tailed prairie dogs cut off every plant over six inches high that grows within seventy-five to one hundred feet of their burrows. This is a safety measure, to clear the view so no enemy can sneak up under cover of tall weeds or shrubs. The less sociable white-tailed prairie dogs are not so fussy. They sometimes extend their more open, loosely-organized towns into scattered woods or groves of aspens.

Prairie dogs can get along for long periods without water. They drink when showers leave puddles, but between times do without, like other dwellers of the arid places. It was once a legend on the High Plains that every prairie dog town was provided with a well, which was dug by the inhabitants. This intriguing yarn was disproven eventually, but not until many professional well-drillers had gone "broke" testing it. Some prairie-dog towns just happened to be underlaid with solid rock only a few feet below the grass roots. In others, drillings a thousand feet deep struck no water.

Where prairie dogs are much persecuted, they become wild and abnormally shy. Showing only their heads above the rim of the mounds, they defy all except the most expert riflemen. A shot must be fatal almost at once if the hunter wants the animal. Even though dying, it will tumble and scramble back down the burrow and out of reach. It was once thought that neighboring prairie dogs would invariably fill up the tunnel of a burrow in which one of the community died, thus sealing the body in a private tomb. On the contrary, a prairie dog in need of a home does not hesitate to move in with a deceased and decaying relative.

Prairie dogs are divided into two general classes.

1. The black-tailed prairie dogs (subgenus *Cynomys*) are rather stocky animals whose tails are more than one-fifth of their total length and are tipped heavily with black. Survivors of the formerly enormous colonies are found on the plains and foothills from southern Saskatchewan and central North Dakota to south central Texas, northern Chihuahua and southeastern Arizona.

2. The white-tailed prairie dogs (subgenus *Leucocrossuromys*) are more slender than the above, and their tails are shorter (less than one-fifth of the animals' total length) and are tipped or bordered with white. They live in the Rocky Mountain region from southern Montana to northeastern New Mexico and northern Arizona.

General description. A plump-bodied, rather large rodent with flattened head, low, rounded ears, short legs, and short, slender tail. Fur rather coarse, close to body. Color pale buffy to pinkish cinnamon grizzled with blackish, grading into white on under parts; terminal one-fifth to one-half of tail black. Total length, 12 to 15½ inches; height at shoulder, 5 inches; weight, 1½ to 3 pounds.

Distinguishing characteristics. Smaller than a woodchuck or marmot, with much closer, paler fur which at most is not as grizzled. Larger and more stocky than the ground squirrels. Most prairie dogs live in colonies on level areas; they inhabit a characteristic burrow completely encircled by a ridge of earth.

Range. Western North America. Southeastern Texas, northern Chihuahua and Sonora, north to west-central North Dakota and extreme southern Saskatchewan; from eastern Nebraska west to western Utah and west-central Arizona.

15. The Chipmunks and Squirrels

EASTERN CHIPMUNK—*TAMIAS STRIATUS*

As it dashes through the shrubbery or along a stone wall, the chipmunk always takes time to stop and satisfy itself about passers-by. A pair of bright eyes in the sharp little face look out with mingled shyness and curiosity. The rusty coat is decorated with black and white stripes, but a pastel quality dispels any suggestion of garishness. In spite of its inquisitiveness, it seldom intrudes and is easily frightened away if it does.

It wants plenty of food and wants it handy. During the fall it piles enough provisions under its bed to raise it to the ceiling. In exceptional cases this may be a half-bushel of nuts and grains. All during the cold winter it doesn't have to get out of its warm bed for meals. It can just reach down under the covers. As the winter wears on and it continues to draw from this pantry, the bed slowly sinks down from the ceiling and by spring it has reached the floor.

From February to the middle of March, the male chipmunk begins to go abroad regularly on pleasant days. Spring has wakened his emotions and he stops cautiously at the doorways of dens where the females are still staying. It is well for him to be circumspect and to go through the proper courting procedure. Female chipmunks are very fussy, and many a brash male has been beaten up and tossed out when he tried to rush things. His squeals of rage and pain bring no mercy. Overpersistent males have died from too many bites by sharp, feminine teeth.

During April, thirty-two days after mating, the baby chipmunks arrive. Most litters number four or five; occasionally there may be but two or three, or as many as six. The young are tiny red beings, entirely hairless and almost transparent. They can only squeak faintly and search for the mother's milk. On the sixth day their stripes begin to appear faintly under the skin as the bands of dark and light hair push outward.

At two weeks they are clothed in very short, fine fuzz, and can stand up. They hear sounds at the age of three weeks and their eyes open when they are a month old. They are now quite like their parents, except in size. By the time they are three months old, they are equipped with a full set of permanent teeth, and their mother now probably sets them adrift to make their own way.

377

EASTERN CHIPMUNK

Young chipmunks are sometimes seen late in the summer and through the autumn. Whether the mother raises two broods each season is not known. Some naturalists believe that the "second" family, at least in some instances, is the "first" litter of a female that failed to breed in the late winter or early spring.

The adventuring youngsters find it easy to locate homesteads for themselves. They don't require much room. Excepting the males when looking for mates, they may spend their lives within two or three acres. Not jealous about territory, they share anything and everything except their bedrooms and their pantries. Occasionally, during the winter, two or three individuals may get together and even use these in common.

Rather sociable, they seem to enjoy talking back and forth. "Cuck-cuck, cuck-cuck, cuck-cuck." In spring and fall especially, a whole community of chipmunks may be calling softly. Their high-pitched voices sound a little like a pond full of tenor-voiced frogs. Sometimes a chipmunk may keep up its monotonous song for a half hour without stopping, repeating the note about one hundred and thirty times each minute. It can even call when its cheek pockets are full of food.

Enemies are an ever-present problem: not only snakes and weasels (both of which can come right into the tunnels and perhaps catch a chipmunk asleep), but foxes; bobcats; the small, falcon-type hawks; screech owls; and barred owls. Cats kill large numbers of chipmunks, and automobiles and small boys with air rifles, .22's, or slingshots are also destructive. In at least one instance a red squirrel became angered by a chipmunk that was gathering nuts from a tree. It leaped upon its small relative, seized it by the neck and apparently broke it or severed the spinal cord.

From all of these hazards the chipmunk's only recourse is flight to the den or some cranny too small to permit the enemy to follow. The approach of any hostile creature is signaled by loud "chip-chip!"s of alarm. A chipmunk that is suddenly surprised gives one very loud chip that runs down in a trill: "Chip-r-r-r-r."

When one of these little striped animals leaves the home nest for the last time, it looks for a range with enough food, cover and water. Unlike some of the western chipmunks, the eastern species generally have plenty to drink, especially in warm weather. In winter, if it goes outdoors, it licks snow.

When necessary, it can swim quite well, and doesn't get its tail wet. Holding it high like a mast but curled at the top, the chipmunk may paddle across a lake a half-mile wide and perhaps wider.

Most of the names by which the chipmunk has been known, particularly by the Indians, were derived from or refer to its alarm call. We have taken one of these to form the word which is used almost universally today. In parts of New England at least, this is shortened at times to "chippie." Other names applied rarely are "hackie," chipping squirrel, striped ground squirrel, and just ground squirrel, but the last three are incorrect. It is neither a squirrel nor a ground squirrel. Although closely related to the red squirrel, it is structurally different. Certainly it is not a ground squirrel even though it spends almost all of its life either on or in the ground.

A suitable house is of paramount importance. So the chipmunk goes to work in a place where the soil is not too hard for its delicate little paws to dig. First it digs almost straight down four or five inches. Then it slopes off a little, but still descends until it reaches a depth of about three feet. The shaft is about two inches in diameter and frequently twists about in its underground course.

As the little miner excavates, it throws the loosened soil behind it. When a load has accumulated it pushes the soil to the entrance by using its nose with hands extended on each side of the face. It is more careful about disposing of soil than many animals. A smart little creature, it has no intention of attracting enemies to its doorway by piling a bushel or so of fresh earth in front of it.

Instead, it does one of two things. It may push it several yards away from the front door. Or, if it feels lazy, it just dumps the earth outside the entrance. Then it makes a new door somewhere else, and comes back and plugs up the old one. The new opening is likely to be under a little bush or an overhanging stone, the immediate surroundings being left undisturbed.

When it thinks some undesirable visitors may be skulking about, the chipmunk shuts the door by solidly plugging the outer three or four inches of the tunnel with earth. It keeps remodeling and extending its home through the four or five years of its average normal life until the tunnel may reach a total length of thirty feet or even more. If no early accident befalls the builder, it may finally have several entrances, a number of short spur tunnels, and up to half a dozen rooms.

One of these rooms, located at the lowest part of the burrow system, is the toilet. There may also be two or three small rooms for storing grains and seeds, and one or possibly two for sleeping. The bedroom is well back toward the rear of the main shaft and is a large room, more than a foot broad and high. The good-sized bed is made of dry, broken leaves or, sometimes, grasses. Underneath, during the winter, are the cold-weather provisions.

An open field and a wet swamp or marsh are just about the only places where one is sure not to find the chipmunk. It demands plenty of shelter and prefers the ground to be dry. However, it will live in damp places such as open woodland where the rocks and down logs are covered with deep moss. Probably the majority of chipmunks were originally forest dwellers, but now they are more commonly found on the forest border, in rock piles at corners and along the edges of fields, and in hedgerows. These sites have an abundance of food. Chipmunks do not object to human neighbors and we sometimes see them scurrying through the shrubbery on suburban lots.

Up at daybreak, the chipmunk comes out to gather breakfast. The meals are chiefly fruits and seeds of a great variety of plants, such as berries of wintergreen and partridgeberry, which are available in early spring, bunch berry, star flower, lily-of-the-valley, wild cherries, viburnum, woodbine, dogwood, and prickly ash; the seeds of many annuals; and such well-known nuts as acorns, hazelnuts, walnuts, hickory nuts and beechnuts. It also likes mushrooms. On summer days, you may see its face streaked with bluish-black. Like an eager small boy, it has been gobbling quantities of blackberries, elderberries, blueberries, and raspberries. It is also fond of thimbleberries, gooseberries, and strawberries, and will scramble about in a shad-bush to get the juicy little applelike fruits.

From this it seems that the chipmunk is not exactly earth-bound. As a matter of fact, it climbs well, but carefully and not lightly like the tree squirrels. It does not attempt to leap from limb to limb, but has been seen in the tops of elm trees, sixty feet above the ground, feeding on the seeds. Because it is heavier and more clumsy, it is probably a little less enterprising in trees than the western chipmunk.

When cultivated grains are convenient, the voracious little rodent naturally goes after them. It will also dig up planted seeds, such as corn, peas, other vegetables, and grains. Many gardeners lose their liking for this tiny neighbor when it excavates and eats their tulip, crocus, narcissus and other bulbs, and fleshy roots such as iris. Very rarely are such depredations wide-spread or serious, however. Unlike ground squirrels, they can usually be checked by live-trapping and removing the offending individuals. The chipmunk is easy to catch in a box-type trap. Even if the trap is unbaited, the little animal is likely to go in just to satisfy its curiosity.

The chipmunk is often a great asset to gardeners. It eats June bugs (all except the hard wings and body shell), wireworms, cutworms, millepedes, a number of beetles, slugs, and even young field mice. It has been seen to stalk and pounce on resting dragon flies. Its liking for earthworms is less to its credit. Worst of all, it has been known to take birds' eggs and nestlings. Around pheasant-rearing farms, it may feast on the downy young which it attacks and kills instantly. At bird-banding stations it sometimes enters the traps and destroys the captives, often merely killing them and at most eating the brain. Here the grain spread to attract the birds may also serve as bait for the rodent. Once in the trap, it cannot resist the nervous impulse to kill the wildly-fluttering birds.

It is very common to find empty, weathered snail shells with a small, smooth-edged hole in one side of the coil. The chances are that it was opened by the sharp incisor teeth of some chipmunk that extracted and ate the juicy mollusk. At times the chipmunk also kills and eats small snakes. This act may be instinctive retaliation for the horrible frights given it by bigger species such as black snakes and fox snakes. These long creatures are always sliding about, ready to chase a chipmunk into its burrow and corner it at the last wall, or to devour a brood of helpless young.

Human bounty is quickly seized. Perhaps the chipmunk is not as intelligent as the sharp face and alert eyes would indicate. But it is quick to find a back door where a hand-out appears regularly. Sometimes it eats on the spot. More often it crams the food into the mouth pouches, filling them until the cheeks and the sides of the neck bulge like those of a boy with the mumps. After biting off any sharp projections, such as the dried calyx stem from the hickory nut, the chipmunk tucks the objects into its mouth, using its hands dextrously and filling each cheek alternately until the load is evenly balanced. Then it scampers off to its burrow.

The enormous size of the load that one of these little animals can carry has excited the interest of many observers. Some of them have painstakingly counted the items crammed away at one time by different individuals: one hundred and forty-five grains of wheat; thirty-one kernels of field corn (amounting to two heaping tablespoons); thirteen prune pits; seven large acorns; sixteen chinquapin nuts; and again thirty-two beechnuts.

John Burroughs once tried an experiment to find out if the chipmunk ever becomes really satisfied with the size of its hoards. In three days, he provided a chipmunk with five quarts of hickory nuts, two quarts of chestnuts, and a quantity of shelled corn. The animal carried it all away. Probably this bushel of provender, in addition to the food it had already found in the woods, was sufficient. At any rate it took no more offerings.

All of the chipmunk's hoard is not stored in the den. It makes little temporary deposits here and there under the bushes. A small hole is dug, the food spilled in by squeezing the cheek pockets with its hands in back-to-front motions, and the earth is replaced. Then a little leaf litter is added carefully for camouflage, just in case a marauding red squirrel snoops around. These little caches are usually intended to be opened before winter, for after the cold really takes a grip the chipmunk in the North generally stays snugly below ground.

Food that will keep (mostly seeds and nuts) is stored at any time during the growing season if it is not needed for that day's use. The chipmunk spends a number of months underground each year and much of this time it may not be asleep.

Because it can depend upon its stores it does not fatten up like the ground squirrels. First comes the period of quiet, during the dry, hottest part of the summer. The chipmunk often goes out on chilly, rainy days in spring and fall, but it can't take extreme heat. During the worst part of July and August, it lounges in the cool underground tunnel and emerges only when the food runs out.

The eastern chipmunk does not hibernate in the South. But in the North it retires about the last of October. During the really cold periods this chipmunk goes dead to the world like the woodchuck. It rolls up like a hoop, or sometimes curls on its side. Its head is tucked between the hind legs and the tail thrown over the back and head. Then it becomes cold and stiff and the blood pumps very slowly. During warm spells, however, it stirs and awakens. It nibbles at the food under its mattress or in the store rooms. It may even go to the doorway and, if the snow is shallow and the sun bright, take a little run.

General description. A small, ground-inhabiting squirrel with flattened and hairy, but not bushy, tail. Upper parts grizzled rusty grayish brown or reddish brown, marked by five blackish stripes running from shoulders to rump along the back and upper sides. The two lowest stripes on each flank are separated by a buffy to whitish band. The cheeks are marked by a buffy streak above and below the eye and a dark stripe passing across the eye. The bright reddish brown of the flanks grades into white on the belly. Total length, 9 to 11 inches; height at shoulders, 2 inches; weight, 3 to 5 ounces.

Distinguishing characteristics. The striped back and upper sides; alert, nervous behavior; high, quick call note.

Range. Most of eastern United States and southeastern Canada, from Nova Scotia and north side of Gulf of St. Lawrence west to southern Manitoba; thence south to southern Louisiana, central Georgia, and east-central North Carolina.

WESTERN CHIPMUNK
EUTAMIAS SP.

In the only area where the western and eastern chipmunks live together, a relatively small territory in the Great Lakes region, they can be immediately distinguished by their color. The western chipmunk is gray, not rusty. Its back stripes are finer and it has more of them. With one exception, it is much smaller, more streamlined, and has a comparatively longer tail.

This modest little creature proves that "the meek shall inherit the earth," or may, if it is persistent. The range of the western chipmunk extends west of the Great Plains, from the frozen Yukon south well into Mexico, and from the lowest valleys far up on the mountains.

As the little gray sprite perches on the end of the yellow pine log making a meal of blue lupine seeds, no musician could handle a flute more gracefully. The long fingers balance and turn the black seed-case with certainty and dexterity while the little animal's pointed nose tests first one side, then the other, as its hands turn the seed-case this way and that. Then a couple of gnaws of the sharp, chisellike teeth and the rich kernel is exposed. Two or three clawed fingers reach in. The shell is dropped on the discards of many previous meals, and the chipmunk delicately nibbles away.

The next item on this seed-eater's menu may be a dandelion or grass head. Each tiny grain is picked off between sensitive fingers, and shelled of its husk before being eaten.

These delicate little hands limit the places where many of the western species of chipmunks can live. Not suited to ditch-digging, they must find soft, loose soil, or woodland where there are many rotting logs, in which homes may be tunneled easily. Some species have branched out to living in crevices in and under rocks, and a few chipmunks are content to take over the abandoned homes of better miners such as pocket gophers and ground squirrels. Usually, however, they excavate their own comparatively modest burrows in the ground

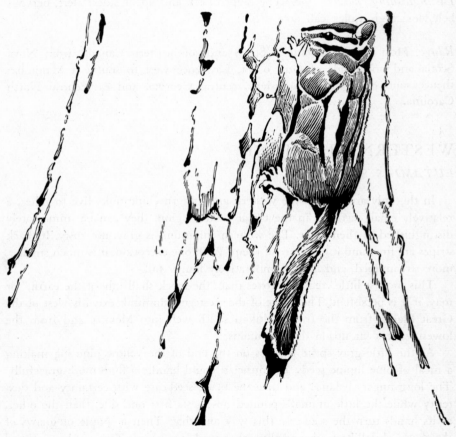

WESTERN CHIPMUNK

or in decayed logs. A few exceedingly flighty individuals have been known to build grass-and-leaf nests in shrubs and low trees instead of in the ground.

In spite of the tremendous abundance of these little animals, especially in newly-made clearings, and around abandoned saw mills and summer camps, little is known about their homes. The few that have been found and opened have been small, about the size and shape of a coconut, and were located under the supporting roof afforded by the roots of a stump or shrub. They were lined with shredded grass, chewed and frayed pieces of bark, or moss. Other dens have been located in rotten logs, and as much as five or ten feet above ground in partly decayed, hollow stubs.

The chipmunk is a clean little animal. It rubs its face with dust, and wipes it off with the paws and sometimes with the tail. Still it has fleas. I have found one to three or four on most of the chipmunks I have examined. Once I captured a chipmunk that was an unwilling host to a great warble which was developing on its abdomen. Ticks occasionally attach themselves also. Unfortunately the western chipmunk sometimes carries sylvatic plague, spotted fever and relapsing fever.

Chipmunks need all their speed and agility to escape from their many enemies: coyotes, wolves, badgers, foxes, wildcats, weasels, martens, snakes, and many predatory birds. Very few wild hunters are too small to kill them or too satiated to ignore them.

When one of these marauders comes into view, all the chipmunks in the vicinity burst into rapid, shrill notes that sound like "tk, tk, tk." They have been compared to the alarm calls of a flock of mildly disturbed juncoes. The graver the danger, the faster and higher-pitched are the notes. Up goes the tail of every chipmunk, straight as a stick, and each one scampers for home to the accompaniment of the sharp, startled chirps. One final "Yip!" and the last one is safe below. If the intruder is a bird, a bold chipmunk may stick out its head and resume a defiant barking. But if the bird swoops, the rodent hastily drops out of sight again.

One shameless chipmunk was known to cry "Wolf! Wolf!" in chipmunk language. When it gave the false alarm, every last chipmunk left the banquet that had been set before them and darted off to its den. Only the faker remained and smugly it ate up the rest of the food.

Since chipmunks are strictly diurnal, they have little fear of night-hunters except such as might dig them out of their homes. They rise early and hustle about at intervals until almost dark. On warm still afternoons in the mountains they talk back and forth sociably. I have heard their slow "Cuck-Cuck" for a quarter to half a mile away. The note is very similar to the "cluck" of the dusky grouse. Another sound, much used, is a series of low, faint "chips," similar to those of the eastern chipmunk.

Most of the western chipmunks are slender, exceedingly agile creatures that are almost as much at home in the trees as on the ground. I have often seen them high up in the tall yellow pines perhaps seventy or eighty feet above the earth, gathering food like any tree squirrel. Feather-weights and clever-fingered, they can skip about on the smaller twigs where even the chickaree (red squirrel) cannot venture. A few species of western chipmunks are rather slow, stodgy animals that may leave the ground only to clamber about in low bushes.

Western chipmunks have a prolonged mating season. A female may produce two litters of two or three to six or even seven young in a season, beginning with the birth of the first brood in late April or May. They remain with the mother at least six weeks. If a stranger comes around, she hurriedly pushes them back into their nest. Near Lassen Volcanic National Park in California a mother chipmunk was once seen on July 29 carrying a young one, apparently about one-quarter grown. She carried it in her mouth by the loose skin of its belly while it held on by curling its tail over her head.

The western chipmunk spends the winter in much the same manner as its eastern cousin. It is more restless, however, and even in the Montana mountains does not disappear until around Thanksgiving Day and comes out again about the middle of March. It has been seen wandering around in late November at eleven thousand feet elevation in northwestern Colorado when the snow was three feet deep and after the temperature had been 'way below zero.

On May 4, 1944 I saw one of these little fellows on the Norris Plateau in Yellowstone National Park when an unbroken blanket of snow twenty inches deep covered the country. As we drove in the narrow cut made just the day before by the rotary snowplow, the chipmunk was too confused or frightened, or possibly too cold and logy, to climb up the vertical wall, so it merely crouched against the snow as we whizzed past. It may have chosen the exposed black road surface because it absorbed the warmth of the bright spring sun.

The chipmunk's soft, dense coat is shed twice a year. The first molt, which generally occurs in June or July, starts at the head and progresses backward along a definite, noticeable line until the change is complete. This brighter, more reddish dress is discarded late in September or early in October, when it falls out hair by hair, here and there. Generally the rear of the animal is changed first and the front last, just the opposite of the summer procedure.

Living as they do in the mountains and other wild areas, most chipmunks never compete with man for a living. Those that settle in fence rows or stone piles on the edge of farms, however, may get into trouble by robbing orchards or by stealing grain which is standing in stacks or piled in storehouses.

When chipmunks are abundant they comb the woods thoroughly for seeds, sometimes preventing regeneration of the forest during the critical year or two following logging. Then the foresters may try to poison the rodents. At other times the chipmunks give valuable assistance by carrying tree seeds into burned areas and forgetting some caches which sprout and grow. A great many forest-damaging insects go into their ever-hungry mouths.

Western chipmunks eat a great variety of food. As they live over such a wide stretch of the continent, with its multitude of fruiting vegetation, I shall name only the types of diet: nuts, such as acorn and hazelnut; berries—currant, blueberry, salmonberry, and huckleberry; other fruits, such as manzanita, buffalo-berries, and dogwood; seeds, as of grasses, thistle, smartweed, and aster; cactus fruits; bulbs of camas and *Polygonum*; mushrooms; tender shoots and flowers of sagebrush, rabbitbrush, willow, and dandelion. They eat many insects: beetles, ants, bees, grasshoppers and their eggs, crickets, aphids, caterpillars and their pupae; and also spiders.

Such an arboreal rodent as the chipmunk might be expected to prey on birds. It has been known to take the eggs of a wood pewee, but a bird the size of a robin might easily fight off a little chipmunk. I once watched several birds, including a piñon jay, join in mobbing a chipmunk that was high in a pine tree. I was unable to determine whether it had gone there after eggs or bird flesh, but it seemed thoroughly unhappy about the consequences. When the coast was clear, it came down the trunk, head foremost, in a great hurry.

The chipmunk eats perishable foods on the spot; but foods that will keep well are carried home for storage in the home burrow or in scattered caches in rotten logs, under stones, in crevices in a cliff, or in a shallow pocket in the ground. The enormous capacity of the cheek pouches is shown by the records of loads removed from animals that were carrying them: one hundred and twelve cherry pits; one hundred and sixty-two cactus seeds; two hundred and sixty-four seeds of buckbrush (*Ceanothus*); one thousand six hundred and fifty seeds of wild cranberry; and two thousand one hundred veronica seeds. One can only begin to comprehend the industry and skill of the little animal that picks up and stores such tiny items.

There is a chipmunk for almost every habitat. A pale little fellow lives on the brushy, arid plains. The tawny chap that has adopted the humid evergreen forests of the northwestern coastal belt has grown almost as big and as brightly colored as the eastern chipmunk. Some western species live in dark rocky canyons while others prefer the open slopes where the tall trunks of yellow pines

stretch toward the sky like columns of a cathedral. We find still other chipmunks thriving on heights where the stunted conifers struggle against the
wind, cold and starvation of rocky, thin soil, and even beyond the zone of
tree growth. Perhaps the only important, extensive habitat from which chipmunks are absent is much of the hot, low desert of the Great Basin and the
lower Colorado River drainage.

Natural selection in such a variety of living conditions has produced chipmunks not only of many different species (see below) but of personalities.
Some are more shy than hunted deer. They race into hiding at the first vibration of a footfall. Most little western chipmunks, however, are less shy and
retiring than their big eastern cousin. They have often come into my camps in
the southwestern mountains to poke around and try to carry off anything edible.
So abundant were they in many places that they became a nuisance.

Over wide areas of the West, rainfall is scant and it may be a long time
between drinks. Accordingly, many western chipmunks have learned to do
without water for months at a time. They extract moisture from green succu-
lents and from the starch of seeds. Other species live where they can drink
regularly.

The many species and races of western chipmunks may be classified in
five groups:

1. The alpine chipmunk (*Eutamias alpinus*) is small and decidedly pale in
color. It lives in the central Sierra Nevada of California at eight thousand to
twelve thousand feet elevation.

2. The least chipmunk (*E. minimus*) varies from small to medium in size.
Its range includes western Canada, the northern Lake States, and much of the
Rocky Mountain area inhabited by the genus.

3. The "western" chipmunk (*E. amoenus*) is small to medium-sized. It lives
in the Rockies from Wyoming and Idaho, and in the Sierra Nevada from
southeastern California, north to northern British Columbia.

4. The "central" chipmunk (*E. quadrivittatus*) is of medium size. Its range
extends widely over the western United States, with an extension into southwestern Canada and an additional species in north-central Mexico.

5. The Townsend chipmunk (*E. townsendii*) is large and somewhat reddish. It is found from northwestern Mexico north to the Puget Sound region.

General description. General effect at slight distance is grayish. Upper parts
marked with 5 black and 4 whitish or buffy stripes from shoulders to base of
tail; flanks grizzled brownish; head gray, with a whitish stripe above and
another below eye, and a whitish spot behind the ear. Tail (which is about half

of the total length) is rather slender and mixed brown and black; under parts grayish. Total length, 7 to 10½ inches; height at shoulder, 1½ to 2 inches; weight, 1 to 4⅓ ounces.

Distinguishing characteristics. A small, slender, ground-dwelling squirrel, with one exception much smaller and more slender than the eastern chipmunk. The western species are grayish, without the bright reddish color on hind quarters, and have much finer and much closer back striping. Smaller and duller in color than the mantled ground squirrel. Quick nervous movements and sharp, shrill call notes. In the Southwest, the chipmunk may be confused only with the antelope ground squirrel which lives on the open desert and barren foothills, while the chipmunk here inhabits the forested mountains.

Range. Western North America mostly west of the Plains, from southern Yukon and southern Mackenzie south to central Baja California and Zacatecas, Mexico; from the Pacific coast east to eastern Ontario, central Wisconsin, western South Dakota, eastern Colorado and extreme western Texas.

RED SQUIRREL

TAMIASCIURUS HUDSONICUS, T. DOUGLASII, AND *T. FREMONTI*

"Tcher-r-r-r!"
"T-Whuk!"

Like an angry alarm clock, going off at 5 A.M., the red squirrel explodes into staccato sound. Any wrong-doer, stealing silently through the forest, is brought up with a start and its evil intentions are exposed to the world. The watchful little tree dweller in the rusty brown coat always tattles. This is probably not so much to give information as to express itself.

If an intruder has designs on the squirrel's storehouse, or pokes around its nest, or just comes too close, the little rodent flies into a rage. Its sharp, rattling barks are varied with spits, sputters and growls that are almost feline. Bouncing and jerking in convulsive fury, it stamps its feet and scolds. All this is a terrific bluff. If it is ignored, the squirrel subsides into sullen silence, broken by an occasional throaty "Wunk!"

When a big black bear raids its caches of seeds, there is nothing the tiny owner can do. Anxiously it follows along, picking up and re-storing the few seeds that the gigantic robber drops or leaves behind.

RED SQUIRREL

If there is no one around to scold, the red squirrel may keep up a constant and cheerful chatter to itself as it works. It is a wonder then that it ever hears or notices anything else. However, it is frequently quiet for hours at a time.

It is natural that such a familiar animal that ranges over a large part of North America should acquire many names. In the western United States, "chickaree" is commonly used. Actually this name originated in colonial New England, and was an attempt to describe the vibrating call of the animal. "Pine squirrel," the common name in the Rocky Mountain region, results from the creature's addiction to conifers. Mountaineers in the Southern Appalachians call it "boomer." Corrupted to "bummer," the term is sometimes used on the Pacific coast.

This self-assured, self-appointed reporter gets the news with no help from anyone. It seems to be the most unsociable of our tree squirrels. Outside of the mating season it keeps pretty much to itself. Occasionally two squirrels, working or resting on their separate ranges, will call back and forth a few times. Sometimes two or three will be seen chasing each other through the trees or over the ground. If this activity is actually play, the animals are probably brothers and sisters. Late litter-mates frequently spend the winter together; the rest of the red squirrels nest alone.

Most red squirrels regard each other more as possible enemies than as friends. Each domain is jealously guarded, and food caches are defended ferociously. Except in times of famine there are few transgressions. Those that step across their boundaries are chased relentlessly. The sharp teeth and claws of the owner seem to be doubly reinforced by righteous indignation, and the intruding squirrel may be badly injured or killed.

Red squirrels pair in late winter and spring. They are seen pursuing each other in the northern states as early as the first of February. The mating season seems to be at its height throughout March in Canada and Alaska, and may last well into April. Both males and females have a pair of glands, located around the vent, which secrete a small amount of clear, pale yellow musk. The faint odor is left on the feces and resting places and probably serves as an identification at least of sex. The gestation period is not known, but it is believed to be between thirty-six and forty days.

The red squirrel is born blind and naked. It is completely dependent on the mother until about one-third grown. One of five or six (occasionally three, four, or seven), it is born in April, May or June in a nest that is usually a tree cavity. Perhaps four inches long, including tail, the body is about the size of one's thumb beyond the knuckle. Its head is over-sized and blunt, while the legs and tail are poorly developed.

The tree cavity, often "borrowed" from a woodpecker, makes the safest nursery. If one cannot be found, the mother improvises a leaf nest among the branches or in an underground den (see pp. 393–394). Sometimes she uses a low, hollow stump. Even if it is open at the top, the rain is kept off by a dense canopy of overhanging spruce, fir or hemlock branches. Occasionally she takes over a man-made bird house or even his attic or vacant room.

The young acquire a decent covering of fine downy fur about ten days after birth. They are nursed until they are five to eight weeks old and one-third the size of the mother. At that stage they begin to venture from the nest and experiment with the aerial roadways through the dancing green leaves far above the ground. Many of them leave too early and are found unsteadily wandering in the woods.

If some danger threatens her brood before they leave the nest, the mother will move them one by one to another nest or temporary hiding place. She grasps each baby in her incisor teeth by the slack of its belly, and it curls its legs and tail around her neck. This is a tremendous load for her when the youngster is a third grown, but she manages it as she jumps from branch to branch.

Most of the earlier broods seem to scatter by late summer or early fall. They may not go far, but find homes for themselves in a rough circle around the mother's territory and lay up their own food stores for winter. Some families, and probably most of the late-born, do not break up until early the following spring.

There are naturalists who believe that many mothers produce two litters in a year, the second one in August or September. Others think that these late broods are the offspring of females that through some mischance did not rear a family in the normal spring season.

The principal factors limiting the population of red squirrels are food and available shelters. But even in one place, the little animals fluctuate in abundance from year to year. They seem to be most numerous in autumn, because they are busy gathering the nut crop and are seen more often.

Some extraordinary records of abundance have been established such as fourteen killed on one acre; and fifteen shot on a wooded village lot measuring one hundred and twenty-five feet by two hundred feet. Generally, one would not expect to find more than one or two red squirrels on an acre of favorable habitat. An ordinary population would be nearer one animal on every four acres. In central Massachusetts, Dr. Robert T. Hatt estimated one pair of squirrels to each six acres of dense, mature white pine, one pair to each two acres of spruce swamp, and one pair to each four acres of mixed conifers and hardwoods.

In addition to haphazard seasonal trips in search of permanent homes, red squirrels sometimes make mass migrations. Little is known about these travels although they probably result from population pressures and food shortages. In the northwestern United States, numbers of red squirrels have been seen crossing lakes, all swimming in the same direction. Swimming with strong strokes of each hind foot alternately, they floated high with most of their heads and upper backs above water. Their tails floated straight behind. No red squirrel is fond of water and after a swim it certainly looks like a drowned rat. But, if it wants to get across, it does not hesitate to swim a swift river at a point where it is fifty yards wide, or to paddle seven miles across a lake.

The red squirrel prefers to live in a stand of mixed conifers and hardwoods. These trees furnish a varied seed supply, plenty of shelter in the dense evergreen foliage, and many dens in old hollow trees. It isn't too fussy, however, and will acccpt almost any kind of woodland or forest border except young sapling hardwoods. Big trees are not required, as red squirrels get along perfectly well in the far north where the spruces are stunted to a height of only thirty feet.

On the border between forest and tundra, tree dens are almost unknown because cavities are scarce and the trunks are too small anyhow. The red squirrel that lives here may make one or more nests of twigs, leaves, and moss, which it anchors firmly on a whorl of branches where they leave the trunk. But it is more likely to build at least the winter home underground. Digging under a tree or stump, or even in a rotten stub, it makes a round room about nine inches in diameter and five inches high. Then it lines the room with shredded bark and almost fills it with soft, warm, dry leaves.

South of this border zone, where hollow trees make almost impregnable little forts and dry, weather-proof homes, the red squirrel prefers them to any other type of architecture. But if it can't find a cavity, it must go to the trouble of building a leaf nest.

The support for the nest must come first. The squirrel looks for a mass of twigs close to a tree trunk, a whorl of many branches, or a witches broom (forced thick growth stimulated by fungus disease, mechanical injury, or other factors) which will form a steady platform. It is usually thirty to fifty feet high or even sixty, but may be as low as six or eight feet. (In the far north, of course, the leaf nests are always comparatively low because the trees are not tall.)

The red squirrel weaves its roundish nest tightly with masses of available material such as hardwood leaves from the ground litter, pine needles, long shreds of cedar or other bark, moss, dry grasses and twigs. It is surprisingly wind-and-rain proof and the thick foliage overhead further wards off deluges or heavy snows. The outside dimensions are sixteen to twenty inches across and ten to twelve inches deep. The coarse material of the outer shell is thickly lined with fine, soft fibers. Within this central core, which is a little less than half of the total diameter of the nest mass, is a snug room about five inches wide and three to four inches high. The single doorway (or rarely two) opens on the side. Sometimes the squirrel hangs a portiere of moss or makes a screen to be brushed aside when it goes out or in. At other times it keeps the house warm by merely stopping up the entrance with surplus nest lining. In cold weather the damp outer shell freezes hard, making the house tighter than ever.

Unfortunately the red squirrel is a slovenly housekeeper. Although it deposits its feces outside, the house is more often dirty than not, and contains numerous parasites. While it is meticulous about its personal appearance and stops every little while to groom its fur and scratch, the squirrel usually carries numbers of fleas and often many mites. Ticks attach themselves and bot flies sometimes lay their eggs on hairs. The fly larvae then hatch, gain entrance into the body, and develop.

The red squirrel often sets up several living establishments scattered about its territory. When the fleas get too much for it, or an enemy becomes interested, it moves across the way or down the "road." In addition to the favorite den in a tree trunk, there may be two or three leaf nests and an underground burrow which is sometimes in a stone pile or wall.

The red squirrel usually digs its underground den under a tree stump so that the roof is strong. One to four or five tunnels lead to the surface or away under the earth in a labyrinth of shallow passages. Numerous small rooms, three to six inches in diameter, are dug for storage of food or nest material. Sometimes the tunnels of the eastern red squirrel are quite extensive. It is surprising that such a passionately curious little creature spends as much time underground.

The home range of the red squirrel is only five hundred to seven hundred feet across. Beyond this it rarely ventures except possibly in mating season or if the food supply runs out. Within this little domain it knows every knot hole, hummock and plant. Most of its life is likely to be spent aloft, for it is adapted in many ways for life in the trees. Racing up and down the pillarlike trunks and along the branches, it can travel with astonishing speed and endurance.

A squirrel building its leaf nest fifty feet above the ground has been known to make twelve trips in twelve minutes with loads of material. One round trip was made in only thirty-five seconds.

When the red squirrel is on the ground, it forages about with short springy leaps. It gets considerable food that grows there and of course many nuts and cones that fall. Although many far northern red squirrels make their homes in the earth, none of them like to get too far from trees. A hungry fox, lynx, bobcat, or other meat-eater might be watching for such an opportunity.

Traveling through the trees, the red squirrel uses a gallop with fore legs and hind legs moving as pairs. On trips downward it goes head foremost and places one foot at a time in a kind of a trot, the back feet being reversed to act as brakes. If its arboreal highway is interrupted by spaces between trees it makes leaps that, for a small animal, are tremendous. Springing with all the power of its taut muscles, it zips through the air with tail extended and legs spread wide to grasp the twig ends. Jumps of six to eight feet, with drops of two to three feet, have been recorded.

No tree dweller, not even the red squirrel with its athletic ability and almost perfect sense of timing and coordination, can go through life without ever miscalculating and falling. Sometimes the squirrel is forced to leap hurriedly from unstable twigs, and misses the intended landing. Usually it is able to grab a lower branch before tumbling more than five or ten feet toward the ground. Once in a great while, however, nothing intervenes. Then the falling animal twists like a cat until it is horizontal, spreads its tail and all four legs widely to increase the air resistance, and drops to the earth. Rarely is it even dazed or stunned by a terrific fall. One squirrel, that fell from the top of a hickory tree one hundred and forty feet high, scampered off five seconds after striking the ground.

Sometimes the red squirrel leaves its nest at night, especially when the moon is shining. As a rule, it works only by day. Its schedule is not too rigid. Getting up is regulated by the emptiness of its stomach, and it rests when tired at midday. It may go indoors to bed for this siesta, but is just as likely to stretch out on a horizontal limb or wedge itself securely into a fork. It loves a good sun bath up in the tree tops.

With all its chatter and dashing about, it is a wonder that the squirrel escapes from as many enemies as it does. In settled regions, small boys with slingshots and men with rifles seem to be all over the place collecting squirrel tails to decorate their hunting hats. House cats get many squirrels, especially the young and inexperienced. In the wilderness other mammal predators are the weasel, mink, lynx and bobcat. The marten is a fast and tireless pursuer that can leap even wider gaps between trees and run even faster than its fear-stricken victims. Successful tree-top hunters are the raptorial birds: red-tailed and red-shouldered hawks, broad-winged hawk, marsh hawk, goshawk. Even the little sparrow hawk has been known to make a meal of red squirrel. Occasionally a squirrel that is foolish enough to keep late hours is gobbled by a horned owl, barred owl, or spotted owl. On trips across lakes or rivers, a swimming squirrel may be picked up by a gull, or swallowed whole by a great pike, pickerel, or trout. Big black snakes climb about the trees and quickly strangle a red squirrel trapped in the nest.

Other animals contribute to the red squirrel's problems. These are the neighbors who sponge on its stored food, the woodpeckers, nuthatches and other birds, the gray and fox squirrels, many lesser rodents, and even bears. Famine (the failure of seed- and nut-crops) is a less obvious but probably more wholesale killer at times. Extensive hot forest fires, especially those that leap into the crowns, may roast or suffocate many tree dwellers, and destroy their stored food and seed-producers as well. With old age comes lessened vigor and ability to withstand falls. After the age of five years the squirrel's teeth do not grow rapidly enough to offset the effects of wear and tear of eating hard foods. Rare indeed is the red squirrel that reaches the age of ten years.

At least ninety-five per cent of the food comes from the succulent growing twigs and buds, flowering parts, and seeds of shrubs and trees, with the latter furnishing the greater portion. Late summer and fall is the squirrel's busiest time. Seeds, which are its bread and butter, are ripening so fast that it is almost beside itself in its haste to cut down cones and nuts. Probably to get ahead of rivals that have the same tastes, and because wind-scattered bits are harder to find and pick up, the red squirrel tries to harvest the seeds from the branches before they are ripe enough to fall. Working at dizzy speed, it jumps from one limb to another and clips them off. Small seeds are usually stuffed into the mouth until it can hold no more. Then the squirrel rushes to some hiding place to unload. It cuts down large items, such as pine cones, throws them outward by a jerk of the head or paw, and picks them up later from the ground.

The red squirrel does not put all of its eggs in one basket. It does, however, put many cones in one heap (called a midden). This may be as much as thirty feet across and two to three feet deep. Centrally located in its domain, it is usually built around a stump, a rock, a large log, or a tree or group of trees, and preferably in a damp spot. The moisture, instead of causing the food to rot, seems to be essential to prevent the cones from opening and losing their seeds. In the Pacific Coast region, pine squirrels are known to store cones in springs or in running water.

The owner generally eats on the top of the midden or on the eminence around which the midden has been built. Husks and cone bracts are shucked off and allowed to fall to the ground. After successive years of use, a midden in autumn consists of a damp mass of debris, on which is piled or spread the gathered crop of the current season. As the winter wears on, the pile tends to become mixed, as the owner burrows into the old trash to hide choice items of food from the top layer, or from other caches.

One squirrel may own several middens of various sizes. Generally they contain three to five bushels of the current year's cones, but may have seven to ten bushels. The squirrel always scatters a portion of its stores, as single seeds or little clusters, in all sorts of places throughout its home territory. These seeds may be hidden in holes in the ground, under patches of leaves, in stone piles or walls, wedged in the angles of tree roots or stumps, or under loose bark on the trunks or limbs of trees. Unlike these carefully hidden caches, the midden lies conspicuously on the forest floor with no attempt made to even pile leaves or litter over it.

The trees that yield their seeds, flowers, catkins, or twiglike tips include all the pines, firs, cedar, spruces, tamarack, hemlock, butternut, walnut, all of the hickories and oaks, cherries, plum, apple, maples, ash, and basswood. Buds and flowers are taken from willows, aspens and poplars, and birches. Among the shrubs, wild currant, gooseberry, barberry, raspberries and blackberries, rose, elderberry, cranberry, blueberry, sumac, partridge-berry, wintergreen, alder, hazel, juniper, ground hemlock, and cat brier are plundered of their seeds or fleshy fruits.

A tree "product" of which the red squirrel is very fond in spring is the sap of the maples and black birch. (Apparently this sweet tooth is shared by all tree squirrels.) The red squirrel sometimes laps sap from the bark as it seeps from natural breaks caused by the strains of wind, frost or other forces. Often, however, this epicure cuts out little saucerlike depressions on the upper side of the limbs, or strips away the bark until the sap flows in satisfying quantities.

It also samples a great variety of food from herbaceous plants, such as the fruits of strawberry and bunchberry, roots, and miscellaneous seeds such as grasses.

If you find a mushroom wedged under loose bark on a tree, or resting in the fork of a limb of a tree or bush, you may be almost sure it was placed there by some red squirrel that intends to come back to eat it. All through the summer, these rodents feed on a great variety of fungi, and spare plants are cached where they will dry and be preserved for the lean winter-time. They even dig for fungi that grow underground on roots or decaying wood. Apparently they are immune to mushroom poison, for the deadliest varieties which would kill a human are eaten by the squirrels without any ill effects.

Nobody knows how many insects they eat. At times, they are seen pulling loose bark from trees to get at the pupae of moths or the larvae of bark beetles or wood borers. They also eat plant lice or aphids, the larvae in tree galls, and the pupae of hornets, wasps and bees (provided the comb has been torn open by other animals and the parent insects have become discouraged and left). Sometimes they capture grasshoppers.

Any carcass lying in the woods is likely to be gnawed by red squirrels. Practically every coyote-killed deer that I have ever seen in the north woods showed evidence of such use. Often in the Rocky Mountain region, and rarely elsewhere, one can find bones that have been gnawed by red squirrels. Frequently these relics, usually leg bones or cast antlers of deer, are dragged and left on the top of the middens, where the rodents can enjoy a little heavy jaw exercise each day. Possibly some of it is necessary to keep the front or chisel teeth worn down if the food consists chiefly of easily opened seeds such as pine and spruce. There is some evidence that female squirrels chew the bony or horny material to get the phosphorus and calcium that is needed for the developing young.

The red squirrel has gained a bad reputation for robbing birds' nests of eggs and young. The little bandit has been seen eating eggs, or pouncing on helpless nestlings. Sometimes the brains or other parts are eaten, or the throat may be cut and the carcass left to rot. Occasionally a squirrel will merely toss the little birds out of their nest, apparently as a defense-of-territory complex.

Possibly there are abnormal individuals in the red squirrel world just as there are among men. The practice of nest robbing cannot be very general. Birds often have been known to rear their broods in the same trees with red squirrels, while the latter looked on and showed no gustatory interest. Some red squirrels have been terrorized by jays and robins, that never permitted the rodents to approach their nesting sites. Dr. Klugh, the Canadian naturalist, seemed to have put the problem in its proper focus when he said: "It is probable that only certain red squirrels are bird-eaters, just as only certain tigers are man-eaters and such individuals should be destroyed as soon as evidence against them is obtained."

For the squirrel that has laid in an ample supply of food, winter is a time of leisure. It does not hibernate, but stays in its nest during stormy weather and through the very coldest periods. At such times it may not come out for two or three days. Generally it makes a round of its little realm, to satisfy an always active curiosity regarding anything that moves, and to tap one or more of its caches for food. After the snow covers up the minor landmarks, an excellent memory serves as a general guide to relocate the buried stores. Once the squirrel is in the immediate vicinity, the sensitive nose takes over. Then it is necessary to dig. Frequently the squirrel makes extensive burrows in the snow about two inches below the surface in order to cross open areas to the caches and to explore the ground beneath for edibles.

Melanistic (black) red squirrels are very rare. Albinos are more common, but are more readily captured by enemies because they are so conspicuous. Normal red squirrel skins are beautiful in their rippling, soft glossiness. Those from Alberta and Northwest Territories bring the trapper twenty-five cents to a dollar apiece. Millions of pelts have been used in the making of "mink" coats. Although handsome, they are easily distinguished from the real mink wraps. Skins of more-southerly red squirrels are sometimes used for trimming, but they are worth only about ten cents each. Among the primitive Indians the skins were used as decorations for clothing and for making ceremonial robes and head-dresses. The flesh is excellent, provided the animal has not become impregnated with resin from feeding on pine twigs. However, the carcass is so tiny that it is hardly worth cooking.

The red squirrels are divisible into three species:

1. The northern red squirrel (*Sciurus hudsonicus*) has white under parts and a yellowish red tail. It is the most widely distributed of the red squirrels, and is found throughout the eastern and northern portions of the range.

2. The Douglas chickaree (*S. douglasii*) has rust-colored under parts and its tail is fringed with yellowish or white. The range is entirely west of the Rocky Mountains.

3. The pine squirrel (*S. fremonti*) has white under parts and a white-fringed tail. It is found from southern Wyoming southward in the Rocky Mountain region.

General description. A small tree squirrel with a flattened, bushy tail; ears generally tufted; manner nervous, alert. Rusty red, brownish or olive, red or gray on head, back and upper surface of tail; sides olive-gray or gray, generally with a black line extending along the flank from back of shoulder to point of hip; under parts white or rusty, depending on the species; tail fringed with yellowish or white. Total length, 12 to 14 inches; height at shoulder, $3\frac{1}{2}$ inches; weight, 5 to $10\frac{1}{2}$ ounces.

Distinguishing characteristics. Smallest of the tree-climbing squirrels that are abroad habitually in daytime. Tail much more bushy than that of the chipmunks, which may occasionally go into low trees. Quick, nervous actions and loud, chattering call. Generally reddish color.

Range. Northern and western North America; from Virginia (northern Georgia in the mountains) to north-central Ungava (except Newfoundland); Atlantic coast northwest to western Alaska south of the tree limit; south to southern Minnesota, southern New Mexico and Arizona, and northern Baja California; absent from the Great Plains and the Great Basin.

GRAY SQUIRREL
SCIURUS CAROLINENSIS AND *S. GRISEUS*

The eastern gray squirrels seemed to overrun the country when the first colonists came to America. They raced in from the forests like swarms of grasshoppers and destroyed the new crops in the tiny corn fields.

It finally became necessary to place a price on their heads. In 1749, Pennsylvania offered a bounty of three pence per scalp, and the treasurer paid out eight thousand pounds sterling for the destruction of six hundred and forty thousand squirrels. Communities offered fame and prizes. Two teams of six Kentuckians each went on a seven-day killing spree about 1840 and tallied a total of nine thousand seven hundred and eighty animals. In the early years of the nineteenth century, as many as two thousand squirrels were killed in a single day in western New York by community effort.

Sometimes "myriads" of squirrels went off on cross-country treks. Apparently they moved when their population reached a peak, even though food still was sufficient, for the travelers were fat. Whatever the cause, the migrations were erratic and unpredictable. No obstacle seemed to stop them; they crossed lakes, streams and mountains, even great bodies of water like the Hudson and the Ohio Rivers. Hundreds of thousands drowned or fell victims to predators, including man. Many also died from sheer exhaustion. But like the lemming hordes, the main body of squirrels pressed onward. A great migration in southeastern Wisconsin in 1842 lasted four weeks. Seton estimated that it may have contained nearly half a billion squirrels. Behind them, the woods were practically deserted. In a few years, however, the same forests seemed as thickly populated as before.

About the time of the Civil War, a marked decrease of eastern gray squirrels began to be noticed. During the following decades, forests were cleared away to grow crops, or were logged or burned. From about 1900 to 1915, conservationists feared that the eastern species of gray squirrel might become extinct. However, reasonable protection of wildlife and forests has permitted it to reoccupy suitable habitats in some numbers. Gray squirrels are even abundant in many city parks, where they become tame and beg for food like so many monkeys.

In the Ohio Valley region, and probably elsewhere, the squirrel population appears to vary in a five-year cycle. A peak occurred in southern Ohio during

GRAY SQUIRREL

1935. After making careful counts on a large area of oak-hickory woodland, biologists estimated an average population in autumn of ten and eight-tenths squirrels an acre. Then came an abrupt decline. A year later there were only two and three-tenths squirrels an acre. In 1937 the animals had begun to increase once more, and the number per acre averaged three and seven-tenths. During 1935 a hunter spent on an average about one and a half hours to bag a squirrel. In 1937 it required eleven and a half hours.

Modern gray squirrels still go on mass excursions like their ancestors. But the movements of today are composed of hundreds instead of tens of thousands. Hunters notice them swimming rivers or moving through the woods, one by one but in the same direction, and telephone the newspapers.

The western gray squirrel has had a less spectacular past. It has stayed at home contentedly and hasn't overpopulated the forests. It is seldom that more than two or three are sighted at one time after the young have scattered.

Gray squirrel hunting requires skill and patience. Unlike their lazy, careless brethren that live in the city parks, woodland gray squirrels are watchful and wary. The sight of a hunter tramping through the autumn leaves sends them scampering into the treetops. A wily old "gray" will flatten out against the upper trunk and carefully worm itself around to keep out of sight of the hunter who is circling. If several men converge from different directions, the squirrel will lie concealed on a high limb or take to a cavity from which it can peep out and watch. Only the crafty, experienced hunter can shoot a full bag. The meat, when stewed, is delicious.

Many people prefer to watch the squirrels than to shoot them. The squirrels' smooth grayish coats flaunt great feathery tails which arch gracefully or jerk with emotion. Perched on a limb against a flaming background of oak or maple foliage, or caching acorns on the forest floor, the squirrels are far more beautiful than when limp in death.

Albinos are sometimes seen and melanistic squirrels are often common. In some localities the black individuals outnumber the "normal" grays. These color phases occur in mixed litters. The dark animals may have many brownish hairs along the back and on the legs, or sometimes they are jet black.

Gray squirrels appear to be a little irregular in their mating times. In the southern half of the eastern range, young have been seen in every month of the year. The vast majority, however, are born in late winter or spring from late February through April in the North, or about a month earlier in the South. A number of litters arrive in late August. These may be the belated efforts of females that failed to mate in the usual mid-winter season beginning in the South during December. The gestation period is about forty-four days.

Almost all gray squirrel mothers use a tree den for their nursery. Only the "under-privileged few" must resort to a leaf nest at this time. They have the entire responsibility of providing food and defense. The father has several mates and is interested in no one but himself after mating season.

A brood may number from two to six young, although four or five is average. They develop slowly, and their eyes are closed for fully five weeks after birth. The devoted mother is affectionate and often strokes them fondly. Sometimes if the home is disturbed, she carried them for quite a distance. Like other little squirrels, they wrap their tails and legs around her neck on such trips. It takes two months for them to develop enough strength and confidence to climb about their home tree and perhaps try to taste of the flowers. They often stay with the mother through the first winter.

In addition to man, the gray squirrel has numerous enemies. From the frantic shrieks that I heard one day when a Cooper hawk swooped down on a gray squirrel that I was watching, I infer that these birds, as well as barred and horned owls, are greatly feared. Both eastern and western grays (particularly the latter) do a great deal of foraging on the ground where they are vulnerable to attack by foxes, coyotes, bobcats and other carnivores. In the trees, the western gray squirrel may be followed through the branches by a hungry marten.

The red squirrels are said to harry and chase their big relatives at every opportunity. Certainly the two species are rarely abundant in the same woodland. It is common belief that red squirrels emasculate the male grays, but there is little evidence. However, the warbles of botflies may do it as they are often found in the bodies of squirrels. Other common parasites are coccidia, roundworms, tapeworms, flukes, fleas, mange mites, and, in the South, chiggers ("red bugs").

About the time of World War 1, an outbreak of mange mites among the gray squirrels of the Yosemite region in California almost extirpated the species over hundreds of square miles of mountains. It was not until fifteen years later that it began to recover. Twenty years after the epidemic began, squirrels were numerous once more.

Tree-climbing snakes often cause trouble, for they persistently poke into holes looking for young squirrels. Sometimes the tables are turned. A hunter near Auburn, Alabama, once saw a five-foot spotted chicken snake sliding along the ground, doing its best to escape from a quarter-grown gray squirrel. The youngster was bravely dashing in and out, nipping at the snake's middle. But it finally gave up and took to a tree when the reptile came to bay.

Gray squirrels do not reach full size and weight until they are two years old, although many mate when only a year old. An occasional veteran may live ten years or even longer in the wild, and several pets have been known to attain an extreme age of fifteen years.

In the East, the gray squirrel prefers oaks, beeches and hickories. A pure stand is not necessary, of course, and these species are often mixed with other hardwoods and occasionally conifers. In the Gulf States, the gray squirrel is most often found on sandy ridges and in damp localities along rivers. The western species lives in the coastal ranges and in the mountains of the Pacific slope. Their usual habitat is between three thousand and eight thousand feet, in mixed stands of oak and pine, or in yellow pine and fir. During the fall when acorns are ripening, the high-dwelling squirrels may visit the lower slopes briefly.

Nuts and large seeds supply most of the food. Acorns, hickory nuts, walnuts and butternuts begin to mature about the first of August, and they make up the bulk of the animal's diet until the following April or even May. The eating habits of the gray squirrel and method of storage of surplus food are similar to those of the fox squirrel (see pp. 414–415). However, I believe that the gray is more apt to keep supplies in its den.

In the Sierra Nevada, the western gray squirrel often robs the caches made by the California woodpecker. This bird's habit of digging small shallow holes in the thick bark of firs and pines and then driving an acorn into each cavity is perpetually fascinating to the squirrel as it is to the tourists from the East. The woodpecker knows what the bushy-tailed thief is up to and often threatens to skewer the robber on its sharp bill.

During spring and summer the gray squirrel lives on a mixed diet: fruits and berries, such as dogwood and viburnum; mushrooms; tree seeds, particularly those of the elms and maples; the larvae and cocoons of insects, and occasionally a fledgling bird. Like its ancestors, it will raid corn and other grain fields if it gets the chance, or growing vegetables such as peas and beans. When the buds of elm, oak, and white and sugar maples are swelling, the squirrel may be seen perched precariously far in the treetops feeding on them and the flowers or catkins. Grasping a stem in its hands, the gray squirrel clips it with sharp teeth, then, revolving the cluster, eats the buds one by one. For three or four weeks each year it lives largely on this delicate fare.

The gray squirrel is most active during the first and last three or four hours of full daylight. It is not as nosey as the smaller red squirrel and is usually content to let the world work out its problems without constant surveillance. It is quite friendly with others of its own race, especially in the winter. It is not unusual to find several gray squirrels using the same den or nest during cold weather. These partnerships generally break up in the spring.

When annoyed, the big squirrel doesn't often become as excited as the red squirrel, but it doesn't hesitate to express itself. First it barks, a quacking "Yak, yak, yak," repeated many times. Then, as its anger increases, the voice becomes more querulous and higher pitched. The complaint changes to a prolonged, harsh "Kuaa-a-a!" The bark is not always an impatient one. I have heard it many times when it was soft and had an inquiring or even contented sound. The animal also has quite a repertoire of little chuckles when it is conversing with other squirrels or even itself.

For a home, the gray squirrel much prefers a den high up in a big tree. As a substitute, it will accept an empty bird house. Occasionally a leaf nest will do, but this is generally used for warm-weather camping, in emergencies, or to starve out fleas and mites when they become too annoying in the den. Also, it is often convenient to have a camp near a particularly fruitful nut tree when a den is not available.

The leaf nest of the eastern gray squirrel is built close to the trunk of a tree, in a fork or on a large limb. First, twigs with their fresh leaves are packed together to make a platform. The surface is leveled up with odds and ends of fine stuff, grass, moss, fresh and dead leaves, and bark. Then fresh leaves or leaves and twigs are woven together and braced or interlaced with dead twigs to form a little house about sixteen inches across inside and twelve inches from floor to ceiling.

Sometimes the nest is made by heaping up dry grass, shredded bark and moss on the platform, then hollowing out a room inside. Regardless of the type of construction, it is usually thirty to fifty feet above ground.

The nest of the western gray squirrel is similar in form. One from northern California was about two feet in diameter and three feet high. It was built in layers: a coarse protecting shell of oak twigs with leaves attached; then a nest of strips of redwood bark, and finally a lining of finely shredded inner bark from the redwood tree.

The fur of our gray squirrel is beautiful, but has no commercial value. Squirrel coats in department stores are made from the pelts of Russian or Siberian animals. (These latter have tufted ears, and in this respect are like our tassel-eared squirrels, the Abert and Kaibab species. See pp. 406–410.)

Our native gray squirrels were introduced years ago into England, France, and other parts of Europe. Most of the animals thrived and their descendants are now completely naturalized.

The true gray squirrels are classified by zoologists in two groups, as follows:

1. The eastern gray squirrels (*Sciurus carolinensis*), which range from the Atlantic seaboard to the western edge of the forest belt in Louisiana and Minnesota.

2. The western gray squirrels (*S. griseus*) are found in the Pacific Coast region. (For details, see Range at end of chapter.) The two species can be distinguished most readily by the distinctly wider tail of the western species.

General description. A large, tree-climbing squirrel with fairly large rounded ears (usually without conspicuous tufts) and long, flattened, bushy tail. Color varies with the species from pale gray to dark brownish and gray on the back; clearer gray on the sides, legs and head; and white or pale gray under parts; feet pale gray; tail grayish black "frosted" with white. Total length, 17 to 23 inches; height at shoulder, about 5 inches; weight, 1 to 1½ pounds.

Distinguishing characteristics. Large size and general gray color of the head, body and legs, together with the gray tail overlaid with white-tipped hairs, distinguish the gray squirrel from other arboreal squirrels. Generally more slender than the heavy-bodied fox squirrel. It lacks the conspicuous ear tufts of the Abert and Kaibab squirrels.

Range. Eastern United States from southern Florida and the Gulf coast north to northern New England, southern Ontario, northern Wisconsin and north-central Minnesota, and from the Atlantic coast west to southeastern North Dakota, central Kansas, and east-central Texas. Extreme western United States from northern Baja California to north-central Washington, excluding the Central Valley and southeastern deserts of California.

TASSEL-EARED SQUIRREL
SCIURUS ABERTI AND *S. KAIBABENSIS*

As it lopes across the sun-sprinkled ground between the tall, pale brown columns of the yellow pines, the tassel-eared squirrel arches its broad plumed tail elegantly. This animal is about the size of a heavy gray squirrel. Tall tufts of hair rise above the ears and distinguish it from all other American squirrels. There is no doubt that they give it an air of aristocracy.

Tassel-eared squirrels formerly lived in one great, presumably happy, family. Circumstances arose to separate them. One was the formation of the Grand Canyon, about a million years ago. The great schism, however, probably did not occur until thirty-five thousand years ago. Even then it was very slow. Obviously, no squirrel or other creature realized it. Warmer climates following the end of the Wisconsin glacial period forced the yellow pine forests to move up the mountain sides. With them went the tassel-ears, which, like most of us, were only creatures of habit. Their descendants continued to live higher and higher in whatever part of the range their grandfathers had been born. Because tassel-eared squirrels never leave their pine forests for any distance, the deep canyon and deserts between their homes separated and imprisoned them.

Isolated, the squirrels developed somewhat different characteristics. Three races evolved. These are the Abert and Kaibab (separated from each other by the mile-deep Grand Canyon) and the Durango squirrel in Mexico (segregated by wide deserts). Their evolution has not gone on for enough thousands of years to standardize racial differences. For instance, an occasional Abert squirrel will turn up wearing a Kaibab black vest, or all-white tail. Sometimes a Kaibab squirrel will appear in a white front and a black tail, apparently borrowed from the Abert race which it has never seen and never will see.

Generally speaking, the Abert has a grayish tail which is white underneath, and white under parts. The Kaibab has an all-white tail and black under parts. Both of them are apt to have grizzled gray coats with a broad rusty band down the back and a black lateral line. The color tone and pattern, however, vary

TASSEL-EARED SQUIRREL

even in their own immediate families. Melanistic Aberts are common, especially in Colorado.

The lives of all the tassel-eared squirrels are very much alike, regardless of where they live. They stay in the tall yellow pines between six thousand and eight thousand five hundred feet above sea level. Occasionally, not often, they go down into the oaks below or up to the firs above, but only for brief trips. Knotholes and cavities are rare in pine trees, perhaps because they are well preserved by their own pitch. So these squirrels nearly always build their houses. The bulky nests of twigs with the needles attached are placed high in the branches where they are seldom noticed. The size of a bushel basket, they are lined with soft grasses and frayed bark, and have from one to three entrances. The dome-shaped outer walls are rough-looking but so well woven that they keep out the winter storms.

Shelter at that season is important to the tassel-ears. Rather than face bad weather they stay indoors, sometimes for a week or ten days at a time. Unlike other squirrels, they do not store much food. During the fall they may have spotted some acorns, pine (or even Engelmann spruce and Douglas and cork barked fir) cones here and there, singly, in the forest litter. But they depend a great deal on yellow pine bark. Crawling out nearly to the end of a branch they bite off the heavy end-cluster of pine needles and drop it to the ground. Then they cut a convenient length of branch, carry it back to a perch and eat the thick white cambium. Sometimes the snow under a favorite pine is littered with needles and the four- to six-inch lengths of stripped twigs.

The tassel-eared squirrels have big feet. They hop like other squirrels, two feet at a time. Occasionally they walk, one foot after the other, but awkwardly. Only their lope is graceful, a series of springy bounds. They spend some time on the ground, rummaging about for food. Against the dull yellowish brown needles of the summer woodland the white tail of the Kaibab squirrel is conspicuous. Numerous times I have watched the long, gracefully waving plume wandering erratically along between the golden brown tree-shafts while the gray body was almost lost in the shadows. It looked a little like the white plume on the hat of the Scotch ghost who stalked invisibly about his castle!

As the higher mountains shed their snow covering the squirrels discard their winter coats. They keep their distinctive ear tufts until early June, when the new summer coats are almost complete. From then until late fall the squirrels have ordinary ears, no decorations, and no swank. The tufts grow quite slowly, but by January they may again be nearly one and one-half inches long.

The three or four little tassel-ears arrive as early as the first of April, although young ones are seen as late as September. No one yet knows for sure whether these later broods are second litters or late arrivals. The earlier squirrels grow up in the world's finest summer climate where only a few July thundershowers interrupt the procession of fine cloudless days and clear cold nights. Under the mother's directions, they get their food from the straight tall pines, eating the spongy sweet inner bark of the twigs, and the male flowers. They learn to hunt mushrooms, the berrylike fruits and spicy roots of the spikenard (*Aralia,* a member of the ginseng family), lupine seeds, and the seeds, fruit and roots or tubers of many other shrubs and herbs. They are no better nor worse than the squirrels of other species, and sometimes rob birds' nests and eat birds that may be caught napping in the trees. They often steal acorns from the Mearn's woodpeckers' caches.

Occasionally tassel-ears create an uproar over trifles. An impatient or angry tassel-ear will bark, grumble, chatter and scold almost as violently as the little western red squirrel that lives in the same forest. Its ordinary call is a "chuck-chuck," much like the bark of a fox squirrel.

It knows when to be silent too. If thoroughly frightened it disappears into the treetops. A patient creature, it may lie for an hour or two without twitching a muscle. Once in a while it may very slowly raise its head to see if the coast is clear. But the hunter who tries to outwait a scared tassel-eared squirrel will not go far that day.

Sometimes the beautiful big squirrels are conspicuous by their numbers. As many as five or six or even more may be seen chasing each other over a single tree. A year or two later it may be hard to find one. Very likely there is a connection between the squirrel population and the size of the acorn and pine seed crops. Some years little or no seed may be produced over wide areas of the mountainsides.

Abert squirrels are found for a great distance along the southern Rockies and other detached ranges of the Southwest. The Kaibab species is restricted to the plateau in northern Arizona from which it gets the name. This great domed "island," about forty miles long and twenty miles wide, is cut off on the south by the yawning moat of the Colorado River. On the east, north, and west, wide treeless deserts bar any attempt at escape. Ruthless hunting or the destruction of the yellow pine forest could wipe out the entire race of Kaibab squirrels. The southern portion of the plateau is within the Grand Canyon National Park, where no hunting is ever allowed; and the state of Arizona and the United States Forest Service protect the Kaibab squirrels elsewhere. Even museum collectors must wait for accidents, such as highway fatalities, to supply them with a few skins each year. Both this species and the Abert squirrel have never learned to beware of automobiles, and the mortality from this cause is comparatively high. The Abert squirrel in New Mexico and Arizona is hunted legally in certain areas where they are numerous.

When protected, the tassel-eared squirrels are tame and confident of their security. They are the objects of attention whenever they appear around tourist cabins or in camp grounds.

General description. Heavy-bodied large tree squirrels with tufted ears and long bushy tails. The *Abert* squirrel is grayish above with a broad reddish stripe down the back (except through central Colorado, where the squirrels lack this band); under parts and upper surfaces of fore and hind feet white, and a white or grayish tail with a gray stripe from base to tip on the under surface, and a wide black band that shows through the white "frosting" on the upper surface. The *Kaibab* squirrel is similar, but has black under parts and an all-white tail. Total length, 19 to 21 inches; height at shoulder, 4 to 4½ inches; weight, 1½ to 2 pounds.

Distinguishing characteristics. Like a large gray squirrel in size and outline, except for the ear tufts. The western gray squirrel is paler gray and has a slate-gray tail "frosted" with white.

Range. Yellow pine areas of the Southwest, from northern Durango (Mexico) north to the Grand Canyon region, thence east to central New Mexico, and north in the Rockies to northern Colorado. The *Kaibab* squirrel is found only on the Kaibab Plateau, north rim of the Grand Canyon, Arizona. The *Durango* squirrel lives in an isolated mountainous region in southern Chihuahua and northern Durango.

FOX SQUIRREL
SCIURUS NIGER

The fox squirrel is the largest of all the squirrels in North America. In the East, it sometimes reaches a length of twenty-eight inches. During autumn, after feasting for weeks on acorns and hickory nuts, it may tip the scales at almost three pounds, twice as much as the gray squirrel.

Fox squirrels are distinguished for more than their size. They have more different colored coats than any other North American family. These may shade all the way from bright orange and yellowish to jet black, depending upon the species and locality in which they live. Now and then there is an albino. The dark head-tops and light ears are ordinarily found in every color phase, but not always.

The majority of fox squirrels have buffy gray coats sprinkled with black hairs, white frosted bushy tails, and buff-colored under parts and feet. Many individuals, especially those in the Mississippi and Ohio valleys, are more striking with the buff replaced by bright orange, yellowish, or brownish orange and tawny.

The black phase is common in the Southeastern states. These are handsome creatures, some being all black except for creamy white nose and ears. Others are black above with buffy or orange bellies, or with an overlay of white on the tail.

A dignified animal, the big squirrel waves its foxlike tail with ponderous decorum. When it slows down to a walk, it practically waddles. If disturbed while poking about in the leaves, it sometimes prefers to bound away over the ground rather than take to a tree. These cross-country dashes are circular, however. It seldom goes farther than a thousand feet from the center of the home range. Its lope is more graceful than its saunter.

In the trees it is definitely awkward, especially when compared with the nimble red squirrel. Perhaps the fox squirrel has grown too hefty for the most efficient arboreal life. Many times my attention has been first attracted to it by a scratching and scrambling as it slipped clumsily in the branches. This is true particularly of the Chiricahua squirrel, a beautiful but gauche relative, that I have watched many hours in the mountain range in Arizona from which it gets its name. When discovered, instead of dashing off through the trees, this brightly furred animal usually clings to the trunk or branch and tries to "play ostrich." It also likes to spend its leisure hours sunbathing on a branch, dozing and scratching at bothersome mites and lice.

Although the fox squirrel takes numerous tumbles, it seems to absorb most shocks without injury. One morning on the campus of the University of Michigan I saw a fox squirrel lose its hold of the elm twigs about forty feet

FOX SQUIRREL

above a concrete sidewalk. Twisting in the air, the animal righted itself and came down on all four feet. It made only a brief pause to shake its head in my direction, as if to say, "Well, what are *you* gawking at?" Then it turned, galloped back to the tree, and ran up as if nothing had happened.

On another occasion, a squirrel was inadvertently trapped in the courtyard of the University's Natural Science Building when the doors in the passageway through which it had entered were closed. The only way out being over the top of the building, the squirrel started to climb. At a ledge about forty feet above the concrete floor of the court, its foot slipped and down it fell to the bottom. A little dazed and nonplussed, this squirrel waited for several minutes before again tackling the wall, and this time it was successful.

The fox squirrel prefers open stands or groves of trees to the gray squirrel's deep forest. However, both species are often found together. In the northern and western part of their range, fox squirrels select dry sandy ridges or well-drained valley bottoms, where oaks, hickories and walnuts furnish plenty of food. In the Southeast they live in the long-leaf pines or along the margins of cypress swamps, but they still insist on having plenty of sunlight and space for the breezes to sweep through. In the sanctuary of city parks and cemeteries, wherever there are shade trees of nut-bearing varieties, they thrive and increase. Quickly becoming accustomed to people, they learn to take peanuts from human fingers and even search pockets for food.

The fox squirrel barks much like the gray squirrel, but is more self-contained. It is not likely to be heard in the morning either, for it often sleeps late. On raw winter days it may not venture out before the middle of the morning, and then only long enough to snatch a lunch. Like any other squirrel, a sudden windstorm and clouds will send it indoors in a hurry. Sometimes, if there is work to be done, the fox squirrel stays up long after other animals have gone to bed. I have watched fox squirrels cache nuts and work on leaf nests until the autumn light was so dim that I could barely make them out. Perhaps the nest-builders were anxious to finish the shelter before the rain began.

Many fox squirrels may inhabit the same woodlot, but they have little to do with each other except at mating season. Old animals, especially males, keep strictly to themselves. Less spritely than the grays, fox squirrels are usually more gentle and easily tamed, and appear to be more intelligent. Individuals differ greatly in temperament, however. Some are tractable and quickly accustom themselves to cage life, but one animal that I kept never lost any of her original wildness and resentment. Her young, which were born in captivity, were just as unmanageable. I have followed some squirrels for hours. Continuously I watched them bury nuts within a few feet of me and I examined each burial.

Another animal, however, would fly into a fury and leave as soon as I began investigating its caches.

Although most individuals are sedate, I once watched a western fox squirrel that was a show-off. Racing stiff-legged around the base of a big red pine, sometimes on the ground and sometimes on the vertical trunk, it kept its tail flattened on its back. At intervals it made single complete somersaults. Gracefully and at high speed, it pitched forward onto the back of its neck and then rolled all the way over until it was on its feet again. Repeating this antic half a dozen times in a few minutes, this ebullient animal may have been trying to secure the admiration of a squirrel that sat about forty feet away. This episode occurred in southern Michigan during early November, when fox squirrels rarely take any interest in the opposite sex. The usual mating period there is January. Then one frequently hears the repeated, low, questioning "kuak, kuak, kua-a-a," and sees pairs of squirrels racing through the trees.

About forty-five days after mating, the young are born in a hollow tree trunk or a leaf nest. In the Lake States region, the latter seems to be the rule. Two females that I had trapped in the wild in southern Michigan gave birth to young on February 21 and March 5, respectively. The litters contained five and three babies, but the "runt" of the smaller brood died in a couple of days and that of the larger litter at the age of two months. In the wild state, the latter would have died even sooner. A mother fox squirrel probably seldom rears more than three or four young of a litter to maturity.

Newborn fox squirrels are pinkish purple. Only their whiskers have pushed past the skin. They weigh about two-thirds ounce each and are four inches long. In ten days a very fine down is discernible over their entire bodies when the still helpless infants are turned on a dark background. The hair does not begin to alter the original flesh color until the animals are more than two weeks old. Then they are able to support their weight of one and one-half ounces for perhaps ten or fifteen seconds.

Their eyes open any time between the fortieth and forty-fourth day. About a week later the most venturesome youngster may poke its head out of the doorway. Through this long infancy the mother nurses her brood. A startled mother was once seen rushing up a tree with three little fellows clinging to her nipples. Ordinarily, if it becomes necessary to move, she carries each one separately, by the skin of the belly, between her incisor teeth. I have seen very young animals, two weeks old, grasped around the middle of the body rather than just by the skin.

In one instance I know of a mother that shifted her three young, weighing about six ounces each, the length of a city block. Each round trip required ten minutes. Because the mother squirrel cannot count, she usually goes back to the abandoned home and searches carefully in the nest to make sure that she has not left a youngster behind.

The young squirrels' lower incisors appear first, when they are three weeks old, and their upper teeth break through the skin at the age of forty-three to forty-five days. At about eight weeks, they begin to eat soft food, such as bits of nut meats that the mother has dropped. They are able to cut through the shells of hickory nuts at seventy-two days. Their weight then is ten to thirteen ounces and they are twelve to fifteen inches long. They object strenuously to being held firmly.

The question of a second brood in a season is unsettled. As a first litter would be capable of making its own living by late May or early June, the mother may possibly take on the responsibility of rearing another brood.

Many persons enjoy hunting fox squirrels, for they become wary and furnish good sport and excellent meat. Their worst natural enemies are raccoons, bobcats and foxes. Undoubtedly, some are killed by horned and barred owls and by several of the hawks. Botflies occasionally lay eggs in their ears, necks and shoulders. Mange often results from mites which burrow in the skin. I have seen fox squirrels that have thus been denuded of hair. The red squirrel is probably no more than an occasional annoyance. Although the natural life span is about five or six years, fox squirrels in confinement have lived to an extreme age of nine or ten.

Most squirrel dens are in hardwood trees, oak, elm, beech and, in the South, cypress and gum. The entrance, which is usually formed by decay of a limb, is three to four inches in diameter and is prevented from healing over by rather constant chipping of the scar tissue by the tenants. Bedding material is made from dry shredded leaves and inner bark.

Leaf nests are of two kinds. The summer nest is a loosely woven mass of leaves and twigs. It can be thrown together in a half hour and rarely lasts longer than a few months. I once watched a fox squirrel that, in twenty-five minutes, made a nest that appeared to be about half a bushel in size. A squirrel may build a new nest every couple of weeks during hot weather, until a dozen in various stages of disrepair are conspicuous in the treetops.

The winter nest, on the other hand, is a very carefully built house. The outer shell consists of a sphere of laced twigs with leaves attached. Against the inner side, layer after layer of damp leaves are pressed, making a wall that will keep out wind, rain and snow. Finally the nest is lined with soft shreds of inner bark and bits of leaves. This kind of structure may last for years.

During the warm months the fox squirrel's diet is varied. It consists of mushrooms, insects, bulbs and roots, fruits (including mulberries, wild cherries, black-berries, and plums), corn, and the buds and twig bark of oak, maple, elm, black birch and basswood. During spring, sap is a great delicacy. In central Michigan I have been told that great damage is done occasionally to maple trees by fox squirrels. They strip the bark from the limbs to lick the sweet sap, as well as to eat the soft cambium.

Bird killing is sometimes charged against this squirrel, although rarely. I tried to tempt some of my caged animals with live English sparrows and found them indifferent. Even when the birds were dead, the squirrels would eat only a little of the brain.

The staple food of the fox squirrel is seeds—acorns, hickory nuts, walnuts, butternuts, beech mast, seeds of maple, elm, basswood, pines and other conifers, and stones of wild plums and cherries. I have watched a fox squirrel eating the bitter meat of the horse chestnut, another cracking open and eating the pits of thornapple, and several in midwinter eating the dried berries of holly and night-shade.

Feeding on nuts begins very early in the season, while the meats are still pulpy, and continues until the supply is exhausted, presumably the following spring.

The fox squirrel is an inveterate hoarder. I have counted as many as twenty-five hickory nuts cached by one animal in half an hour. The instinct appears early; even my two-and-one-half-month-old squirrels were hiding acorns in the litter of their cage.

Nuts are cached separately, in hundreds of little holes in the ground. They are cut from the trees and dropped to the ground as fast as possible, until the frost catches up and brings them down in showers. They may be buried no more than one hop length from where they landed, but it seems to be against the rules to cache them on the exact spot.

In a study of this habit in Michigan, I found that a very high percentage of stored food is recovered. Periodic examination of two hundred and fifty-one marked caches of acorns and hickory nuts revealed that about ten per cent were emptied before January 1. By spring, all but two of the caches were empty and only one of these nuts was good.

Further experiments that I carried out on captive squirrels proved that they readily recovered nuts buried in moist soil. In very dry ground, however, they located them only after much fumbling. It appears that squirrels use their memory to reach the vicinity of their caches, after which they rely on their very sensitive noses.

Of course, this high percentage of recovery does not mean that our nut-bearing trees will be exterminated. The squirrels miss some acorns and nuts, which sprout and grow. Occasionally a squirrel dies of disease, old age, or is killed and eaten by a predator before it has a chance to recover many of the caches. Squirrels have lived in the trees and "on" them for thousands of years, and always enough seeds have escaped to perpetuate the forests.

The following species are included in the Fox Squirrel group along with *Sciurus niger* (described below):

1. The Chiricahua squirrel (*S. chiricahuae*) closely resembles a yellowish-brown fox squirrel. It occurs in the United States only in the Chiricahua Mountains of southeastern Arizona; thence south into Mexico.

2. The Arizona gray squirrel (*S. arizonensis*) is grayish with a brown dorsal band. It is found in New Mexico and Arizona and south to southern Durango. Although it most nearly resembles the true gray squirrel, it is classified by zoologists as a fox squirrel.

General description. A large, heavy, tree squirrel. Color very variable, most commonly grizzled buff or rusty tawny brown above and pale reddish or yellowish brown below. In the Southeastern states, melanistic animals (black or dark brown, with white nose and ears) occur frequently, also a gray phase in which the top of the head is black, and nose, ears, feet and under parts are white. Total length, 19 to 28 inches; height at shoulder, 5 inches; weight, 1½ to 3 pounds (average 2 pounds or less).

Distinguishing characteristics. Large size and grizzled reddish or brownish color.

Range. Eastern United States, from the Atlantic coast west to eastern South Dakota, central Kansas, and Texas; Maryland, western New York, northern Michigan (lower Peninsula) and central Minnesota south to southern Florida, the Gulf coast, and the Rio Grande.

FLYING SQUIRREL
GLAUCOMYS VOLANS AND *G. SABRINUS*

The flying squirrel does not fly—not in the sense that the birds and the bats move freely through the air. But for thousands of centuries it has been trying, and in the meantime has become an expert glider.

On a limb far in the top of a tall tree, perhaps sixty feet above the ground,

FLYING SQUIRREL

it gathers its feet together and with a great spring leaps off into space. Immediately it spreads out all four legs at right angles to its body. This stretches out the "wings," which are folds of skin covered with fine, close-lying fur. Extending from the sides and lower flanks as far as "wrist" and "ankle," they connect its fore and hind legs on each side.

The air, rushing by underneath, bows the skin of the "wings" upward. Deftly the squirrel sails downward through the air for one hundred and fifty feet, or twice as far if it takes advantage of sloping ground. This is pretty good for a little animal less than a foot long that weighs only three to five ounces.

It can go in practically any direction. By varying the slack in one or both "wings," it may control the angle, speed, and course of the glide. Mostly, however, it steers with its tail. In the take-off jump the tail is brought down with a jerk until it is straight out. Throughout the glide the legs and tail vibrate with tension, ready to twist, raise or lower as circumstances demand. This may mean a sudden turn of ninety degrees or more. Many lesser twists are required to avoid twigs and trunks of trees.

Just as the little animal seems about to crash into the ground at full speed, it flips its tail upward. Abruptly the body turns up, the speed checks, and it lands on a tree trunk. Flattened out, spread-eagled, it makes its landing facing upward. Apparently the hind feet strike first and absorb much of the shock. The squirrel may stop where it first lands, usually ten or fifteen feet above the ground. (Motionless, it is almost mistaken for a fat, gray-brown lichen.) Or it may expend surplus momentum by running up the trunk to gain altitude for the next trip.

If the flying squirrel is traveling through the woods, it runs surefootedly over the treetops, as long as this highway is continuous and promises to be interesting to its palate. Then it starts gliding downward through the air. At each landing tree it must climb up and begin all over again. Some hops may be short (great leaps rather than glides) and lose little altitude. In taking long flights, it makes an angle downward of forty to fifty degrees, but probably never less than thirty.

It seldom lands on the ground. When it does forage there, it makes for a tree awkwardly and hastily if startled. Once in the chosen home, it is more adept and nimble than any other arboreal mammal, even the marten and the fisher.

"I would think a flying squirrel could make ten jumps while a red squirrel was getting ready for one," Dr. C. H. D. Clarke recently wrote me. The well-known scientist further described the little animal's agility: "At the Ontario Fisheries Research Laboratory camp on Lake Nipissing, the boys had a pet brood. They used to play catch with the squirrels across the room. No matter how hard you threw your squirrel, he could check himself. Each time he would reach the catcher with the momentum of a feather. None of the brood seemed to resent this game.

"Flying squirrels are like coiled springs. One instant on the table, next on the window sill, they leave the observer blinking in amazement at not having seen the jump."

The big-eyed little squirrel wears a brownish fur coat that is soft as velvet. The hairs of its flattened tail grow out like the vanes of a feather on a rib. Gentle and friendly, it gets along well with its relatives. As many as fifty flying squirrels have been found living together in one hollow tree. When a martin house with several compartments was taken down for the annual fall cleaning, it was found to be occupied by six screech owls, about twenty bats, and as many flying squirrels. Caged flying squirrels have preferred to sleep together in one nest box in summer, even when a number of boxes were provided.

Perhaps some couples mate for longer than just the breeding season. A male and a female have been found living in nests only fifteen to fifty feet apart in isolated patches of woodland where no other flying squirrels were known. No fathers are permitted to see the young while they are tiny, but they are sometimes found in dens with mothers and their well-grown young. One handsome male was reported living near the family nest and running around with the mother at night.

Northern flying squirrels appear to have only one breeding season, in February and March. In the southern half of the eastern United States many females mate twice, sometime between January and early March, and again from late May to the middle of July. The gestation period is forty days. A litter may contain from two to six young; generally the number is three or four. At birth, eastern flying squirrels (*S. volans*) weigh but one-ninth to one-fifth of an ounce. They are naked, dark pink in color, and their eyes and ears are sealed shut. The "wings" are fully-spread, transparent webs of skin. The little animals are especially helpless, lying on their sides and squirming continually. They are not well furred until they are almost two weeks old, and their eyes open in twenty-six to twenty-eight days. For the first five weeks their only food is the mother's milk. Then they begin to nibble at soft foods such as insects and tips of twigs.

Up to this stage, there is no more devoted mother in the world than the flying squirrel. She hardly leaves the babies, taking only a few seconds to go to the toilet outside, or a few minutes at dusk and just before dawn to snatch a bite of food. As a rule she nurses the young every hour or two, standing over them on her haunches while they burrow upward between her "wings," which she spreads apart with her hands. Captive mothers have been known to accept strange young of the same age as her own, and even white rats whose eyes had not yet opened.

The mother is fearless of any danger if her young are threatened. In a number of cases, the mother squirrel whose young were taken from their den after the tree was felled climbed up the clothing of the human kidnapers and took the offspring, one by one, from their hands. Rolling each baby into a ball, she grasped it by the slack skin of the belly, climbed a nearby tree and glided to another where a cavity offered a new home. Successive trips were made until the whole family was in safety. Young squirrels up to almost half the mother's weight are sometimes carried up trees and through the air in this way.

Before the young are two months old, they can comb their hair and give themselves good baths. Using their nails for combs and their tongues for wash cloths, they reach almost every part of their body, including the end of the tail.

At six to eight weeks they look much like their parents, except for their somewhat smaller size and tousled baby coats. Good climbers, they are still only capable of making short glides. When they are about three months old, they get their adult coats of thick fur. Thereafter they make only one complete change every year. Each September the new fur begins to push out the worn reddish hair on the sides. The process extends to the back and finally to the shoulders and head. It takes about two months to get a completely new suit.

Sometimes the youngsters scatter to make homes in nearby hollow trees. More often the family stays together until a new litter is imminent, as much as a year later. At that time some of the young rear families of their own. Others do not breed until they are two years old.

When the mother flying squirrel is able to leave her offspring for longer periods at night, she does not forget them for a single moment. At the sound of their first cry, she hurries back to the nest. She may even respond when humans imitate it, trying to climb up on their clothing to locate what she thinks is a baby squirrel in distress. The father never pays any attention, nor would he be allowed to when they are still very young.

Flying squirrels begin to grow old at the age of three and they seldom live past the age of five or six. They have too many enemies—the larger owls, an occasional hawk, the raccoon, marten, weasel, bobcat, and other carnivorous mammals, and the tree-climbing snakes. Their remains were once found to be more numerous than those of any other kind of prey at two ravens' nests in the mountains near Lexington, Virginia. Man is an indirect yet very serious enemy, since he burns and cuts down the forest and eliminates many nesting places while "tidying up" his managed woodlands. He also harbors cats, which prey extensively on flying squirrels that try to live near towns and farms.

The flying squirrel is rarely seen alive by humans. Unless it is frightened out of the nest, it almost never leaves it before dusk, and hastens back by dawn. Very few persons know that the clan is widespread and often more numerous than the red squirrel. Trapping records reveal that over wide areas of favorable habitat there may be three to five or more flying squirrels per acre. Frequently they live in the shade trees on our town streets. They like old woodland best—plenty of nut trees, with decaying limbs or standing snags where, during the day, woodpeckers love to hammer and make the chips fly.

Sometimes at night you can hear flying squirrels chipping softly like small birds; not a soft drowsy tone, but wide-awake, a somewhat staccato note; like a chipmunk a long way off. When alarmed or threatened, they burst into angry squeaks and squeals.

One can often find signs of a night's activities. On the ground, under favorite feeding perches, may be the empty shells of hickory nuts, whole except for a roughly circular opening either on the "blossom" or stem end. Fine tooth marks on the edges show that the opener was the neat flying squirrel, and not its red relative which leaves broader, rougher chisel marks. Other tree squirrels and the chipmunk break or cut the shell into many small fragments. White-footed mice cut into the side of the shell opposite each meat half.

Rapping sharply on rotten trees or hollow snags will probably frighten the sleeping animals from their dens, providing one raps on the right "door." A forest of old trees may have many likely-looking stubs, but only one in a hundred may be occupied when you call. Trapping is likely to be more fruitful. Rat-traps or live-traps nailed high up on tree trunks are apt to catch the little fellows. Nuts or bits of meat are suitable bait. The animals are unsuspicious and curious, making them easy marks for such nefarious schemes. In fact, fur trappers are often exasperated by the number of flying squirrels that are killed in their traps, thus preventing the capture of valuable fur-bearers.

Although the flying squirrel has the equipment for traveling far, it stays close to home. Probably it is satisfied with an area of four or five acres.

Its favorite home is a woodpecker's hole. No one knows how often it uses force to drive out the owner to secure a ready-made house. It is not likely that it would dare to pick a fight with the larger woodpeckers, the pileated or the hairy, but a little downy woodpecker should be easy. It may be significant that the squirrel is most often found in an old residence of the downy. As a rule, however, most forests have enough abandoned woodpecker holes to more than go around.

The den chosen is usually in a very rotten stub or tree, so far gone that often it can be shoved over. Downy woodpeckers are weak chiselers and seldom have the energy to work on a dead tree that is still hard. The squirrel can use a spacious home, but really needs only enough room to hold sufficient nest material to keep it warm in winter. Of course, it must have a doorway large enough to crawl through. The smaller eastern species can squeeze through a hole only one inch in diameter. When the squirrel moves in, it throws out the woodpecker's bedding and makes up a new bed of finely-shredded inner bark or lichens. Then it is settled, perhaps for life.

The great majority of flying squirrels are born in a tree den. In the Pacific Northwest, the nursery is frequently a leaf nest in the treetops or in a tangled thicket. Adults here use this type of home fairly often, at least in summer. It is built on the general plan used by the other tree squirrels. The stick platform holds a mass of leaves and twigs which are encased in a protecting framework of twigs and lined with shredded dry grass, leaves, and inner bark. Some naturalists think that most of these leaf nests are the abandoned quarters of red, gray or fox squirrels, and that the flying squirrel seldom, if ever, does more than renovate. Certainly it is an opportunist that is quite ready to use an attic or a cupboard in a human dwelling, a wooden bird house or a woven nest, as well as the woodpecker hole.

The squirrel's staple food is nuts and seeds, especially those of hickories, beech, white oak, pines and firs. Many other types of vegetation are eaten. Some are mushrooms, persimmons, serviceberries, apples, wild grapes, bark of many hardwood trees, and blossoms of the sugar maple. Grain fields or storage bins are sometimes raided, but the damage is not serious. I have never known this squirrel to eat any part of a corn kernel except the germ. The rest, made up of starch, is always discarded.

The flying squirrel is the most carnivorous of the tree squirrels. Sleepy birds may be captured in the treetops, and eggs and nestlings are eagerly devoured. Moths, beetles, and larvae of many insects are eaten. Besides stealing trap baits, this squirrel would never miss a chance to nibble at meat hung in cabins or attics.

During the fall, surplus nuts are stored in the den or nests and in the ground. The latter nuts are hardly buried. The squirrel brushes a little dirt aside with the forefeet, then presses a nut down with its nose, and scatters a bit of soil and perhaps some grass or leaf litter over the place.

A steady supply of water is a necessity, especially in hot weather. A pet flying squirrel that I once kept escaped from my room when the door was left open one summer evening. Several days later, after I had searched the house, including the furnace and flues, I found him half drowned in the basement toilet.

There is much dispute over the flying squirrel's hours of work. Some say that it is active all night long, while others think that it takes a nap at midnight. According to my own experience with the animals, the latter view is probably correct. At least, a squirrel that I once kept in my bedroom one summer left his nest box at dark and stayed out only a couple of hours, then went to sleep until about three in the morning. After scampering about for another couple of hours, he retired again at dawn, which came about five-thirty. Because of his friendly or curious attitude, and his interesting habits, the flying squirrel makes an entertaining pet, being active and playful without being destructive or mischievous. But he is nocturnal and one must stay up at night to observe him.

My squirrel enjoyed climbing up the window curtains to the pole, then gliding to my bed. Morning after morning, about three or four o'clock, I was awakened by the thump of his weight as he commenced the second installment of the night's frolic. Once I awoke feeling a tiny pressure on my chest. In the first dim light of dawn the squirrel's face was just above the end of my nose. His great eyes, enlarged and thrown out of focus by their proximity to my own, were like those of a goblin. Only by exercising the greatest restraint did I stifle a yell that might have frightened him to death. After about three weeks of such nightly frolics, I had to take my pet back to the woods and give him his freedom.

I have handled a number of wild adult flying squirrels without gloves, and not one ever threatened to bite. It is safest to protect one's hands, however, as occasionally one may encounter a vindictive individual. Above all, never squeeze a flying squirrel. The soft body is easily injured by a pressure that would not hurt a red or a gray squirrel in the least. Many of the little "fliers" that I have caught alive have died within a dozen hours, apparently of shock or fright.

Flying squirrels of various species are found around the world north of the equator. Two of them occupy a great expanse across North America from Florida and southern Labrador to central Alaska, and thence south to Utah and southern California. Others live in eastern Europe and most of Asia. The latter continent boasts of the greatest variety of species, including the largest in the world, four feet from nose to tail tip!

Our two American flying squirrels prefer distinctly different habitats, although there is some variability. The smaller species, of the eastern United States, wants beech-maple forests, although it is often found in other hardwood trees such as oak and hickory. The somewhat larger squirrel of Canada, Alaska and the western and extreme northeastern United States likes coniferous woods, with hardwoods scattered through it.

Flying squirrels are divided into two groups:

1. The eastern flying squirrel (*Glaucomys volans*) is the small species. The fur on chest and belly is white to the roots. It is found in eastern United States, southwestern Ontario, and two areas in Mexico (see below, under Range).

2. The northern flying squirrel (*Glaucomys sabrinus*) is the larger species. The light-colored fur of its under parts is gray at the roots. It ranges from Nova Scotia and southern Labrador across Canada, south of the tree limit, to central Alaska; south in the Appalachians to northeastern Tennessee, to central Minnesota, and in the western mountains to the Black Hills, western Wyoming, and southern California.

General description. A nocturnal, small, tree squirrel with very soft fur, large eyes, horizontally flattened tail, and a "wing" of furred skin extending from each side between the front and hind legs. Color variable with the species and region: cinnamon, snuff-brown, reddish brown, grayish, or blackish brown above, and pale pinkish, cinnamon, white, or yellowish white below. Total length, 9 to 14 inches; height at shoulder, $2\frac{1}{4}$ to $2\frac{3}{4}$ inches; weight very variable, depending on the species, $1\frac{1}{2}$ to $5\frac{3}{4}$ ounces.

Distinguishing characteristics. Very soft, velvetlike fur, large eyes, flattened tail, "wings" of skin, and nocturnal "flying" habits.

Range. Most of forested North America; absent from Newfoundland, south-eastern Florida, the Great Plains, Great Basin, and southwestern desert region. South of the United States, flying squirrels are known to occur in two isolated areas, one in central Mexico and the other in southern Mexico and adjacent regions of Guatemala.

16. Chisel-Teeth (Part I)

POCKET GOPHER—FAMILY *GEOMYIDAE*

No miner in North America can match the pocket gopher. Not even the mole, that digs long but not deep tunnels. Man, who sometimes fancies himself as a builder of tunnels, must use complicated tools and explosives. The gopher excavates an amazing labyrinth with nothing except its muscles and hands. Sometimes, in sandy soil, it makes two hundred to three hundred feet of tunnel in a single night. A one-hundred-and-fifty-pound man would need to dig a trench seventeen inches in cross-section and seven miles long in ten hours to equal the record of a one-pound gopher.

The pocket gopher's mining activities are sometimes expensive to man. Unconscious of sabotage, it and other burrowing animals may tunnel through earth dams, causing floods and loss of crops and other property. Gophers become abundant in fields and orchards, devouring forage, grain, roots, and other vegetables, cutting off entire root systems of small fruit and nut trees and girdling larger ones.

The farmer tries to destroy his unwelcome guests by flooding irrigated fields, setting "scissor"-type traps in the runways, and fumigating the burrows with automobile exhaust gases or carbon bisulphide. Another method calls for dropping in the runway one-inch cubes of carrot or sweet potato which have been coated with a strychnine paste. Over a ton of poisoned grain was used by a district highway board in one month.

The pocket gopher is named for its remarkable fur-lined pockets. Placed one on each side of the head and neck, they are complete pouches, not merely bulging cheeks outside the molars like those of the chipmunk. The openings are long slits in the skin under each jawbone. Lined with fine soft fur, they extend backward along the side of its head and neck as far as the shoulders. The only other North American mammals that have these fur-lined pockets are the pocket mouse, kangaroo rat and spiny mouse.

Using both hands so fast that the human eye can hardly follow them, the gopher inserts food or nest material first in one pocket and then the other. Long flexible pieces of grass or slender roots are shoved back farther and farther until they coil into place. Big, unwieldy clumps of food may be eaten on the spot, or

POCKET GOPHER

dragged along the ground into the burrow, or cut up into two- or three-inch fragments and stuffed into the cheek pockets. This is carried either to the store-rooms or to the bedroom.

The gopher keeps a good deal of food in bed. When there is too much spoilage, the rodent leaves it to the swarm of spiders, mites and other arthropods and scarabaeid beetles that feed on decaying debris throughout the system of burrows. Eventually as many as seven or eight of these abandoned bedrooms may accumulate.

The pocket gopher never wets its bed but is careful to go to an inside toilet. When this toilet has been used long enough, the animal throws in more refuse and closes it permanently, and digs another.

The pocket gopher tends to take on the color of the earth in which it spends most of its life. It may be anywhere from pale gray or buffy to very dark brown, almost black. Seven to fourteen inches in length, it is stoutly built, with heavy shoulders resembling those of the mole. The neck and legs are also short, and the tail thinly haired. But on other points it is quite different. Although near-sighted, the black eyes are as conspicuous as good-sized glass heads of pins, while the mole's are almost invisible. The roundish ears lie close to the head but well outside the fur. The "nap" of its coat does not brush forward and backward like that of the mole, but lies in one direction. The "hands" are long with large, very sharp claws and wristlets of long, stiff hairs. The hind feet are much smaller, with short toes, short claws and no anklets.

The pocket gopher spends most of its life in the dark, but needs no light. It has an excellent sounding system, both in the front and in the rear. If it is going forward in the tunnels, the whiskers are sensitive feelers that keep it from bumping into the walls. If it has to back up through a hallway, the nerve endings on a nearly hairless tail serve as guides. A well-developed sense of smell also helps to detect food and enemies in these pitch-dark corridors.

When the pocket gopher is traveling underground, it is not going anywhere in particular, but is just looking for another dinner. It prefers to mine in treeless places where deep rich soil supports a fine growth of succulent plants. Here it naturally grows bigger and fatter.

It does not waste time cutting out high ceilings. The round tunnels are only large enough to get through. The gopher's legs are short, and by crouching down perpetually it is brought even lower. The passageways are but one and one-half to three inches in diameter, depending upon the owner's size. Instead of pushing its way through the ground just under the surface, as the mole does, it makes deep, clean-cut tunnels. It does not dump all the debris in one pile at an entrance, but throws it out at several points. It spreads the soil fanwise, beginning a few feet away from the hole and working in. This dump may be spread out two or three or even four feet across, but is only six to perhaps twelve inches deep at any point.

The last loads of dirt are always used to plug the doorway tightly. The spur shaft of each entrance slants down and opens into the intricate maze of feeding galleries which in general are on the same level. This may be as little as six inches or as much as three feet below the surface. It all depends upon the density of soil, the length of plant roots and the danger of badgers.

At several points, little rooms are located just off the travel route or at the end of spur tunnels. These are the upper storerooms. Some contain the remains of food left over from the previous winter; others are filled with freshly gathered supplies. There may be as many as eight or ten rooms. Stocks containing two thousand three hundred grass cuttings and one hundred and seventy-five bulbs have been found in one cache alone. The pocket gopher's eyes are bigger than its stomach and it always brings home more than it can eat. The result is that much of the food spoils. Some of the old galleries are packed solidly with all sorts of refuse—moldy and dried bits of roots, tubers, tops of plants, old bedding, feces, and soil from newer tunnels.

From this complex system of upper tunnels, a shaft drops almost straight down to the central home of the little owner. It may be more than eleven feet below the surface, but it is generally less than half so deep.

In an old burrow system the lower tier of galleries may be complicated, but it is never as extensive as the upper foraging tunnels. The latter may be a half mile long, and the lower ones but fifty feet. They seem to be extended only as new sleeping rooms or food storage bins are needed.

Usually but one bedroom is in use. It is nearly globular, nine or ten inches in diameter, and almost completely filled with bedding. This is made from "bales" of grass, leaves and similar material torn very carefully into fine pieces and shreds.

Such a home is used by the pocket gopher in the north, wherever the ground freezes for two feet or more during winter. Farther south, the lower tier of passages is dug nearer the surface, until in warm climates there are only the upper, general foraging galleries. Here a somewhat smaller nest is used as less bedding is required. A similar sized bedroom, about five or six inches in diameter and close to the surface of the ground, may be found also in the north during summer.

The pocket gopher of Texas and western Louisiana carries this house raising to an extreme. Living in the lowlands where the ground is apt to be wet, or even flooded at times during winter and spring, it has trouble keeping dry. It solves this problem by bringing up earth from below until a mound is established that may be as much as six feet in diameter and two feet high. Then it makes its nest, toilet, and food-storage chambers in the mound above ground. During dry seasons it may hollow out rooms in the ground, but keeps the mound apparently for protection and for reinforcement of the roof.

In the winter the hardy mountain gopher spends much time above ground, under the snow. Grass nests, ten to fourteen inches in diameter with a single entrance on one side, and droppings have been found. In such cases the gopher still continues to extend the underground burrow below the frost line. The excavated earth is pushed out and off through snow tunnels. When the snow melts the next spring, the long sinuous cylinders of earth are left exposed. Sometimes the ground is covered with a veritable network of these earthen plugs, impressive evidence of the work that the gopher does much of the time but which usually goes unnoticed because it is out of sight.

The pocket gopher is an efficient digger. With the hind feet spread wide, it attacks the earth with powerful downward strokes of the hands. The long sharp claws cut into the soil and sweep it back under its belly. At short intervals the hind feet are used together to kick the accumulation farther to the rear.

When a good-sized handful of dirt has accumulated, the pocket gopher reverses itself in the narrow low tunnel by turning a somersault. With astonishing quickness it pokes its nose under and back between the hind legs. Then it turns over with a twisting motion that ends with being on its feet and facing the pile of loose soil which nearly blocks the passageway. At once it drops on its chest. Placing the front paws at either side of its face, the claws are pointed up and out at about forty-five degrees. Like a little animated bulldozer, it shoves forward with the hind feet. It moves by jerks, a few inches at a time, pushing the dirt ahead up the tunnel. At each pause it pulls its head and hands back slightly to reassemble the load. With a final flip, the fine soil is thrown violently out of the doorway.

Digging is a messy job and the pocket gopher's fur, especially on its face and front, is often powdered with bits of earth. These are quickly brushed out of the slightly oily fur without soiling it. While it is actually digging or moving dirt, the gopher's ears are closed tightly by means of valves. Its eyes are small and the lids fit so closely that grains of sand rarely get underneath.

If the soil is so hard that claws are not effective, the pocket gopher uses its huge upper front teeth. Pinching the lips together behind them, but over most of the lower incisors, it bares its upper teeth like closely-paired gouges. With downward strokes, they tear at the clay and gravel, while the closed lips behind prevent dirt from getting into the mouth. Gophers that live in regions where the soil is exceptionally hard have especially protruding incisors for shovels.

An entire tunnel system is built and inhabited by only one of these small rodents. There is little sociability in this underground world. Sometimes two or more gophers are caught in traps placed in the same runway, but usually these animals are captured several days apart. This indicates that the second animal broke into the tunnel and, not hearing any activity, adopted the passages as part of its own foraging territory. Otherwise it probably would have plugged the break hastily and gone about its solitary way.

Pocket gophers that meet usually fight viciously. First their teeth chatter and grind with rage. Then each tries to grab the other by the nose with its teeth. As they struggle, they squeal excitedly. If the loser is unable to get away, it is often killed on the spot, or quickly bleeds to death through gashes from the opponent's sharp incisors.

The late Professor H. M. Wight told me of an incident which ruined some of his experimental work with live pocket gophers. Two plumbers, coming into the laboratory early one morning to fix the steam pipes, noticed the animals in their separate cages. With sadistic glee, they took two gophers out and put them together. The resulting battle was so entertaining to the men that they started another. This was repeated several times. When Professor Wight arrived, the laboratory was a shambles and most of the animals were dead.

There is only one time in the year when wild pocket gophers seek the company of others. As the winter or spring rains encourage the grass and other vegetation into green luxuriance, the male pocket gophers become restless and strangely reckless. According to J. R. Brown, they leave the safety of their tunnels mostly at night but sometimes in broad daylight and go hiking off across country. By some mysterious sense they find the females that are secluded in their underground homes. Following successful mating, the males leave and usually return to the home burrows they left.

In some areas, at various times, there is a great surplus of females. Because of their retiring natures, many of these must remain spinsters.

The mating season in the gopher world varies with the climate, from early November in southern California to May in southwestern Canada. In any one locality it may cover two or three months. Since the search by the males seems to get little or no help from the females that apparently stay in their burrows, the meeting is something of a hit-or-miss proposition. If gophers were conditioned to mate during only a week or two each year like many other mammals, the race would probably die out.

When time for the birth of the young approaches, the pregnant mother has her storerooms stocked with plenty of fresh roots and green shoots. The nest is put in good condition, or a new one built. About four weeks are required for prenatal development of the young. The litter varies greatly in size, not only with the species, but with individual mothers. Occasionally there is but one offspring or twins. Some species rarely produce more than three in a litter. At the other extreme is the prolific mother that gives birth to as many as nine youngsters at a time. If any average can be struck from such wide differences, it might be set at four or five.

A newborn gopher is a fat, stubby creature with short legs and tail. It weighs about one-fifth of an ounce. The naked dark pink skin seems almost twice too big and hangs loosely in many wrinkles and folds. The eyes and ears are sealed shut. In most species the cheek pouches are no more than slight furrows in the skin. Only occasionally are they deep enough at birth to be called pockets. Frequently they do not develop until the animal is a month old.

As early as the age of three weeks, young gophers begin to eat green food. Because their eyes do not open until they are about five weeks old, their vegetable food is brought to them by the mother. The youngsters remain with her until they are six weeks to two months old and then scatter to find their own individual homes. If a vacant burrow is nearby, it is taken over by the first finder, which repairs it little by little. Sometimes a half-grown young may wander for a mile or more and still not find any such ready-made home. Then it must start digging from scratch. Its first attempt is a short, shallow tunnel. If it survives, the tunnel is lengthened and deepened tremendously as time goes on. Some species ordinarily do not shirk digging when they leave home. They pick a spot within fifty feet of the burrow in which they first "saw darkness," excavate lustily, and settle down.

When once established, the pocket gopher seldom leaves its tunnel system except to find a mate. Only at rare intervals does it pick up and move overland. In case of a severe drought when all of its food dries up, it may try to find a moist valley. Such a migrating prairie pocket gopher was once seen swimming across a river about three hundred feet wide.

With few exceptions, most species of gophers have only a single litter of young each year. However, if food suddenly becomes abundant, as when areas are put under irrigation and planted to alfalfa, clover, or other ideal food, breeding may increase. According to Joseph S. Dixon, as many as three large broods may be reared in a year by one mother under these conditions. When the population multiplies with such great speed, they may soon eat themselves out of house and home and into a decline.

We might think that, as long as it stayed underground, the pocket gopher would be assured of a long though dreary life. On the contrary, it has numerous foes even there. The badger is a faster digger, and likes to dine on a fat juicy pocket gopher. Predatory reptiles, such as the king and bull snakes, and the relentless weasel, go right into the home runways if all entrances are not solidly closed. Hungry snakes have been seen trying to worm their way through a poorly packed door-plug. Other predators that search for the pocket gopher above ground are wolves, coyotes, foxes, skunks, house cats, the horned, barn and long-eared owls, and the red-tailed, roughleg, and Swainson hawks. Although the gopher is a clean animal, it often carries lice, and may also be host to mites, roundworms, and flatworms. Perhaps the worst dangers are floods, which drown or at least drive the miner from the protection of its home. Avalanches may also sweep the mountain-dwelling gopher to destruction.

The pocket gopher is active the year round, but when it takes a nap, it sleeps soundly. Captive animals have been picked up from their nests and laid on a table without awakening. In one instance the pocket gopher did not wake up until three minutes later.

Winter is the only season when the pocket gopher's coat is not moulting. The process starts in spring at its rear and slowly works ahead until, in early fall, it has reached the nose. A very noticeable narrow belt extending around the animal marks the old from the new fur.

It seems useless to attempt to list the food of the pocket gopher. It eats practically any vegetable matter that it can reach. In dense growth the gopher may drive a tunnel to the surface and come out to forage briefly on top of the ground. It does this mostly at night, but may do so also on cloudy days. One such sultry day in July, I watched several gophers gathering blue flag and wild geranium in a little mountain park in the southern Rockies.

First each miner's blunt nose and beady, alert eyes appeared in the craterlike mound of fresh black earth. Then in a twinkling a little brown animal scooted out about ten inches. With one clawed hand pushing on a stem, its jaws rasped once, twice, sometimes three times, and the plant went over. Grabbing the cut end in its mouth, the gopher backed into its burrow in one swift movement and in a moment the upper end of the stalk had disappeared. This happened repeatedly. Each trip required far less time than it takes to describe; every movement counted. The little animal's timidity at being in the great open unknown was striking. A man retrieving his hat from a den of lions at the zoo could not have been more nervous.

Although I stood in plain sight about six feet away from one of the gophers, its eyes were not keen enough to see me clearly. When I had watched it long enough I tapped the ground with one foot. Instantly the animal flashed backward into its burrow and hastily plugged it with earth.

The pocket gopher eats some meat. It devours small mammals such as mice that may be killed in traps, and even its own kind, but does not seem to want to go out and do its own butchering. Apparently it does not care for any of the many insects and arthropods that live in its burrows.

The most fundamental difference between the pocket gopher and the mole is that the gopher is a rodent that lives almost exclusively on vegetation, while the mole lives on insects. Instead of a long series of pointed teeth, the gopher has a pair of chisellike teeth in the front of each jaw for cutting off roots and stems and a row of flat-topped teeth on each side for grinding pulpy material.

The pocket gopher has an enormous range in southeastern, middle and western North America and Central America. The family lives in many habitats, from sea level to more than thirteen thousand feet high, well above timber-line, in mountain parks, open forests, prairies, valleys, on sandy ridges in the Gulf region, moist meadows, arid deserts, and grassland. Sometimes the ground is so hard and stony that it seems impossible that an animal only seven or eight inches long could burrow through it.

Almost everyone knows this burrowing rodent by one name, except in Florida. There, people call it "salamander," while the term "gopher" is applied to a turtle.

The pocket gophers are valuable to man despite the damage they sometimes wreak. For countless centuries, generations of gophers have been working and reworking the soil. They have covered humus to rot and thus added its fertility to the ground. They have mixed the various layers and aerated the whole mass.

As Dr. E. Raymond Hall has pointed out, pocket gophers are sometimes valuable in range management. In the western United States, where most of the species live, the seasons are alternately wet and dry. To live through the droughts, the plants have developed relatively large root systems which makes a feast for the gophers. When too many cattle or sheep are crowded onto the range, the grasses are depleted. This permits coarse, succulent "weeds" to multiply because there is more nutriment and moisture for them and they are less tasty to stock. Thus the pocket gophers increase as the grasses decrease. If the range is protected from cattle and sheep, this "weeding" by large numbers of pocket gophers hastens the return of valuable grasses.

All except the peak populations of pocket gophers and those living in critical areas can be controlled by natural enemies, if these predators have not already been removed.

The numerous kinds of pocket gophers north of Mexico are grouped into three main classifications or genera. They are very much alike externally, and can be distinguished with certainty only by grooves and ridges on the front surface of the upper incisors.

1. The western pocket gopher (*Thomomys*) has very slightly grooved upper incisors. It is the most widespread member of its family, being found from the Pacific coast of the United States and Mexico (Jalisco) to eastern Dakotas, western Nebraska, western Texas, and western Vera Cruz (state); north to eastern Alberta and central Saskatchewan.

2. The eastern pocket gopher (*Geomys*) has deeply grooved upper incisors. The range is divided into two parts. The western portion extends from northwestern Minnesota to the Gulf coast of Texas, and from the eastern foot of the Rockies to the Mississippi River; in the southeast, central Florida north to central Georgia and Alabama.

3. The chestnut-faced pocket gopher (*Cratogeomys*) is similar to *Geomys*.

Its upper incisors have one groove. The range is from southeastern Colorado and western Oklahoma to east-central Mexico.

General description. A burrowing rodent with broad, flattened head, small eyes and ears, short, stout legs equipped on the forefeet with long, heavy, sharp claws; short neck, heavy body, and thick, rather short tail. Fur fine, soft and close to body. Color varies with the species from very dark dull brown, chestnut, sooty gray or buffy to very pale sandy, becoming lighter or white on the under parts; a white spot appears frequently on chin or throat; feet paler than body, or white; tail scantily haired and pale in color. Total length, 7 to 14 inches (usually 8 to 9); height at shoulder, 2 to 3½ inches; weight, 2¼ to 18 ounces. Females are 20 to 40 per cent smaller.

Distinguishing characteristics. An underground dweller, larger than the mice and shrews. Best known from the piles of earth excavated from the tunnels and thrown out on the surface of the ground. The pocket gopher is the only mammal with cheek pouches that does not forage commonly at a distance from its underground burrows. Compared with the mole, the pocket gopher has much longer claws on the front feet, more conspicuous eyes, and the fur lies flat instead of standing up like plush.

Range. North America, from eastern Alberta and central Saskatchewan south to Costa Rica; the Pacific coast, from Puget Sound through Baja California to Jalisco, Mexico, east to southeastern Wisconsin, eastern Illinois, and central Louisiana; also central Alabama and eastern Georgia south to central Florida.

SPINY MOUSE

LIOMYS IRRORATUS TEXENSIS

The spiny mouse has fur-lined cheek pockets and is bristling all over with flattened "spines." Spreading thickly through the soft fur, especially over the back and flanks, these coarse, stiff guard-hairs are conspicuous by their darker shade.

The coats of the several species vary a good deal in color. Most of them are some shade of gray but some are brown or buffy. Each species has evolved a coat that is best suited to its environment, a dark one for the deep forest, a paler one for open scrub on the desert. The "spines" vary from black to pale gray. (Those of the Texan mouse are quite light.) Between the "spines" are the normal fine hairs of the coat which may be anywhere from gray to yellowish brown. (Buffy in the Texas species.)

Neither the spiny mouse nor its immediate relatives will have anything to do with cold weather. They live throughout the Central American countries and in northern South America. Only one, the Texas species, ventures north beyond the Rio Grande over a few miles of the lower valley.

A retiring animal, the spiny mouse never willingly shows its face in daylight. It lives in a series of tunnels in the ground, only part of which are in use at one time. Periodically, repairs are made. It carries the earth that has fallen from the roof and dumps it here and there. Careful to keep the small doorway well hidden under leaves or a log or rock, it does not draw attention to it by heaping fresh earth immediately on the threshold. The best place to look for the burrows is in a hedgerow or dense brushy border on the edge of a field. South of the Mexican border, most species live on semi-arid plains and mountain slopes, but others inhabit damp jungles.

TEXAS SPINY MOUSE

Litters of spiny mice contain three to five—usually four. They may be born during any season, but spring and early summer is customary. They are well furred from birth but their flattened bristles, instead of being stiff, are soft and lax. In a couple of months, when the mice are a little more than half grown, molting spots appear on the head and middle of the back. Gradually the process is extended until the new adult spiny coat is complete. This apparel must last for about a year. Before the next early summer, when the mouse gets a fresh suit, the fine fur is worn back more than the "spines."

A spiny mouse in its new clothes has a fresh, spruced-up appearance as well as being lighter in color. The adult's molt is quite irregular; it may work progressively from a patchwork beginning, or it may be an almost imperceptible replacement of one hair by another all over the animal.

Its diet consists mostly of many kinds of plant seeds, including those of weeds and daisy-type species. In southern Texas it is known to be fond of hackberry seeds and mesquite beans. Blooming and fruiting are spread over a large part of the year in the tropics and subtropics, so this mouse can dine amply and well during most months by taking seeds as they ripen on different shrubs and herbs. Nevertheless, it stores reserves in its burrow against a time of possible need, using the fur-lined cheek pockets to carry them. Green leaves and tender twigs are also eaten.

Spiny mice are often abundant. They are seldom noticed until some farmer discovers that they are stealing his crops: wheat, corn or other grains, castor beans or garden beans. In a few places considerable damage has been done. Owls, ringtails, foxes, coyotes, weasels, ocelots, and many snakes help to keep the mice in check.

General description. A large mouse with fur-lined cheek-pouches, long, hairy tail, and many spiny bristles scattered through the fur. Pale grizzled gray and brownish above, becoming paler on the flanks and white on the feet; a light brownish band on the sides; tail grayish above and around tip, white below. Total length, 9 to 10 inches; height at shoulder, 1½ inches; weight, about 1 ounce.

Distinguishing characteristics. The stiff flattened bristles distinguish this mouse from other small rodents that have cheek pockets.

Range. Southern Texas through Central America into northern South America.

POCKET MOUSE

PEROGNATHUS SP.

This little miser never overeats. It stints and saves for the rainy day, and works hard and fast. Rearing back a bit on its long hind legs, the tiny white hands reach for food. They become a quick blur, moving between the food supply and the fur-lined pockets that lie along each lower jaw. Each hand works independently, like an automat on a machine. Only a steadily increasing bulge of each cheek, and a disappearing pile of food, confirm the evidence that the flying hands are busy in their task of filling the pockets.

Just as it seems that the mouse's cheeks will burst, it turns and races away to the tunnel store rooms. In a few minutes it rushes back and begins hastily to refill its empty pockets.

Each cheek pocket holds about one-eighth to one-half of a teaspoonful, depending upon the size of the mouse. Perhaps six to twenty mesquite beans make a comfortable load. Most of its food is much finer. The smallest species of the pocket mouse, timed while gathering tiny mustard seeds, was found to carry away and store almost three thousand seeds in one hour.

The pocket mouse empties its pockets by squeezing out the food with sweeping motions of the hands. It takes but a few seconds. If cornered by an enemy, it will instantly sweep its pockets empty before running, probably to lighten its weight and increase its speed.

Pocket mice are all on the small side, as mammals go, but the numerous species vary as much as three hundred per cent in weight. The big California pocket mouse is nine inches long and weighs an ounce. The tiny Pacific mouse is the smallest rodent in North America. It is only four and one-half inches long, counting its rather long tail with the bushy tuft, and one-third of an ounce in weight.

Big or little, pocket mice are gentle and inoffensive. I have handled many right from the traps and have never been bitten. If they are not injured or squeezed, but held loosely or covered, they quickly recover from their first panic. Never try that with the white-footed mice or meadow mice. They will gash your hand badly with sharp chisel teeth.

The death rate of the pocket mouse is enormous. The average one probably dies before it is many months old. By an exceptional combination of circumstances, a few pocket mice may live far longer. In tranquil capitivity they have been known to live for four to six years. One pocket mouse, which was captured in Nevada when fully grown, lived in a cage for seven years. He was at least seven and one-half years old, but his teeth were not greatly worn when he died of unknown causes.

Pocket mice in the wild seldom die in bed. They have too many enemies. Badgers dig them out of their dens. Coyotes, skunks, and gray and kit foxes pounce on them at night. The grasping talons of the owls, especially the burrowing and short-eared owls, may snatch at any moment. Weasels and snakes are always creeping about looking for a meal. The grasshopper mouse and the white-footed mouse are almost as dangerous.

Unless the pocket mouse can use its superior speed, these carnivorous little relatives will kill and devour it. A poisoning squad once examined a large number of white-footed mice and pocket mice that had been killed on the same area. Not one carcass of a white-foot had been injured, but one hundred and seventy pocket mice had been partly devoured by their white-footed enemies.

Most pocket mice do not need water. They manufacture it in their stomachs

POCKET MOUSE

from the starch of seeds, and of course they get some moisture from their green food. The Kansas and Baird's pocket mice that I have kept in captivity drank a little water occasionally, as it was kept before them. They probably would have remained healthy without it. A Nevada pocket mouse (pages 437–438) that lived in captivity for seven years was never given water throughout that time. After refusing to look at green vegetation that was offered during the first few weeks, it was allowed to be happy on a diet of bird seed and nothing else.

Except during mating season, the pocket mouse is a hermit. There is not enough food on its little home range for more than one adult. Any other pocket mouse is immediately challenged and driven away. If it finds any evidence of pilfering, it is likely to pack up and move all its food to new store rooms.

In captivity the pocket mouse will quickly attack another animal of its own kind, and there is likely to be but one survivor. The tiny Baird's pocket mouse seems to be an exception. I have kept two of these delicate little creatures for more than a year in a cage about twelve by eighteen inches in size, without any arguments of which I was aware.

The mating period is irregular, at least in the south, for young may be found throughout the warmer months. In this climate the female has two litters a year, generally in spring and in mid-summer. In the Pacific Northwest the little mice are born between early June and the middle of August. Here the mother does not always have two litters a season, but two are more frequent than one. Three to four weeks elapse between mating and birth of the young. The number varies widely with the species and circumstances from two to eight but is generally four, five or six. They soon learn to shift for themselves.

In south-central New Mexico are two areas of vividly contrasting color, the dazzling White Sands, which are almost pure gypsum, and the black Malpais or "bad country" of jagged lava. The pocket mice that live in these two places, as well as several other short-ranging mammals, have become so thoroughly adapted to their environment that they have evolved coats that match the ground. Over the centuries, predators took the mice that could be seen most readily. Now the pocket mice that live on the Malpais are grizzled blackish. Only thirty or forty miles away, the pocket mice that inhabit the White Sands are almost snow white.

Pocket mice live only in North America being typical dwellers of the dry or semi-arid plains west of the Mississippi River. Mountain regions are shunned unless they are exceptionally dry. The smaller species are restricted to valley bottoms where the soil is soft and tunnels can be dug by weak little miners. The bigger ones may live on hard and even stony ground, and at the foot of cliffs and canyon walls. Some pocket mice inhabit grassy plains; others prefer the miniature open "forests" of creosote bushes and mesquite and catclaw shrubs of the hot deserts.

The builder starts its house-tunnel at the side of a rock, or under the protection of a cactus clump or a thorny shrub, or even out in the open on bare ground. Frequently it kicks together a low broad mound, twelve to twenty-four inches across, on which to start. Scooping out a circular doorway, it drives the tunnel down steeply.

A young animal usually makes a short burrow, with a sleeping room at the end but still under the same slab of rock where it began. Older animals take more precautions, digging out a number of tunnels with storerooms and other chambers. After digging steeply below the entrance, some kinds of pocket mice level off their burrows so that they may be no deeper anywhere than six or eight inches. Others keep on going down to a depth of as much as six or seven feet. Those deeper galleries may spiral or loop sharply so that the horizontal radius of the whole tunnel system may be only twenty to twenty-five inches. Deep burrows may be branched into three or four tunnels near the ground surface, but they have only one main passageway below.

An intricate, branching network of tunnels is a good defense against small enemies that may try to trap the pocket mouse in its home. Usually it plugs up the doorway when inside. If a marauder breaks down the door, the little pocket mouse has one more trick. It rushes into a side tunnel and plugs it with dirt. This often fools the bloodthirsty white-footed mouse or other assassin into thinking that the burrow is empty.

The sleeping room is either at the end of the main hall or on a short spur rather near the front doorway. It is globular, about three inches in diameter, and contains a nest of seed shucks and short lengths of grass and weeds.

Some of the desert mice that I have known do not pile up earth outside the tunnels. These doorways are perfectly round little openings on the smooth earth. Other species frequently heap up mounds of very fine soil on the thresholds. These piles are similar to those of the pocket gopher, but usually are not nearly as large. In late summer they are evidence of great activity below the surface. The little animals are busy digging new tunnels and store rooms to take care of the fall crop of seeds.

When the pocket mouse is especially busy carrying in the crops it may work in the sunlight, provided the ground is covered with grass or weeds for shelter. Ordinarily it is nocturnal and does not venture outdoors until the twilight hunters have gone to roost. Then it tears down the door and scurries out to find some supper. It hates a wetting and rarely goes out in the rain. In the arid or semi-arid country, rains are not frequent during the warmer months of the year.

Fully three-quarters of the pocket mouse's diet consists of seeds from plants that grow in the vicinity of its burrow. Practically all small seeds are gathered, but the mouse seems to like best those of the flowers of the Composite Family, and of grasses and sedges. Among others that have been found in the store rooms are Russian thistle, pigweed, spurge, morning glory, wild parsnip, croton, dalea beans, mesquite, creosote bush, snakeweed, wild mustard, and juniper berries. Sometimes it even stores the fecal pellets of the cottontail rabbit. Greens are usually available only in spring and early summer, but the pocket mouse is fond of them. It clips tender leaves, buds, and succulent stems of grasses and herbs. At other seasons it has to be content with the pulp of prickly pear "leaves."

Possibly some species of pocket mice are strictly vegetarian. The prairie pocket mouse in Oklahoma seems to eat insects found around its burrow and stores some for future use. Caged animals have killed live grasshoppers, and eaten the heads, abdomens and legs in preference to the brittle thorax (chest region).

For such a small animal, and such a short-lived one, the pocket mouse accumulates a good-sized pantry. It will ordinarily maintain several underground caches, each containing from a tablespoonful to a cupful of many hundreds of tiny seeds.

This food is essential during the long droughts that are normal on the plains and deserts, and also through the winter. Although the pocket mouse does not hibernate like the ground squirrel, it does stay indoors during cold as well as wet weather. On the southern deserts this may be only three or four times in a "winter," for perhaps a week each period. At the northern end of the mouse's range it goes below for as much as three months, and comes out only on a few warm, windless nights. Cold, even well above freezing, makes it drowsy. The male usually emerges first in spring and starts out looking for a mate.

Farmers are not often annoyed by the pocket mouse because, individually, its size is small, and its appetite is moderate. Occasionally the clan will increase and multiply on the edge of a cultivated field and the resulting depredations may become serious. Kernels of planted corn and peas are dug out of the rows, and heads of small grains are cut off and carried to the subterranean store houses. Apparently the animals are attracted to wheat, barley or oats only when the grain is over-ripe, shattered on the ground, and already lost to the farmer.

Results of a trapping experiment that I once made in the San Simon Valley of eastern Arizona indicated that the population of desert pocket mice was about two thousand three hundred per square mile. Despite a prolonged drought and an overabundance of livestock, signs of the pocket mouse were everywhere.

In fact, seed-eating rodents often increase with over-grazing and the resulting replacement of grass by weeds. Pocket mice thus may increase, while cattle starve.

About twenty-six species of pocket mice are known in America north of the Rio Grande. These are further subdivided into more than sixty subspecies. For general purposes it is sufficient to know that all these kinds are grouped in two main divisions or subgenera:

1. Pocket mice of the subgenus *Perognathus* are small to medium in size, and have soft fur without stiff bristle hairs. Most of them live in the Sonoran or desert and chaparral zones, and in the warmer areas of the pine country.

2. Pocket mice with bristly pelage are placed in the subgenus *Chaetodipus*. They are medium to large size, and live mostly on the hotter deserts and on grassland.

General description. A fairly small mouse with short to medium-long tail, long hind legs, small ears, and fur-lined cheek-pouches. Color of the rather coarse fur varies widely with the species: upper parts, from black through shades of brownish and grayish to pale pinkish buff or white, usually sprinkled with blackish hairs; under parts reddish, buffy, or usually white; a dark or buff-colored line runs along each side from nose to end of tail; the latter grayish above, white below. Total length, 4½ to 9½ inches; height at shoulder, 1 to 1½ inches; weight, ⅓ to 1 ounce.

Distinguishing characteristics. With the exception of the spiny mouse, which has a very limited range north of Mexico, this is the only mouse-sized rodent with fur-lined cheek-pockets that open outside of the mouth. The pocket mouse is not easy to distinguish from other mice without close examination. Most of the kangaroo rats are larger than pocket mice and their hind legs are proportionately longer.

Range. Western North America from southern British Columbia to the Valley of Mexico, and from eastern parts of South Dakota, Kansas and Texas to the Pacific coast.

KANGAROO RAT

DIPODOMYS AND *MICRODIPODOPS* SP.

Turn off the paved highway some clear summer night when you are driving across the southwestern deserts, and follow a winding dirt road through the

KANGAROO RAT

scattered, thorny shrubs. The filmy smoke-tree and the tortured, ghostly cholla look unearthly in the light of the car lamps. Here is a place out of the world, where only spirits live.

Down on the earth, between the wheel tracks ahead, shines a little dull light. Ruby-red, it glows steadily like a far-away railroad signal-lantern. It winks out—no, there it is again. One can dimly see that the light is the reflecting eye of a little gnomelike creature. It is a miniature kangaroo! As the apparition suddenly leaps away and disappears, there is left only the mental impression of a round head, a chunky, pale brown-and-white body perched on two stilt legs, and a long slender tail.

The kangaroo rat is not a rat, nor a kangaroo. It is a clean, native American, that is most closely allied with the pocket mouse. The average kangaroo rat is bigger, ten to fifteen inches from nose to tail-tip. It also has a white stripe on the thigh that the pocket mouse lacks. Hopping along like a kangaroo on its hind legs, it uses its tiny front paws as nimble hands. The slender, black-and-white striped, brush-tipped tail, which is longer than body and head together, is a balancing organ. The great black eyes that shine red at night are round as those of the owl and proportionately larger. Active only at night, the kangaroo rat gathers food stores in capacious fur-lined pockets.

The different species vary greatly in size, in shade of the buffy or brownish coat, in habits and personality. They are all much alike, however, in their choice of home. This is dry plains country as high as seven thousand five hundred feet elevation in the foothills. The vegetation is chiefly grass, and shrubs or trees, if any, are spaced wide apart. The smaller kangaroo rats generally prefer to live on loose sandy soil where digging is easy. Some of the bigger, more powerful species are able to burrow even in hard, stony ground.

The entrance to the house of this miniature "kangaroo" is usually a mound of earth. Set in a clearing, the mound may have three to a dozen round holes, each one about four to six inches across. Depending chiefly on the species of the builder and age of the dwelling, the mound may be up to fifteen feet in diameter and four feet high. Occasionally some of the holes are plugged with earth; but usually they are wide open. If a caller thinks that means he is welcome, he is mistaken. Should he tap or scratch even gently near one of the holes, he is likely to hear from within the mound a series of rapid thumps. Sometimes they are grouped in series of two, with two or three seconds elapsing between pairs.

"Go 'way! Go 'way!" the owner is saying with its big hind feet.

A large mound is formed slowly through many years by the work of successive generations of kangaroo rats. Most of it is brought up from below—excavated soil from tunnels and rooms, seed hulls and spoiled food which is cleaned out of the living quarters, and droppings which are kicked out in general housecleanings. As the mound grows in bulk the galleries within are extended, until it may be four stories high.

Some kangaroo rats, principally the smaller species, build their homes entirely below the original ground level and without the benefit of a mound. Even some individuals of the mound-building families may neglect it. These animals usually have taken the precaution of locating their front doors under the protection of a rock or shrub. One can find all grades and sizes of mounds, from a few handfuls of earth up to bulky structures that can be seen from a long distance. Presumably the advantage of the mound is that the doorways can be located above the general ground level so flood waters do not run down into the passages.

These hallways may be quite short, or they may entwine in a complicated labyrinth that extends to two, three or even four levels. Usually they dip down into the original ground as much as twenty inches and there they frequently extend several yards outside the perimeter of the mound. Blind passages strike off here and there, as much as three and one-half feet deep. Ramps lead up and down between series of galleries. The dimensions of the hallways vary with the size of the owners, of course. Those of the larger "rats" are about four inches high and a little greater in width. They expand here and there into rooms, most often at tunnel junctions.

Food caches are located in a number of places, along the widened passages just mentioned; in little thimble-sized pockets in the walls, and in spherical rooms that may be as much as ten inches across. Depending on the climate and soil drainage, the pantries are located where they will be driest. If the lower strata are likely to be damp, food is stored within a few inches of the surface. In very arid regions, where the greatest danger is from sudden deluges that may wet only the top of the ground, the caches are found at depths of six to twenty-four inches.

Finally, usually near the bottom of the tunnel system, often as much as two feet below the ground level, and at a dead end, is the bedroom. This is a roundish cavity about seven to ten inches in diameter. It contains a varying amount of bedding composed of fine soft grasses and rootlets, and often a quantity of seed hulls. Sometimes the bedding is limited to a flat mattress, and in many cases extends entirely around the chamber so that the owner, by worming carefully through the bed clothes, is snug and warm in a little nest about four inches in diameter.

The kangaroo rat has no toilets. Only its bed and food are free from droppings. The pellets completely litter the floor of the many hallways, and are found even in the pantries. Mixed with chaff and bits of grass, and usually dried by the desert air, they are seldom objectionable. The kangaroo rat keeps its body spotlessly clean and spends much time taking dust baths and grooming its fur.

Every burrow system is changing almost by the month. New hallways are being dug, and the earth is thrown out on the mound or used to plug up old entrances and undesired passages or rooms. The mound may be broken here and there by rainstorms or trampling animals, especially where the soil is light and crumbly. It is such a honeycomb of thin-walled passages, some of which may come within a couple of inches of the surface, that it is little wonder that breaks occur and must be repaired.

Numerous small tenants move in on the kangaroo rat. They take advantage of its industry and poor housekeeping. Those that have been found in the burrows include toads, horned toads and a number of other lizards, gopher-, king- and rattle-snakes, and many invertebrates such as centipedes, scorpions, spiders (including black widows), crickets, wingless locustids and cockroaches, dung- and other beetles, ants, sowbugs and millepeds. No one knows how the kangaroo rat feels about these hordes of house guests.

After the original owner dies or is killed, or the burrow is abandoned for some other reason, it may offer shelter to other kangaroo rats, pocket- and grasshopper mice, ground squirrels, wood rats, cottontail rabbits, and many of the lesser creatures mentioned above.

During the day, the kangaroo rat sleeps and putters around inside its house. Apparently it is watchful at least part of the time because most callers will be met by an angry thumping from within. Almost never, unless dug out, does it leave home between sunrise and sunset. In fact, many kangaroo rats will not emerge until it is completely dark. They do not feel comfortable as long as other creatures can see much. Even full moonlight is too scary and on such nights the little animals generally stay inside until the moon has set. Juvenile rats, however, are less cautious and often wander about and gather food by the light of the moon.

When it decides that it is safe to venture out, the kangaroo rat sometimes stops back of the doorway and thumps out a series of knocks. (Perhaps this is to bait any enemy that may happen to be standing nearby into betraying its presence.) The rat waits a minute or so, then hops out. As it stands there, erect, up on its hind legs, we know why the ceilings and doorways are so high. For a little while it is very cautious, and stays within the cleared area around the burrow. The slightest sound or movement will send it back indoors in a flash. But at last it gathers enough assurance that enemies are not close by and proceeds out along one of the numerous trails that radiate from its home.

As it hops along on its hind legs, the kangaroo rat stops here and there to pick up a seed, or to pull over a grass head with its hands. Quickly it clips it off between the stout incisor teeth. Some grains are eaten on the spot but most food is tucked away in the fur-lined cheek pockets and carried into the den. This instinct to store, to put away against the long days or the rainy or moonlit nights when it cannot or dare not leave the den is a passion with most of the race. It is exercised as long as anything edible is within its territory, and ends only when it draws its last breath. The underground stores are likely to be the biggest in autumn and winter. This rat does not hibernate and unlike some desert rodents does not drowse or sleep away the midsummer drought periods. Therefore it tries to keep food always on hand.

As much as one hundred and seven quarts (almost fourteen bushels) of seeds and dried grasses cut in short lengths have been found in one burrow. Amounts ranging between twenty-five and fifty quarts are quite common. This food is usually stored most methodically, each kind of seed by itself, or, if several varieties are piled in the same bin, each kind is segregated in the heap. Probably this happens because the seeds mature and are gathered at different times. Or, when harvesting, the little animal concentrates first on the fruit that it likes best and, when that is all gathered, turns to its second choice.

There are several exceptions to this family habit of thriftiness. The little Merriam kangaroo rat, among others, rarely stores anything. Instead, it often steals from the caches of its bigger and more provident relatives. If the little pilferer is caught the big "rat" will kill it immediately.

In addition to caches in the dens, many species of kangaroo rats bury small amounts of food in numerous places in the ground nearby. A hole about an inch wide and deep, or larger, is scooped out with the hands, the food is deposited and tamped down with the nose, and some dust is scattered over the place. These caches are grouped closely, only an inch or two apart. In some instances they are apparently temporary, the food being dug up after the harvest rush is over and taken below ground to the pantries. Possibly these surface caches are made to cure partly green food by the warmth of the sun. Giant kangaroo rats (*Dipodomys ingens*) have been known to cut the heads of brome grass and stack them neatly in piles about four inches wide, twenty-four inches long and two inches deep. Shallow stacks as large as four by six feet and four inches deep have been recorded.

The food of the kangaroo rat is made up very largely of seeds. It gathers almost everything in that line that grows within its foraging limits. Grass seeds, chiefly the bromes, gramas, fescues, and needle and panic grasses, are most important. Among the other seeds that are eaten are those of mesquite, vetch, poppy, telegraph weed, pepper-grass, carpet-weed, evening primrose, snake-weed, solanum, filaree, bladder-pod, wild oats, clover and lupine. Occasionally a puff ball or other fungus is brought home. Whenever tender green grass is available (mostly in late winter and spring, and after the summer rainy season) the kangaroo rat eats it heavily. It also cuts the stems and blades into short lengths, stuffs them into the cheek pouches and carries them below. However, because it usually prefers rich dry seed, its industry often out-runs its appetite for grass. Much of it spoils and must be thrown out.

Insects seem to be important. Beetles and crickets are picked up between the front paws, but lively kinds like grasshoppers and moths must often be chased. This is very entertaining to watch. The kangaroo rat hop-skips about ludicrously, dashing frantically back and forth on its hind legs, trying to cut down the elusive insect. When it succeeds, it often eats the head on the spot, then tucks the remainder into a pocket to take home.

Its thirst is very slight. Green leaves and stems quench some of it. This "rat" sips dew, when available, and sometimes gets a drink from a puddle after a rare storm. The lower tunnels of the burrow, being cool and somewhat damp, help to conserve body moisture. Some water is converted from starchy food. When drought strikes the range, it is able to retain body fluids and reabsorb water through the walls of the bladder.

As it goes about its darkened domain, the kangaroo rat ordinarily moves by a series of hops about six inches long. Its "arms" are carried close against its chest. It may hop almost steadily for a half-hour or more without showing signs of becoming tired. When nosing about for food it drops its jaunty carriage and descends to all fours. If food is plentiful, the evening foraging trip may take less than an hour, after which it goes back downstairs for several hours. The second venture outside may be long or short, but always ends by daybreak.

Narrow beaten paths often lead from one den to another perhaps one hundred yards away, indicating that kangaroo rats pay visits to their neighbors. It is very rare, however that two adults of the same species of large *Dipodomys* are found in one burrow except at mating time. In only one instance have I ever trapped two from the same mound. In that case it is possible that the second one moved in later that night and cleared out the doorways that I had plugged to test the possibility of dual occupancy.

The larger kangaroo rats are most unsociable. They almost always drive away mice, or kill them if they are not quick enough to escape. Any small kangaroo rat that pokes about the big fellow's burrow, in hope of stealing some grain, takes its life in its hands. If cornered, one mighty blow from a hind foot will break its back or tear open its flank.

I have kept a number of banner-tailed kangaroo rats of the *spectabilis* species and found them quite "uncooperative." The most careful efforts to pair them were unsuccessful. Fighting began almost at once. Leaping and sparring, each "rat" tried to knock out the other with a hind foot. With baleful eyes and flying limbs, they kept on fighting silently until one or the other had been beaten into a stupor. The vanquished usually died in a short time as a result of shock and many punctures from the long sharp nails.

Kangaroo rats apparently never rely on their teeth in such battles. Although I have handled many of them, I have been bitten but once, and then very ineffectually. On that occasion I had made a grab for a "rat" that was leaping to escape. I missed the body but my fingers closed on the tail. Instantly, before I could release my hold, the skin covering the rear half of the tail ripped off. Under this great provocation, I could not blame the animal for turning and grabbing my finger, but the blunt incisor teeth did not break my skin.

Only when badly hurt or suddenly frightened have I heard an adult kangaroo rat utter a sound. Then it was one short, high-pitched squeak. Some naturalists say they have heard foraging kangaroo rats utter low chuckles from time to time.

In contrast to the evil-tempered big kangaroo rats are the little Merriam species. They are the most gentle and friendly creatures imaginable. They may be thieves, but they are charming ones. I once kept sixteen of these engaging little animals in a cage measuring three by six feet. Only one casualty from fighting occurred in two years. Although I provided six nest boxes, all sixteen animals frequently preferred to sleep in a heap in one box.

Instead of glowering at me from the corners as did the banner-tailed kangaroo rats, the little fellows would gather around me when I entered their cage. Full of curiosity and hopeful of something new to eat, they smelled my shoes and climbed into my trouser-cuffs. I had to use great care to avoid stepping on them. In their native desert these small kangaroo rats live in colonies. As many as several hundred dens may be closely grouped, and the connecting trails indicate that the animals run back and forth numerous times each night.

The caged Merriam "rats" amused themselves playing tag. At times, for no apparent reason except from good spirits, one of them would leap straight up about six inches, or perhaps sideways. Lone kangaroo rats of the bigger, solitary species have been seen to do this in the wild, though probably not for fun. The ability to leap suddenly provides a means of escape from enemies. Even the smallest member of this family, the dwarf kangaroo rat, has been known to jump repeatedly out of a tin can seventeen inches deep and only ten inches in diameter, without touching the sides.

Living as it does in a dry climate and working in dry, warm sand, the kangaroo rat needs a constant supply of oil to keep its skin and fur from drying out. To meet this need it has an oil gland on its back over the shoulder blades. Frequent grooming with its paws distributes this oil through the hair. Twisting and pushing its body through dry dust removes the excess which would mat the fur. This is the kangaroo rat's bath. It abhors water (except to drink) and a few drops on its body is enough to give it the jitters. It stays at home during rainstorms and until the ground has dried afterward. Even a fog will keep it indoors.

Among the kangaroo rat's enemies are the coyote, kit- and gray foxes, badger, bobcat, and the horned and barn owls. To escape them, it relies on speed, timed as high as seventeen feet per second, and an exceptional ability to dodge and twist while running. When in top form it leaps eighteen to twenty-four inches at a time. It zigzags with every jump and, with the help of its counter-balancing tail can turn almost ninety degrees. It keeps this up, however, for only a couple of hundred feet, so it rarely goes that far from home. For additional safety it usually digs three or four temporary refuges, which are located at strategic points on the domain. They are simple straight tunnels with from one to three entrances and one or two blind side passages, one of which leads to a bare, unfurnished room. A little food may be stored there for emergency use when a persistent enemy tries to outstay the rat.

If a badger starts to dig into the main burrow while the kangaroo rat is at home, the latter may decide to make a run for it to one of the emergency shelters. Instead of dashing out of a doorway, which the badger might expect, the kangaroo rat will probably burst through a wall where it is especially thin and so gain a head start toward a possibly safer hiding place.

In the open, the kangaroo rat can detect enemies very well, for it has good sight and smell, and extraordinarily sharp ears. One observation led a naturalist to conclude that a kangaroo rat heard a barn owl on the wing when the bird was at least thirty feet away.

Against smaller foes, the kangaroo rat is not so well equipped. It almost always is annoyed by a few fleas which breed in the chaff and dust that clutter the burrow. A small tick attaches itself to the ears, and roundworms have been found inhabiting the internal organs.

Perhaps because the larger kangaroo rats are such confirmed hermits, the breeding season of the species is prolonged. It may take a reluctant individual from January to August, inclusive, to come to the point, but the greatest number of matings seem to occur in March and April.

The two to five young are tiny, pink, and much wrinkled. Their hind legs and tails are proportionately much shorter than the mother's. If she finds it necessary to move them, she either carries them in her arms (with a firm mouth-grip on their backs) or drags them while clinging to her nipples.

The youngsters' eyes and ears open at about fifteen days and within a week later they are weaned and changed to a diet of the softer kinds of solid food.

By then their new adult coats have replaced the very dark pelage that previously covered the upper half of their bodies. Young Tulare kangaroo rats have been found to weigh about one-tenth-ounce at birth, one-half-ounce at three weeks, and one and one-quarter ounces at two months. Even the latest-born kangaroo rats are able to produce young the following spring or early summer. Judging by the low annual birth rate, mortality is not very high. The life-expectancy of a kangaroo rat is perhaps two years.

The burrows of kangaroo rats added to those of pocket gophers and ground squirrels sometimes destroy small earthen dams. The "rats" rarely do damage to cultivated crops because their homes are destroyed by plowing or even shallow harrowing. Stockmen accuse them of eating a great deal of forage on the range. During years of severe drought it seems that the loss of seeds of annual plants may seriously decrease the stand of forage species that would grow the following season. Ordinarily, the kangaroo rat does little or no harm. By stirring up the soil around the den, the giant kangaroo rat of the San Joaquin Valley of California is known to increase the amount of filaree and brome grass more than five times, thus benefiting the sheep industry.

Mammalogists have described at least twenty species and more than fifty races of kangaroo rats. They are grouped into two genera:

1. The genus *Dipodomys* is much the larger of the two principal groups. Its members are the true kangaroo rats. From nose to tail-tip, most of them exceed 9 inches, and the smallest are more than 8 inches long. Perhaps the best known species are the huge *spectabilis,* which is from 13 to 14 inches long, and the little Merriam kangaroo rat, which measures but 9 to 10 inches.

2. The dwarf kangaroo rat (genus *Microdipodops*), only 6 to 7 inches in total length, looks like a good-sized pocket mouse with large head and heavy body. Its range is limited almost entirely to the Great Basin of Nevada, southeastern Oregon, and extreme eastern California. Dwarf kangaroo rats are rather rare and are found only locally within the general range.

General description. A large mouse- to rat-sized mammal with large head and big eyes, external fur-lined cheek pouches, stocky body, long hind legs and short forelegs. The long black-and-white striped tail of the true kangaroo rat ends in a dusky or blackish tuft. That of the dwarf species is brown above, white below, and black on the terminal third. Fur long and fine; pale buffy, cinnamon buff, or brownish on upper parts, with dark brown or blackish at base of whiskers, eyelids, and ears; a crescent-shaped blackish mark over nose; under parts white. Total length, 6 to 14 inches; height at shoulder in normal walking position, 2 to 3 inches; weight, ½ to 6½ ounces.

Distinguishing characteristics. The "kangaroo" form; long hind legs, small forelegs and long tail. The kangaroo rat, the pocket mouse, the spiny mouse, and the pocket gopher are the only four native mammals with external fur-lined cheek pockets. The gopher lives underground. and the pocket mouse lacks the very long hind legs and long tail of the kangaroo rats. The back of the spiny mouse is sprinkled with flattened bristles.

Range. Deserts, plains and valleys of western North America, from the Gulf coast of Texas and southeastern Montana west to southeastern Oregon and Baja California; south to the region of Mexico City.

BEAVER

CASTOR SP.

The giant beaver that lived in North America thousands of years ago was longer than a black bear. Counting the tail, it measured seven and a half feet. The head was probably only four inches shorter than that of a lion. Perhaps it was too big for its own good. At any rate it became extinct.

The modern beaver never stops growing, but doesn't grow fast enough nor live long enough to acquire any great stature. An average lucky beaver may expect to live ten or twelve years. In captivity a maximum of nineteen years has been recorded. Three to four feet long, the beaver weighs fifty to seventy pounds, or one hundred if very fat and old.

The world's first engineer was the beaver. While our ancestors were still living in trees and caves, this brown rodent was sleeping peacefully in its island lodge, secure from practically every enemy. If attacked at home, the beaver and its family could dive into the water from a back door and swim to safety. It was not until hundreds of thousands of years later that a human warrior learned from the beaver to turn a stream into a wide moat surrounding his castle.

Even in ice water, the beaver's heavy coat over a warm suit of underfur keeps it comfortable. As soon as it comes out of the water, it wipes and combs itself dry with the combing claws on each of the two inner toes of the hind feet. This redistributes the oil and makes the animal waterproof again. Sometimes it takes half an hour to do the whole body properly. Someone has suggested that, after its meals of wood, it uses the split nail on the second toe to take the splinters out of its teeth!

Huge webbed hind feet and a large, black, flat scaly tail enable the beaver to paddle rapidly through the water. Ten to twelve inches long and six inches wide,

BEAVER

the tail is used for several purposes. An efficient rudder in the water, it may also serve as a scull when the animal wishes to move very slowly. Slapped vigorously on the water, it expresses warnings, anger, disgust, and possibly exuberance. On land it is used as a fifth leg. Standing up on the hind legs to cut down a tree, this extra prop gives the beaver additional support and leverage.

The valves of the nose and ears close automatically when it goes under water and open again on reaching the surface. A pair of small eyes in their tightly fitting lids are only fairly keen in the air, but seem to be more efficient under water. The lips are so loose that it can draw them together tightly behind the protruding teeth. In this way a submerged beaver can cut and chew wood without getting its mouth full of water. The extra-large lungs and liver permit it to carry enough air and oxygenated blood to stay under water for as long as fifteen minutes at a time.

The beaver is the largest rodent in the world, except the capybara of South America. Yet it is a modest animal that works hard and never attacks any other race unless severely provoked. Adults are always sober, some even more than others. (A worrying, left-handed beaver once had the nervous habit of stroking its chin with its right paw.) Usually there are no signs of fighting except during mating season. At that time a beaver may be found with a torn coat and tail.

The beaver works hard and fast. It will cut down a willow tree five inches thick in three minutes, and has been known to fell a tree as high as one hundred and ten feet, with a trunk five feet seven inches thick. All this with only its teeth! Sometimes two or three beavers work together, but ordinarily it toils alone.

Selecting a tree, the beaver rears up on the hind legs and braces itself with its flat tail. Cutting a notch at a convenient height, it next shifts to about three inches below. Then, with a wrench, it tears out the intervening chunk of wood. The cutting work is all done by the lower incisors; the upper teeth merely hold on. Soon the ground around its feet is littered with chips, and the tree begins to creak and sway. The average tree cut is between four and twelve inches across the stump, but a big tree may require a number of nights of labor. As it snaps, the beaver runs.

Crash! Boom! The beaver, and usually all of the family, duck into the pond and listen. The crash may have attracted the attention of an enemy. If one member of the family hears or smells something suspicious, *Ker-slap!* Down comes the broad tail on the water and the sharp sound warns every other beaver within hearing. Perhaps it is also intended to startle a skulking land enemy into jumping "out of its skin" and betraying its location.

If everything remains quiet, the animals return to their logging area and cut up the tree into convenient lengths for handling, two to six or eight feet long.

The trunk and limbs larger than about five inches in diameter are usually left lying where they fall, although some of this bark may be stripped off and eaten on the spot.

Some people think that the beaver knows how to cut trees so that they will fall into the water. Actually it cannot control the direction in which they fall. It simply cuts, then gravity does the rest. Because trees growing near streams tend to lean toward the opening they usually fall in that direction, and the beaver gets the credit. Other felled trees lie in almost any direction. Small trees are cut through from one side, medium-sized trunks may be attacked from two sides, and bigger ones will be chipped all the way around.

After chopping the tree into portable lengths, the beaver seizes a log in its mouth and drags it over the ground to the water's edge. Once the log is afloat, hauling is much easier. Swimming alongside, the beaver tows it across the pond. The teeth grip it firmly and the broad tail is set at an angle to prevent the beaver from traveling in a circle.

During autumn, when the beaver is busiest gathering food for winter and fixing up its dam and lodge, the tote or haul roads are often worn down to the raw dirt and are two or three feet wide. It uses the slopes to advantage to make the hauling easier.

If it has to go too far in level country, it digs canals. A couple of feet wide and one to two feet deep, they may be as much as seven hundred and forty-five feet long, and make it safer to work farther from the pond and also save much labor in getting in the logs. In the Upper Peninsula of Michigan, and elsewhere, I have seen canals built on two or three levels. The lowest was filled with water which backed up from the pond, while the upper levels were filled from springs or seepages. These canals with their "locks" are less conspicuous than dams, but they are much more difficult to plan properly. They are the most remarkable structures that are built by this extraordinary animal.

The beaver builds canals, dams, reservoirs and houses that last for many years. Yet its intelligence is rated at only fifty compared to a horse's or dog's one hundred. When it comes to picking a site for the dam, the beaver is not clever. It may be located where all factors are well suited to the purpose, or it may be so poorly situated that the dam washes out repeatedly and finally is abandoned. I have seen a number of dams that, if they had been placed one or two hundred yards up or down stream, could have been built with much less material and labor. Perhaps there are smart and stupid beavers, but the choice of a dam site seems to be generally a "hit-or-miss" proposition.

Why does a beaver go to so much trouble to make a dam? It must be assured of having a body of water at least two or three feet deep the year round.

It needs the pond as a refuge from enemies, a highway to float food and lumber, and a cache for its food.

Alone, or with the assistance of the family, and rarely the neighbors, the beaver begins building a dam. It heaps up mud, stones, water-logged sticks, driftwood, food sticks from which the bark has been peeled and eaten, and limbs and logs cut for the purpose. It may even toss in a deer's antler. Poles, from two feet up to five or six or rarely longer, are laid compactly side by side on the downstream face of the dam and parallel to the course of the stream. Some of them may finally come around into a crisscross position and they are all weighted and fixed in place with muck, stones and masses of water plants. At first the water may pour through in thousands of little streams. Eventually these are stopped up by mud, which the beaver plasters on the upstream face, and by the water-logged debris, especially masses of fallen leaves that float down with the current until they lodge and sink against the dam.

No two dams are exactly alike. Some are straight, but the majority have one or more twists and angles. An extreme example was a large dam that I once saw on Mount Desert Island, Maine. Although the distance between the two ends was only about ninety feet, the dam zigzagged like the letter W and must have been twice that length along the crest. Such an irregular dam may be the result of a swift current which, during the building process, breaks the structure in one or more places and pushes sections of it downstream before the animal can anchor them. Frequently the dam bends to avoid obstacles or, more often, to take advantage of some natural support such as a tree, boulder, or dense clump of alders.

Probably the longest dam recorded was one that measured two thousand one hundred and forty feet. It was located on the Jefferson River near Three Forks, Montana. Once in a while a height of eleven or twelve feet may be reached in the central part of a dam. The base probably would measure fifteen to twenty feet in thickness. Such a dam, or a very long one, may be the work of a number of generations of beavers. Most dams are less than four or five feet high and under three hundred feet long. An old dam may become very compact and can be crossed by a man or even a horse with perfect safety and without doing any damage to the wall.

Not all beavers build dams to surround their houses with water. Many live on deep ponds or rivers where, even at lowest level, there is ample water for their needs. Many streams are too large or swift to permit the construction of stick dams.

On most of these streams where the water level is subject to considerable fluctuation, the beaver may live in a burrow which it digs in the bank. The den is located above the average high water if possible, otherwise the owner must move out during floods. The chamber is two and one-half to three feet across and one and one-half to two feet from floor to domed ceiling. It is connected with the water by a tunnel which may be as much as fifty feet long but generally is much shorter. The beaver plans that the lower end of this passageway shall open under the level of low water. Thus it may pass in and out without exposing itself on the bank or on the surface of the water.

In case an enemy starts to dig into the house through the roof, the beaver plunges down the hallway and into the submerged lower end. Swimming under water, it may come to the top at a safe distance to see what goes on, or it may dive directly to another refuge along the bank and wait out the trouble unseen. It has been known to swim submerged for half a mile before coming up for air.

The beaver that lives in a bank is often called a "bank beaver." It does not belong to a separate species, and may be living in the bank only temporarily. Frequently the bank-den is located so high that its roof is no thicker than the undisturbed sod and roots. For safety's sake it may be dug under a stump or tree or pile of driftwood. If the roof is broken or collapses, the beaver is likely to repair it by heaping sticks and earth across the opening.

The lodge-house is the home of most beavers. (A "lodge-beaver" may also have one or more bank dens for emergency or part-time use.) The lodge may be close to or quite a distance from the dam. It is erected on shore, on an island, a floating marsh, or out in shallow water. If the latter, the beaver must build an artificial island. The level top of this foundation is often only an inch or two above the pond. The one essential for a house site is proximity to deep water so that one or more tunnels may open under the winter ice.

When construction of the lodge starts, sticks are dragged together to form a rough circle or oval, at one or more sides of which are the slide-hole doorways leading to the water. Stones, mud, boughs, and logs build up the walls. As they rise to a height of two or three feet, they are built inward and finally roofed over. More and more sticks are dragged by one end up onto the walls. Eventually the lodge looks like a great mass of peeled poles and sticks, most of which are built into the structure, and some plastering is generally done to make the walls tight. As long as the lodge is occupied, the owners continue to add sticks and mud from time to time. Sometimes it is seven feet high, and thirty to thirty-nine feet in diameter.

When a beaver wants to do a little plastering, it sweeps together a double armful of mud between its arms and chest. Walking on the hind legs and steadied by the trailing tail, it steps easily over the rolling logs and climbs up the rough side of the house.

There is only one room in this big house, but it is large enough for a man. John Colter of Yellowstone fame is said to have made his remarkable escape from the Blackfeet Indians in 1809 by diving into a creek and crawling inside a beaver lodge. Depending upon the number of offspring in residence, the combined bed-living-dining room may be as much as four or five feet across and three feet high.

The adults sleep on the bare floor, but new babies get a soft mattress. This is made of leaves, grass, twigs and roots and, economically, can be eaten later on. The walls are fairly uniform for the beavers have trimmed off the projections. If more room is needed they dig into the walls. As the roof sags with weight and age, it may be necessary to cut away some of the ceiling also. The room is irregularly shaped and once in a great while two adjacent lodges may be merged. The rooms are then thrown into one.

Sometimes a lodge is the home of only one beaver. However, it is much more usual to find a number of animals living together and working as a group. The colony may contain as many as a dozen beavers of all ages, but an average family is about half this size. Ordinarily it is made up of father, mother and their last two litters of young.

The male head of the family seems to take care of the daily repairs on dam and lodge, but when a big job has to be done, the whole family turns out and "works like beavers."

If both parents survive, the union is probably life long. Due to the fighting and traveling of males at this time, there is no doubt that many males seek more than one mate. Actual mating has been observed very seldom. Although they have been seen standing up in the water with their arms around each other's neck, they were probably only wrestling. Mating occurs in January or February when the ponds throughout most of the northern range are frozen over. The young are born a little less than four months later.

Shortly before their arrival, the even tenor of family life is interrupted. The set of children who are now two years old are driven out of the home or leave voluntarily. Possibly the mother, who has been a model of affection up to now, suddenly turns on them. One set of year-old children, besides the new litter to nurse, is enough. Two-year-olds of beaver families kept in captivity are killed if they cannot get away. At this age they are nearly mature and may wander forth to look for mates and to raise small, late-season families of their own. Finally the father leaves the lodge to take up temporary quarters in a nearby bank-den. The mother, made waspish by her condition, is left alone with her brood of the previous year. She gathers materials for a nest from the bank of the pond, and waits.

In late April, May or June, the three or four young arrive. (The number may vary from one to six.) They average slightly less than one pound, although they may weigh from eight to twenty-five ounces. Including the three and one-half-inch tail, they are about fifteen inches long. Their eyes are open from the first and their bodies are covered with soft, fine fur. Probably the only frivolous moments in a beaver's life are when it is first old enough to play water tag with its brothers. Apparently it needs no swimming lessons.

A litter of four Michigan beavers that weighed fourteen to fifteen ounces each at birth were weighed regularly. At one month they scaled three and one-half to four pounds; at six months, ten to fifteen and one-half pounds; at nine months, sixteen and one-half to twenty and one-half; and at one year, twenty and one-half to twenty-six and one-half pounds. A three-year-old beaver will weigh almost fifty pounds.

Sometimes you can hear, through the walls of a house, the litter of young wailing. Adults have quite a repertoire of sounds: soft churrs, mumbles and whines. When angry, they hiss. A frightened beaver, or one that has been hurt, will cry out pathetically like a human child.

Beavers of both sexes have a pair of musk glands which are located in the rear of the abdomen. The musky liquid was once believed to have medicinal values, and the glands or "castors" were sold for ten to twenty dollars per pound. They no longer have any commercial worth. The musk is probably a sex identification odor, and is much more evident during mating season. It is deposited, at least in spring, in the "sign heaps," conical or flattened piles of mud about a foot across and two or three inches thick, that the beavers often leave along the streams.

The beaver has its enemies, of course, despite all precautions and a comparatively protected life. If ambushed on land by a carnivore, it prefers to rush back at a clumsy gallop to safety in the pond. Unfortunately its best pace is no better than a fat man's run. The formidable teeth are enough to discourage a small predator, but against the wolf, coyote, bear, wolverine, cougar, lynx and bobcat the beaver has little chance. There is also the arch predator, man, with his steel traps and deadfalls. Most beavers are parasitized at times by blood-sucking beetles. They are also subject to diseases, the nature of most of which are unknown. Sometimes a beaver miscalculates and is struck and killed by a tree that it is cutting. The death rate from all causes, however, is not high.

Many people think that the beaver eats nothing but the bark of poplar trees. Actually it has greatly varied menus, for a vegetarian. In summer it eats many aquatic plants, including duckweed, eelgrass, waterlily roots and duck potato. It has also been known to cut raspberry canes for their delicate flavor. After a long winter on an exclusive diet of bark and a few underwater plants, the northern beaver is probably especially eager to sample grass, herbs, roots, shoots, buds and leaves of many small land plants and shrubs.

In addition to aspen, cottonwood and poplar bark, the beaver likes maples, willows, beech, cherry, alder, the black, white, and yellow birch, and sometimes other trees. Some woodsmen will swear that the beaver will eat the bark of conifers only when faced with starvation. At times, however, it dines on pines, cedar, spruce, fir and hemlock by choice. I well remember seeing all the lower branches cut from young jack pines that grew along the shore of a small lake in Chippewa County, Michigan, while plenty of luscious young aspens stood untouched. The peeled pine twigs, bearing the tooth marks of beavers, lay in the shallow water. According to Dr. C. H. D. Clarke, captive beavers "go wild" over a midwinter treat of a few cedar boughs. The beaver is an individualist. You can count on its upsetting the charts of the most expert dieticians among the naturalists.

In the north, thick ice would cut off the beaver from its food supply if it left the food piled on the bank. It must sink its stores in the pond below the ice level. Because many fall-cut logs would not waterlog and sink before being frozen in the ice, the beaver has to tow them to the winter pantry in the bottom of the pond. Here it either rams them fast into the mud, or piles stones on them.

After the pond has frozen and the world is covered with a white blanket, the beaver swims under water to its larder. Selecting a juicy poplar or other log, it returns to the lodge for an appetizing meal of bark. (You may be sure it shakes itself well in the hallway before going into the warm bedroom-dining room.) When it has finished dinner, it tosses the white, stripped log back down the hallway into the pond, and resumes its conversation with the family.

The life of any beaver colony is dependent on its food supply. An average beaver requires an aspen tree between one and three inches thick at the butt, or its equivalent, each day. As the animals of successive years and generations log off the nearby timber, they must go farther and farther away for supplies. The labor of hauling and the danger of being caught by predators increases rapidly after passing the distance of three hundred feet. If a good canal cannot be built, beavers will not go farther from the pond edge than five hundred to six hundred and fifty feet. Then the colony is abandoned and the animals must migrate. Years later, after the forest has returned, another family will probably settle on the old site.

As early as the seventeenth century, the search for fur, principally that of the beaver, was the greatest single urge that sent white men into the most remote corners of unexplored America. From Florida, the Rio Grande and the head of the Gulf of California north to the open tundra of Alaska and Canada, the trappers found beavers by the thousands.

The beaver pelt became the basis of value, not only of other skins but of all commodities and articles. A beaver skin would buy a pound of tobacco, a one-pound kettle, four pounds of shot, or one large and one small hatchet in the posts of the Hudson's Bay Company during 1670. It took six beavers to purchase a laced coat, and twelve fine ones to acquire a long rifle. Some of the most fabulous fortunes of the United States and Canada, such as the Astor millions, were founded on this barter. The beaver has taken a place on the coat of arms of the Dominion. Its name was given to hundreds, more likely thousands, of places from counties and towns to meadows, mountains, lakes and streams.

Until about 1840, most beaver pelts went into the manufacture of high "silk" hats. Fur coats and accessories took the rest. The total drain on the beaver population was enormous. Between 1853 and 1877 the Hudson's Bay Company alone sold almost three million beaver skins on the London market. Trappers pursued the animals into the most distant wildernesses of northwestern Canada and Alaska. Inevitably the species declined even there, and in most of the United States it became extremely rare or extinct. Given advantage of protection, however, beavers have again become abundant in many regions.

In parts of some states, they are even numerous enough to be an agricultural liability. When the Idaho Fish and Game Department received thousands of complaints that beavers were flooding fields and roads, they promptly took steps to remove three thousand of the animals to sparsely settled mountainous regions. Many other game commissions have done the same thing. Here live beavers are more valuable than dead ones. They make reservoirs of water that prevent erosion (including the carrying of damaging silt on to irrigation projects) and provide water facilities during drouths for grazing livestock as well as wildlife.

About fifty thousand skins are marketed annually from the United States, twenty thousand from Alaska, and one hundred and five thousand from Canada. Most of them are used for coats, collars or other trimmings. The market price of a good pelt just before World War II was about thirty-five dollars. Northern dark colored skins are most valuable.

General description. A very large rodent with heavy body, short legs, large webbed hind feet and broad, horizontally flattened, scaly tail. Dense fur, varying in color with the species from reddish chestnut to rich deep brown and almost black, which becomes paler on the lower chest and abdomen; naked tail almost black. Total length, 3 to 4 feet; height at shoulder, about 15 inches; weight, 40 to 50 up to a normal maximum of 70 pounds, although very fat animals have scaled as much as 110 pounds.

Distinguishing characteristics. Large size, webbed hind feet, broad flattened naked tail, and aquatic habits. The only similar mammals that live on waterways are the otter and the muskrat. The latter is much smaller and has a slender tail that is flattened in a vertical plane. The otter is much more slender and has a conical, furred tail.

Range. Most of North America from northern Florida and extreme northern Mexico northward to the limit of trees, exclusive of the southern halves of California and Nevada.

GRASSHOPPER MOUSE

ONYCHOMYS LEUCOGASTER AND *O. TORRIDUS*

It is a night for murder. A big, hunter's moon stares over the eastern horizon of the plains. A blocky little mouse with stubby legs and a short, chubby tail comes out of its burrow under an overhanging sagebrush. Plump and placid, it smooths its velvety, dun-colored coat and immaculate white vest. It looks comfortable, benign, at peace with the world. Then, sitting back on the haunches, it points its nose toward the faintly glimmering stars, opens its mouth, and utters a faint, very shrill, long whistle. The sound can scarcely be heard ten feet away, but there is something wild, untamed in it.

Once again calm and smug, the mouse trots slowly down the little trail that leads toward a gnarled rabbitbrush. Suddenly, as if jerked by a string, it stops and stiffens. The nose goes down; sniffing, it feels about. The scent is warm on the tiny delicate footprints of a pocket mouse which, a few minutes before, crossed the path with a load of seeds. The hunter's ears are back, the black, beady eyes sparkle, and gone is its air of benediction.

Like a hound on the trail, it turns and eagerly follows the scent. Just as it is unraveling a puzzling tangle of tracks at the edge of a grass clump, a pocket mouse incautiously walks around the corner. With a rush the chunky hunter is upon it, clutching with sharp-clawed fingers. A short, fierce struggle! Then the grasshopper mouse has its paws around the victim's throat. A final choked squeak, the knifelike lower incisors slash into the base of the brain, and the pocket mouse goes limp.

Tearing and biting, the grasshopper mouse devours the brain and much of the carcass. Soon there is little left except scraps of skin and a few bits of bones. The mouse's white vest is spattered with blood, and it will require much scrubbing and grooming to get it clean again.

The grasshopper mouse kills many pocket mice, harvest mice, meadow mice, white-footed mice and small species of kangaroo rats. It even eats other grasshopper mice if opportunity offers. Carrion is accepted if fresh, quivering prey is not available.

With its heavy build and short legs this little killer cannot run down swift prey. Instead, it ambushes them, and with a short rush, like a miniature lion, it overwhelms them. The lizards that it captures are probably caught only when napping.

Over one-half of the grasshopper mouse's food is made up of smaller game—insects. One-fifth of its diet consists of beetles, which provide almost the entire food supply throughout the summer months. One of its alternate names is "scorpion mouse," acquired from its habit of preying on those fearsome creatures.

GRASSHOPPER MOUSE

(For the same reason, this name is even more frequently applied to the Sonoran white-footed mouse.) Other insects eaten in quantity are grasshoppers, caterpillars, crickets, bugs and moths.

Only a little over one-tenth of the mouse's food is vegetation, mostly seeds of grasses and grains. It depends upon these especially in winter when insects are scarce or dormant in the ground. However, it is able to locate some hibernating insects and their larvae by smelling about. Eagerly it digs them up and devours them.

Leading a rather hand-to-mouth existence in the wild, it alternately gorges and starves, but has developed a huge capacity to accommodate food when it is handy. A captive grasshopper mouse weighing four-fifths of an ounce has been known to devour half its own weight in mouse flesh and blood, insects, and a little rolled oats, and to repeat this feat every night for weeks.

Regardless of its bloody reputation, the grasshopper mouse is much more amenable to captivity than most of the mammal prey species. It is calm and self-possessed. I have kept a number of Coues grasshopper mice of Arizona and have found them generally friendly toward each other in captivity. Quarrels were uncommon. Perhaps an ample supply of food, always before them, removed any incentive to murder. However, they objected strenuously to being handled and their sharp teeth were weapons to be respected.

Grasshopper mice are found only in North America. They are grassland animals, living on the dry treeless plains and in desert scrub growth or foothill country. The majority of the species live where the climate is warm or even hot for much of the year.

They do not hibernate. Not even the northernmost mice, in southern British Columbia and Saskatchewan, retire for the winter. During the worst weather, they stay inside but not for any long sleep. They store up enough carbohydrates as fat to make them almost rotund. Their tails become especially plump. Spare food is cached in their burrows and hoarded until no more food can be found on the range.

The grasshopper mouse is well fitted to dig and often makes its own den. Equally often it saves itself the trouble by taking over an abandoned gopher tunnel or a burrow belonging to a ground squirrel, a kangaroo rat, or other mice. Sometimes it moves into a corner of an old badger digging or a prairie dog hole. Those that I have kept in captivity tunneled into the cotton bats supplied them for bedding, but did not bother to fluff it up or otherwise make it over to suit their individual tastes.

The first litters of the year arrive in the north in May; those along our southwestern border are born a month earlier. They contain three to six, generally four or five naked, toothless offspring that weigh about one-tenth of an ounce each. They get their first teeth, the incisors, at ten days of age, when they also begin to hear sounds. Their eyes open when they are two weeks old. About ten days later they are weaned. At that time they appear to be about one-third the size of the mother.

Much remains to be discovered about the private lives of grasshopper mice. From the fact that partly grown young just out of the den have been seen as late as September, it is inferred that the mothers may rear more than one brood in a season.

Like all good hunters, grasshopper mice have sharp eyes and ears, and very perceptive noses. Except for occasional forays in shrubs to pick up insects, especially the larvae, they confine their hunting to the ground. Persistent trailers, they get excited on a hot scent and utter a succession of sharp squeaking barks.

Because they are practically never out by day, grasshopper mice do not worry about the hawks or shrikes, or mammals that do not dig for a living. Owls, snakes, badgers, and coyotes are fearsome enemies.

On the whole, grasshopper mice are man's allies. They do not eat appreciable amounts of grain but kill and devour quantities of destructive insects. Some of the small mammals on which they prey also are detrimental to man's interests.

Two species and more than twenty geographic races of grasshopper mice have been described. The two main groups are distinctly different. They may be recognized as follows:

1. Mice belonging to *Onychomys leucogaster* are heavily built, and their upper parts are clear to dusky pinkish buff. They are found from extreme northern Mexico north and east to the limits of the tribal range.

2. The various races of *Onychomys torridus* are smaller, more lightly built, and have relatively longer tails than those of the *leucogaster* group. The upper parts of most members are bright tawny. They live only in the arid Southwest, mainly on the hot low deserts. Where the two species occur in the same region, *leucogaster* is found at somewhat higher elevations.

General description. A plump mouse with short, tapering tail that is thick at the base. Fur soft and silky; grayish or blackish brown to reddish brown or pale pinkish cinnamon, abruptly changing to pure white below. Total length, 5½ to 6½ inches; height at shoulder, about 2¼ inches; weight, 1 to 2 ounces.

Distinguishing characteristics. Short, thick tail as compared with the long, slender tails of the white-footed and jumping mice; white under parts instead of gray as in the house and meadow mice, and most of the red-backed mice.

The last named also have distinctly reddish backs, which the grasshopper mouse lacks.

Range. Western North America, from central Texas, eastern Kansas and western Minnesota west to the eastern foothills of the Coast Range in Oregon and California; Baja California, northern Durango and San Luis Potosi, north to central British Columbia and Saskatchewan.

HARVEST MOUSE

REITHRODONTOMYS SP.

Sometime, in marsh grass or a weedy fence row, you may run across an odd little nest made of firmly woven grass and sedges. It is about the size and shape of a baseball. There is only one entrance, perhaps half an inch in diameter. The woven sphere is probably four or five feet above ground in a bush, or attached to the lower grass stems, or on the ground. A padding of soft, warm, finely shredded plant fiber and cottony material makes the walls about half an inch thick.

Captive harvest mice have been watched weaving their nests. After gathering materials on the site, the mouse goes to work. Pulling some grasses underneath its body, the little animal weaves the ends upward into a cup. As it continues, the cup becomes a sphere. The busy little hands and teeth weave and pat and jerk the material together overhead. Turning continually, it patches and fills every space until only the round doorway remains open. When the walls are thick enough, it gathers cattail down, milkweed floss, or fine soft grass blades and carries it into the house. This is worked into the coarser material until the soft lining is complete.

Once in a while a harvest mouse will make its nest in a tunnel in an earth mound or in a haystack. It has even gone to the other extreme and settled in a tree. On very rare occasions, it uses an abandoned woodpecker hole, a deserted bird's nest, or even a knothole in a fence post. If it desires extra protection, which is quite often, it will locate the ball-shaped house under a board or a fallen tree trunk on the edge of a field.

Open, grassy fields, brush borders and meadows, are where harvest mice are found. In the tropics, where they live in the mountains, their homes are located in the brushy, grassy savannahs of open-growing forests of mixed oaks and pines. Various species have their own preferences for building sites. Some like dry places; many want plenty of moisture, while a few live in salt or fresh

HARVEST MOUSE

water marshes where the grass often grows with its feet in the water. None of the harvest mice are hardy enough to live north of the United States. They prefer warmer climates—Central America and northern South America—where they are sometimes found in great numbers and variety of species.

Several other small mammals make globular nests of woven grasses. Those belonging to cotton rats and rice rats are much larger. Those of the white-footed mice and jumping mice are usually underground.

The dainty little harvest mouse is retiring and seldom noticed. It is not at all rare but has no conspicuous features. For this reason, the ordinary observer is likely to pass it off as a house-mouse reverted to life in the fields. The two species look much alike. A long, slender, almost naked tail, large ears, and dull, nearly uniform color are similar. However, the harvest mouse is generally a little smaller, more slender and has a proportionately longer tail. The surest method of identification cannot be used until the mouse has been killed and can be examined. Each upper incisor of the harvest mouse has a deep groove running down the face of the tooth from gum to cutting edge. The incisors of the house mice are smooth.

Harvest mice rarely move in with humans. They are too independent or timid, or both. Always immaculate, they are in striking contrast to the house mice who trade cleanliness for an easy thieving life.

Probably there is as much variation in the personalities of harvest mice as among human beings. Some of them are quick-tempered and resent intrusion on their privacy. The desert and the dusky harvest mice are especially quarrelsome and pugnacious. Others are very gregarious and will live tenement-fashion all mixed up with the neighbors. In captivity, on the average, only one pair occupy a nest. However, a strange male was once placed in a small cage occupied by a pair of harvest mice with new-born young. He was accepted without protest as a part of the family. A perfect gentleman, he returned this hospitality by never harming the babies. Almost any other species of mammal would have killed the intruder, or driven him away immediately. Other captive harvest mice, however, have slain every newcomer as soon as it entered.

Except in the northern colder parts of the range, two broods of young and sometimes three are raised. April and September are the mating months for most adults, although there is considerable variation and in the tropics young may be born in any month. During these romantic interludes, male golden harvest mice have been heard singing. The very shrill bugling has a ventriloquil quality, and can barely be heard by human ears. It is not only very faint, but is almost too high-pitched to register in our limited range of hearing. Twenty-three or twenty-four days later the young are born. A litter usually numbers two, three, or four, but up to seven have been recorded.

When born, baby harvest mice of our central Great Plains region weigh only one twenty-fifth of an ounce and are slightly more than one-quarter inch long from nose to tip of tail. When they are two days old, a little brownish fuzz begins to appear over their backs. The eyes and ears open and both sets of front teeth poke through the gums in seven or eight days. At ten days they have tripled their birth-weight and have become quite active, walking about a little unsteadily.

The mother begins to wean them when they are two weeks old. By then they look and act much like small editions of herself. A week or ten days later they leave her and go out to make their own living. They are full grown, weighing about one-third ounce at the tender age of five weeks. If the weather is warm and food is plentiful, the precocious youngsters may be looking for mates before they are three months old, but four months or a little over is more ordinary. No one knows their life expectancy; probably it is little more than a year.

From the name, one might expect the harvest mouse to keep a well-stocked pantry. Perhaps some individuals are more provident than others, but food seems to be stored only occasionally and not in large quantities. The harvest mouse has no storerooms. Any food that is put away is kept in the nest. It may consist of seeds of grass, including brome, crab, witch, and fescue, wild oats, foxtail, filaree, and clover. Although the mouse may climb after these tiny grains and cut them from the stalks, fallen seeds can be picked up from the miniature "forest" floor during many months of the year.

Most of the mouse's diet is seeds, with some tender sprouting grass-tips for greens. It eats most heavily after the long day's sleep, between dark and about ten or eleven p. m. Sometimes it carries seeds home for the meal, or may eat them on the spot. After finishing its dinner, it washes its face and hands much like a cat and smooths down its fur. Running the tail between its hands, it scrubs the entire length with its tongue. Finally, if water is handy in a rill or puddle, or as drops of dew on the grass, it takes a drink.

Captive harvest mice kill and eat moths so readily when given to them that they probably prey on these and perhaps other insects in the wild. On seeing a moth, the mouse crouches like a cat. Slowly and carefully it stalks forward a few steps, then rushes. Seizing the moth, the mouse bites it to death and then hastily chews down all the appetizing portions. On occasions when a good-sized moth was able to fight off a little caged harvest mouse, the frustrated mammal nonchalantly called it quits and wasted no more attention on the insect.

North of Mexico, harvest mice rarely become so abundant that their pilfering from grain fields is noticed.

In their grass jungles the harvest mice are active throughout the year. They do not like the daylight, another reason that we seldom see them. At dark they leave their nests and go out to forage. Apparently they ramble about rather haphazardly instead of confining themselves to established routes. Other, heavier mice make good roads and trails, which the harvest mice follow at will. Good climbers, they swing about on grass stalks and in the bushes.

Little is known of their special enemies. They are practically lacking in offensive power, and their only defense is quickness, agility, and watchfulness. They are preyed upon by most of the smaller carnivorous mammals, as well as birds and reptiles. Apparently harvest mice live on friendly, or at least neutral, terms with white-footed mice.

North of Mexico harvest mice get along on one suit for an entire year. Most of them change in late autumn. In brushing through the vegetation and climbing laboriously over the "down timber" of thickly fallen grass and weed stems, their clothes get hard wear. By early summer the ends of the outer fur are scuffed off, exposing in most cases the somewhat browner tones beneath. When the next hair begins to grow in, all over the body at once, the old coat is faded and often ragged. Harvest mice of the tropics are less regular about molting, although the majority go through the process sometime during the second half of the year.

General description. A small mouse with large ears and long, slender, scantily haired tail. Color varies with the species: dull blackish, brown, buffy or reddish tawny, darkest along the back and merging gradually into gray, grayish pinkish white, or white under parts; tail sharply bicolored, brownish above and grayish white below. Total length, 4½ to 7 inches; height at shoulder, ⅞ to 1 inch; weight, about ⅓ to 1 ounce.

Distinguishing characteristics. Closely resembles a small house-mouse, but is browner or buffy instead of gray, and has somewhat more hairy tail. The upper front teeth, incisors, are grooved longitudinally, unlike those of any other small mouse.

Range. Lower elevations of North America, from Virginia, Kentucky, northern North Dakota and central Washington south through Central America to Ecuador.

WHITE-FOOTED MOUSE
PEROMYSCUS AND *BAIOMYS* SP.

Take any spot in North America south of the Arctic Circle. If mammalian life is possible, there you will find the white-footed mouse, from the last stunted shrubs on the highest mountains to the bottom of Death Valley, two hundred and seventy-six feet below sea level. Conditions can hardly be too severe—too hot or cold, too wet or dry. Hardly a square mile of this continent and far into South America fails to support the white-footed mouse.

These mice are often called deer mice because the color and pattern of their coats are similar to those of the white-tailed deer. They build their homes in deep forests, thickets, on open prairies, along sandy beaches, in swamps, salt-water savannahs, on the southern deserts, northern muskegs, and in the cliffs of the mountains. They will even move into a town house or wilderness camp and take advantage of its shelter, stores of food, and protection from their normal, outdoor enemies.

WHITE-FOOTED MOUSE

When the white-footed mouse occupies a human dwelling, it never goes unkempt like the house-mouse. Its coat is just as smoothly brushed, its white vest, nose and feet are as immaculate, as those of the white-footed mouse that never smells a human footprint in a lifetime. It is unfortunate that the name "mouse" has been given such disrepute by that ubiquitous parasite from the Old World. Our native species is a dainty little creature that lives on the choicest of seeds and other vegetable matter. Few American animals are more retiring and clean. It is the social antithesis of the prying and frequently dirty house-mouse.

In its personal toilet, it is indefatigable. It scrubs, combs and arranges every hair, until the brown-and-white coat and long, haired tail have achieved the height of mouse elegance. But when it comes to housekeeping, it spends neither thought nor energy and is almost more careless than any other mammal. It loves to eat in bed, and bits of food, husks of seeds, discarded shells of nuts and acorns are dropped in the nest cavity and even in the nest. Worse yet, the mouse often does not bother to go outside to the toilet, and the nest becomes not only lumpy and messy, but damp and smelly. It gets so bad that it can seldom be used for more than a week or two at a time, so the mouse has a number of homes and moves from one to another in rotation.

White-footed mice are accomplished. They can sing. When "in good voice," their very shrill buzzing may be prolonged for five or ten seconds, and be audible for as much as fifty feet. If disturbed at any time, a nervous white-footed mouse will thump rapidly with its front feet. On resonant leaves or a similar surface, this will make a tiny drumming sound.

Only a short acquaintance with white-footed mice is enough to find that they vary widely in temperament. Some species are easy-going and quiet. I have found the desert mouse (*Peromyscus eremicus*) easy to handle, and the big California parasitic mouse (*P. californicus*) even more gentle. Other species and races are highly nervous, and in spite of the best treatment in captivity they continue to be wild. The eastern wood mouse (*P. leucopus*) seems to be a perpetually irascible species. There are mice and mice, and some individuals of any race may be relatively tame, others shy and nervous.

A number of species of white-footed mice spend much of their time in trees and weave their round nests among the branches. They travel with great skill. The long tails are used, like the arm of a balancing man, whenever the twigs start to bend. I have noticed that the brush-mice of the southwestern mountains usually take to trees as a means of escape in preference to running along the ground. They climb readily, although not rapidly, and seem to have no fear of falling. A mouse that once escaped me while being transferred from a trap to a cage climbed a ponderosa pine and disappeared in the crown forty feet above the ground. Another fugitive ran into an oak tree and, when I threw a stick at him, jumped off the perch. With all four legs thrust out stiffly, the little animal parachuted twenty feet to the ground. He landed upright and, without a perceptible pause, raced off to safety.

Under the ideal conditions of cage life, white-footed mice mothers of the more prolific species might each produce as many as fifteen litters in a year. Although it is not likely that any such production-line effort would occur in the wild, these white-footed mice do rear several broods of young each season. The number varies with the species. Some of the larger ones have fewer litters with less offspring in each one than the mice of smaller stature. The breeding season also varies in length, according to latitude. In the northern tier of states it extends from March to October.

Although many mice pair off for the winter, most of them live alone during that time. (Sometimes these partnerships are with animals of the same sex.) As spring breaks, each male sets out to find a mate. Usually the female fights him off at first, but not for long. As soon as she changes her tactics, the male suddenly becomes coy. It is now necessary for her to pursue him. When she gets him, the two occupy her nest for a few days. Then the male leaves or is thrown out. Apparently these successive unions through the season are very short, for adult males and females are seldom found living together during the warmer months of the year.

Development of the first litter of the season requires twenty-one to twenty-five days before the little mice are born. Many white-footed mice mothers then go out and acquire a mate within a day or even a few hours. Others wait as much as several weeks.

The number in a litter ranges from one to nine, depending largely on the species. The mothers of one species will consistently bring forth six to eight young at a time, while others may average only one to three. Young of the smaller species weigh but one twenty-fifth to one-twelfth of an ounce. Those of the largest may be as much as one-fifth ounce. There is some individual variation in the number and size of young, for one mother may sometimes have successively larger litters than another mother of the same race. Even the size of offspring frequently differs in the same litter.

All young white-footed mice are much alike in appearance. Wrinkled and pink, they are so transparent that a milk-filled stomach shows through the skin as a tiny white sac. Blind and deaf, most new-born white-footed mice are naked except for their "whiskers." At most, the area along the back may be darkened by the fur that is developing under the skin. This appears above the surface by the second or third day.

About two weeks after birth their eyes open. At this time the smaller types of white-footed mice are about four inches long and weigh approximately one-quarter ounce. With their first new teeth they begin to eat solid food.

Weaning is a flexible process. They may go on a solid diet when as young as three weeks if another litter is born. In only rare cases can a white-footed mother feed two broods at a time. Nursing, however, is quite apt to slow up the growth of the developing embryos, and it is seldom that the youngsters already in the world are cast off as early as three weeks. Generally they stay on a milk diet for about twenty-five days, and occasionally for more than five weeks. They are ready to mate at from five to eight weeks old, but do not achieve adult size until they are ten weeks or older.

The mother white-foot is a model of solicitude and maternal care. Except for running out briefly to mate and get food, she devotes every moment and all her energy to the young. Before they were born, she had built a nest of the softest materials available, fluffing these out with her teeth and paws. As she reworked the grasses, cotton or rags into a fine little home, her paws and mouth were as dextrous as three human hands. A plug of material closes the doorway and keeps the house warm.

Much like a brooding hen, the mother hovers over the babies to keep them from being chilled. Balanced on her straddled hind legs, her soft belly is arched over the squirming youngsters and her paws are drawn close to her chest. If necessary to move them during the first few days of life, she takes them in her mouth, one at a time, behind her long incisors. Beginning at about a week of age, the young take a "death grip" on the mother's nipples, and often hold on for hours. So tight is this grasp that she can pull the whole brood around or even up a tree without having one of them let go. If one should happen to fall by the wayside, she returns, grabs the slack skin of the youngster's belly and races off. It helps her considerably by automatically holding on with all four feet and curling its tail over her head.

When a new litter of young is about to arrive, the mother usually does not drive away her just-weaned family. Instead, she moves out herself and builds a new nest for the next litter somewhere in the neighborhood. In this way the new babies arrive in more sanitary conditions and the adolescent mice have a better chance to survive where they are familiar with food supplies and escape routes.

The first coat of young mice is a fluffy, rather woolly dress. It is a uniform dull gray on the head, back and sides, and white below. Within a few months it is gradually shed, usually a hair at a time here and there over the entire animal. In the new suit the gray areas are replaced by brown. Generally this is a duller and paler shade than the brown dress worn by adults, which all growing mice acquire before they are a year old. The individual hairs are also shorter. The final shift into adult pelage is similar to the previous change, a replacement of hair by hair all over the mouse. Subsequently, every autumn or late summer the change is made uniformly, beginning at the head and working back to the rear.

This coat must last the mouse for an entire year. As the weather grows cold, more hairs grow in and make it heavier. Enough drop out the next spring to make it thinner during the summer than at any other time of the year. Very gradually the dusky tips of the fur are worn away, exposing the brighter and paler brown tints below. Only a little of the fur needs to be worn off to give the mouse a much gayer appearance. It is often believed that a mouse in such a bright tawny or reddish-brown coat is very old. However, any fully adult animal may go through a period of splendor each year, if only the dusky "nap" of its suit wears off before renewal in the fall.

The size of the home range and foraging territory of the average white-footed mouse is difficult to define. Undoubtedly it varies with the habitat and abundance of the right kinds of food. Ordinarily the female mouse does not travel more than about three hundred feet from home, but a male may wander much farther when looking for a mate that will be accommodating enough "to chase him." On the other hand, some males prefer to stay home at all times, especially when there are plenty of females conveniently at hand.

White-footed mice are just as strongly attached to their home territory as are many of the huge mammals. They fiercely defend the inner circle of their ranges against aggression by other white-footed mice. At a little distance from home, they are not so particular, and there is considerable overlapping of the outer portions of individual territories. In experiments to test the homing instinct, these mice have been live-trapped and marked, then transported varying distances and released. While a few of the animals settled down at their new location, most of them returned to their original homes from distances up to several hundred yards. A number of mice found their way back from a mile or more. One of the little creatures succeeded in returning to its home across two miles of country.

White-footed mice build their houses in a great variety of places. The location depends on the species and habitat. The old field mouse of the southeastern states digs a burrow with an entrance one inch to one and one-half inches in diameter. The tunnel dips steeply about a foot below the surface, then levels off and leads to a round chamber in which the nest is built. In many cases another shaft extends upward within an inch or so of the surface. Presumably this is an emergency escape hatch which can be broken open if the owner should be cornered in its home by an intruder. This whole burrow system may require the excavation of a quart of soil, which is dumped just outside the entrance. Some of the loose dirt is used to plug the doorway in case of heavy rains or floods.

A white-footed mouse in Florida, called the gopher mouse, also lives underground. It saves labor by moving into the burrow of a tolerant gopher turtle. (This is how it got its common name.) To avoid collisions in the narrow passageway, the gopher mouse may take the trouble to scoop out a short side tunnel.

The prairie deer mouse sometimes tunnels, or may be lucky enough to find a protecting cover such as a large flat rock, a discarded plank, or even a substantial clod of earth. Under this roof, a cavity is scooped out and a globular nest woven of the stems and roots of grasses, sedges and other plants. A single round entrance at one side gives access to the interior, which is lined with some soft material such as thistledown or bird feathers.

Similar sites, or hollows in logs, stumps and trees above ground are selected by the wood mouse of the eastern United States. Homes of this species have been found fifty or more feet above the ground. Sometimes a wood mouse uses the abandoned cavity of a chickadee, a bluebird, or woodpecker, or a secondhand den of a flying squirrel. It then replaces any old nesting material with a soft globe-shaped nest like that of the other white-footed mice. At other times it may move into a bird nest in the fork of a shrub, after roofing it over and converting it into the usual spherical house.

Leaf nests which have been abandoned by squirrels also make good houses for remodeling. Some tree-dwelling white-footed mice build their own nests of leaves and pine needles. These are bulky, lined with fine, shredded bark, and vary from three to eight inches in diameter.

Many species of mice build their nests in cracks and crannies in cliffs. I have found canyon mice living in crevices at the rear of caves, where they were safe from all except their very smallest enemies. Sometimes they move into brush heaps or old woodrat nests. In fact, they have been known several times to live in the walls of a woodrat house while the owner still occupied the room inside. Almost any kind of white-footed mouse might be expected to take up residence in an attic, an unused chimney, or a basement of a house that was located conveniently in its range.

Practically every meat-eater, up to and including the cougar, preys on white-footed mice. Among those that do so quite regularly are the weasel, skunk, coyote, and red and gray fox. The larger shrews sometimes trap and kill mice in their nests or tunnels, where snakes also may overcome them. The hunting hawks and owls, especially the latter which are abroad at night, swoop on them from the sky. Even such a mild-mannered bird as the wood duck is known on at least one occasion to have gulped down a white-footed mouse. Fleas and lice frequently draw their share of blood from these mice.

Our laboratory pathologists take advantage of the white-footed mouse's susceptibility to a number of human diseases, including cancer, to do experimental work on captive animals. Among its unfortunate similarities to man is a tendency toward epilepsy. When excited, a mouse that has inherited this defect will whirl in a tight circle, sometimes for more than half a minute at a time. It may fall over on its side, unconscious, and even die. Because such mice do not have control of their movements during such fits, they probably are eliminated rather quickly in nature by their ever-alert enemies.

These trials and tribulations combine to attack and reduce the peaks of white-footed mouse populations that "explode" at intervals until the woods and thickets seem full of the little brown animals. Even in "average" times, due to predators, the life expectancy is probably very low. It certainly does not even approach the six to eight years that a number of white-footed mice have attained in sheltered captivity.

Although the white-footed mouse is not furnished with fur-lined pouches like those of the pocket mouse, the ample cheeks can hold at least a teaspoonful of seeds at a time. As a rule, the mouse does most of its harvesting at night. Unless driven by hunger, it stays inside during the day. As the sun goes down, the more restless venture outside their nests, and by an hour or so after sunset the majority of the population is on the move.

The little animals gallop from place to place. Thus their footprints, paired two by two, are easy to identify from the single-footed trot of the meadow mouse or shrew. They dislike to make even a few leaps away from shelter, because they know that speedier enemies are everywhere. Even a small boy can run down a fleeing white-footed mouse in the open. These mice do not make beaten trails, as do most rodents. However, they will readily use smoothed paths that have been established by other species.

On a dark night, the mice spend the first couple of hours in satisfying their hunger. Then many of them return home until early morning, when there is another, more prolonged, period of activity. As dawn begins to break, the animals retire, and by sunrise the last one is in bed for the day.

No one knows how far the mice travel during a nightly round. In a laboratory cage, a prairie deer mouse once turned a recording wheel twenty-five thousand times during one night. This was the equivalent of ten miles of running. Of course, in the wild they would not have the advantage of roller-bearing transportation!

Moonlight is dreaded by the mice in proportion to its intensity. Many of them stay in their nests until moonset, or, if they leave for food, they make short trips and take special pains to stay under cover. Only if deep snow provides shelter do the mice often leave their homes during the daylight hours. Then they tunnel their way over the ground, staying safely under the thick white blanket.

Because white-footed mice are practically omnivorous in their diet, it is impossible to go into the details of the food habits of such widely distributed animals. At the head of their general preferences are dried seeds and nuts, and berries. Depending upon the region of the country, this class of food would include the fruits of rose, nightshade, thornapple, cactus, wild strawberry, blueberry, raspberry, serviceberry, wild cherry, viburnum, bittersweet, and hackberry. The seeds of maple trees, pines, junipers, mesquite, acacia, screw bean and all kinds of grasses and sedges, smartweed, dandelion, beach rye, jewelweed, mullein, and a long list of other herbs are also eaten in great quantities.

This fondness for seeds sometimes gets the white-footed mice into trouble with man. They raid grain fields, particularly after the crops have been shocked. In these convenient shelters they build their nests in order to avoid traveling across the open ground which they fear so greatly. Sometimes they come into barns and storehouses, and have been known to feed on the buds and bark of orchard trees. Foresters complain that, when very abundant, these mice destroy entire crops of tree seed in the wild at times vital for reforestation. Or the animals may dig up and eat planted tree seed, just as they sometimes follow the farmer's drill along a field border. On the whole, white-footed mice are much less harmful in agricultural regions than are meadow mice and many of the ground squirrels.

White-footed mice are believed to eat a good deal of miscellaneous vegetable matter such as sprouting shoots, bark, and buds. Their carnivorous propensities are better known. During the summer they consume many insects, catching them by pouncing like a cat and then beating and biting the creatures to death. Among the species particularly enjoyed are beetles, grasshoppers, woolly bear and other caterpillars, carrion beetles, crickets, flies and sowbugs. The mice also eat snails, slugs, centipedes, millepeds and spiders. They will even dine on the carcasses of small birds and mammals that die or are killed by predators and left unconsumed. If one of the victims is a member of their own race, it does not lessen their appetite. Quite likely a hungry white-foot would not hesitate under some circumstances to attack and kill a crippled or young fellow mouse, but little information is available about this kind of crime.

Numerous times in northern Michigan I have noticed in the snow the dainty tracery of white-footed mice tracks around carcasses of deer that had been killed and never recovered by hunters. Such a find would ensure easy living for an entire winter.

These little animals do not count on rare windfalls. The northern species regularly store many tree nuts and seeds, from acorns and hickory nuts to seeds of pines, spruces, basswood and beech. Several quarts of red clover seed have been found cached in a stump in a clover field. Nearly a peck of beechnuts has been hidden within a cavity thirty feet above ground in a large beech tree. Other seeds found in storage are chokecherry, wild grape, catbrier, dogwood, viburnum, wild cherry, and raspberry. Cocoons of the luna moth are sometimes put away against a time of need.

No food is too tiny to be rejected by the industrious mouse. Whole spoonfuls of the minute seeds of blueberries, huckleberries and woodbine are heaped up and hoarded. It eats the pulp away from these and other fleshy seeds, and shucks the husks from grass and clover seeds until they are clean and smooth. Then, stuffing them into its cheeks, it carries them to one of several hiding places in the ground, in logs or stumps, or in standing trees.

The great variation in environments that are inhabited by white-footed mice has produced many types. More than fifteen species and over seventy-five geographic races or subspecies have been named north of Mexico. Only a few have been given popular names such as desert mouse, canyon mouse, golden mouse, old-field mouse, gopher mouse, beach mouse, and wood mouse. The widely used term "deer mouse" is a generic term that is loosely applied to many species, particularly in the eastern half of the continent.

Because it is obviously impossible to give a simple key that would provide ready identification of every group of all these mice, it seems best to omit any listing of them. The reader is referred to a good manual, such as H. E. Anthony's "Field Book of North American Mammals."

Mice of the genus *Baiomys* look much like *Peromyscus,* with which they were formerly classified. Some of their habits, however, are very different. *Baiomys* make runways for their routine travels in search of food. They are much less quarrelsome among themselves. Quite unlike white-footed mice, *Baiomys* fathers help their mates in taking care of their progeny.

General description. A small to medium-sized mouse with large, thinly haired ears, rather large eyes, and fairly well-haired tail that is almost or quite as long as head and body. Fur soft and fine. Color varies with the species from very dark brown to gray, tawny, or pale creamy buff above; white, creamy white, or occasionally buffy on under parts, legs and feet, and lower face; tail brownish above and white below. Total length, 5 to 10 inches; height at shoulder, about 1½ inches; weight, ½ to 1¾ ounces.

Distinguishing characteristics. Somewhat resembles a large house-mouse, but with hairy tail and pure white under parts (instead of dull gray), sharply distinct from the darker upper parts.

Range. All of North America except northern portions of Ungava, Keewatin and Mackenzie, and the northern half of Alaska; south to Panama and northern Colombia.

RICE RAT
ORYZOMYS PALUSTRIS

These rats were given their name because of the enormous amounts of rice that they consumed when it was grown extensively in the southeastern United States. They were hated and cursed by planters. Not only did they eat the growing rice at all stages; they even dug up the seed.

RICE RAT

Looking rather like an under-sized house-rat, the rice rat is much cleaner. It does not move into human slums, and is very particular about its appearance and immediate surroundings. A great deal of time is spent fussily combing the dark brown coat and yellowish vest. Using its nailed fingers, it arranges and smooths the coarse outer hair and goes through the dense fine inner coat. Then it washes its tail and paws with its tongue.

The real home of the family of rice rats is South America. A number of overflow species, however, occupy Central America, and two occur in the United States. The swamp rice rat spreads across the Gulf states and up the Atlantic coastal plain as far as southern New Jersey. The other species has an outpost across from Mexico in the Rio Grande delta. Its territory in the United States, the southern tip of Texas only, is very small.

In the tropics and subtropics, rice rats produce families throughout the year. Although this activity is practically continuous in southern Texas and the tip of Florida, it is interrupted by cold weather in the rest of the United States range. In the lower Gulf states, rice rats begin to mate during February, and the urge does not abate until the following October. In the northern portions of the range the season lasts only five or six months.

The animals are very promiscuous. A female that is ready to mate goes out looking for a male. The union is short-lived; in a few hours at most, she turns on him and drives him off. Twenty-five days later the offspring are born. No time is lost; within ten hours she mates again. It would be only by chance, however, if she met the same male again.

The mother rat produces four to five young at a birth, although the number may be as few as three or as many as seven. They are blind, much wrinkled and weigh only one-ninth ounce apiece. A fine down on their backs and legs is the first sign of a fur coat. On the sixth day their eyes open and their soft, reddish-brown hair coats with white stomachers are complete. Immediately they make exploratory trips from the nest. The mother stops nursing them when they are ten to twelve days of age, for her strength is required to develop the coming family. Within the next week she drives the youngsters from the nest if they still dare to loiter around.

Until full grown, they are grayer and duller than their parent. They do not have to be highly specialized to make a living. Their basic diet consists of the tender portions of many green plants, mostly grasses and sedges which occur in profusion. They also eat seeds of grasses and grains. Like the rice, the grain is eaten at all stages, including planted seed.

Although not as important economically as many other species of rodents, rice rats may become so numerous at times that they do considerable damage in restricted areas. One rat will normally eat about twenty-five per cent of its own weight in food every day. Each adult female may produce eight or nine litters of young in a year. Worse yet, these young are ready to mate when only fifty days old. While the broods produced by these immature females average some-what smaller than those of mature mothers, it is easily seen that the race has enormous potentialities for sudden expansion under favorable conditions.

Rice rats eat meat as well as vegetables, at least at times. They are said to prey on crustaceans and on shellfish, including mollusks. After diving, they can swim rapidly for some distance before coming up for air. Dense woolly under-wear keeps them fairly dry. Highland dwelling rice rats south of the United States border swim only in emergencies and do not have this type of pelage.

More northerly dwelling rice rats have somewhat longer fur in winter. This wears down, becoming more rusty as the lower portions of the hairs are exposed. Molting may occur at any time during the warmer months of the year. It does not proceed systematically. Old hairs fall out individually here and there and are replaced by new ones.

Our North American rice rat lives in marshes and wet meadows, or on dry upland slopes that are covered with tall grass, weeds or brush. When selecting a home, it seems to consider that dense cover, for food and protection, is requirement number one.

If the ground is dry, the rodent builds its house on the ground under a tangle of weeds or brush or a down log, or sometimes even in a shallow burrow in the sand. The nest is a sphere of the finer parts of sedges and grasses. Dry leaves are gathered and shredded and then loosely woven together.

In marshes and on tidal flats the rice rat naturally elevates its home enough to keep it above high-water level. Here it suspends the nest in tangled grasses or other vegetation. A network of runways and tunnels under the rank growth shows the industry of a large population that are rushing about making a living. The rice rats share these roads with cotton rats and smaller rodents such as harvest mice and white-footed mice.

Like their neighbors, the cotton rats, rice rats are quarrelsome. Badly wounded rats are killed and eaten. Sometimes unfortunate victims of traps are set upon and devoured by their neighbors. During battles the air is filled with shrill, angry squeaks of the combatants. At other times, softer sounds express contentment.

Because they are almost entirely nocturnal, they escape some of the common daytime enemies. However, their nests are not proof against prying rattlesnakes, water moccasins, skunks, minks, and weasels. At night the owls, especially barn and barred owls, harass the small mammals. Against these attack from the air, as well as those from the ground, rice rats can depend only on their speed to save their lives. They are very quick and can get into thick cover or take to the water instantly.

In South America the rice rats are found from sea-level marshes through the uplands to the high mountains. This wide range of vegetation, soil and climate has been responsible for producing many different species and geographic races. Over one hundred and fifty kinds have been named and described. Both in variety and number the rice rats take the place in South America of the white-footed mice of the northern continent.

General description. A ratlike mammal with thinly haired, scaly tail that is about as long as head and body combined; whiskers short; ears small and hairy. Fur coarse and long, grizzled grayish brown or buffy above, white or yellowish white below; tail brownish above, grayish white below. Total length, 9 to 12½ inches; height at shoulder, 1½ inches; weight, 2 ounces.

Distinguishing characteristics. Much like a brownish house rat, but smaller and with a shorter, more hairy tail; much larger than the native field or meadow mice, whose habitat it often shares; smaller, with coarser, grizzled fur, than the finely haired wood rat.

Range. Southeastern United States, from southern New Jersey to southern Florida, west through the Gulf States to eastern Texas, northward irregularly to southern Kentucky and Illinois and southeastern Kansas, south along the Gulf coast into Mexico and practically all of South America.

COTTON RAT

SIGMODON SP.

Sometimes this rat will steal as much as a peck of cotton from the bolls of a nearby field to line its nest. The "ginned" seeds provide an extra course for dinner. As it darts through the dense grass, it looks like an oversized meadow mouse. It has much the same form and coarse, shaggy, grizzled fur coat. Even its habits and nervous jerky movements are quite similar. However, if it pauses long enough for a good look, you can see that an adult of the smallest species is considerably larger than even a huge specimen of the meadow mouse family. A young cotton rat venturing into the world for the first time is about the size of an average meadow mouse, but can be distinguished by its longer tail.

The cotton rat thrives best in hot climates. Most of the species and a great majority of the individual members live south of our boundary, from Mexico to Peru. The northern limit of the range is in our southern states. Although our cotton rats are restricted to about fifteen races which are grouped in three species, they are found from coast to coast and at times in enormous numbers.

These rodents are excitable and pugnacious. The female is much the deadlier of the species. But she is an excellent mother and doesn't mind having several generations of her children in the nest at the same time. I have kept numerous cotton rats of all ages together under crowded conditions in cages, but it was seldom that a mother rat became so upset as to kill a bothersome child. On the other hand, a strange male or perhaps even the average father is likely to make a meal of several young if he can get to the nest while the mother is away.

Cotton rats have strong likes and dislikes and are always quarreling. When trapping Berlandier and least cotton rats for museum specimens, I have had to discard over half of all the animals captured, because of scarred hides or muti-

COTTON RAT

lated tails, all caused by fights among themselves. No doubt some of the battles result in fatalities.

Trapped cotton rats are often attacked and killed and then at least partially eaten by other members of the colony. In cages, adult cotton rats, especially of the opposite sex, are apt to fight furiously. Prospective mates must be introduced carefully and by degrees. Even then the unfortunate male may be killed by his ill-tempered spouse. Toward their human hosts, caged rats remain wild and hostile and, if handled, will bite viciously.

The cotton rat reproduces almost as fast as the house-rat. Although an occasional litter may contain only two or three young, I once counted eleven that were born to one mother in captivity. Many times my caged animals produced five, six, or seven youngsters at a birth. Covered with fine chestnut-brown hair, they can run about when only a few hours old. Although the eyes of most little cotton rats open between eighteen and thirty-six hours after birth, sometimes an animal is born sighted. A backward individual, however, may be nearly three days old before reaching this stage. There is much variation in size as well as rate of development of a large litter.

Weighing but one-eighth to one-third ounce at birth, the little rats grow like weeds. They gain more than double this birth weight every ten days for the first three months. By then they have reached practically adult stature. The female at that age may already be a mother! As soon as the little cotton rats can see where they are going, they dash about with even greater agility than their parents. They can survive and change over to a vegetable diet when only a week old, but their mother usually nurses them about twice as long if no accident befalls her. Youngsters that are properly nourished for at least their first two weeks make more rapid growth to maturity than do those that must eat solid foods earlier.

The mother rat not only has large litters but frequent ones. As often as not she mates within a few hours of the birth of her young. The next brood, like any other, requires only twenty-seven days for development before being born. If food is abundant, several successive litters may stay in the home nest, one generation mixed with the others. With no thought of the evils of inbreeding, sisters blithely mate with brothers and half brothers. Females often pair when seven weeks old, and sometimes a week earlier, before they are full grown. Young that are born in spring reach sexual maturity somewhat earlier than those that arrive during autumn. In captivity, cotton rats produce offspring throughout the year. Under natural conditions in the southern United States, breeding commences as early as February and continues as late as November. Very likely it is a continuous, year-long process if the food supply is ample and the temperature remains high enough.

Although grassy cover is essential to its existence, the cotton rat lives in many diversified types of country—damp meadows, dry fields, roadside ditches, waste borders of cultivated lands, and even salt marshes of tidal flats and brackish expanses of rank grass in the Everglades. I once lived with and studied a colony of cotton rats in a lush cattail swamp with a border of sedges. This was located on the state line between New Mexico and Arizona, where the animals were isolated from their nearest relatives by many miles of inhospitable desert. At the other extreme are those rats that live in the dense growth of scattered forests as high as seventeen hundred feet elevation in the Southern Appalachians.

If you part the screen of their thick cover, you will find a network of trails which are used by day as well as at night. Highways three inches wide are beaten down to the ground by many small feet. They are paved with bits of food plants that have been discarded or lost by generations of scurrying animals. Branching and crisscrossing from these avenues are secondary roads and trails in all degrees of wear. Any highway may lead to a down log or an old stump. Here loose mounds of black soil show that under the protecting cover are the tunneled homes. Perhaps the road will drop abruptly into the abandoned den of a spotted skunk, a ground squirrel, or other small mammal, or the long twisting tunnel an inch or two beneath the ground that a cotton rat has dug itself.

In one of these underground retreats, or half sunk in a bowllike depression on the surface, is the small nest. This is built of dry grass and fibers stripped from the stems of larger plants. Although the climate is warm, damp cold rains require a certain amount of bedding. When available, the pilfered cotton is often used.

The cotton rat's food consists largely of grass and sedge. All parts are eaten— stems, leaves, and seeds. Roots uncovered while digging, or that are growing into the tunnels, are cut off and devoured. The same parts of many other soft herbaceous plants are also taken. The rats get at the choice upper sections and fruiting parts by cutting off the plants near the base, then drawing them down through the surrounding "forest" of standing vegetation.

Many cultivated grains are relished. When the rats are abundant, they some- times cause heavy financial losses to farmers. They like all kinds of vegetables and at times do a great deal of damage to truck gardens. Squashes and sweet potatoes may be ruined, and the flesh and seeds of tomatoes eaten out until only the green-skinned shells remain. Sugar cane growers have at times lost as much as three-quarters of their crops to these animals.

Cotton rats are highly carnivorous. Ordinarily their craving for meat is satisfied by insects, including grasshoppers. During spring and summer, how- ever, they are always on the lookout for quail eggs and young chicks, as well as eggs and nestlings of other ground-dwelling birds. As far as is known, these rodents do not climb shrubs or trees to reach higher nesting species. However, investigation has shown that at times they exert a highly detrimental effect on quail populations, not only by destroying the eggs and young but by eating at least thirty kinds of important quail foods. Other flesh foods of cotton rats are crayfish and fiddler crabs, which they pounce on along the ditches and mudflats.

Apparently the cotton rat never goes hungry on its range in the United States, not even in winter. It does not have to lay up stores, either in under- ground pantries or on its back in the form of fat. Neither does it hibernate, for it lives in a land of year-round plenty.

The population of cotton rats often declines in late winter, probably because constant natural losses are not being replaced by an adequate number of young at that time. At intervals of four or five years, the rodents become very scarce. These periodic setbacks are probably due primarily to fungus diseases which, aided by wet weather, sweep through the population and remove most, if not all, of the adults. At such times cotton rats have had severe infestations of internal parasites and cases of coccidiosis. Dried-up mummies of the deceased can often be found in the nests.

Soon, however, the enormous reproductive capacity of the species begins to assert itself. At times when an attractive food is plentiful the numbers of cotton rats reach very high levels. In one instance, in Florida, systematic poisoning in a one-acre plot of sweet potatoes killed five hundred and thirteen of these rats. Quite likely others escaped, or crawled away before dying, and could not be found and counted.

In the South this rodent is the principal food of numerous predators. Among them are the rattlesnake, copperhead, pilot snake, alligator, and other hunting reptiles; barn, barred, and horned owls; marsh and numerous other hawks; house cats, dogs; mink, raccoon, gray fox and the lesser fur bearers. By feeding fur mammals and serving as a "buffer species" between predators and such game birds as quail, the cotton rat partially compensates for the damage it does to crops.

The various kinds of cotton rats are placed in two groups. Those of the *hispidus* group have harsh or "hispid" coats and their tails have only a scattering of hairs. Animals in the *fulviventer* group have soft fur and well-haired tails.

General description. A medium-sized, ratlike mammal with chunky body, narrow head, and short rounded ears almost hidden in fur. Tail slender, thinly haired, and equal to about one-third of total length of animal. Fur long, rather coarse, grizzled dark gray and black, brownish, or light buffy gray. Tail dusky, feet brown, under parts gray, grayish white, or white. Total length, 9 to 13 inches; height at shoulder, 1¾ to 2½ inches; weight, 3 to 6½ ounces.

Distinguishing characteristics. Much like a gigantic meadow mouse; easily distinguished from all other rodents by the rough, grizzled coat.

Range. Southern Virginia to Florida; west to southwestern California; south through Central America to Peru.

WOOD RAT
NEOTOMA SP.

The only North American animal that is interested in bringing home useless objects is the wood rat. It is the original "art and curio collector." Other animals concentrate almost entirely on filling their stomachs.

WOOD RAT

Nothing is too trifling to be added to the wood rat's collection. Bits of broken china, a vanity mirror, coins, kitchen cutlery, small stones, fragments of harness, old buckles, sticks and straws, bits of cow chips, droppings of horses and other animals.

In the western mountains, one sometimes hears of lifelong partnerships being ruptured by mysterious thefts. The loss of money or a watch may sow the seeds of suspicion, only to have the missing valuables turn up later in a nearby wood rat's cache. Some Colorado miners once missed several pounds of tallow candles. Later one of the men found them carefully piled on a ledge behind the timbering, about thirty-five feet down the mine shaft, where a wood rat had taken them. Even dynamite sticks have been lugged off and hidden. Prospectors who have carelessly left their false teeth beside their bunks at night have lisped and gone hungry on a soft diet for days afterward. I have had the shoelaces stolen out of my shoes. One Allegheny rat went so far as to go off with things it didn't want. Finding a woodsman asleep on a bed of small hemlock boughs, it could not resist its obsession for thievery. Stealthily it pulled every bough from beneath the man without waking him, and scattered them about the nearby woods.

Because of the habit of packing home so many objects, this rat is often called a pack rat. It frequently leaves something behind in place of the forks, watches or dentures that it steals. This may be only a stick or a straw or a bit of rock, but old-timers of the western ranges thought that these exchanges were evidence of honesty. Because of this peculiarity of trading one article for another, they gave it a third name, the trade rat. As a matter of fact, it is probably trading only for its own interests. If it comes across something that it likes better than what it is packing home at the moment, it drops the first object and goes off with the new find. Anything that is shiny or glittering is especially appealing.

The wood rat is one of the most persistent creatures alive. As an experiment, a naturalist once replaced in a wood rat's den a bit of stick that the rat had been seen to carry out and discard. Immediately the offended animal brought it out again. The naturalist put it back. The rat promptly removed it. This was repeated a dozen times in rapid succession. Perhaps this performance would have gone on indefinitely, but the human experimenter gave up after the twelfth trial.

Universal repugnance for the house-rat has helped to create disdain for many rodents. No American species has been more maligned by this comparison than the wood rat. No two animals could be more different and still look so much alike. The wood rat is a soft-furred mammal whose large ears are not naked like the house rat's but well covered with short fur. The tail is haired also, instead of being bare and scaly. In fact, the bushy-tailed wood rat is almost as well covered aft as a flying squirrel. The wood rat's white or pale buffy vest and stomacher sometimes get stained with fruit juices, but usually are kept spotless. It is a much more agreeable companion than the house-rat. When around man, it is curious rather than furtive, although its "taking ways" are sometimes exasperating. The great black eyes are as inquiring as those of the red squirrel. Of course, they are adapted for use at night. When a flashlight is turned in their direction in the dark, they reflect an orange-red light. The whisker feelers act like sensitive, outstretched fingers to save it from bumping into objects. They vibrate rapidly and the nose twitches in almost continuous sniffs.

When merely curious, the wood rat may sit crouched over on its haunches with both forepaws drawn up against the chest. More likely, it puts one front foot on the ground. The tail may be flat on the ground, relaxed, or acting as a prop, or may be arched over the back. If the wood rat is in a tree the tail may hang down from a limb, or extend stiffly to balance the body.

When alarmed, the wood rat will thump with one or both hind feet, or vibrate the outer third of its tail rapidly up and down on the ground. Against dry leaves these taps can be heard for some distance. Probably they act as a signal to other wood rats. Caged animals have been heard to thump to each other, varying the speed and volume of the sounds apparently to communicate messages. An angry wood rat, before or during combat, may click or grate its teeth, or utter short shrill squeals. The voice is used at times but not often. Low chirps have been heard at mating time as one animal pursued another. A brief shrill chatter, something like the call of the red squirred only much shorter, apparently is an alarm call. A rat that is seized by an enemy will give a despairing squeal or shriek of terror.

The wood rat's home is remarkable. It may be six feet high on the ground, twenty feet up in the trees, or in a long roofed-over ditch in the ground. The nest itself often follows the usual rodent pattern, a globular mass between six and ten inches in diameter. It is woven of fine soft grasses, shredded bark, cactus fiber, cotton rags, or other warm material. The two-inch entrance on one side leads to the three- to four-inch cavity. The bushy-tailed wood rat's nest is built much like that of a bird, open at the top.

Around either type is an extraordinary protecting structure. If the nest is located in the crevice of a cliff, the wood rat builds a thick grillwork of sticks across the opening, until a would-be snooper is faced with a forbidding tangle that is wedged and crisscrossed between the rocks. The amount of this material varies with the industry of the rat, age of the habitation and size of the opening to be blocked. Nests are sometimes placed at the rear of large caves instead of in narrow fissures. In caverns in New Mexico, rat homes have been seen containing twenty to fifty bushels of debris.

On the arid plains of the Southwest the wood rat digs a series of trenches and covers them with a mass of sticks and other material. It is not a capable miner and rarely goes below the surface unless to tunnel under the roots of a tree or spreading cactus plant that is in the way. Sometimes this type of dwelling is only a short, shallow pocket in the ground. When blind side passages go down a foot or two from this pocket or the trenches, they are probably the remains of an old, partly distintegrated burrow system of a kangaroo rat. It is very seldom that a wood-rat den in the ground will have as much as a bushel of excavated earth lying around outside. Once in a while a rat will pick a site at the base of a hollow tree, extend a tunnel into the cavity, and fill it with the nest, food stores and debris.

The wood rat's house that is built on top of the ground may be great or small. Sometimes it consists of only one or two dozen sticks from a few inches to two or three feet long, or a few cactus joints. An average house will cover four or five feet square and rise about one and one-half feet above the ground. The builder uses any material within reach: twigs, branches, bark of oak, pine, juniper, mesquite, catclaw, or paloverde, leaves of yucca or sotol, or joints of prickly pear or cholla. Other items of little or no value except for bulk are usually added. These include dried droppings of cows, horses and other animals, bones, small rocks, and many other "museum pieces."

The house may be circular in outline, or it may be irregular to conform to circumstances such as sheltering trees or shrubs. When built largely of sticks it may look much like a beaver's lodge. Two to six doorways, generally at ground level, open into the passageways that wind through the structure and lead to corridors in the ground.

Many other animals find shelter in the house besides the builder. Most of them are small—daddy longlegs, crickets, tarantulas, mites, millepeds, bugs, isopods, beetles, bumblebees, wasps, "woolly bear" caterpillars and numerous other moth and butterfly larvae and cocoons. Among the rat's backboned companions may be lizards, snakes, salamanders, tree frogs, white-footed and harvest mice, shrews, and rabbits. Moles often tunnel under the house to feed on the insects that thrive in the decaying wood and leaf mold. Quail and other low nesters have been known to build their nests on top of the jumble of sticks.

A wood-rat house that is well located in a good foraging spot will be occupied for many years. When the builder dies or is killed, another wood rat is likely to move in. Each successive tenant adds material to the structure. Generally a fine large house will be occupied by a big husky animal. There is some evidence that an old wood rat may be driven out of its mansion by an unscrupulous neighbor and forced to spend its declining days in a small "shack." The bigger houses are prized because they naturally offer better protection to the occupant.

When placed under thorny shrubs or in a patch of cactus, the house of a desert-dwelling wood rat offers double insurance. If built largely of cholla joints or portions of prickly pear plants, it is an almost impregnable fortress. The terrible recurved spines of cholla will repel a coyote, or even a man who is not equipped with tools. Although a house built of spineless sticks may not keep out a determined mammal, it is still a good shelter from hawks and owls. Also, despite its loose structure, it sheds rain quite efficiently. The wood rat's cellar rarely is soaked unless a cloudburst floods the whole ground surface.

The wood rat is always doing something. If not collecting curiosities to add to its museum, it is piling more sticks or other material on the house for better protection. Small sticks are picked up in the jaws; big ones are grasped by one end and dragged as the animal backs and tugs. It is amazing that the desert-dwelling wood rat can handle cactus such as prickly pear and cholla without discomfort. It seems to have no more regard for the thorny plants than for a piece of smooth paloverde.

It arranges bits of cholla and prickly pear pads on each side of its trails, especially for several yards outside the house. Woe to any bird or mammal so rash as to pounce on a fleeing rat as it rushes to such a protected home! The slightest contact against the cactus fence will saddle the enemy with a searing pincushion. When careful, the rat can climb about over a cholla without getting a single spine in its soft, bare, pink-soled feet. But when it rushes too hastily to escape an enemy, it may itself become painfully injured or even impaled and trapped on the recurved needles.

Wood-rat houses on the Pacific Coast are sometimes six feet high. These are roughly cone-shaped and built in chaparral, of branches, twigs and leaves, as well as herbs, moss, and earth. The underground section of the house is small and because of the moist climate the nest is placed in the central part of the upper structure. Passages are cleared by gnawing off projecting sticks. They lead from the outside to one, two or more rooms up to six by twelve inches in dimension. Only one of these contains a nest which may not occupy the entire room but is placed at one end. Usually one of the other rooms is located in the lower part of the house, on the first floor, so to speak, where it serves as an observation post. Here the owner pauses to listen for enemies before going outdoors. The whole house is generally chinked with small twigs, leaf mold, or earth, and it sheds all except the heaviest rains. Support and added protection is often found by building around a tree, in the low crotch of a multiple-stemmed tree or shrub, or in a tangle of brush and vines.

Occasionally an aerial-minded wood rat, especially one of the dusky-footed species, will place its home in a bush or tree. Few of these homes are more than six or eight feet above ground, but some have been seen twenty feet or even more up in the branches. One species of wood rat in Mexico sometimes builds in the tops of mangroves that stand in shallow water. Because any wood rat dislikes swimming, these animals travel through the thick mangrove crowns perhaps one hundred and fifty to two hundred feet to reach shore and their foraging grounds without getting wet.

Wood rats live alone except when mating or rearing offspring. They occupy one home throughout the year, and generally for a lifetime. However, paths that are well worn at all times of the year often lead from one house to the next. Neighbors may not enter each other's home outside of mating season, but apparently they do some visiting back and forth as they go about their feeding. In regions where the species is scarce, an animal may have to leave home and travel a half mile or more to find a mate. But it usually returns after accomplishing its purpose.

Under ordinary circumstances the wood rat seems to have a small home range, often restricted to less than fifty feet in any direction from its house. To this it is definitely attached. The white-throated wood rat sometimes has refused to leave even after its house had been torn down and scattered. A completely wrecked dwelling is seldom rebuilt, however. Rats have returned home through woodland after being live-trapped and released a quarter of a mile away. One such kidnapped rat, released a half mile away, did not return.

About one out of every four or five wood rats that I have trapped have had frayed ears or scarred tails, apparently the result of fighting among themselves. In captivity, when two are placed in the same cage, they generally battle to the death. It seems to make no difference whether the animals are of the same or opposite sex. Three out of four times there will be only one live rat left within twenty-four hours.

However, the successful mating is more lasting than most rodent unions. The male's presence in the cage is tolerated even during the female's pregnancy and after the young are born. As soon as the offspring are weaned, trouble is likely to start. Both parents are upset and on edge. In the wild it is probable that the juvenile wood rats are driven out of the adult's territory to find a vacant range if possible, or otherwise to perish.

The time of mating, birth, and length of development of young may vary in the different species of wood rats. Some of them apparently have only one litter a season, while others rear two or possibly three. Those in the latter group include the eastern Allegheny wood rat and the white-throated wood rat of Arizona.

The male rat takes the initiative in courtship. As early as the first of January he becomes restless and apt to make nocturnal excursions beyond his home range. A long narrow gland down the center of the abdomen becomes active in both sexes. The animals often rub this on the ground, leaving traces of a strong-smelling, greasy secretion. When the male locates a female, she is no dewy, yielding maiden. She has nothing but threats and blows for him. Even after she finally accepts the persistent suitor and allows him to take up temporary quarters in her house, the pair do a good deal of sparring.

Allegheny wood rat couples have been seen to rear on their haunches and tails, then push and strike like boxers. At times they pause briefly, whiskers trembling with excitement, while each rat's paws rest on the other's shoulders. Although they seldom use their teeth, their sharp claws make the fur fly and even draw blood. After mating, the fighting is less vicious for two or three weeks, or sometimes longer. Then the female's temper begins to rise again. The male cannot endure his waspish mate much longer, and soon departs.

The time required for development of the young may depend on the species and condition of the mother, and on her food supply. At any rate, the gestation period has been estimated by different naturalists at twenty-three to "at least" thirty-eight days. The number in the brood ranges from one to four. In most species three young is the maximum, and the average two. The earliest young arrive about the first of March and the latest soon after September first. The late summer births are probably second or possibly third broods, for most young wood rats are born in spring.

New-born rats are darkly pigmented or grayish on the upper surface and pink or red below. They are blind and deaf. Measuring about four inches along their curved length including the tail, they weigh one-third to a little more than one-half ounce. Almost at once they crawl and nose about until each one finds a nipple and gets its first meal. The middle incisors appear in a few days. These four milk teeth grow in such a manner that, when the jaws are closed, a diamond-shaped opening is left between them. When the baby wood rat takes a firm grip, the mother's nipple completely fills the space but is not cut or bruised.

When the mother wishes to go away from the nest for food she usually leaves the babies at home. A straight-line pull would only cause them to cling harder to the nipples, so she pinches each youngster on the neck or jaw with her teeth or twists them off. Squeaking loud protests, they let go, but resume their hold as soon as she returns. If the family is disturbed the mother can dash from the nest to safety without even pausing to grab the offspring. They just hold on and are dragged along beside or between her hind legs.

By the fifth day their coats of silky pale gray fur have developed enough to protect the tender skin from scratches and cuts as they slide and bounce over rocks or up tree trunks, should it be necessary for the mother to flee to save their collective lives. So tightly do the infants maintain their hold that seldom is one lost. After the danger has passed, the mother will return to search for any possible stray. Asleep or awake, the youngsters keep their hold on their mother most of the time until they are about three weeks old. By then their front teeth have gradually straightened in their jaws until the clamping V's have closed and the grip is no longer secure. Their weight is then about one ounce.

Young wood rats begin to eat solid food about the time their eyes open at fifteen to twenty-one days. If allowed, they will continue to nurse for about a week longer. Caged rats have nursed their young for more than two months. As a rule, the mother probably forces the young to leave home before they have reached this age. However, well-grown adolescents have been found in a nest with young half-brothers and sisters a week or two old. At three months of age the wood rat's weight averages about five ounces. They appear practically adult and their fur takes on the buffy tint of older rats. They mate late in the following winter when they are almost a year old.

No one knows the normal life expectancy of the wood rat, although many of the race have lived in captivity for at least three or four years. The comparatively low birth rate indicates that wild wood rats are more successful in escaping enemies than many of their closer relatives among the rodents. Due to their efforts at barricading their nests, they are fairly safe while there.

Outside, and occasionally even at home, wood rats fall victims to badgers, coyotes, foxes, skunks, bobcats and ringtails. This last sharp-faced prowler is a particularly feared enemy who prefers wood rats above all other food. Slinky and persistent, it worms through the stick-and-twig barricades in the cliff crevices and corners the wood rats. Rattlesnakes and fox, bull, and king snakes also slide into these retreats in search of food, and may invade the valley houses despite the most elaborate defenses of cholla spines. Owls, especially the barn and horned owls, are other dangerous enemies.

Many kinds of parasites live on wood rats at times, including various species of mites, fleas, ticks, and assassin bugs. Bots or larvae of the warble fly frequently develop to huge size after the mother fly has laid the eggs in the skin of the neck or chin. Although serious in appearance, an inch long and nearly one-half inch in diameter, these blood-sucking grubs never do much harm to the wood rats, as far as I have been able to determine. Some of the huskiest and best-conditioned rats I have ever trapped have carried one or two big warbles. Blind rats also have been seen in the Alleghany Mountains.

Wood rats are subject to diseases, including bubonic plague. Epizootics, the nature of which was unknown, have swept off rat populations, leaving as evidence the mummified bodies in the houses. Populations as high as twenty rats on an acre are sometimes counted on the mesquite-cactus plains of southern Arizona. Such concentrations are probably reduced in short order to an average of about five an acre. No evidence has ever been found of regular fluctuations or of population cycles.

On one occasion I trapped a wood rat that was abroad on a cloudy afternoon at least two hours before the sun was due to set. Other naturalists have seen rats out of doors in full daylight, sitting on the house soaking up sunshine after a rainy spell. The animals are often awake and alert indoors during the day, for a human caller at the houses is frequently met by thumping sounds requesting him to leave at once.

Usually the wood rat does not come out until dusk has fallen. It is most active during the first few hours of the night, and again before dawn. Apparently the southern wood rats at least are not fond of cold weather, for the little available information indicates that they move about less and less as winter comes on. Only great hunger will force them out into a rainy, cold night.

From the activity records of caged animals, we may infer that free rats thoroughly cover all of their small home ranges during a night. Captives have run recording wheels for an average of five and one-third to eleven and one-half miles a night. One rat set a record of more than thirty-three miles in one night. Of course no wood rat would be likely to run around any such distances on the ground.

Practically all of the wood rat's food consists of vegetable matter which varies widely with the region as well as season of the year. Even in a single locality the food of two individuals will be widely different, principally because on such restricted home ranges the plant species will differ enormously. The wood rat eats what is available within fifty or one hundred feet of home. If delicacies aren't there, it apparently does not go adventuring for them.

In the Southwest, the wood rat eats mostly the pulp of cactus joints, stems and fruits, and the leaves, twigs, bark, flowers and seeds of mesquite. Then come a long list of miscellaneous herbs, including grass, carpetweed, and mimosa, none of which is of material importance in the diet. Less than one per cent of the food is of animal origin which is made up mostly of ants, termites and beetles.

Gnawed remains of a snake and a ground squirrel were found in a nest in southern California, and part of the body of a myrtle warbler in another.

The dusky-footed wood rat of the Pacific Coast has a more diversified list of green foods. The more important are oaks, deer brush, Oregon myrtle, Douglas fir, crab apple fruit, Christmas berry (*Photina*), mountain mahogany, honeysuckle, rose, dewberry, cottonwood, madrone, manzanita, kidneywort, hazel, elder, willow, poison oak, buckthorn, currant, snowberry, vetch, and monkey flower.

The wood rat eats a good share of its food on the spot, as is proven by bits of cuttings, seed shucks and other debris under the plants and at eating stations, on stumps and rocks and on little stick platforms in trees. The animal also takes quantities home, both to consume at once in greater safety than in the open, and to have enough for lunches during the next day. This food is stored in the nest chamber and in crevices along the passages near that room.

Provisions are also put away in the house for winter use. These are mostly seeds, nuts, acorns and berries, although quantities of leaves of shrubs, and entire plants of small annuals, are often packed away. Sometimes up to half a bushel of milk vetch, pepper grass, and limoncillo are stored in one den. In a dry state they may serve a useful purpose during bad winter weather. As much as two gallons of dried pods of mesquite beans have been put away by one rat, and over a pint of hackberry fruits by another. A Texas rat gathered and stored nearly a bushel of pecans. Catclaw beans are another important source of cold-weather food. If several kinds of seeds are stored, they are usually segregated in separate caches. The stores of the wood rat in the Southwest are raided by foresters for the piñon pine seed.

The wood rat harvests twigs and leaves by cutting them off the branch slantingly with its teeth about three to six inches from the end. It allows each one to drop to the ground, then proceeds to the next twig. After a number have been cut it descends and starts carrying the harvest off to the storage rooms.

At intervals the dusky-footed wood rat clears out bits of food, seed hulls, and unused stores from the house. This waste is pushed out of the doorways and allowed to slide downhill, or is shoved off a little way on flat ground. Old houses may be recognized by their large garbage dumps as well as by decayed material around the base. Quantities of the dark colored, elliptical droppings about one-third inch long are mixed in the middens, for the wood rat deposits them almost anywhere along trails or in the house, with the sole exception of its nest. Their peculiar sweetish musky odor hangs about all wood-rat dwellings and over the trails and feeding places.

Some individuals drink considerable water. Others, especially the desert-dwellers, have little use for it. Instead, they eat succulent food. Probably they are able to convert additional water from the starch that they eat. The white-throated wood rat apparently depends largely on pulpy cactus flesh for liquid. During hot weather, it eats much more cactus and less of the substantial foods. Wood rats are never hearty eaters compared with many other rodents. A daily amount of dried food equivalent to less than five per cent of their body weight seems to be sufficient.

Accusations of ranchers that wood rats consume large amounts of stock-nourishing grasses apparently have been disproved by research. The amount of grasses eaten by these rodents is insignificant. They sometimes cause damage by eating the bark of fruit or nut trees, thus killing them, but such cases are unusual. The rats seem to resort to bark only when other food, especially succulent growth, fails. They must be given credit for being valuable soil-builders, for the nitrogenous material in the abundant feces enriches the earth. The growth of grasses and other herbs is often noticeably ranker around wood-rat houses than elsewhere.

An important source of food for carnivores, wood rats are also good eating by human standards. The flesh tastes like quail, and is much more delicate than squirrel. For centuries many Indian tribes, especially those of the Southwest, have depended on wood rats for appetizing, nourishing meat. These rodents are also eaten by most Mexicans of the laboring class, both in the Southwest and throughout northern Mexico, and are generally on sale in country markets "south of the border." By these people, wood-rat meat is considered better than rabbit or chicken, and especially suitable for sick persons.

Scientists have described a total of twenty-eight species and about fifty sub-species of wood rats. They live in several types of habitats. Generally they are found among rocks, chiefly because of the protection offered. The eastern wood rat usually lives among boulders or in rocky crevices in the wooded mountains, or on open slides of frost-shattered rock. To a lesser extent it frequents rock formations such as the Palisades along the Hudson River, limestone cliffs of southern Ohio and Indiana, and limestone caverns of Virginia, Tennessee and Kentucky. One of the most conspicuous evidences of wood-rat presence are white stains on the cliffs. These are limy materials contained in the urine. Sometimes the deposits are an eighth of an inch thick.

In western America, wood rats range from sea level far up on the mountains, at least in the Sierra Nevada and in the southern Rockies. I have found them within the lower edge of the pine zone on the desert ranges in Arizona where the elevation was about eight thousand five hundred feet. In Colorado, the bushy-tailed wood rat lives on the very upper slopes of Pike's Peak, over fourteen thousand feet high. The race is found as far north as southern Yukon but here they tend to avoid the added rigors of high altitude and stay much lower.

Most of the western woodrats are found in predominantly rocky areas such as canyon walls and sloping slides, but some are content with small outcrops and mere heaps of a few boulders. These jumbles of talus or fissured cliffs may be surrounded by trees or brush, or be entirely in the open. Sometimes, even in rocky country, one finds the untidy stick nest of the wood rat piled against a tree or log, or on the bare forest floor.

Where rock outcrops are rare or non-existent the wood rats may still thrive. West of the Sierra Nevada in California and Oregon they are numerous in the live oak forests where scrub growth and chaparral occur. There tree trunks and branches serve to back up the houses and give them a little added support. On the flat deserts of southern Arizona, wood rats seek shelter in the thorny shrubs and masses of cactus that send their roots deep into the sandy plains. Cholla and prickly pear are the favorite plants. Wherever these formidable cacti are scarce on the desert, wood rats too are apt to be low in numbers.

Wood rats are divided into three subgenera or divisions:

1. The round-tailed wood rats, a group of species with moderately hairy tails (subgenus *Neotomia*), range from the northern United States to Nicaragua, and from New Jersey and Florida to the Pacific coast. However, large areas of the eastern United States are not inhabited. These rats are distinguished accurately from those of the following group only by skull characters.

2. A group of species (subgenus *Homodontomys*) that live along the Pacific coast from northern Oregon to northern Baja California. By some scientists they are combined with the above.

3. The bushy-tailed wood rats (subgenus *Teonoma*), found in western America from the Great Plains (Black Hills) to the Pacific coast, between northern Arizona—New Mexico and southwestern Yukon.

General description. A rather large ratlike animal with large ears, large beady eyes, and fairly long tail that, according to the species, is sparsely covered with short hairs or well furred with long hair. Fur long, soft. Color above, cinnamon, brown, gray, yellowish gray, or creamy buff; feet and under parts white or creamy white; tail blackish or buffy, paler on under side. Total length, 13 to 17 inches; height at shoulder, about 3 inches; weight, 6 to 18 ounces. Females are about 20 per cent smaller.

Distinguishing characteristics. Much larger than the mice. The uniform coloring immediately distinguishes it from such ground squirrels as may be about the same size. The soft fur, well-haired ears and tail, and clean habits distinguish this native species from the alien house rat.

Range. North America, from southwestern Yukon to Nicaragua and Guatemala; from the Pacific coast east to eastern Montana, southwestern Missouri and extreme western Florida; also in the eastern mountains from western Connecticut to western Kentucky and Tennessee, and in a wide Atlantic coastal belt from southern South Carolina to central Florida.

17. Chisel-Teeth (Part 2)

LEMMING—*LEMMUS* AND *DICROSTONYX* SP.

Like many animals, especially the other rodents, lemmings are very scarce at times, and then multiply to enormous numbers. But instead of living and dying on the same small areas as most mice do, some lemmings pick up and move on when their tundras become over-crowded. These migrations, especially of the common lemmings (*Lemmus*), have been famed for many hundreds of years.

Giving birth to five or six young, or even up to eleven, the female lemmings make a big showing for their race. When conditions are favorable, each mother produces several litters in rapid succession between April and the end of September. The collared lemming (*Dicrostonyx*) is known to keep right on breeding during winter under the snow.

In peak years, parts of the tundra may swarm with lemmings. The sedges, grasses, and other plants melt away under the onslaught of millions of tiny jaws, champing to satisfy millions of little stomachs. Whether set off by threat of starvation, fouling of runways, or merely the pressure resulting from over-crowding, some lemmings can no longer resist the urge to wander. For centuries this instinct has coursed through the blood streams of the race, and once more it rises.

Sometimes the population of an entire lemming "city" will start out simultaneously. Moving almost entirely by night, the lemmings travel in a straight course or down the valleys, regardless of obstacles. They clamber through the sedge and past the spruces that are dwarfed and flattened to the ground by the howling Arctic blizzards. Rocks and ridges are hastily surmounted. Almost in a frenzy they dash through the bog pools. If the streams are not frozen over, they rush up and down the banks searching for calm-water crossings. Many of them are swept into the churning rapids and drowned. They hurry into lakes and swim across without hesitation.

In Scandinavia, the lemmings sometimes follow their course to a particularly dramatic climax. If the sea is reached before the travel urge is spent, the mass of little animals rush into it. They have no means of knowing that this tumbling expanse of water is not another lake. Those that survive the surf swim on. Even the wash from a passing vessel is enough to overwhelm them. Several miles at sea their strength begins to ebb fast. Determined, but enfeebled, they sink and drown in the cold green waters.

At times vast numbers of lemmings reach the ocean, or at least the coastal bays. In 1868 it took fifteen minutes for a steamer in Trondhjem Fiord to pass through a great band of swimming lemmings.

Migrations of American lemmings are smaller and occur less regularly than in Scandinavia. Usually disease or other natural forces strike our lemming hordes before they leave their homes. Collared lemmings have been known to die of a brain affliction resembling encephalitis. Many records show, however, that great numbers of American lemmings trek across country sometimes. These migrations occur in late winter or in spring.

During peak populations, thousands of lemmings fall victims to the clutching talons and beaks of birds of prey, and to the claws and teeth of carnivorous mammals. The owls, ravens, glaucous gulls, jaegers, skuas and hawks feast, as do the weasels, foxes, wolves, wolverines and lynxes. The huge brown and polar bears overturn stones, snapping up the hiding lemmings or watching their cubs devour them. Even the caribou vary their herbivorous diet when their pastures become overrun with lemmings. Crushing the little rodents between their flat-crowned molars, they swallow them whole. Their great splayed feet mash down countless others, unnoticed.

LEMMING

Although some lemming migrations move concertedly, most of them have little unity. The rodents start out at different times; choose different paths and directions, and pause here and there as luxuriant foliage tempts them individually.

None of them ever stops long enough to make a home again. They continue to push on until death overtakes them. Females may linger now and then to produce young and rear them briefly. During the emigration mania, the litters are much smaller and less frequent. The numbers of adults dwindle rapidly as diseases and enemies wreak havoc. Usually in but a few weeks in America, the exodus halts. There are no travelers left to travel. In Scandinavia, it is thought the emigrations may last as much as a year or two.

Back on the tundra where an exodus started, a few stay-at-homes remain. From this seed-stock the pendulum starts to swing back. Once more the lemming population is rebuilding. The peak is reached in about four years. Occasionally the cycle takes three years or as much as five.

The cause or causes of lemming emigrations are uncertain, but most naturalists believe that they have their origin in overcrowding. Once the migrants have started, the travel instinct which seems to be lacking a brake keeps them moving onward. One early "scientist," however, maintained that the Scandinavian lemmings were seeking their ancient home on the submerged island of Atlantis. The sudden appearance of lemming hordes led primitive people to evolve simpler theories. According to a legend that appeared in literature as early as 1532 and was common among both the North American Eskimos and the peasants of northern Europe, the animals came down from the heavens in snowstorms. Old Eskimos have gravely sworn that they have seen the creatures spiraling down among the swirling flakes. Eskimos in the western Canadian Arctic call the collared lemming "quilangmiutog" (the sky one). *Lemmus,* the common lemming, is "nunivaktog" (the land one).

Lemmings are found all the way around the globe in the northern portion of the continents. True lemmings (see p. 507) are arctic or boreal animals. In North America they are not found far south of the limit of trees (except along the Rocky Mountains to western Alberta). They live chiefly on the barrens or tundra, although the collared lemming extends its range into the tree zone. Even there it prefers to live in the clearings. It keeps to the higher, rocky or gravelly slopes, while the common lemming lives on the low, damp flats. In fact, the latter prefers the hollow spots there, perhaps because the vegetation is more luxuriant and drifted snow gives better protection in winter.

Although lemmings swim well, water is a hazard. During a wet spring, when the sun melts a heavy snow blanket and thaws the upper inches of the ground, the lemmings may be flooded out of their homes and drowned by the thousands.

These rodents look like big, chunky meadow mice. But their tails are stubby and their fur is so long and fluffy that it completely hides their ears. (They must not be confused with the lemming mice (see p. 519) that generally range much farther south.) The common lemming, also called the brown lemming, is grayish, black and brownish throughout the year. These colors are grizzled and vary according to the species, but the effect is bright and rich.

The collared lemming is the only mouse in the world that changes its coat to match the snow. It is pure white during the winter. The change is slow. As cold weather comes on, white hairs begin to grow in the brown summer fur, first on the top of the head and along the back. Then the belly becomes white, and at last the flanks. The new growth is not very orderly. During the process, the animal's coat is often spotted and streaked like a crazy-quilt. The summer coat is acquired in much the same order or disorder. In this apparel, the lemming is well concealed among the rocks and vegetation. Also called "banded" and "pied," the collared lemming in Alaska may wear a brilliant variegated brown, reddish brown and gray, or just a dull brownish gray during summer. One species of collared lemming, that from Unalaska Island, was able to conceal itself from scientists during a search that lasted more than a quarter of a century. Numerous skulls were found in owl pellets and fox droppings, but it required many years of trapping before anyone knew what the animal looked like in the flesh.

Albinos are rather common among lemmings in some regions. Of course they remain white the year round.

Another remarkable feature of the collared lemming is the thick horny shield that develops in autumn on the lower surface of the two middle claws of each front foot. They are shed (sloughed off) in April or May. No one knows the reason for these growths. It is possible that they serve to protect the claws against wear while their owner is tunneling and cutting through packed, crystalline snow. However, the brown lemming tunnels even more extensively, and its ordinary set of claws seems to suffice and last a lifetime. Collared lemmings are sometimes very numerous, but do not flourish in such myriads over extensive regions as the brown lemming. Neither do they make as great migrations.

The lemming's bed is in a ball-shaped nest four or five inches in diameter. It is usually made of grass but sometimes includes some saxifrage and potentilla. A lining of moss, grass, hair (fox, caribou or muskox, if available), and feathers from abandoned birds' nests keeps out the chill from the ground. When the bedroom is under the ground, it is reached by a tunnel, which in the case of the brown lemming is long, winding, and with many forks. The collared lemming usually lives underground and makes only a short, simple burrow, but often adds a side tunnel which ends in a little toilet. In spite of its greater burrowing activities, the brown lemming frequently nests on top of the ground. Both species make extensive foraging tunnels through the moss and other plants on the surface as well as below the ground to get at roots. The collared lemming seems to be more cautious than its relative, and is careful to avoid making a roadway right up to the door. The home of the brown species is easily found by following its trail.

Most lemming homes, whether subterranean or not, are in the open, among grass or other low plants. Collared lemmings that live among trees, however, often select a site under a log or bush or similar protection. Their summer homes are usually underground. The winter nests that are above ground are of course covered and protected by snow.

Adult lemmings are spunky little animals, full of growling fight when cornered. They have been known to stand up on their hind legs and furiously bite a whip handle, when presented, and even to go after and attack it. They will defy a man on occasion, "dancing" with rage or frenzy, and will bite if picked up. A collared lemming was once seen to come to bay when attacked by a team of dogs. Since the latter were hampered by their heavy sled, the tiny animal could have escaped by running. But it chose to fight, and was devoured.

Courage does the lemming little good when confronted by its larger enemies, but sometimes it can give a weasel something of a tussle and even a sharp nip or two before being killed. Young lemmings are quiet and very curious. If gently handled, they seldom bite. They are born in a hollow ball of grasses on the surface of the ground or in an underground den. Their juvenile coats are much duller and usually more gray than those of their parents. Two weeks after birth they venture outside and probably gather some green stuff to eat. They must grow up very fast to make way for the two or three other litters that may follow in as many months.

The runways of the lemmings intertwine and often those of a colony will extend over acres. Paths lead to the pastures, where the animals feed on a great variety of green plants. Much of the forage is cut down and carried to the owners' doorways. Here they eat, sitting up on their haunches, handling their food with dextrous paws. At other times grass may be cut into four-inch sections and, held by the ends, carried below ground for emergencies (particularly when enemies dally overhead.) Among the foods that have been identified are willow catkins, sedges, blades of cotton grass, edible parts of mosses, bearberry leaves (*Arctostaphylos*), saxifrage, and roots of grass, "liquorice root" (*Hedysarum*), and silene (pink family). In Northwest Territories, lemmings store the big taproot of *Hedysarum, Polygonum,* and miscellaneous small bulbous roots under stones and in their burrows for winter use. With the help of their dogs' sensitive noses, the Eskimos often find and dig up these caches to add to their own provisions. *Polygonum* roots are called "Kogmollik potatoes."

Although there is little good evidence, it seems likely that lemmings eat insects. Butterfly wings have been found outside their dens, as if the edible bodies had been devoured there. In winter, the rodents raid human food caches, especially for caribou fat of which they are very fond.

It is not surprising that these mouselike rodents must sometimes go on short rations. Their appetite is enormous. A pair of collared lemmings was once released in an enclosure of twenty-five square yards. The ground was covered with a lush growth of grass and a few buttercups and plantains. About two weeks later the female gave birth to five young. Just eight weeks after the experiment began, the two adults and their fast-growing brood had eaten every blade of green vegetation and had made considerable progress on the roots. The plot had become a desert and the lemmings would have starved shortly had they not been removed.

Although lemmings do not hibernate, they do not have a very hard winter. The snow blanket covers their range three, four or more feet deep, and protects them from the birds and beasts of prey that travel on or above its surface. Snug in their thick winter fur, the rodents keep their runways open and live much as they do in summer. Occasionally an animal will make a tunnel to the surface of the snow, possibly to reach the top of an especially desirable shrub. It cannot stand intense cold (forty degrees below zero), and scuttles back under the warm blanket in a hurry. According to Dr. George M. Sutton, winter tunnels of the brown lemming that he uncovered on Southampton Island hugged the ground, while those of the white-coated species often turned upward and cruised through the drifts, just under the surface.

If the wind sweeps the snow away from the lemming townsite, or a rain and chinook wind melt it suddenly, the animals may become confused. Losing their way, they wander about and are frozen to death or are seized and devoured by some ever-hungry enemy. Great numbers of lemmings were once seen out on the sea ice of Queen Maud Gulf, between Perry River and King William Island. Some were as much as thirty-five miles from land. They have also been seen at least twelve and four-tenths miles out on the Greenland ice cap. As there could be no possible food in such places it seems evident that the unfortunate creatures had become lost. Insufficient snowfall, which may be swept away by the wind, also exposes the animals to cold and to attacks by carnivores.

In spring, the lemmings may often be seen running about on top of the snow, probably seeking mates. At such times they are extremely nervous. The first hint of an enemy's presence will drive them to cover in a hurry. Although ungainly in appearance because of their long thick hair, they are quick as a flash.

It is very seldom in America that migrating lemming hordes invade cultivated lands. (Individuals, however, often make themselves at home during winter in trading posts and other buildings, feasting on human stores for a sumptuous change.) Occasionally they cause damage in northern Europe and even devour the crops of whole fields. Lemmings are important to man indirectly because they help to sustain such valuable fur animals as the Arctic foxes. Little parkas, trousers and other garments are sometimes made out of lemming pelts to clothe the dolls of Eskimo children.

Two genera or groups of true Arctic-dwelling lemmings are recognized:
1. The common or brown lemming (*Lemmus*) is bright or grizzled brownish, black or grayish throughout the year. The group is divided into six or more species in the New World.
2. The collared lemming (*Dicrostonyx*) in summer is gray or brilliant brownish and gray; in winter, white. About four species are known in America and on the islands of the Arctic Ocean. The two middle claws of the front feet become very long in winter, while the nails of the common lemming remain the same the year round.

General description. A medium-sized mouse. Resembles a large, short-tailed meadow mouse. Ears very small and hidden in long fur. Body chunky; forefeet large with large claws; soles of feet hairy; tail very short and covered thickly with fur. Pelage grizzled yellowish brown, cinnamon brown, or buffy blackish, with reddish tints on hindquarters, gradually becoming paler on sides and under parts. (The collared lemming turns white in winter.) Total length, 5 to 6½ inches; height at shoulders, 1¾ to 2¼ inches; weight, 2 to 4 ounces.

Distinguishing characteristics. Much like a thick-set meadow mouse, but with a tail less than 1 inch long. With the exception of a few species, the tails of most meadow mice are at least 1½ inches in length. Lemmings must not be confused with lemming mice (*Synaptomys* and *Phenacomys;* see p. 519). Lemming mice are somewhat smaller and generally range much farther south.

Range. Arctic North America, from Labrador (Straits of Belle Isle) to Bering Sea, the Alaska Peninsula and Unalaska, St. George and St. Lawrence Islands; Grinnell Land, Ellesmere Land and Baffin Land east to the east coast of Green land; south in the Rocky Mountains to western Alberta.

MEADOW MOUSE

MICROTUS SP.

The meadow mouse and the other American voles are the busiest mammals north of Mexico. Taking only a few hours out for sleep here and there, the meadow mice rush about day and night. Finding and eating their own weight in food every twenty-four hours keeps them fairly well occupied. The rest of their working time seems to be spent dashing up and down the trails through their grass forests.

Families are born and reared on the fly. It is possible for a mother to produce seventeen litters during a year. Weaned within two weeks, the young females mate when less than four weeks old. They are not yet full grown, and still have their juvenile coats. Three weeks later *their* babies are born and spend only a few days in the nest before leaping on life's merry-go-round. Because of this continuous mad rush, the meadow mouse's life is a short one. The average mouse is burned out and succumbs before the first birthday. A mouse that is eighteen months old is ancient and doddering.

Meadow mice, pine mice, red-backed mice, tree mice, and lemming mice (bog lemmings) are the American members of the vole family. In the United States voles are often called "field mice." Because they are similar in appearance and habits, they are included in this chapter under the general term "Meadow Mouse."

The best known, most abundant, and most widely distributed of the voles are the true meadow mice (*Microtus*). The popular name is only an approximation. They do not all live in meadows, by any means. Many inhabit the central plains and prairies, and dry weedy fields. Some live on sea beaches and in tidal marshes, while others like the woodland. More than one hundred species and subspecies or races of the meadow mouse have evolved, each one adapted to make the best of its particular niche anywhere between sea level and timber-line, throughout North America. Wherever they exist, they are highly important animals—to man, because of their voracious appetites; to carnivores, because of their food value.

The meadow mouse begins its hectic life as one of five to nine—rarely up to thirteen. Since they are born absolutely hairless, the mother must be an adept nest-builder. Their home is a little hollow globe of woven grasses, sedges or other plants that grew on the site. Frequently it is lined with finer, softer fibers than those in the outer wall. Some baby meadow mice have their nurseries luxuriously padded with milkweed floss, or cattail down, or perhaps a little moss.

Many mothers select a thick grass jungle with overhanging stems and blades, or the center of a grass clump, in which to weave their nurseries. Others locate them underground where most meadow mice live during the summer. The subterranean nests are smaller than the surface nests, but are built on the same plan. One or two doors in the side walls give access from the tunnels or runways.

New-born meadow mice weigh between one-twentieth and one-tenth of an ounce. They are blind, deaf and hairless. Through their delicate pink sides one can see the blood coursing through the vessels. Even the liver shows up, darkly. The skin is very loose and wrinkled. Apparently it needs a head start to take care of the rapid growth of the body.

Hair begins to appear within eight to twelve hours after birth. At first it is only a clouding of the skin on top of the head. By the time the mice are four days old they are well covered with very fine gray fuzz which is longest, about one-eighth of an inch, on their backs. Their incisor teeth work through the gums on the sixth or seventh day, followed in a day or two more by the opening of eyes and ears. For a number of days their vision is limited to less than ten inches but their hearing is better.

They nibble on tender shoots, and push rapidly under the bedding or litter

MEADOW MOUSE

if something disturbs the nest or alarms the mother. Should the trouble be serious, they will even dart out of the house and away down the maze of runways. It is a couple of weeks before they become skillful or have much endurance.

Baby meadow mice are surprisingly tough. They will survive exposure to cold that would kill almost any other young rodent of comparable age. A day-old mouse may be swept from its nest by an icy flood and, if rescued within a few minutes, seems to be none the worse for the wetting and chilling. New-born meadow mice have resumed breathing after being completely submerged in water for half an hour. This hardiness is a characteristic of adults as well, for they seem to be unaffected by exposure to cold and starvation that would be the death of white-footed and grasshopper mice.

At two weeks of age the youngsters are finding their own food. Each day they gain almost half of their original birth weight. If all goes well they maintain this growth until their eighth week. Then they are about two inches long including the tails and weigh between one and one and one-half ounces. Although not yet fully grown, the females have already produced their first litters. From now on they grow more slowly, and attain practically adult size by the time they are three months old.

Meadow mice change their gray juvenile coats for the grizzled pepper-and-salt attire of grown-ups during their eighth and ninth weeks of life. This molt progresses methodically, beginning along a line running down the center of the belly and working upward to the backbone. If they live long enough to get another coat, the change is irregular, starting in many spots and spreading until all fur has been renewed.

The mother has no time to admire the progress of her youngsters. The chances are that she left them temporarily within one to six hours after their birth to mate again. Having few dislikes, she mated briefly with the first male she met, and then returned home. For the next couple of weeks she tends strictly to her babies and is a model mother. If it becomes necessary to flee from her nest and one of the infants loses its grip on a teat, she risks her life to return and try to rescue it. But within a few days after her brood is weaned, the embryos within her begin to stir vigorously. Their development takes only twenty-one days. She must either put her two-to-three-weeks-old youngsters out to make their own way, or depart and make a new nest somewhere in the neighborhood. She can weave a new home that is warm and almost rain-proof in a couple of hours.

Of course the fast-maturing original brood quickly outgrow the nest because of their increasing bulk. Besides, they are soon restlessly looking for partners and their own homes. Although the females can mate successfully when only four weeks old, the males must wait for at least another week. This difference may be a natural device to shuffle the families and reduce inbreeding. Otherwise, if brother and sister meadow mice reached reproductive capacity at the same age, the members of each litter would probably mate with each other.

The kind of world into which the juvenile meadow mice first venture depends upon their race. Some live in alpine meadows, other in lush vegetation on the border of a lowland lake or river. Open forests, thickets, or dry plains have attracted still others. Civilization does not discourage the species and they often persist on vacant city lots. Most field mice desire dampness, and often they are found living in hummocks or "niggerheads" where water stands in the intervening pockets for much of the year. In such wet environments the less fortunate members of the mouse population live in the lower hummocks.

Even if these are flooded every year or two, the inconvenience is not really serious. Meadow mice are good swimmers and even those living in the higher grass crowns of swamps must take to the water to reach fresh supplies of food. The dense fur is not water-proof, but it is water-resistant. Those that do not have to swim frequently may live in rank grass which at times is fairly dripping with rain or dew. They may be out of doors for hours in such sopping jungle, yet their coats are wet only on the outside. Under such conditions many other species would look like drowned rats.

A meadow mouse in southeastern Michigan once swam a distance of eighty to ninety feet, ten of which were under the surface, in an attempt to avoid pursuers. It entered the marsh at a run and seemed to race across the top of the water for about three feet before sinking enough to begin to swim.

On one occasion I started to stretch out on the ground to get a drink from a small stream on the headwaters of Savage River in Mount McKinley National Park, Alaska. A young meadow mouse, hardly more than a few days out of the nest, slipped from the grass between my hands and plunged into the water. Bobbing and twisting in the rushing current, the little mouse paddled desperately. As it disappeared from sight around a bend it was still master of its course. Just below, however, the rivulet dropped underground, and I was unable to learn the youngster's fate.

Except when pursued by an enemy, the meadow mouse ordinarily stays within twenty or thirty feet of home. It is able to run like a streak for fifty to one hundred feet, but does so only in case of necessity. Of course there are always exceptions to the rule. Males are generally more venturesome than females and sometimes move several hundred feet to unsettled habitats. Mice of both sexes wander farther than customary while seeking mates, but in general a female will live out her life on no more than a quarter of an acre. The male will require almost twice as much room, especially in the drier types of grassland. When a mouse dies or is killed, the vacant area is usually filled in a short time by one of the new generation.

At times meadow mice are forced to hike unusual distances to find food. In dry prairie, mouse trails have been traced three hundred and fifty feet away from any den. But there is no such thing as a definite migration such as is made by the lemmings (not lemming mice). Populations may multiply and food supplies dwindle, but the adult meadow mice cling to their original homes and endure starvation rather than leave for the outer and unknown world.

For their busy comings and goings, the meadow mice stick closely to their trails. These paths begin as mere traces in the grass where a mouse has pushed its way through a few times. As travel grows heavier the mice use their sharp yellow teeth to nip off the grass stems flush with the ground. Decaying litter, leaves and twigs are cleared away from under foot. The passage of hundreds of tiny, hurrying feet compacts the soil. Soon a smooth highway, one to two inches wide, zigzags across the grassland. Spurs run off to feeding places, and branches connect with other trails. A populous field will become a network of paths and roads, most of which are concealed by the overhanging curtain of the grass forest and by the fallen layers of last season's herbage. The labyrinth exists only to enable the mice to run safely and easily to and from their home-nests or burrows to food plants. They are not interested in seeing the rest of their little world.

Here and there on the sides of the trails, or at the ends of short spurs, are the piles of droppings that mark the toilets.

Although they often live in close quarters and use the same runways and some of the same burrows, meadow mice are not truly gregarious. Each adult lives quite independently and has its own nest. There is little or no cooperative enterprise. They are peaceable and quiet as a rule when alone or with known neighbors, but will fight a stranger viciously. Clicking their teeth in rage, two meadow mice will rear and strike hard, downward blows with their front feet. Their claws can slash through fur and skin, but the sharp incisor teeth are the most dangerous weapons. One bite may cut through an opponent's nose or almost sever a paw.

Under sticks or overhanging grass clumps are numerous round holes about two inches across. These are the doorways to the underground tunnels. They form a shallow system of burrows equally as extensive and intricate as the trail system above. Flattened piles of earth are the mine-dumps of the mice—excavated soil pushed from the tunnels. These shafts (as well as trails above ground) are traveled the year round, but in the winter they are used mostly in emergencies.

Oddly enough the meadow mice are likely to leave their summer underground homes and build above ground during the winter. Melting snow in spring often reveals these bulky grass structures, as well as the trails and patches of stubble that mark the mice's pastures. By going below ground in summer the animals escape the heat.

The majority of young voles never reach maturity. This is especially true of the most prolific member of the group, the meadow mouse. Despite the enormous birth rate, immature mice which are "on their own" exceed the number of adults only when the mouse population is expanding rapidly (see page 516).

Natural enemies are legion. Many of them lie in ambush along the runways, or invade the underground tunnels—garter, fox, bull, milk and pilot snakes as well as blue racers, copperheads and rattlesnakes. More than one-third of the rattlesnake's diet in Pennsylvania has been found to be composed of meadow mice. Bullfrogs and snapping turtles sometimes devour mice that are swimming.

Many mammals also kill and eat great numbers of meadow mice. The more voracious range from the tiny shrew through the weasel, mink, skunk, marten, raccoon, badger, red and gray foxes, bobcat, lynx and coyote. Even the wolf, the black bear and grizzly dine on mice at times, especially when the little creatures reach their peaks of abundance. Generally, however, they are only tidbits for the vast appetites of these great mammals. To the list of wild enemies of the mice, must be added the domestic dog and cat.

Many birds prey on mice whenever they get an opportunity. Some of this predation is only occasional, but a number of birds depend on mice, at least seasonally, for a considerable share of food. The ring-billed, herring, and California gulls eat many small rodents during summer. When irrigation water is turned into fields and the mice flee from the burrows, the California gull on occasion has gobbled them until it could hold no more. Then, after vomiting its victims, the bird greedily resumed its feast.

Other winged hunters of meadow mice are the long-tailed jaeger of the far north, the bitterns, great blue heron, sandhill crane, crow, raven, magpie, and northern shrike. Hawks and owls are most destructive, foremost among them being the marsh, red-tailed, red-shouldered, rough-legged and sparrow hawks, and the long-eared, short-eared, barn, barred, and screech owls.

Of all these predators, the smaller weasels are the most fearsome! They are rapacious hunters. Not only do they pursue the mice aboveground, but they are small enough to chase their terrorized prey through their tunnels. One or more least weasels will often move into a mouse meadow and proceed to slaughter all of the inhabitants. The mice have no defense against this predator. Frequently it kills so many of them that it can eat only parts of the bodies. Replete, it curls up callously in one of its victims' nests and sleeps off its gluttony. As soon as it awakens, it begins killing and gorging again. Sometimes the fresh snow is marked and bloodied by the carcasses that it drags over the ground to the particular mouse den that it has selected for a local headquarters.

It seems likely that the hordes of hunters may account for the almost complete absence of white meadow mice. There seems no good reason why albinos should not occur, at least once in a while. However, in the series of over five thousand eight hundred skins of field mice in the collection at the University of California, not one is an albino or even piebald. Evidently white meadow mice die young because they are too conspicuous.

Parasites and disease are always stalking the mice. The latter in epizootic form is the outstanding factor that prevents these rodents from overflowing the earth. Ticks, mites, lice and fleas live in the thick fur, and botfly larvae sometimes burrow into the skin. Flatworms have been found in the intestinal tract, bladder and liver. A number of other lower animal parasites, such as spirocetes and flagellates, find lodging in the blood stream or other internal parts. Plagues occasionally sweep off enormous numbers of mice. The animals become sluggish, their breathing slow and heavy, and their coats rough. Pus collects in their eyes, and after sitting for a time with hunched backs the little animals die. Since the same bacillus causing this disease also is responsible for arthritis, erysipelas, and septicemia of hogs, meadow mice may be accused of transmitting the disease. Great losses of hogs have followed outbreaks in Europe and to a lesser extent in the United States. Swine erysipelas also may be communicated to man.

Nature has not stacked all the cards against the meadow mouse. She has given it a fairly good stock of intelligence. And it doesn't have to waste time craning its neck. Since its forehead recedes above the bulging, small eyes, it can see directly above without tilting its head. In fact, without moving, the mouse can see about two hundred and seventy degrees both vertically and horizontally. Everywhere except beneath itself, which isn't important, and directly behind it, which is. For this reason, it likes to keep its back up against a rock, grass clump or other barrier whenever it stands still or eats in the open. Sounds that are barely perceptible to the human ear will cause a meadow mouse to look around or cringe. It also has an excellent sense of smell.

Dashing about day and night, the meadow mouse divides its time into periods of two to four hours. At the beginning of each period it is extremely hungry and works hard and fast to fill its stomach. Then it quickly sleeps or rests off the effects. At the end of each period it is hungry again and must hurry off to resume its feeding.

Of course many things may happen to modify this schedule. If a hawk or fox settles down to watch a burrow entrance, the occupant cannot go foraging on its normal schedule even though very hungry. Hot weather, about eighty-five degrees Fahrenheit, causes the meadow mouse considerable discomfort. In order to keep cool, it stays much longer underground. It may dash out frequently, but much more briefly, for lunches. Very cold weather is apt to keep it in the winter nest above ground eighty-five per cent of the time. The snow blanket provides good insulation.

The meadow mouse eats more food during cold weather than when it is hot. Vegetable matter makes up ninety-nine per cent of its food. This consists chiefly of seeds, flowers, leaves, tender stems, and roots of grasses and sedges. Plants furnish not only food, but much of its water, shelter, protection from enemies, and nest material. Each day the meadow mouse eats its own weight in green food when available. This is necessary fuel for its usually busy body.

Felling grass in a dense, tall stand is a big job for the little lumberjack. Often it must make successive cuts, discarding three- or four-inch lengths, until the upper tender portion of the plant and the flower or seed-head are dragged down through the forest and within reach.

The list of incidental plant food, even of species that at times are eaten in quantity, is too long to be given here. The mere names would fill a book. Grains of all kinds, clovers, vetches, and alfalfa are cut down when nearly or quite ripe. All kinds of tubers and bulbs, such as tulips, turnips, artichokes and cattail are dug up. Hardwood trees and shrubs, occasionally conifers, and woody vines (as grape) are girdled by the mice in winter in order that they may eat the cambium layer. Slender saplings may be cut completely off, like beaver work but of course on a much smaller scale. Most of this work is done near ground level or at least under the snow-line, but occasionally the mice climb to the branches. Frequently very serious damage is done to orchards of apples, pears, and cherries.

Meadow mice are not as carnivorous as many of their relatives, but they eat meat. They will eat carrion flesh, and even murder their own kind in order to satisfy this craving. They like crayfish and snails. Whenever insects are in season the mice hunt them down and devour the edible parts. During colder weather, the rodents dig up many pupae. Red-backed mice and possibly other associated voles have been credited with eating about sixty per cent of all larch sawfly cocoons. For this reason, they are the most important control of this very destructive forest insect

Indians took advantage of the industry and foresight of the meadow mice in storing food. Every fall they probed for the underground pantries. Often they were rewarded by finding as much as five or six quarts of edible roots, bulbs and tubers in one storeroom. Many species were included, the most important being bulbs or roots of dandelion, morning glory, wild artichoke, sunflower, wild onions, blazing star (*Liatris*), juniper berries, and hog peanut. The latter was originally called "wild bean," and a race of meadow mice that stores the roots in large quantities has been given the name "bean mouse."

On the tundra of northern Alaska the Eskimos rob the caches of little grass bulbs, which the mice hide on top of the ground by covering them with grass and moss. Boiled, the tubers are considered a very special delicacy by these vegetable-hungry people.

Food, cover and other necessities permitting, meadow mice ordinarily number up to perhaps fifty per acre. Periodically, approximately every four years, the population doubles and redoubles. No one knows whether it is vitamins, or the weather, or a psychological uplift! Litter follows litter in rapid succession. More young mice are produced at a birth. The breeding season is lengthened, sometimes into or even throughout the winter. Predators feast, and the many natural forces take their toll. Yet the mouse hordes continue to increase. Four to six times the usual population is commonplace at these times. Sometimes the peaks are incredibly high: an estimated eight thousand to twelve thousand mice an acre in the Humboldt Valley, Nevada, in 1907; two thousand four hundred an acre in the Sutshan District, Russian Far East, in 1927.

During the Nevada "explosion," the mice ruined orchards, vegetable gardens, grain fields and alfalfa crops. After devouring all of the alfalfa above ground the mice burrowed and ate the roots for six to eight inches into the ground. Of twenty thousand acres of this forage crop, fifteen thousand acres had to be plowed up and replanted. Mouse burrows perforated the fields, often as many as one hundred and fifty to one hundred and seventy-five a square rod—no more than a step apart. Great numbers of predatory mammals and birds fed on the swarming mice.

It was disease, however, supplemented by poison, which defeated the army. Once the attack started, the myriads of mice melted away within three or four months. Six months after the tide turned it was difficult to find a mouse in the whole valley.

This mouse plague was estimated to have damaged crops to the extent of a quarter of a million dollars. The work of meadow mice and other voles is usually much less spectacular but nevertheless important to individual farmers. Fruit trees are girdled, shocked grain is raided and eaten, root crops, flower tubers and bulbs are devoured along with the tops of these and many other cultivated plants. A quite ordinary concentration of one hundred mice an acre will eat nearly three hundred pounds (one-seventh of a ton) of alfalfa, or ninety-six tons of hay from a section (six hundred and forty acres). At least twice as much more would be cut and wasted. The best means of controlling mouse outbreaks are by clean tillage to reduce mouse protection, by encouraging natural enemies, and by the proper use of poison.

With the exception of the meadow mouse and the pine mouse, voles seldom become troublesome. There are two reasons: they do not seem to have the reproductive powers of the meadow mouse, and do not live where crops exist to tempt them into trouble. Even the two offenders, the meadow mouse and pine mouse, have their virtues. They provide food for many animals that are valuable to us, and they are interesting creatures.

The family of voles inhabits only the northern part of the world, but it reaches all the way around. Beginning at the edge of the Arctic Ocean, voles are found as far south in America as Guatemala, and in Asia as far south as Burma and Yunnan Province, China. Preferring the colder climates, voles do not do well in the tropics. The southerly members of the family live in the higher mountains and avoid the hot humid lowlands. Provided plants can grow to furnish food, no climate is too severe. Voles are found from sea level in the Arctic and as high as twenty thousand feet in the Himalaya Mountains.

Many of them live in open places, but some prefer forests or marshes and rarely go into fields. They all burrow in the ground, at least at times, and most of them make many yards of tunnels. Their habits differ only in details, depending on the species and the region and habitat in which each species or subspecies lives. In broad outline, their ways of life show marked similarities.

A few of the more interesting habits of voles other than the meadow mouse follow:

The tree mouse and the lemming mouse may breed in almost any month of the year, but none of the voles have as many litters in a season as the meadow mouse. The number of offspring in each litter is about the same, however, except with the pine mouse which usually has only two to four. The gestation periods as well as the histories of development of the young are similar.

The lemming mouse and pine mouse make nests that are quite similar to those of the meadow mouse. They may be either above ground, in dense grass, or below as part of the burrow system. The home of the red-backed mouse is usually more bulky, and more often has the added protection of being located under a stump, a flat stone, a log, or in a stone wall.

The tree mouse may live in a tree or in the ground. The male is more likely to nest in the ground, while the female usually prefers to live aloft. She picks out a fir or other conifer and settles at any height, often thirty feet or more above ground. She does not weave her nest as other voles do. First she finds a small cluster of branches or perhaps an old squirrel nest for the foundation. Then she gathers a mass of fir twigs and the central spines of fir needles from which the fleshy lateral parts have been nibbled for food. Twisting, patting and shaping this loose material, she forms a room in the center of the pile.

Pine mice live in forests and open fields alike. They spend most of their time underground. Being weak miners they need loose soil that is fairly free from stones in order to construct their shallow tunnels. Lemming mice are highly adaptable and are found in cool coniferous forests, in sphagnum bogs, on dry hillsides, and in weedy fields. Their tunnels and surface runways are much like those of the meadow mice. Red-backed mice are forest dwellers. In the southern part of their range, within the United States, they use spruce and cedar swamps, and sphagnum bogs where the tamarack grows.

The voles are a populous group of small rodents, of which the meadow mice (*Microtus*) are the most numerous and widely distributed. Voles are generally similar in size and appearance. Because they are stocky, short-eared, and blunt-headed, with long loose fur that hangs low, their legs look shorter than they are. Some of the species can be distinguished from each other only after close examination and the taking of measurements. Most of them make long or intricate burrows in the earth. In addition to the meadow mouse (see page 519), the members of this group are as follows:

1. A meadow mouse (*Lagurus*) which is very similar to *Microtus* but has a shorter tail and paler, loose fur. It is a western animal ranging from western North Dakota, Alberta and Washington south to southern California and Utah.

2. The pine mouse (*Pitymys*) has especially small ears which are hidden in the fine glossy brownish fur. Because of the close, smooth pelage it looks like a small mole. The tail is only slightly longer than the hind foot. The pine mouse is found from central New Hampshire to Florida, westward to eastern Iowa and Louisiana.

3. The red-backed mouse (*Clethrionomys*) is below medium size. The tail is distinctly longer than the hind foot. The pelage is rather long, and distinctively marked by a band of dark chestnut sprinkled with black which extends the length of the mouse's upper surface from back of head to base of tail. This is a mouse of the northern forests, from New Jersey, Nova Scotia, Labrador and Ungava westward to northern California and southern Alaska; south in the Alleghenies to North Carolina, and in the Rockies to southwestern New Mexico.

4. The tree mouse, also called "lemming mouse," (*Phenacomys*) looks like a small meadow mouse, and can be distinguished from *Microtus* only by tooth and skull characters. It ranges from the Gulf of St. Lawrence and Labrador west to southeastern Yukon; south in the Rockies to northern New Mexico and in the Sierra Nevada to east-central California.

5. The lemming mouse or bog lemming (*Synaptomys*) must not be confused with the lemming (see p. 501). It is very much like a small, short-tailed meadow mouse from which it can be distinguished only by comparing the teeth and skulls. It can be told from the tree "lemming" (*Phenacomys*) by smaller size (total length, 4½ to 5½ inches), longer tail (slightly longer than the hind foot), and grooved upper incisors. The true lemmings have ungrooved teeth. The range of the lemming mouse includes the northeastern quarter of the United States and eastern Canada, thence west through central Saskatchewan to a large area extending from northern Washington to western Alaska.

General description. A medium-sized, stocky mouse with small eyes and ears, and short tail covered with short hair. Fur loose, rather long, blackish, grayish brown or yellowish brown heavily sprinkled with black hairs resulting in a grizzled appearance; darkest on the back and shading into gray, ashy, or buffy on the under parts. Feet not grizzled; tail dusky above, slightly paler below. Total length, 4½ to 8½ inches; height at shoulder, 1½ to 1¾ inches; weight, ¾ to 2½ ounces.

Distinguishing characteristics. The generally grizzled pelage and chunky build. In the northern part of the range, meadow mice usually can be distinguished from lemmings by the tail measurement (more than 1½ inches as against less than 1 inch in the case of the lemmings).

Range. Practically all of North America from the Arctic Ocean south to Guatemala.

WATER RAT
NEOFIBER ALLENI

The water rat lives only on the Florida peninsula and the Okefinokee Swamp which extends into southern Georgia. It looks like a miniature muskrat with a round tail. In fact it is often called "round-tailed muskrat." Although both names describe it, it is not a thoroughly aquatic animal.

WATER RAT

Unlike the muskrat, which is twice as big, it spends most of its time on land, or on that oozy, wavering table of muck and vegetation that lies above the watery world of the everglades and bogs. It likes salt marshes, tide-water savannas, grassy flats around inland lakes, and sphagnum bogs of the Okefinokee. In the Florida Everglades, however, it often lives on dry ground, even in cultivated fields and gardens. It can swim well and frequently does, but the hind feet have only the beginnings of webs between the long, slender toes. Excursions by water are not this rat's forte, and life under the water even less so. For such an animal, expanses of open water are hazardous. It never swims far from shore, and prefers to stay in the protecting plant cover of land.

Here a maze of twisting three-inch runways thread their way between the stems of sedge and saw grass. Water stands in the trails in places, even during the dry season. Enough grass stems are cleared by the rats so that, if necessary, they can hustle down their paths without tripping. Every few feet the trails are routed under the cover of beds of sphagnum or protecting thickets of fallen grass stems. Occasionally they disappear in tunnels which lead underground. Some of these passageways are feeding shafts, while others may lead to nests.

It is only an exceptionally fortunate watcher who sees this rat, which is one of the most secretive of all rodents. Generally it takes the precaution of approaching its house built on top of the ground via secret underground corridors rather than on surface runways which are conspicuous to any passer-by.

Trundling slowly down the surface trails, the rat pays no heed to the puddles. It depends on the dense inner fur to keep the dampness away from its skin. Splashing through the water, it reaches the three-inch round plunge hole which is the entrance to the outer hallway. Down it goes without hesitation into the mucky water, and out of sight. As it paddles with its feet, the tail makes circular sculling motions.

It swims three to six feet or farther through the water-filled tunnel in the black muck. This hallway turns upward and ends in the single room of a grass hut out on the surface of the ground. A little light filters through the thick but loosely constructed walls. It is a mound-shaped structure, made of grass or other plants gathered on the site. Sometimes slender roots make up a considerable proportion of the building material. Outside, the house is between one and two feet in diameter, up to a possible three feet. When new, it is about the same height. But a little time weighs heavily on it and soon it sags. The walls are too thick to allow much room inside. There is scarcely a half-inch to spare ahead of the owner's nose and behind its rump when it stretches out. The nest is usually damp. The floor, a mass of muck and vegetation, is hardly an inch above the water level, and is surrounded by water. It is located on a "drier" spot among the stems of a mangrove, a buttonbush, or other bog plants, or sometimes in a hollow stump of an old mangrove or cypress.

The water rat always takes the precaution of making two exits. Three or four, up to six or seven, inches apart, they are located on opposite sides of the room. Each one opens into separate shallow tunnels which lead away in different directions. If an enemy starts in through one subway, the water rat is off through the other. Frequently it plugs the entrances from the inside with a round mass of muck. Material dug out of the tunnels lies in a heap outside each entrance.

The house is such a hastily built affair that it stays habitable for only a few months. Construction doesn't take long, so the rat does not hesitate to abandon a home when it begins to decay, and to put up a new one. Often a bog will be dotted with houses, many of which are abandoned. Possibly the old homes may occasionally be used for temporary or emergency shelters. Sometimes, ants move into these structures in such numbers that the original owner finds no comfort or peace if it returns.

Feeding platforms are built by the rats throughout the marsh or bog. At first these are small heaps of moss and muck which barely rise above the water level. They are just large enough for an animal to rest comfortably. Two paths, perhaps only two or three inches long, one on each side of the platform, run into tunnels that descend into the bog. During the course of months, discarded bits of food and other debris from many meals increase the size of the platforms considerably. The plunge paths are no longer on the edge of the platform, but become merely openings in the flooring material. The floors are packed and smooth from heavy use.

Undoubtedly these escape routes save many a rat's life. When a barred or horned owl swoops overhead, the rodent has only to dive down either tunnel to safety. Since usually it stays at home under cover during daylight, and also eats many of its meals at home, it seldom has to worry about hawks. The otter and perhaps other mammal hunters, however, could easily crash into its flimsy home. Hungry reptiles—alligators, turtles, and such snakes as moccasins, rattlers and water snakes—may enter through the tunnels. If these are closed they can worm their way through the walls of the house.

Paddling about or swimming, the water rat gathers stems of numerous plants that grow close by the feeding platform and climbs up to eat them. They include stems and seed pods of arrowhead, iris or flag, stems of purple bonnet (*Brasenia*), and seeds of arrow-arums (*Peltandra*). Small water-filled holes and little heaps of muck here and there in the marshy thickets show where the water rat digs for rhizomes, bulbs, and other underground parts of plants. It also kills and eats many crayfish.

The houses of water rats are often close together, but this does not mean that the animals enjoy each other's company. Apparently they are not particularly aggressive toward each other, at least toward familiar neighbors. The territory seems to be shared on a communal basis. Several adult male rats have been found using one feeding platform, one after the other. However, water rats probably are quite indifferent toward each other except for mating purposes.

Young rats may be found during any month of the year, at least in southern Florida. At the northern extremity of the range, Okefinokee Swamp, births occur throughout the winter and spring months. Little is known about the beginning of the rat's existence, except that a few days after birth it is still blind and very sparsely furred. Apparently special beds of soft dry grasses are provided for the new litters.

Water rats are almost completely without the strong musky smell of their relatives, the muskrats. Unlike the muskrat, the water rat's outer fur is thin and short so the pelt has practically no value.

General description. Much like a small, round-tailed muskrat with very short ears and short, soft underfur which is overlaid with shining guard hairs. Tail is scaly and almost naked; hind feet have small webs. Color dark brown above and white or yellowish below. Total length, 12 to 13 inches; height at shoulder, 2 to 2½ inches; weight, about ¾ pound.

Distinguishing characteristics. Easily separated from the muskrat by small size (little more than half as long), round tail (instead of being flattened in the vertical plane), and small webs on hind feet.

Range. Florida and extreme southeastern Georgia.

MUSKRAT
ONDATRA SP.

It was after sunset, but not yet dusk. The golden and brown leaves of the cottonwoods and willows flickered dully as they drifted down through the quiet air, then lost their glow when they settled noiselessly on the surface of the little river. Autumn was bringing a hint of cold, a cold which would become penetrating before dawn. A gurgling murmur came from the shallows below the river's bend. Elsewhere the water moved hesitantly across the deep pools, with only a swirl here and there to mark its progress. On the steeply shelving banks and surrounding fringe of woodland the scattered grasses were turning brown with the early frost.

Near the margin of the stream a small, thick-set animal swam slowly. His brownish black back scarcely rose above the water. The pale brown face turned this way and that. Little eyes, like twin black beads, searched the bank and the huge clods that had tumbled into the water at its foot. The muskrat was searching for a home territory. It was vitally important that the homeless wanderer locate one soon, for winter would bring cruel hardships.

Although this muskrat was only eight months old, he was already well developed. Probably he weighed one and one-half pounds. The head and chunky body were a foot long. His ten-inch black, scaly tail, flattened vertically, floated at ease or waved listlessly with the stronger movements of the swimmer. Only the upper edge of the tail showed above water. Whenever he changed course, it curved and stiffened, acting as a rudder.

MUSKRAT

Little swirls showed that the alternately moving hind feet were steering as well as propelling. In the dark water it was impossible to see the closing of each foot as it moved forward in the vertical plane. Then the long toes were spread to stretch out the webs between their bases as the foot swung backward on the ankle as a pivot. A fringe of stiff backward-pointing hairs about one-tenth of an inch long on the side of the toes and foot increased the propelling area.

The muskrat did not use his small, long-clawed front feet while swimming on the surface. They were held, palms in, against the chin. Once when he dove briefly, however, he paddled a stroke or two with them to help bring the fore parts back up to the surface. There he relied solely on his hind feet which now stroked in a horizontal plane through an arc of about ninety degrees. As each spread foot shoved backward and inward, its motion was opposed by a vigorous outward swing of the tail. The effect was that of two sculls moving toward each other, which kept the animal on a straight course instead of swinging abruptly from side to side. Even when striking out rather vigorously he did not swim faster than two or three miles an hour.

Several times he left the water briefly to amble slowly along the bank. Cold water dripped from his soaked outer fur, which in its wet condition looked jet black. The very dense, short inner fur, however, kept him dry and warm. The scaly tail dragged on the ground and bits of leaf mold and soil adhered to its wet blackness. He walked without noise and when he entered the water, swam off just as silently. Once he paused to scoop up and eat a mouthful of tiny seeds that the wind had drifted together on the water.

The muskrat had been wandering and searching in this manner for a week or two. Because he was in strange country, he usually did not venture out before dusk, and he tried to find a safe hideaway under a brush pile or the roots of a stump before each sunrise. At every likely appearing territory he found one or more muskrats already in possession. Usually older than he, these householders were doubly fortified by a righteous sense of early possession. Muttering "n-n-n-n" and snarling through exposed yellow teeth, they savagely drove off the wanderer. Meekly he continued his quest. After a number of nights of this buffeting he was becoming anxious and harried. Desperately he began searching in full daylight each afternoon, instead of waiting for darkness.

At last he found a vacant area that might be used—a creek bank in an open pasture. But foraging cows had stripped off all shrubby growth. Broken tunnels along the banks and track-pocked ditches in the shallow water gave evidence of muskrat homes that had been destroyed by the hoofs of the cattle. Wooden stakes, and, sometimes, bits of steel chains and wire were evidence of man's successful trapping forays. Discouraged, but not yet despairing, the muskrat pushed on.

Fully twenty air-line miles from his birthplace, he had swum and walked much farther on his erratic course. Dogs, coyotes—once, even a fox—sniffed and yelped around his day-time refuges. Occasionally a weasel, an otter, or the much-dreaded mink loped and twisted through the piles of driftwood where the muskrat hid, trembling. By night he watched along the creek bank for that masked hunter, the raccoon. Cooper's and marsh hawks and eagles swooped by day on whistling wings, but those of the night-prowling great horned owl made no sound. Snapping turtles were a constant menace as they had been since the muskrat, a youngster, had gone for his first swim. Cold weather, of course, would end the activity of those particular raiders for that season. Not until spring would they again be able to pull down and drown the biggest muskrat. The large pickerel and pike which could have swallowed him when younger, were no longer much of a threat.

At last, on a quiet stretch of the little river, a combination of circumstances rewarded the long quest. A stream bank pitched steeply to deep water that would not freeze to the bottom in the coldest winter. The clay soil would hold a tunnel secure from caving. Above, a heavy sod and a thicket of brush was an added safety factor. A narrow fringe of woodland beyond gave assurance that temporary refuges would be near at hand whenever spring freshets should flood a muskrat from his bank-den. Other coverts existed along the water's edge—overhanging banks, fallen trees, under-cut stumps, and masses of lodged debris. Here the muskrat would be safe from enemies until he could complete his future home. Later they might save his life in emergencies.

Beyond the woodland lay a cornfield where delicious grain could be found even through the winter if the farmer were a little careless. Across the stream, on the long, low flat, natural food grew in abundance—willow, cottonwood, ash, box elder, nightshade and other woody species, and such herbs as goldenrod, shepherd's purse, Jerusalem artichoke, aster, clover, grasses and sedges. In an old, long-cut-off oxbow on the flat were pools of shallow water. They supported many succulent water plants including little groves of those plants so especially appetizing to muskrats—cattails.

Careful investigation of the vicinity made it certain that no other muskrats had established themselves. There were tracks in the bank, little, handlike, five-fingered tracks, those of the hind feet being much the larger, about two and three-quarters inches long. These were deeply imprinted over and a little to the outside of the marks made by the forefeet. An average grown muskrat made a forefoot track about one and one-eighth inches wide and one and one quarter inches long, with a stride of three to four inches when the animal was walking unhurriedly. On muddy spots between the rows of prints was the long, slightly curving mark about one-quarter inch wide which was left by the lightly dragging tail. However, all signs indicated that most of these muskrats had been wanderers passing through, probably youngsters like the would-be settler. The others were made by muskrats that ranged occasionally into the area from their regular beats up- and downstream.

The muskrat immediately went to work on his new home. Selecting a bank where the gentle current swept against it, he dove to a convenient depth, about a foot, and began to scratch a hole with his hands. Fortunately the stream was low but still deep enough at that point to make a long entrance corridor unnecessary. In building on a gently sloping bank it would have been essential to start digging well out in the stream, so that the tunnel mouth would be concealed under water as much as possible through low stages.

The sharp claws of the muskrat made good progress in tearing away the first few inches of soft mud, which went swirling away in the current. From there on, digging went much more slowly. Sometimes he could not even cut as much as an inch of clay before he was forced to the surface for air. Slowly the tunnel, five or six inches in diameter, extended upward into the earth at an angle of thirty to forty-five degrees. Two or three nights of work placed the upper end above the water line, which permitted the rodent miner to work more continuously in the air pocket. Most of the earth debris, kicked back down the tunnel, was washed out into the river. That which settled on the floor of the sloping corridor was easily scratched and swept out.

The tunnel was continued until root-tips of grass and shrubs warned the muskrat that he was close to the roof. Although intuition or signs on the banks told him that flood waters would sometimes rise above the present level, he could dig no higher. So here he scooped out a round sleeping room about eight inches across and six inches high. Finally he swam across the stream and gathered several mouthfuls of dead, dry cattail leaves and the lower parts of stalks. Carrying them into the den, he shredded them to bits and made a soft, clean nest. The fact that the material was well soaked by being ferried across the river and through the submerged lower tunnel did not bother the muskrat. His wet fur would further dampen the bed every time he returned home from the shortest trip. When the mattress became moldy, he would simply throw it down the hallway into the stream and then in a few minutes gather material for a new one.

This home was only a simple one. As he grew older, he might extend the tunnel to reach a spot of greater safety, real or fancied. He would be quite likely to dig another exit tunnel, to either side or above or below the original one. This might save his life if a mink or otter swam in the front door.

A female particularly would be almost sure to make an elaborate underground dwelling for herself and her young. She would have two or three chambers, a number of inter-connecting passages, and as many as five or six doorways below the water level. The ceilings of the rooms might be within a few inches of the ground surface, or as deep as two and one-half feet below. In time a number of crisscrossing tunnels might be built in a bank. Occasionally a tunnel would be driven completely under a stream, from one bank to the other, like a miniature Hudson River tube.

Like all muskrats, the new householder was extremely clean about his person and dwelling. He had two or three outdoor toilets. These were rocks, smooth earth hummocks, or logs that were near the water's edge or stranded on shallows in the stream. The black, oval droppings were almost always voided on these places, three to a dozen at a time. Only occasionally were they deposited haphazardly on shore, or in the water while the animal was swimming. In spite of working in muddy places, the muskrat never permitted his lustrous fur coat, or his black hands, feet, or tail, to stay soiled. Right after completing a messy job he shook himself, combed and smoothed his fur coat, and licked his fingers clean.

Although our young muskrat had only the customary quota of a few mites and fleas, which belonged to species well adapted to withstand frequent wettings, he might become afflicted later in life with more serious parasites. The intestines of muskrats sometimes are infested by great numbers of flatworms and roundworms. Cysts of the tapeworm have been found in the liver and the omentum or "apron" that hangs between the intestines and the inner forward wall of the abdomen. Sometimes liver flukes are acquired by eating snails, which serve as intermediate hosts for these parasites.

Food was no problem during the remainder of the autumn. The muskrat had only to swim across the narrow river to the flats where a variety of plants was to be had for the taking. Whether he sought food by night or day, his keen nose helped to find the choicest. He was most likely to waddle first to one of the marshy spots where the tall, tender cattails grew—for this was his favorite. He then reared on his hind legs, rested both paws on the stem, and steadying himself by his tail, attacked the plant. A few bites with his sharp incisor teeth, and the cattail, weighted by the heavy brown head, came swinging to the earth. The stem was cut into sections five to ten inches long, and neatly piled up or eaten.

Bitter experience through a long race history has made all muskrats uncomfortable in the open. Too many unpleasant things may happen to him who lingers there. So this muskrat, in spite of his youth, was not able to really enjoy the juiciest cattail stalk or root unless he was under cover or within one jump of some shelter. A recess between several leafy cattails was cozy until frosts shriveled and slashed the foliage. Then he was more apt to lunch while crouched on his haunches in shallow water near shore. Here a litter of food discards on the muddy bottom showed where many meals had been enjoyed. In case of sudden attack, one splashing dive would send him into deep water.

The muskrat apparently never ate in the bedroom, but had a special dining room in a recess of the same steep bank. There he was nearly as safe as in the burrow. Downstream a short distance, were two solid earthen clods that had lodged at the stream's edge under the overhanging bank. A many branched young willow, its roots undermined, hung downward from the edge of the bank. In this protected recess between the clods, with the added screen of the willow, the muskrat had scratched a little feeding platform about a foot square. To this place he ferried many a delicious bundle of green food, and roots dug from the soft muck across the stream. It was not likely that an otter could approach without giving him sufficient warning to escape into the water.

Although it meant a hazardous trip, the muskrat made several nocturnal journeys each week through the woods to the cornfield. He was inordinately fond of the flinty yellow kernels which ranged in rows down the long ears. Sometimes he ate on the spot, in the shelter of a shock. Sometimes he carried an ear, crosswise in his jaws, to the river bank and ate in greater security.

Although the winter was now coming on, and the quieter pools of the river bore thickening skins of ice, the muskrat did not attempt to store food. Unlike the beavers upstream, he would continue to forage each night for his daily meals. Methodically he continued to draw food plants from the same patches and groves across the river until each group in turn was depleted.

Occasionally a lone muskrat, one or another of several downstream neighbors, swam by on some errand. Among them was an enormous old patriarch. He weighed twice as much as the average two-pound muskrat, but stolidly minded his own business. The recent settler watched the passers-by casually, or chattered his teeth in angry warning if they came too close to his shoreline.

Once in a while three or four muskrats may sleep together for warmth during the winter. As many as twenty-five were once reported in a burrow on a wildlife refuge. Generally, however, muskrats prefer solitude. Certainly this one did for he neither wanted nor tolerated companionship. One night, finding a shivering wanderer in his dining nook, he rushed furiously at the stranger. Squealing with rage, he sank his sharp teeth again and again in the other's back and along the tail. There was no quarter given, no leniency toward a homeless fellow-'rat whose fate had almost been shared by himself. Soon the unfortunate muskrat was bleeding in a dozen places. With a low squeak of pain, he fled into the dark river. Weakened further by the cold, he died a few hours later a short distance away along the shore. The following night the householder found the carcass and ate several ounces of the cold flesh. Cannibalism is not an everyday occurrence among muskrats, but neither is it extraordinary.

Minks, arch enemies of the muskrats, were abundant on the river. They devoured many a homeless muskrat that was new in the region and did not have escape methods worked out to a fine precision. Only alertness and speed saved our muskrat settler. Numerous times he dodged into the burrow just a few inches ahead of the flashing teeth of a big brown mink. Strangely, the marauders did not follow. Despite their strength, their sharp teeth and their weasellike swiftness, they were not so desperately hungry that they cared to risk a battle with a cornered muskrat in the narrow tunnel.

Like others of his kind, the muskrat was stout-hearted. With his back against a wall, he would have fought to the last gasp, even against man. At one time a mink took up residence for several weeks in a hollow stump on the bank only a few yards from the muskrat's burrow. It passed his doorway a number of times, but did not get up enough courage to attack him.

Throughout the autumn another danger had menaced all muskrats along the stream. In his spare time, a young farmer had added materially to his income by trapping. His steel traps, set along the river for muskrat, mink, and other fur-bearers, were cleverly designed. Those intended to fool the muskrats were placed just under water near shore, with a piece of apple, carrot, turnip, or other root, hung overhead. When reaching for the tantalizing bait the animal would find it convenient to step on the trap-pan. As the steel jaws snapped shut the muskrat instinctively would dive for the safety of deep water. The trap-chain, sliding down a rod or steel wire, would foul and so drown the victim. Occasionally a trapped animal would escape drowning. Then, in the hours before the man returned, the animal would stoically gnaw through skin, flesh, tendons and bones just above the trap, and so escape. Although some of these unfortunates lost as many as two or even three feet by self-amputation, they did not seem to be greatly hampered in their efforts to make a living.

With the arrival of intense cold, the river froze over solidly from bank to bank. Upstream tributaries were choked off by the hand of winter and the main stream flowed only sluggishly. When the water level dropped, the ice buckled and collapsed, then froze again. The upper doorway of the muskrat's enlarged home was exposed to the icy air and the gaze of all passersby. For warmth and safety the owner plugged it solidly with mud from the river bottom. Freezing at once, the plug effectively sealed off this exit. At one time an ice jam blocked the lower door for several days. Then the muskrat was forced to claw his way laboriously through the frozen clay to open a new exit.

A lean and dangerous time followed. Wandering over the nearby ground, he picked up anything that passed for food. Carcasses of starved birds and mammals and the leavings of carnivores were taken eagerly. Discarded nubbins of corn were the greatest delicacies. He ate quantities of dried grass, sweet clover, mint, violets, even the coarse smartweeds and cockleburs. A number of times he desperately cut down willows, as much as one-half to one inch in diameter, to feed on their twigs, buds and bark. He even ate wood and rotting plant stems. Tenaciously he clung to his home territory. Even on a nearby solidly frozen rivulet the muskrats refused to leave, preferring to face hunger rather than the unknown. Deprived of all water, they heaped grass and weeds over their doorways and made the best of it. Internecine warfare broke out, however, and many muskrats carried festering sores from bites.

On the main stream the ice jam was broken after a few days, and our muskrat's doorway was opened again to the lower stratum of the river. The ice sheath above did not impede or frighten him. In fact, he could now swim freely, almost without fear of enemies, even in the daylight that filtered through the ice. Here and there, in spaces between water and ice, were air pockets where the muskrat could get fresh air. Exhaling and taking a deep breath, he could get enough oxygen for a swim of several minutes.

Down here in the dark water the muskrat made a fairly good living even in winter. There were aquatic sedges, arrowheads, burreeds, pondweeds, bulrushes, and other succulent and delicious plants. He not only ate the tops, but even dug up the roots. Around the upper bend of the river, in a quiet back-eddy, was a small clump of water lilies. He liked this plant so well that by the middle of winter they were practically exterminated. He rooted into the mud for the big fleshy tubers and even chipped and dug into the under-surface of the ice to get a final inch of the upper stems. The top-most leaves, of course, were frozen fast.

Animal prey was abundant. The muskrat caught and devoured crayfish and salamanders. He surprised swift water dogs by a sudden dash. Sometimes he succeeded in creeping onto a fish when it was cooped up in a pocket by the ice. A good many victims were dead or dying—carp, suckers, catfish, other still-live fish, frogs, and the smaller turtles that had buried themselves in the muddy bottom. By far the greater part of the flesh food, however, was freshwater clams and mussels. Up and down the stream, the heaps of neatly parted shells could be seen on the bank or on the ice where the various muskrats had carried mussels out to eat. Apparently they pried the valves apart with their teeth. To some extent the muskrats would continue eating shellfish and other aquatic food throughout the R-less months, but not to the degree that they were seeking them in cold weather.

At last the sun built up enough heat to break the back of winter. From hundreds of hillsides melting snow poured into the river. The ice broke and surging flood waters rose over the banks in many places. The muskrat was forced out of his burrow and narrowly escaped being crushed to death when he surfaced between jostling cakes of ice. He was more fortunate than some of his kind, however, because the brushy woodland afforded him shelter from enemies and swift currents. For several days, until the water subsided, he lurked in thickets and under some grounded ice fragments.

Thus far in his adult life the muskrat had kept strictly to himself. The sight of another aroused only irritation. Now, with the approach of his first spring, he felt a strange restlessness. Wandering downstream, he stopped at every bank burrow to investigate. At strategic places near the water's edge he sniffed eagerly for information. Sometimes a strong musky odor told him that another male had passed. Then he would grate and click his teeth with resentment.

Another smell was that of the female. It excited the muskrat in a new way. From the recently swollen pair of slender musk glands about one inch long that lay under the skin of his lower abdomen, he excreted a few drops of oily, yellowish scent. This was a message of warning to any male that came that way, and an invitation to any female. Then he hurried on. During the course of his short journeys he had several quarrels with members of his own sex, and a couple of pitched battles. His wounds were not serious and were soon forgotten, for in a week he found what he was looking for. He met a female muskrat that welcomed his attentions. After mating briefly in shallow water on the bank of the stream, he went on his way. Unless he was an exceptionally fortunate muskrat, he could hardly expect to find two mates in a season. Males slightly outnumber females and harems are not collected.

This female muskrat was a big, glossy animal. She, too, had wandered a mile or more from her home, which was in a big marsh where the river spread and meandered across the plain. Because there were no steep banks here, the muskrats had built lodges. They were much like small beaver houses. Instead of wood, they had used mostly dead cattail stalks of the previous year. Sometimes other coarse vegetation was added and occasionally a few sticks. The spaces were plugged with handfuls of water plants, moss, rootlets, and mud or peat.

The big female's house was located near the edge of the marsh. Safely surrounded by water a couple of feet deep, it was built on a little island of decaying vegetation and muck that she had scooped and heaped together from the adjacent bottom. At first, in the autumn about eighteen months before, it had been a modest affair. Shaped like a little wigwam, it had been about three feet in diameter at the base and two feet tall. Its simple, round room was about twelve inches across and six inches high.

Two years later, the desultory additions of material had swelled the lodge's bulk to eight or nine feet across and between three and four feet high. It had lost its peak and was simply a roundish heap. Two entrances from below the water level led through narrow passageways upward into opposite ends of the irregularly shaped chamber. It was nearly sixteen inches long, ten inches wide, and seven inches high. Slight constrictions of the walls gave an effect of marking the room into three sections, two of which contained a bed of damp, shredded cattail leaves and grasses. As the roof settled, the female had to chew the inner side away and add more material on the outside. Even with remodeling, the house would probably not last more than three years.

It was flimsy and could be easily broken into during summer by such enemies as coyotes and otters. But a few days of freezing hardened its walls into flint. It became a real fortress when the owner needed protection most. In case of dire food shortage, she could stave off starvation by nibbling at the more edible parts of the walls.

The damp interior of the muskrats' houses often was an attraction to other small animals. Among them were insects, spiders, skunks, frogs, toads, and snakes. The larger of these creatures used the vacant lodges, but also sometimes burrowed into the roofs of others. Turtles occasionally laid eggs in the mass.

The big marsh was dotted with muskrat homes, some on shore, others far out in the shallow water. Most of them were concentrated among or near the wind-tattered cattails, for these were as important to muskrats as aspens are to beavers. They furnished food and building material. The largest house apparently lodged two families, for there was a nest at each end. Probably nine tons of material had been required to build it. Twenty-two and one-half feet long and ten feet wide, its top was two feet eight inches above the water line.

Scattered here and there were miniature houses. Some were so small that they looked like fallen clusters of reeds. These were the feeding shelters to which many marsh-dwelling muskrats carried their food to eat under cover. Open platforms and rafts were also common. The muskrats cut cattail stalks, towed them to selected spots and matted them, butts together, in a radiating pattern. One of these rafts would support two muskrats.

Not that they ate only water plants. Almost every night they went ashore for whatever food was available. This varied somewhat from the meals of the muskrat which lived in a bank. Depending on the season, they found tender grass stems, goldenrod, smartweed, ragweed, cockle-burs, shepherd's purse, wild oats (*Avena*), bark and leaves of tree seedlings, poison ivy, acorns and thorn-apples. More green food was obtained from the land when the cattails were older and tougher.

Converging on each house, unless it stood in fairly deep water, was an irregular system of water-filled ditches and surface runways. Holes revealed underground tunnels, some of which led from the house to the feeding hut or platform. Doubtless the tunnels were used on those sunny days when the musk-rat became hungry but did not care to risk wandering far on the surface. In their shelter he could safely dig for roots and tender underground shoots.

Generally only one muskrat lived in a house, but occasionally three or four adults, or even more, might be found together. As with the bank muskrats, this was more likely to be during the fall and winter, when the animals might like to huddle together for warmth. These partnerships often broke up suddenly and without warning after enduring for months.

The big female was not one that took in roomers. Her temper this spring, never very sweet, grew steadily worse until no muskrat in the vicinity dared to swim near her house. Then, late one night about thirty days after she had met the male muskrat on the river, she gave birth to nine blind and practically hair-less young. They weighed about three-quarters ounce and were about four inches long. (Sometimes the gestation period may be as short as twenty-two or twenty-three days, or as long as thirty-five.) Being a large animal, her brood closely approached the possible maximum of eleven and was more than the average of four to six.

The birth took place on her feeding raft. As soon as the ordeal was over, the mother started moving her young to the lodge. One at a time, she grasped the skin of the belly between her yellow incisors and swam off. Each trip required eight to ten minutes and she worked away steadily. All went well until the seventh infant was safely in the lodge. Then she suddenly lost interest, or forgot that two children still remained on the raft. Perhaps she did not care to rear an overly large brood in this crowded muskrat marsh-world. The two foundlings squeaked more and more feebly in the chill night air, but with the extreme tenacity of their race they refused to die. Soon after sunrise, a prowling snapping turtle found and devoured them.

In a week's time the surviving young were clothed in coarse gray-brown coats. Although they were beginning to tumble over each other and to explore their home, they spent much time slowly suckling the mother's breasts. So firmly were they attached to her nipples that once, when she rushed outside suddenly, more than half of the children were dragged into the open water. There they let go and, squeaking protests, floated or swam about blindly.

The mother soon returned and started grasping each baby in turn by the skin of its belly and swimming with it back to the lodge. She held each one as high in the water as possible to keep at least its head above the surface, while her counter-balancing tail waved in the air. Several kits blundered into floating or emergent vegetation or the foundations of their home, and so saved themselves. As the cold water soaked into their skins, they set up a rising crescendo of squeaks. So insistent were they that the mother, which had commenced to show indifference to these last ones, at length was unable to ignore them any longer. Before she got around to them, however, one had drifted off across open water and drowned.

A week later a heavy rain raised the water level of the marsh, and tore and beat at the lodges. The muskrat family was forced out of the bedroom onto the roof of the house. High waves washed at them, and the weakling of the remaining brood was drowned. Then the rain ceased and peace returned.

The survivors, now reduced to six, grew rapidly. Their eyes opened in thirteen to sixteen days. Those of the smaller animals opened first, while one over-grown youngster did not gain sight until it was twenty days old. At two weeks their coats had lost some of the early coarseness and brownish tints, and had become gray, soft and woolly. They varied in weight from two to four ounces. Ten days later the more precocious young had ceased to nurse and were seeking their own food. Tender, blanched parts of grasses and other plants near the lodge were their first solid meals. Because there were too many children for the mother's supply of milk, they did not grow as fast and were weaned nearly a week later than families of only two or three young.

They could swim and dive well at this early age. A hovering hawk was the signal for them to crawl under marsh plants or litter, or to submerge, sometimes for more than three minutes at a time. They weighed three and one-half to seven ounces apiece and were approximately nine to eleven and four-tenths inches long from nose to tail-tip. Some of them began to change back to a brownish color, while others remained gray until autumn.

As soon as the young were weaned, and not later than about thirty days after birth, the mother turned on them savagely and drove them from the lodge. She knew that another brood was due at any hour and that the present, protein-hungry youngsters would immediately devour their new-born brothers and sisters if she permitted them to be together. She was ruthless about enforcing the exodus. In fact, she bit one reluctant juvenile so severely that it died the following night. That left five young muskrats, an average number of autumn survivors for a brood that started out with nine or ten in the spring.

The young did not move far. They burrowed into any kind of shelter, abandoned lodges, heaps of trash, or piles of drifted vegetation, between fifty and two hundred feet from their birthplace. More distant wanderings were met with hostility and attacks from the thickly settled community. Winter life of the muskrat marsh would be strained from over-crowding, but in summer and fall the apparent abundance of food restrained the young from wandering long distances. Later in life, when they knew more, they were permitted to go into lodges where nursing young were housed.

Enemies of every kind gathered here to prey on the muskrats. By the time the surviving young were two months old they were as wary and cunning as their elders. They swam under water a good deal, although perhaps more to explore the bottom than from caution. Sometimes they covered nearly two hundred feet before coming to the surface. They "dog-paddled" with all four feet. On their starchy diet, occasionally varied with a body of a murdered comrade, or crayfish and other slow creatures, they grew fast. At three months they were sixteen to nineteen inches long and weighed eighteen to twenty-five ounces. They would be capable of mating when nine or ten months old. In the north, this would be midwinter. Along the Gulf Coast there is no closed season on family cares, although they reach a low point during the coldest months and again at the peak of summer. The average adult female has three litters a year.

After the early summer rains, no more fell for a long time. The marsh dried up as it had not done for years. Fortunately no fire started. The muskrats dug their tunnels deeper, and hollowed out new rooms in the now-exposed base of their lodges. Many animals had nothing to drink; only moisture in the roots of iris, cattails and sedges kept them from dying of thirst. They all became especially susceptible to coccidiosis, a common disease caused by protozoans.

Their archenemy, the mink, found it easy to kill as many muskrats as it wanted. Internecine battles became more frequent and deadly. A number of the most poverty-stricken muskrats gave up and wandered away in a do-or-die attempt to find food, water, and shelter. In general they fared even worse than the majority that stayed at home. Before the drought was past, the colony had been decimated. So resilient was the species, however, that a few favorable seasons would bring about another problem of over-population. In Canada the cycle of abundance recurs about every ten years and is parallel to similar cycles in the numbers of snowshoe hares and other species of mammals.

Muskrats live over most of North America north of the Rio Grande, including tidal marshes along the coast. From imported stock that was released in Bohemia in 1905 and in the British Isles about 1927, as well as other introductions, muskrats have spread over most of central Europe, Holland, Belgium, and eastern France. Although welcomed by trappers, the animals have been an almost unmitigated curse to farmers. Their burrowing habits have been especially serious in regions where dikes are of vital importance. These structures, as well as railroad embankments and earth dams, may be weakened and destroyed by the big rodents. Determined efforts have nearly exterminated them from England and Scotland, but they are still spreading to new areas on the continent of Europe.

In its native America the muskrat is one of the principal assets of the fur trade. A century ago a skin was worth only a few cents. Following World War I the price rose to the all-time high of four dollars or more, but the average current price for prime dark skins is about two dollars and fifty cents. More than ten million pelts are marketed annually, far more than any other wild American mammal. Louisiana alone produces about three million skins, or as many as all of Canada. Despite this enormous drain the species is able to maintain itself because of its high rate of reproduction. Practically all skins taken are made into women's coats. They are either in the natural form (usually "mink-dyed") or "Hudson seal" (sheared to remove the guard hairs and then dyed black or brown). Muskrat carcasses are sold as "marsh rabbits" in Washington, Baltimore, Philadelphia, St. Louis, and numerous other places. By act of the state legislature in July, 1944, the official name in Louisiana is "marsh hare." The dark red meat is fine-grained and tender and tastes like wild duck or terrapin. The trapper obtains about ten cents a pound or fifteen to twenty cents for a carcass plus the price of the pelt. Dried muskrat musk is used in the manufacture of perfume and for trapping scent.

General description. A large, stocky, heavily furred aquatic animal with small eyes and ears, stocky body, and short legs. Long, scaly, sparsely haired tail flattened in the vertical plane. Hind feet partially webbed, and considerably longer than the front feet. Fur dense, consisting of a close, gray underfur which is covered by long, glistening guard hairs of a blackish, brown, or rusty red color which shades to nearly white on throat and belly; feet dark brown; tail naked, black. Total length, 17 to 25 inches; height at shoulder, 4 to 5 inches; weight, 2 to 3¾ pounds.

Distinguishing characteristics. Easily separated from the other inland aquatic mammals, the otter and beaver, by its small size and vertically flattened, scaly tail. (The tail of the otter is furred and taperingly cone-shaped; that of the beaver is scaly but flattened in the horizontal plane.)

Range. Most of North America north of Mexico, from central Georgia, southern Louisiana, and southern Arizona north to Newfoundland, northern Ungava, northern Manitoba, Mackenzie River delta, and the Yukon River basin of Alaska. Absent from all of California except extreme eastern and southern portions.

HOUSE MOUSE
MUS MUSCULUS

Now and then a house mouse sings loud enough for a human to hear. Its musical but rather monotonous songs are made up of runs of chirps and chippers which range through about two octaves. The notes, uttered rapidly at the rate of two to six or more per second, can sometimes be heard twenty-five feet away. This is rare, however; usually the song is so faint as to be inaudible more than ten feet off. The Chinese are said to have kept these rodent songsters in cages, as we keep canaries. Perhaps all house mice sing, but most of their music is pitched too high to register for our ears. The very few that we can hear are the great bassos of their tribe. They have been known in the United States, China, Europe, North Africa, and Mexico.

During their infrequent disagreements, ordinary untalented house mice scold each other in a series of rapid squeaks. In moments of calm, a shrill exclamation may be chirped. Now and then a house mouse, more loquacious than others, has quite a repertoire of notes which express emotions and convey messages to its companions.

Everyone knows the house mouse; the ubiquitous little creature has made its way across the world. All dwellings, even the most modern steel and concrete apartment buildings, afford it rent-free shelter and food at times. The musical talent of a few of the family has given it no prestige. Socially, it is on the bottom rung of the ladder, along with the house rat.

All mankind condemns it as a thieving parasite. Our "mouse," the German *maus,* the French *mulot,* the Latin *mus*—all these names are descended from the ancient Sanskrit word *musha,* meaning thief.

There is almost nothing that the little animal will not plunder. Its ancestral food, grains, come first. Much damage often is done to valuable seed stock. It devours anything, vegetable or animal, cooked or raw, that is eaten by man. It also chews up leather. It seems especially fond of book bindings, because of the delectable paste and glue flavor. While the stomach capacity of a single mouse is small and crumbs and waste food are often enough to sustain it, a large colony of the animals may cause great losses. Besides the food that they consume or destroy, much more is contaminated. Their strong, sharply musty odor will seep through everything with which the animals or their body discharges come in contact. Clothing, hangings, rugs and upholstery are also shredded for nest material.

Although they are not as outstandingly filthy as rats, house mice frequently live or run about in unsanitary conditions. They have been found carrying germs of typhus fever, as well as an infection resembling infantile paralysis. They are suspected of being carriers of choriomeningitis and several other diseases that affect man.

Unfortunately for us, house mice are very prolific. They may start mating at the age of two months. A single female can produce five to eight litters in one season. Although cold weather inhibits breeding, she is ready to start producing

HOUSE MOUSE

offspring as soon as the average temperature reaches fifty degrees. She may make a warm nest of cotton or wool threads or bits of cloth under a haymow or in the walls of a building. If she lives in the open, she uses grass, and perhaps feathers, to line the walls of a burrow in the ground of an open field or orchard. Here she gives birth to her tiny pink, blind, and naked young. The average litter contains five of the little squirming creatures, with a usual range from four to eight and an occasional extreme of ten or eleven. They are weaned some three weeks later when their growth is about half attained. Then they scatter to adjacent territories, where they will soon start their own families. In the meanwhile the mother mates, often long before her infants are able to leave her. If she is nursing a large litter the usual gestation period of three weeks is prolonged as much as three days.

Whenever factors are in their favor, house mice rapidly increase to vast numbers. In arid or semi-arid regions a wet spring and plenty of green vegetation may produce an "irruption" of the animals. Such circumstances in 1941 and 1942 provided an unusual abundance of the creatures in the Central Valley of California.

Years earlier, in 1926–27, this had been disastrous. Both house mice and meadow mice in enormous numbers moved out of the fields of milo maize and barley in the drained bed of Buena Vista Lake, and devastated the surrounding ranch lands. With great suddenness, waves of mice traveled in a night or two as far as ten miles. The swarming animals devoured grass and maize, and even the roots of many plants. Buildings were over-run. At one ranch more than two horse-cart loads of house mice were poisoned with strychnine. Stacked barley was riddled and the grain devoured. Ninety-one sacks of barley which had been sown on a quarter-section of land was entirely consumed. The owner, examining his devastated field by lantern light, said that the swarming house mice were "thicker than mosquitoes!" Gulls, short-eared owls, hawks, ravens and other birds, as well as coyotes and other flesh-eaters, had a field day. Apparently disease brought an abrupt end to the phenomenon.

Man's traps and poisons, as well as cats, are constant controls that usually prevent such high peaks of population. Perhaps of equal importance is the vicious rat. The little house mouse cannot possibly defeat this fierce marauder. It must depend on its keen senses to avoid trouble and on its small size and quickness to reach crannies too small for the rat to follow. With luck, the house mouse may live fifteen to eighteen months. Only if it is in confinement under special care can it expect to attain the extraordinary age of six years.

Ordinarily the house mouse is not a great traveler. When it can find food and water close to a good nest site, it is satisfied. A methodical animal, it follows established trails, under protecting cover as far as possible. When it is necessary to leave the shelter of tables, benches, piles of crates, rubbish, or other objects, it scurries across the open floor as fast as possible. If a wall is near by the mouse follows it closely. On that side, at least, it feels safe. Humans with murderous intentions often take advantage of these habits. They set traps and poison where the mouse will find the bait most readily.

It takes practice to be a really good climber. Young mice are awkward and timid when aloft. Older mice use their long tails to keep their balance, waving them stiffly and slowly or jerking them from one side to the other as circumstances require. An animal that loses its balance will use its tail as well as its long toes to try to get a new hold. A mouse that has lost its tail shows great reluctance to venture out on a narrow rod, and is unable to regain its balance once it wavers to one side. House mice often leap fearlessly across openings or from one beam to another and spring onto tables when an overhanging shelf prevents climbing. They swim well, although they dislike getting wet and seldom enter water if they can avoid it.

Unlike the common rat, the house mouse has a good disposition. White mice, which are merely albinos of this species, are often kept as pets for children. These thoroughly domesticated animals are more docile than other house mice. Even in the wild, house mice are models of sweetness and peace when compared to house rats. Of course one of the house mice, when cornered and faced with death, is no coward. It will bite viciously, inflicting severe cuts on a person's hands. The mother mouse will sometimes fight to the end rather than flee to safety and leave her little ones in danger. But usually house mice are among the most timid of mammals and would much rather run than fight if any avenues of escape are open.

Because albinos can be inoculated with numerous human diseases, easily bred, handled, and kept in close confinement, great numbers are used in medical laboratories. Many thousands serve in other biological experiments, and in research on genetics. Thus some house mice partially reimburse mankind for the damage that the rest of the family inflicts.

Folklore and fable have been much more kind to the mouse than to the rat. While the rat is universally regarded with loathing, the cleverness, curiosity and adaptability of the smaller rodent have won grudging approval. The proverb, "When the cat's away, the mice will play," describes high human mischief. A playful child may be as "merry as mice in malt." Plautus, the Roman comic dramatist, said in "Trunculatus" about 190 B. C., "Consider the little' mouse, how sagacious an animal it is which never entrusts its life to one hole only."

The house mouse's sight is not good and it often will explore for food in a lighted room where people are sitting quietly. The big ears, however, can pick up slight sounds to which it reacts instantly. A sudden sharp noise, as the tap of a fingernail on a table, and the mouse jerks an inch or two into the air. With its life in danger every instant, this "timorous beastie," as Robert Burns called it, is always on the alert. The nose twitches and trembles as the mouse sniffs keenly for trouble. It is very susceptible to odors, some of which, oddly enough, it just can't abide. Householders sometimes take advantage of its delicate nose by scattering napthalene flakes over clothing, books, or other possessions. Among other repellent odors are those of sulphur, lime, many petroleum products, pine tar, pyrethrum, nicotine sulphate, ammonium sulphate, and oils of citronella, peppermint, wintergreen, and cedar.

The house mouse is no upstart; its family tree is very tall and interesting. Long before the dawn of human history, its ancestors lived in central Asia. Small, scaly tailed rodents, their grayish to brownish coats graded imperceptibly into paler color on the bellies, as they do today. They lived on dry grasslands and even in deserts. This region was the cradle of mankind. No doubt house mice stole seeds and grains from the stores of the first human beings who also lived on the steppes.

As the primitive people migrated east, west and south, the mice went along. Living on the scanty supplies of wheat and barley, traveling in baggage, the mice eventually reached Japan, the southern tip of India, and even northeastern Africa. Colonies of mice were established everywhere that people stopped or settled. Before the end of the Stone Age the little rodents had made their way around the Mediterranean Sea, and later spread northward across all except far northern Europe.

Most of Asia and Europe between the Pacific and Atlantic Oceans, as well as northern Africa, were inhabited by wild house mice even before the beginning of recorded history. They all belonged to one species, but four races or sub-species have been recognized by modern science.

Three of these races produced "commensals"—mice especially adapted for life with man and, in a sense, fitted to live and eat with him.

The house mice that now inhabit the United States and Canada are commensals. They are descendants of wild mice of the Wagner race which originated in Russian Turkestan. Ages ago mice of this race migrated along the caravan routes through Asia Minor, across North Africa, and thence to Italy and Spain. In these two countries, different climatic and other conditions caused their separation into two distinct strains, the *brevirostris* or "short-nosed" and the *domesticus*.

From Spain the "short-nosed" house mice were carried by ship to the extreme southern sections of the United States which were originally colonized by the Spanish Crown, and to South and Central America. House mice of the *domesticus* race spread from Italy into the Balkans and eastern Germany, then west to France, the British Isles, Iceland and Norway. English and French ships brought them to America, presumably about the time of the Revolution. Eventually the race spread over the northern half of the United States, all of inhabited Canada and Alaska, Hawaii, and Australia.

The "short-nosed" and *domesticus* races in America are very much alike, and can be distinguished only by careful examination. Nevertheless, despite their opportunities to become mixed in the United States by traveling north and south on railroads and trucking lines, the two races still retain their essential characteristics. Once established, the races seem to merge only where their ranges meet and there is a great deal of interbreeding.

Of course America has no truly wild house mice. Wild species have no way of getting over here from Asia since they rarely travel with man. Also, once a strain becomes established in an area, it generally seems to be able to subdue all other strains that may arrive later. The tails of wild mice are always shorter than the head and body combined. Also the white of their bellies is distinctly set off from the darker color of the sides. Commensal house mice have developed longer tails, often considerably longer than the head and body. (Those of our short-nosed and *domesticus* commensals in the United States, however, are about the same length as head and body.) Bellies of commensals are usually tinted gray or sometimes buffy, and this coloring merges indistinctly into the darker upper parts. Skull changes also have occurred. In Europe and Asia, where specialization has gone on for ages, commensals have evolved which show these characteristics most distinctly. Other commensals, less specialized, may live in the wild state.

American house mice, which have been here only four centuries or less, have not had time to work out distinctive ways of living. When conditions are favorable and most nearly resemble those under which their ancient ancestors lived in Asia, our mice can still "go back to Nature" very easily. I found such a colony thriving in the grassy fringe around a swamp in an Arizona desert. Only natural foods had been available for many years since the abandonment of the ranch buildings where the mouse colony had first gained its start. In severely cold or moist, rainy climates, many American commensals move outdoors into grassy fields or thickets for the summer or dry seasons, returning to the shelter of man's buildings when the weather becomes unfavorable.

General description. A small mouse with large ears and a long, scaly, almost naked tail. Fur lies snug to body. Color uniform dull yellowish dark brown or grayish brown above, merging into light gray under parts; tail dark gray. Total length, six to eight inches; height at shoulder, 1 inch; weight, ½ to 1 ounce (average 3/5 ounce).

Distinguishing characteristics. The dull coloration; ashy gray under parts, and long, scaly, almost hairless tail. The meadow mouse is larger, much more stocky, and grizzled; the white-footed mouse has a sharply bicolor pattern with white under parts, and a hairy tail. The harvest mouse is much like the house mouse but is more slender, has a proportionally longer tail, and is usually but not always smaller. Its upper incisors are grooved lengthwise, while those of the house mouse are smooth.

Range. All inhabited areas of North America.

HOUSE RAT
RATTUS NORVEGICUS AND *R. RATTUS*

Shadows stretch outward into space and dusk deepens over the great cities. Along the Broadways and in the residential areas, the lights hold night at arm's length, but in the squalid alleys, between warehouses, and in the city's financial districts, darkness thickens. The distant hum of the living sections of the city becomes an undertone for strange night sounds. For these cobbled streets, alleys, canal banks, and cavernous, shadowy buildings are not deserted. Night, which has banished human beings, wakens another population—the rats.

Creeping along buildings, poking into rubbish heaps and garbage cans, they look for food. Like swiftly moving shadows they swarm to overhead beams. Nimbly they walk up sheer walls and over roofs. Long mooring cables form their narrow highways to ships. Water itself is no obstacle, as they swim to opposite wharves or gather floating garbage. The rustling ceases only at the sound of a human footfall or as a light flashes. In the darkness, squeaks and sharp screams rise at intervals as the rats quarrel over food or territory. Only dawn and the rising roar of the city will quiet the slinking creatures, for another twelve hours.

Each night, in practically every city around the world, this scene is repeated. In the sticky heat of the tropics and the gripping cold of the far northern and southern settlements, rats forage and prey on man's supplies. In varying degree, ramshackle tenement districts and trim little villages act as unwilling hosts to these rodents. Practically all farms are inhabited by them.

Rats often outnumber humans. They are among the most prolific of mammals. If living conditions are suitable, a female will breed throughout the year, although in the northern United States and Canada comparatively few litters are produced during the winter. The number of young varies from two or three to a dozen or more. As many as twenty-two embryos have been counted in one female. The average number of youngsters produced is about eight. They are naked, blind and helpless, but grow "like weeds." Their eyes open when they are fourteen to sixteen days old, and the mother weans them at three weeks.

She may mate again within a few hours after the birth of a litter. As the gestation period is between twenty-one and one-half and twenty-two and one-half days, the next brood in this case would be born simultaneously with the weaning of the first. For this reason the period may be prolonged several days, to provide for proper development of both the actual and the embryonic litters.

Young rats waste little time before starting families of their own. A female

HOUSE RAT

only eight weeks old has been known to give birth to eleven young and rear them all. Normally, the first breeding age is three months. At two years rats have passed sexual maturity. The very exceptionally old rat may live as much as a year longer, but it is blind, toothless, and almost hairless. It goes out of this world just about as poorly equipped as when it was born.

Assuming that three to six litters of nine to ten young are produced each year and that each of these breed when three or four months old, one pair of rats and their progeny theoretically would result in a total of more than three hundred and fifty million rats in three years. Of course nothing like this ever takes place. Apparently the number of female rats is considerably less than the number of males. Losses, especially of young rats, are enormous. Man destroys great numbers; natural enemies include the *Buteo,* rough-legged, and marsh hawks, the great horned and barn owls, and such mammals as skunks, weasels, minks and foxes. Diseases sweep off tremendous numbers when the population approaches a peak. Rats are ferocious enemies of each other, and cannibalism is a common occurrence when the regular food supply runs low. Nevertheless, the theoretical rate of increase gives an idea of the capacity of a rat colony to increase under favorable circumstances and to recover from disaster.

There are two species of house rats—the brown (*Rattus norvegicus*) and the much smaller black (*R. rattus*). The brown rat is a burrowing rodent in its native home in Asia. In America it normally lives in burrows under or near buildings, or in the lower walls of structures. Although not fitted to dig extensively, these rats often congregate in such numbers and supplement each other's efforts so well that a maze of tunnels results. The shafts are comparatively shallow and rarely exceed a depth of seventeen inches. Among them are the dens—globular cavities a foot or more in diameter, well lined with grasses or scraps of cloth, paper, excelsior, old mattress or upholstery stuffing, or other soft material. Rats are often communal and a number of adults, or a mother and several youngsters, may occupy a single nest.

Brown rats climb as readily, although not as skillfully, as their black relatives that often live in trees. Although agile and quick, neither of these rats is a very fast runner and it can be overtaken readily in the open. Rats have plenty of courage. To "fight like a cornered rat" is the phrase of tribute paid to any desperate, vicious defense against attack.

Many rats, either by choice or because they are crowded out of more sheltered quarters, take up residence in open fields. Ditch banks and trash or garbage dumps are favorite locations, especially if close to grain fields. On the Atlantic and Gulf coasts, rats are common in salt marshes.

They often make seasonal migrations, leaving their crowded quarters in spring and moving to the open fields. As cold weather approaches they return to the warmth of man's buildings. Sometimes rats move in great numbers to new territory. In addition to the vast, historic incursion of the brown rat into Europe in 1727, other lesser migrations have been seen. One of these occurred during 1903 in Mercer and Rock Island Counties, Illinois. An eyewitness testified that one moonlit night a great army of rats rustled through the fields and crossed the road on which he was walking. All of the rats were traveling in the same direction, and the hordes stretched away in the moonlight as far as one could see.

The rat is positively our worst mammal enemy. Its appetite is enormous—it will eat one-third its own weight in twenty-four hours and waste as much more. Although rats clean up immense quantities of garbage and other refuse, they also devour enormous amounts of useful goods. They eat everything that is humanly edible and much that is not. Grain and its products, meats, all sorts of packaged foods, leather, paint, soap, cloth, even books. Insulation may be gnawed from electric wiring, causing short circuits and fires. They eat vegetables and fruits of most kinds, both in storage and in the field. One was caught devouring bank swallows which it had trapped and killed on their nests. Many rats invade poultry houses, stealing eggs and killing chickens. Once started, they seem to go wild. They have been known to kill hundreds of baby chicks in a single night. Even full-grown hens, young pigs and lambs sometimes fall victims to these savage creatures. Property may be damaged by gnawing or flooding—rats often gnaw through lead pipes, apparently to get at water which they hear running. It is estimated that rats cause an annual loss in the United States of almost two hundred million dollars.

Appalling as this is, rats are far more of a menace to human health and lives. They have been responsible for killing more people than were destroyed in all the wars of the past five thousand years. In fact, the history of mediaeval Europe was molded more effectively by rats than by kings and their armies. Most of the armies of the Crusades were defeated and practically destroyed, not in battle, but in camp by epidemics spread by rats. Typhus was one of the worst of these diseases. Bubonic plague, the "Black Death" of the Middle Ages, is a rat disease which also afflicts man. During the fourteenth century, one of every four inhabitants of Europe died from its effects. Other rat-borne diseases of man are sodoku (rat-bite fever), spirochetal jaundice, tularemia, rabies, trichinosis, and food poisoning.

Although the house rat has contributed some members of its race to man's benefit (the albino rats of medical research laboratories) it is practically always our enemy. It should be destroyed whenever and wherever possible.

Nearly everyone knows the brown house rat by sight. Many descriptive names are given to it: gray rat, brown rat, wharf rat, sewer rat, barn rat, and Norway rat. These merely indicate its versatility. The common (brown) house rat often varies so much in color (gray to brown, fading into dirty silver or light yellowish brown on the belly) as well as size, that people often think that there are many instead of one species.

The black house rat is not only much smaller than the brown one, but it prefers warm climates. While abundant in the tropics, it is common north of the Rio Grande only in the Gulf states and at seaports. Northward in the United States, the black rat colonies are only sporadic and small. Here the much larger and more powerful brown rat crowds out or actually kills its darker relative.

The two house rats and the house mouse of the United States and Canada belong to the family Muridae, the group of true rats and mice. This is the largest group of rodents on earth, comprising almost three hundred species. It was limited originally to the Old World, all of Europe, Asia and Africa, with the exception of Madagascar.

Even today, we have only three full species to represent the family in the United States and Canada. (See also section on house mouse, pp. 538–544.) Both the brown and black rats are believed to be natives of Asia. The smaller species migrated to Europe in the twelfth century and soon spread to all seaports. It came to be known also as "roof rat" because it was peculiarly suited to life well up in buildings or other structures. This is in marked contrast to the brown rat which usually likes to make its nest under houses or in the lower sections of them.

Consequently the black rat became a common pest in practically all ships, and by this means reached America. Although its arrival was not recorded by the historians or immigration authorities, undoubtedly this was very soon after the first colonists began to take foodstuffs ashore, and sailors to lay their ships on the beach to make repairs and scrape bottoms. By the year 1700 the species was common along the Atlantic seaboard.

In 1727 the larger brown rat entered Europe by moving overland from Asia. Apparently urged by a tremendous pressure of population in the rear, the rats pressed on westward. No barriers—rivers, mountains, heat or cold, or the enmity of man, were so forbidding as to turn them back. They invaded the castles of the mighty with as little respect as they entered the hovels of the lowliest peasants. By 1750 the rodent flood had reached Paris. This greatest city of Europe, with its poverty, filth and extensive labyrinth of sewers, was a veritable paradise for the newcomers.

Other rats, attracted by food supplies, smuggled themselves aboard ships. At various ports individual rats went ashore. Colonies were established and the rodent migration was augmented from new centers of dispersal. Some of the water-borne rats arrived in England during 1728 or 1729. Finally, America was invaded by the brown rat about 1775. At once the species started on its march westward, to complete its encirclement of the globe.

Rats traveled in covered wagons and in army transport trains. They hid in and lived on the grain and other food-stuffs, and in forage for the oxen and horses. Forts, relief stations and trading posts were taken over. When the railroads were put into operation, the rats found their travel problem greatly simplified. Carloads of grain or other merchandise were ideal for a long trip, for they contained an inexhaustible supply of rations. Every town along the routes became populated, and in time adventuresome rats spread to every suitable habitat within reach. Only in the arid Southwest and in the high mountains was progress slow. The house rat did not become established in Wyoming until 1919 and in Montana until 1923. At most places in the interior the black rat, if it reached them at all, was exterminated by its larger relative.

By about 1910 rats in the United States and southern Canada undoubtedly exceeded the human population. In the cities, rats were at least as numerous as people, while in small towns and on farms the rodents were far in excess of this ratio. Due to modern buildings, the replacement of the horse by the automobile and truck, improvements in care of food, and better sanitation, rats have declined about fifty per cent in the larger towns and cities. They are, however, still very abundant on farms, especially in the northern half of the United States and in southern Canada. For example, even in one county in Texas with a human population of thirty-five thousand, more than one hundred and fifty-three thousand rats were killed in six weeks, and of course many escaped.

This high incidence is due to the rat's adaptability and capacity to get along in competition with other creatures, including man. It is an intelligent animal. No matter how much we may loathe it for its bad habits, we must admit that it is able to take advantage of the slightest opportunities. If food is not abundant and shelter present, it moves on. When it finds conditions suitable, it settles down and reproduces at a rapid rate. Man's strenuous and continuous efforts are necessary to keep the rat millions from taking over completely.

Two species of Old-World rats are found in North America:

1. The brown rat (*Rattus norvegicus*), which is relatively large and stocky, with a tail that is shorter than the head and body combined. The fur is grayish brown to gray, becoming pale dirty gray or yellowish white on the belly.

2. The black rat (*R. rattus*) is considerably smaller, and its tail is longer than head and body. It is dusky black or gray above, and white, pale buffy, or pale gray below.

General description. A rather large rat with large, hairless ears and long, scaly, ringed, nearly naked tail. Fur somewhat coarse, blackish, brownish, or grayish above, becoming paler gray below; feet grayish or whitish; tail dark gray. Total length, 15 to 18 inches; height at shoulder: black rat, 2 inches; brown rat, 2½ to 3½ inches; weight, 8 to an extreme of 25 ounces; average, 10 to 12 ounces.

Distinguishing characteristics. The drab coloration and nearly naked, ringed tail serve to distinguish the house rat from practically all native rodents of its size. The wood rat has white or creamy white under parts and its tail is at least fairly well haired (in some species, bushy). The smaller black or roof rat is rare and found only in the warmer of our southern states.

Range. Practically all inhabited parts of North America.

MOUNTAIN BEAVER
APLODONTIA RUFA

The white man has given many misnomers to animals, but he has done his worst by this burrowing rodent of the Pacific slope. The mountain beaver is not a beaver. It doesn't even have a tail, that is, to speak of. "Boomer" is the name applied in Oregon, but it never booms. Neither does it whistle, although "whistler" is what some people call it.

The Chinook Indians used the animals' skins for making fur robes, which they called *sewellel.* In writing about the Chinooks, Lewis and Clark confused the rodent with the robe, and stated that *sewellel* was the native name of the animal. This has been a widely accepted "book name" ever since. Others taken from various Indian languages of the Northwest, are *showt'l* or *showtl, squallah,* and *sh'auch. Chehalis,* a term used in the Olympic Mountains, is also probably of Indian origin.

The mountain beaver actually does cut down trees sometimes. Perhaps that is where it got its most common name, but it is a lumberjack in a very small way. The trees that it fells must be saplings; they can seldom be larger than three-quarters of an inch in diameter. It does not chip out pieces all around the trunk. As the big beaver does with small trees, it, too, makes only one slanting clean cut. Compared to the beaver that is three times as long and twelve times as heavy, the mountain beaver is "very small potatoes!"

MOUNTAIN BEAVER

It looks more like a big edition of the pocket gopher. All except the tail, which is so short as to be barely visible beyond the fur. Its dark brown coat is much like the muskrat's. The under coat is so scant that the pelt is thin and has no commercial value. About the size of the muskrat, it is twelve to seventeen inches long and weighs two to three pounds.

In many of its habits, as well as general appearance, the mountain beaver is similar to the pocket gopher. Indefatigable burrowers, two or three mountain beavers will create enough signs of activity to give the impression of a big colony. However, they are only slightly more sociable with members of their own kind than the solitary gophers. While trails and connecting passages often lead from one mountain beaver's burrow system to another's, the number of animals living together is never more than two, or a mother with young. Any uninvited stranger would probably be killed if it were unable to get out of the burrow first. In captivity these animals will allow no familiarity. A vicious quarrel follows any physical contact. The animals have very sharp teeth and, for their size, great strength.

Although the mountain beaver may live at high elevations, it prefers the foothills and lower canyons. Sometimes it lives on the flats but seems to like sloping ground. Probably it seeks drainage, for in the rainy Northwest even the hillsides are soaking wet much of the year. It must have a reliable supply of water and seldom settles far from a stream.

Much of this animal's range was originally covered by dense forests of great spruces, firs, or redwoods. Since the country was settled, a vast acreage of this woodland has been cleared away. Some of it has been cultivated, but the rougher slopes and unfertile areas have grown up to a jungle of shrubs, herbs and vines. The mountain beaver has found this growth much better suited to its needs than the original forest. There is an abundance of food in great variety practically throughout the year. The dense tangled growth of vegetation is good insurance against birds of prey. Many stumps and down logs offer refuge from coyotes, foxes, skunks and other digging enemies, and against soaking rainstorms. Perhaps other foes—martens, bobcats, and cougars—find the heavy underbrush as much a handicap as an advantage in concealing their movements. The mountain beaver has very poor sight, and is at a grave disadvantage on cleared ground. It feels highly uncomfortable there and seldom goes more than a few yards from cover.

Its most dangerous enemies are the weasel and mink. These swift marauders pursue their prey into the deepest tunnels.

With its stout long claws on the front feet, and well-muscled shoulders, the "beaver" is well fitted for digging. In its chosen home in loose soil it burrows along eight to twelve inches below the surface. Its erratic course depends on many factors. A patch of food will entice it to swing to either side. A prone log, offering overhead protection, will cause the miner to turn upward until it is just underneath. There the tunnel becomes a trench or possibly a mere path on the top of the ground, while the log acts as a roof. If it is only a short distance to the next log, the runway stays on the surface.

Unlike the pocket gopher, the mountain beaver seldom utilizes the underground portions of plants. It wants the upper sections, and the tunnel is merely a passageway to reach those plants in greater safety than by traveling above ground.

The size of the tunnel varies with the nature of the ground. In hard soil it is only three or four inches in diameter, but if the digging is easy the passageway expands to as much as ten inches. At short intervals a shaft is driven straight out to the surface. Through this opening the miner dumps the excavated soil, pushing it ahead of its chest, outspread arms and blunt nose. It propels itself by shoving with the hind feet. As it throws the load on the downhill side just far enough to clear the tunnel mouth, it falls in a fan-shaped mound. Spoiled food, droppings, and old musty nest material are also thrown out of these openings. Other doorways are cut wherever the mountain beaver wishes to collect food.

Like the course of the tunnel, the doorways are located almost entirely by chance, wherever the builder wants to go out. Generally they open under a thick shrub or clump of ferns, for safety's sake. There may be as many as a dozen exits in an area twenty feet square. Unlike the true beaver, there is nothing systematic about the mountain beaver. It is often downright slipshod, failing to repair the tunnel roof which is frequently so thin that it collapses in many places. If the debris interferes with its work, the beaver just scoops it up and shoves it out.

The tunnel is often two hundred or three hundred feet long. If the mountain beaver's favorite food plants are abundant it does not need to cover as much ground and the tunnel is comparatively short. On the other hand, a scarcity of food will force it to extend the feeding range and thus the runway will be longer.

Each tunnel system has one or more nest chambers. They are located within two feet of the surface and, for protection, under spreading stumps or logs. Sometimes they are excavated under a mound of earth and debris formed by the roots of a wind-thrown tree. Often the room is an enlargement of the main tunnel, or it may be at the end of a blind passage. Globe-shaped or sometimes flattened, it is sixteen to twenty inches in diameter. It contains a nest made of dried grasses, ferns, twigs and attached leaves, and similar material.

During late winter or early spring—March at lower elevations in the Northwest—mountain beavers enter the rutting season. Little is known about this period, but it lasts about six weeks. At its end the males are very thin, but bear no marks of fighting among themselves. After two or three weeks of normal eating they recover their usual plump figures.

Mountain beavers require about four weeks for development before birth. Each mother produces two or three young. At the age of about a week they weigh approximately three ounces, and are covered with very fine pale brown fur. Their heads are large and they are still blind. Youngsters about six weeks old and weighing half a pound may still be nursing. They are supposed to leave the mother's bed and board at the age of two or three months.

This species has a low annual birth rate, but is generally sheltered and free from destructive enemies. Most of the young mature very slowly, especially in comparison with other rodents. By the end of their first winter they weigh only three-quarters as much as their now unrecognized parents. Very few of them attain sexual maturity until their second year.

Mountain beavers are almost exclusively nocturnal although they may be out foraging in the dusk or dawn, or even at mid-day if the sky is heavily overcast. Because their legs are short, they are poor runners. Apparently they depend on their hearing to guard against danger, but stay above ground as little as possible. Almost all food is cut and carried or dragged to the burrow entrance. Then, if it is too unwieldy, it is cut into sections, carried below, and eaten or stored. Seldom do they risk an attack, or nervous indigestion, by eating in the open.

Although it is a strict vegetarian, the mountain beaver has considerable variety in its diet. Almost any kind of green grass, clover, herbs, and leaves and twigs of shrubs and trees are eaten. It prefers deciduous species among the woody plants, including willow, alder, hazel, dogwood, maple, elderberry, currant and gooseberry. Thimbleberry, raspberry, bracken, sword fern, horsetail and skunk cabbage are also favorites during the summer.

When winter comes and plants drop their leaves and the twig tips of deciduous trees become woody, the mountain beaver turns to the evergreens—cedar, western hemlock, Douglas fir, salal, Oregon grape and evergreen ferns. It also eats the bark of both coniferous and deciduous trees and sometimes girdles them a foot or more in diameter.

On the heel of each "hand" is a protuberance. This "thumb" makes it easy for the mountain beaver to grasp and manipulate food. Sitting on its haunches like a squirrel, it clips short pieces from long stalks, passes them back into its mouth and chews them thoroughly.

As autumn approaches, this rodent cuts quantities of its favorite summertime herbage and stows it away in chambers underground. Some of these storage rooms are wide places in the main tunnel, while others are cupboards in the walls of the bedroom. When full, they each hold two to four quarts. Fern roots, and leaves and stems of nettles have been found in such reserves. Because they spoil relatively quickly, these stores must be renewed every few weeks. As the season wears on, cedar and fir twigs are put away. The "beaver" apparently brings in too much food, for its refuse heaps and even the storerooms often reveal quantities of spoiled and useless vegetation.

During summertime years ago, some naturalists noticed little bundles of grasses and other small plants lying near the openings of mountain beaver burrows. These were arranged with the butts of the stalks more or less even, and often "hay ricked" on sticks laid parallel on the ground. It was thought that the animals were curing hay for winter food. Now it is believed that these bundles of vegetation are dried for bedding, not to eat.

The mountain beaver wastes no time hibernating. Even in the higher mountains where the snow piles up and stays on the ground for several months, it maintains its daily routine. Tunneling about on the surface, it forces its way through the snow to reach the bases of trees and shrubs which it strips of bark. Sometimes it comes to the top of the snow and runs about on the crust. This permits it to reach another supply of food at a higher elevation. The following summer reveals elongated piles of earth on the ground, evidence that the mountain beaver had continued digging below the frost line and had dumped the earth in the snow tunnels after the manner of the pocket gopher.

Although it cannot scramble up a tree spread-eagled like a squirrel, it often climbs as high as fifteen feet if side limbs provide a ladder. Cutting off the branches as it climbs, it leaves stubs two or three inches long. This makes it possible for the "beaver" to come back down on a series of steps.

During the prolonged rains, water frequently runs in streams along the bottom of the mountain beaver's tunnel. It doesn't seem to mind, but splashes along regardless. It tries to assure itself of a dry bed by digging several sloping tunnels to draw off any seepage and to divert the streams coming down the hallway, but does not attempt to dam water as the true beaver does, nor does it actually like water except to drink. It swims well, although slowly, but probably does so only when strictly necessary.

The musky odor of the mountain beaver is immediately and extremely noticeable to the human nose. It is much like that of the muskrat, and is not repulsive to most people.

Ordinarily silent, this creature will whine when annoyed or in pain. A fight between two mountain beavers is punctuated by loud squeals of rage.

In capitvity, mountain beavers are pugnacious at first, but quickly lose their fear, abandon all attempts to bite and will take food from a person's hand within a few hours. They seldom live more than a few weeks in confinement. During that time they never show the least response, affection or enjoyment of caresses, as some tame animals do. It seems likely that they have a definitely limited intelligence and set of reactions.

In their normal habitat, mountain beavers rarely do any harm. Even their most extensive cutting is hardly appreciable in the lush, fast-growing vegetation of the rain forests. Occasionally they invade small fields and appropriate all kinds of growing crops, cutting off portions above ground and carrying them to their burrows. Sometimes they become destructive by tunnelling into roadbeds and walls of irrigation ditches. These animals can be easily caught in box traps, or in steel traps set in the tunnels. In fact, they will blunder into almost any contrivance that is set across their paths.

Structurally primitive, the mountain beaver is not developed for a specialized life. Zoologists recognize but one species, which is found only in North America. The total range does not exceed sixty-three thousand square miles. In the Tertiary Period, which ended about a million years ago, the range extended over most of the present western half of the United States.

General description. A medium-large burrowing rodent about the size of a muskrat, with stocky body, short legs, and no appreciable tail. Head short, eyes and ears small, and neck short. Fur slightly coarse and stiff. Color pinkish cinnamon to buffy ochre with a grizzling of black hairs especially along the backbone, fading into brownish gray on the under parts. Total length, 12 to 17 inches; height at shoulder, about 5 inches; weight, 2 to 3 pounds.

Distinguishing characteristics. Larger and uniformly browner in color than other burrowing rodents of its habitat, it lacks a visible tail.

Range. California (Marin and Mono Counties northward), through western Oregon and Washington (Pacific slope of the Cascades westward) and extreme southwestern British Columbia.

JUMPING MOUSE
ZAPUS AND NAPAEOZAPUS SP.

The beautiful little jumping mouse is one of the world's champion leapers—for its size. Some insects outrank it, but undoubtedly it is first among the mammals. Weighing less than an ounce, it can cover ten to twelve feet at a single bound. The great gray kangaroo of Australia, which stands about eight feet tall and may weigh as much as two hundred pounds, can jump no farther than thirty-two feet at the most. A human broad-jumper scaling one hundred and fifty pounds is exceptional if he can exceed twenty-six feet. If man and the kangaroo had the same percentage of propulsion energy as the jumping mouse, they could bound across the country making single leaps of four and one-half and six miles respectively!

Few persons know that the jumping mouse exists. Yet jumping mice are rather common in suitable places over most of Canada, Alaska, and the United States as far south as North Carolina, New Mexico, and south-central California. Sometimes they are seen at night disappearing into the darkness with mighty leaps, or crawling awkwardly through the weeds on all four legs. By day a mowing machine may startle them into leaping across the tall grassheads to safety.

A ten-foot leap is stimulated only by terror. The mouse is more likely to make a couple of zigzag jumps, each four to seven feet long, and then freeze motionless for as much as forty minutes if necessary. Its yellowish brown coat with a sprinkling of blackish hairs over the back blends with the surrounding leaf litter or grass stems. It becomes almost invisible, and the average meat hunter is likely to search in vain for it.

The tail, almost twice as long as the body, serves as a balance. This is very important to an animal that makes long jumps and quick turns. Without it, the center of gravity would be far ahead of its long hind legs. In making leaps there would be no equalizer for this sudden violent push upward and forward. When landing, the animal would be unbalanced. A mouse that has the misfortune to lose its tail in a trap or in the jaws of an enemy is hopelessly handicapped. Attempts to jump send it somersaulting and sprawling on its back. Losing the tail is almost as serious as breaking one of its slender rear legs. This latter accident is probably not rare, for the jumping mouse sometimes leaps through the grass forests with rash abandon. Even a young mouse has been seen to leap three feet high in an effort to clear high grass.

Jumping mice are nervous, high-strung little creatures. Because of this char-

JUMPING MOUSE

acteristic, they rarely become at ease in captivity. When they breed in cages, the mothers usually destroy their young. Even when first caught, however, they can be handled gently without fear of being bitten. Fastidiously clean, elegant little rodents, they spend much time licking and arranging their white fur vests and golden brown coats. While eating, they sit back on their haunches and long shanks and use their paws like hands. Sometimes they may tuck a few seeds into their ample cheeks to take home and munch on them at leisure.

The voice is a pleasant deep note rather than the high-pitched "shriek" of the deer mice and field mice. Drumming by vibrating the long tail against leaves or the ground is another method of communication. A woodland jumping mouse was once seen hopping about rapidly and erratically. As there did not seem to be any objective (insects, for instance,) the observer concluded that the mouse was going through a kind of "dance," as do so many other species of mice.

Two kinds of jumping mice are known, the grassland (*Zapus*) and the woodland (*Napaeozapus*). In their winter coats, they are almost identical in general color pattern as well as size. Most people could not distinguish between the two if it were not for the white tail-brush of the woodland jumping mouse. This species lives in woodland—provided there is a stream or lake nearby—in a sphagnum bog or willow-alder swamp, or among the rank weeds in a little opening on a forest stream. Water is essential. The woodland mouse never establishes a home in dry fields, and rarely in the open.

The grassland jumping mouse, which has a blackish tail-tip, likes a moist grassy habitat, but occasionally lives in open meadows and fields where the ground is fairly dry. Probably it can get along without water for long periods, managing with the dew and moisture in its food plants. It often lives on sagebrush flats, in thickets, shrubby forest borders, fence rows, and sometimes in moist woods. It ranges farther south in the lowlands, while the woodland mouse is not found far below the northern tier of eastern states except in the Appalachian Mountains.

During summer each jumping mouse lives alone in a small globular or conical nest of grass and leaves. Its outside diameter is four inches or a little more, and it has a tiny opening at the side that leads to the two- to three-inch room within. Sometimes fragments of moss, or even stray bits of string, cotton, wool, or feathers are used. The nest looks so much like the surrounding vegetation that it is very difficult to see. It is usually built on the ground among grass or weeds but often it may be suspended a few inches aloft in grass, shrubbery, or in a brush pile. Sometimes the mouse digs out a shallow hole in the ground an inch or two deep and builds its nest in the depression so that only the upper half is visible. Or again, it may locate its summer home in the shelter of dense overhanging grass, in a hollow tree, a stone wall, under a fallen log, or buried three or four inches in soil.

The woodland jumping mouse is more likely to build completely underground. A nest of this species that was once found in a short tunnel in sloping ground near Lake Nipigon, Ontario, has been described as follows: about a foot from the entrance, which was plugged with earth during the day, the one and three-quarter-inch passageway was enlarged to form an oblong rounded chamber four and one-half to six inches in diameter and three and one-quarter inches below the surface. The nest of aspen and wild sarsaparilla leaves completely filled the den. Beyond it the tunnel continued on about two feet where it ended. Possibly this was a drain to carry flood-waters away from the nest, or perhaps the owner intended to extend the burrow deeper for a winter home.

The winter residence is a small leaf- or grass-lined den deep enough in the ground to escape the frost. It is usually located in a bank or on sloping ground to ensure drainage. Jumping mice dig their own nest-burrows and rarely or never use tunnels of other mice or shrews.

Although the summer and winter coats of the woodland jumping mouse are very similar, the summer fur of the grassland species is generally brighter, and the dark band on the back is more noticeable.

The shedding of summer coat and the great increase of weight are the indications that the mice are preparing for a long sleep. As the fatty layer thickens over their backs and abdomens, and especially in the groins, their total weight is increased a third. They grow so obese that their movements are awkward and slow. More than ever, they are vulnerable to the meat-eaters who are also storing up reserves for the winter ahead. Nevertheless, many of them manage to survive and to find time and energy to prepare properly for their well-insulated dens. During the late summer and fall (earlier in the north, later in the south), all but mothers with autumn-born young retire for the winter. About a month later these tardy ones follow.

Months of storms and cold pass unnoticed. When the jumping mouse finally emerges from its winter's sleep, it seems to have no fear of bad weather. It fares forth bravely on cold, rainy nights as readily as on warm clear ones. Although it always prefers darkness, it may sometimes be seen abroad by day even when it has not been routed out of the nest. It does not make distinct trails like those of the methodical field mice or deer mice. A leaper cannot be trammeled by established routes. It may use broad avenues such as paths of bears, moose, and deer, but the grassland jumping mouse, anyway, is likely to go hopping off in any direction. The woodland relative usually follows its stream bank in a general way. Both species often climb through dense weeds, tangles of blackberry and raspberry vines and blueberry bushes, and even into alders to gather fruit and seeds.

Water is no hazard to either of them. They swim well, using only their hind feet while their hands on comparatively short arms are held up against their chest. To hold their head high, the tail is arched as a counterbalance. They can swim vigorously for at least five minutes which undoubtedly is more than enough for a little animal that has only quiet pools to cross occasionally. Grassland jumping mice in Idaho have been known to swim to little "islands" in a creek to get oatmeal which was used as trap bait. Another jumping mouse was seen to swim three or four inches under water all the way across a three-foot ditch.

Little is known about the social life of jumping mice in the wild. They seem to be mildly companionable, foraging on the same territory without argument. But in their homes they are definitely solitary except perhaps briefly at mating time. This occurs in spring soon after the mice emerge from hibernation. A second breeding period follows in late summer. Probably this second season is of minor importance, for it would seem that late-born young would not be as well fitted to survive the winter as would their older brothers who have had three or four months' advantage in growth.

Although the period required for gestation is not definitely known, it apparently is rather long for a mouse, possibly as much as thirty days. The tiny young, weighing only one-thirtieth of an ounce, are born sometime between the last week of May and the middle of July. The litter usually contains between two and six young, although an enormous family of nine young was found in early September on Mount Desert Island, Maine. At birth the youngsters are poorly developed, being small, blind, and naked, and even lacking the "whiskers" with which most animals are provided from the very first. They are no longer than one and three-quarters inches at most. The tails are very short, only half as long as the head and body. Those of adults are almost twice as long.

At the end of a week their tails have grown noticeably, and those of the woodland jumping mouse have developed the family badge of the white tail-tip. This color results from the hairs pushing up under the pink skin, for even at seven days of age the youngsters still lack all covering except the stumps of their future whiskers. At this period they are quite noisy, squeaking long and loudly if disturbed or a little hungry.

Two weeks after birth the young are almost three inches long, the tail being almost as long as head and body combined. Their backs are covered with short yellow fur through which the black hairs of the back stripe are beginning to appear. The legs and feet are still mostly bare but a thin covering of white hair on the belly hides most of the pink skin. At three weeks their eyes and ears are wide open, they weigh about one-third of an ounce, and except for their paler backs look much like their elders. They attain full adult stature and weight when only six weeks old.

In good times a jumping mouse will consume a daily ration equal to about one-half its own weight. Most of this consists of grass seeds, which the mouse secures by cutting or bending down the stalk until it can reach the head. A feeding place will be marked by little piles of stems which are cut into three- to four-inch lengths. Starchy roots are dug up, chewed well and eaten. Because it can reach so much higher than meadow mice, the jumping mouse cuts longer sections of grass. Its work therefore can usually be distinguished from that of the short-legged species of rodents such as meadow mice whose grass sections are rarely over one and one-half inches in length.

When daisylike plants are in bloom the mouse will run up the stem until the top bends to the ground, then cut off and eat the flowering head. It is fond of the fruits of raspberry, blackberry, blueberry, wintergreen, May-apple and many other plants. Tender shoots, including new needles of spruce, are staple food. Its stomach often contains numerous insects including larvae and adults of beetles, flies, butterflies and moths. Spiders and centipedes are also taken. Like other rodents it will eagerly devour meat, including the bodies of its own relatives. It will even eat fish found as carrion.

All of the enemies of very small mammals prey on the jumping mouse. Its long legs like steel springs, its habit of fleeing by hopping zigzag, and its furtive ways help to keep it alive. They are of no avail against more insidious foes such as lice and fleas, which drink its blood, and the larvae of bot flies which sometimes burrow in the body.

Jumping mice are distributed unevenly. In some localities that apparently are suitable to their requirements it may be impossible to find a single jumping mouse. In other places they outnumber the common shrews and white-footed mice. They fluctuate in numbers from time to time on the same area. A biologist who systematically trapped an area of seven and one-half to nine acres of dry and marshy grassland in southeastern Michigan was able to catch only one jumping mouse during an entire summer. The following year in late June the population on the plot rose to a peak of twenty-nine jumping mice. Then, near the end of August, the number shrank suddenly to about thirteen. On the portion of the plot where the mice occurred they numbered as many as five per acre, but they decreased to about two on an acre before autumn. This loss was due partly to deaths from attacks by enemies and partly to emigration to other habitats. In fact, some movement of mice was going on throughout the summer. For a couple of months the number of newcomers was enough to balance the losses and to keep the population stable. Males seemed to be more afflicted with wanderlust than females, for a larger number of strange males appeared on the plot during the summer.

These Michigan grassland jumping mice lived close together along the marshy shore of a pond and drainage ditch, and wandered from there onto the drier and less desirable ground. Some of the mice required as much as two and one-half acres, while others were content to stay within fifteen-hundredths of an acre. The average jumping mouse required about nine-tenths of an acre. These individual ranges of both males and females overlapped considerably, especially in the best part of the area where the mice were concentrated. They seemed to move at intervals, but most of them returned after absences of one to five weeks. They stayed an average of three weeks, then moved away again. Records of woodland jumping mice that have been marked indicate that they rarely travel more than one hundred and fifty feet from the point of their first capture. It is unusual for one of these animals to wander more than three hundred and fifty feet in twenty-four hours.

In a forest of mixed white pine, hemlock and birch in central New York, a total of fifty-one woodland jumping mice were trapped in twenty nights on a strip about one-half mile long beside a small stream. An unknown number of animals remained. The following year fifty-seven mice were captured on the same trapline in only two weeks. This shows that in favorable places jumping mice are numerous, and that they may recover rapidly from catastrophes.

Two genera of jumping mice are distinguished by the color of the slightly bushy tail-tip, and by the presence or absence of the upper premolar teeth:

1. The grassland jumping mouse (*Zapus*) has a blackish tail-tip. Including an upper premolar on each side of the jaw, it has a total of eighteen teeth. Approximately eleven species and fifteen subspecies range from the Arctic Circle as far south as North Carolina and south-central California. None are known outside of North America.

2. The woodland jumping mouse (*Napaeozapus*) has a white tail-tip. It lacks the upper premolars and therefore has only sixteen teeth. A single species (divided into four geographic races) is found from southern Hudson Bay and Great Slave Lake southward into the northern United States and, in the Appalachian Mountains, to North Carolina. Another species resides in Asia.

General description. A small to medium-sized mouse with small ears, small forelegs, very long hind legs, and very long, slender, tapering tail. Fur rather long and coarse; dark to pale yellowish brown or buffy, sprinkled with more or less numerous black hairs which are concentrated in a band down the back from crown to base of tail. Under parts and feet white or pale yellowish, sharply distinct from upper parts. Tail grayish brown above, white below. Tail-tip of woodland species is white; of grassland, blackish. Total length, 7½ to 10 inches; height at shoulders, 1¼ to 1½ inches; weight, ½ to 1 ounce.

Distinguishing characteristics. Long hind legs. Very long tail which is brownish above and white beneath. Brownish yellow color on upper parts. The kangaroo rat is considerably larger; has external cheek pockets; and has black markings on the head and a tail which is black above and below and white along either side.

Range. Northern North America, from the Arctic Circle south·to North Carolina, Missouri, and south-central California.

PORCUPINE

ERETHIZON DORSATUM AND *E. EPIXANTHUM*

Some mammals escape their enemies by running. Others hide, or use their wits in various ways. A few prefer to attack. One animal can protect itself by merely bristling up its coat—the porcupine.

From the top of its head, or even cheeks, to the end of its heavy tail, the hairy coat is thickly sprinkled with slender, very sharp, hollow quills. They are white or yellowish ivory with black tips. Each one is half an inch or less, up to a possible five inches long. About one-quarter inch from the outer end, the quill suddenly tapers into a long point which is covered with very fine, black barbs. Each one of the barbs overlaps the one behind it, something like scales on a fish. The number on each quill varies greatly. (Rarely an animal will be found whose armament is perfectly smooth, like the point of a needle.) Ordinarily every quill is furnished with several dozen barbs, each one so small that the outer surface of the quill is scarcely roughened to the touch.

The base of each quill is constricted and is lightly connected to a layer of muscle which lies just under the skin. By means of this muscle sheet, the quills can be pointed rigidly upward, or allowed to lie flat and at ease.

Ordinarily the porcupine gives the appearance of being mostly fur. If the coat is of more than average thickness, the quills are largely concealed except on the tail. Its short heavy body with arched back is a mass of coarse guard-hairs which

PORCUPINE

are brown near the base. These grade in the eastern species (*Erethizon dorsatum*) into dark brown or blackish. Many of them are tipped with white. Those of the yellow-haired species of the West (*E. epixanthum*) are tipped with yellowish. Underneath the overcoat of each species is a suit of fine, brown underfur.

Little shoe-button eyes are almost buried in hair. The blunt-nosed head, with its small ears, is connected to the humped shoulders by a short, almost imperceptible neck. The legs are short and bowed. Bearlike, the long-clawed front feet toe in. The tail is short, thick and blunt at the end.

Albino porcupines are known, but are rare. They are creamy white, with pink eyes, and the quills and claws are whitish with the merest trace of brown.

As it waddles slowly along, its nose to the ground, the porcupine looks like easy quarry for any meat-eater that chances by. Appearances were never more deceiving.

If a dog rushes up, the porcupine instantly raises every quill so that it stands on end. The reaction is automatic, probably like the erection of hair on the back of the head of a startled person. The animal humps up in the middle, pulls back its unprotected nose and face, and raises its tail slightly. The quills seem to spring out of the short undercoat, which is often so thin on the lower back over the hips that bare skin is exposed. Most of the guard-hairs are bent forward by the erection of the shoulder quills. Now we know why it is also called "quill pig."

Somewhat taken aback, the dog circles, trying to find an opening. As it does so, the porcupine revolves jerkily on its front legs as an axis, always keeping its rear toward the enemy. The hind legs throw the body around in little hops. It grumbles and chatters its teeth in warning. Its tail jerks threateningly from side to side. Its breath comes in frightened gasps.

The dog gets impatient and makes a quick rush. A grab at the neck, a quick snapping jerk, and its quarry will lie dying of a broken neck, so it thinks. But— too suddenly for a human eye and mind to record the details, the porcupine acts. It twists its rear to meet the sudden attack. The quill-thatched tail jerks upward with all the force of the powerful, heavy muscles. It strikes the dog under the chin and in the throat. The momentum carries the dog's head into the radiating forest of quills on the porcupine's back. Instantly the long slender points of hundreds of these darts slip through the dog's hide and into its flesh. Its lips and open mouth are stuck like a great pincushion. Every quill burns like fire. Yelping with the pain and terror of this strange, horrible torment, the dog races away.

Any effort to paw away the fire will only drive the quills deeper. As the barbs of the quills become moistened, they expand slightly. Each movement of the muscles causes the quills to work deeper. Only a strong pull by a human hand, aided by pliers, will remove them. Otherwise they will continue to inch their way along through the flesh. Some will push on and out, or become absorbed, doing little harm. Others may sometimes reach vital spots, such as eyes, large arteries, lungs or heart, and cause death by mechanical action or through infection. The wild animal whose mouth has been badly stuck is generally believed to die of starvation because of inability to eat.

There is some dissension about this theory, however. "I once examined a wolf that had quills in mouth and throat, œsophagus and stomach, some of which had penetrated adjacent tissue," Dr. C. H. D. Clarke has written me. "They looked harmless and soft. The wolf was in good shape, though the œsophagus showed some reddening around the quills. Apparently quills are absorbed fast in some tissues, slowly in others. However, I have never heard of an animal full of quills that was even in poor shape."

Can the porcupine shoot its quills at an enemy? Not ordinarily. They grow, mature, and are shed, just like the real fur except that they last longer and the entire set is not replaced seasonally or at one time. An old quill may be attached so loosely to the tail that, when the appendage gives a mighty flip, the quill may be thrown as much as five or six feet. This flying dart may strike the enemy with enough force to penetrate the skin and, with the aid of its barbs, to work into the flesh. Such an occurrence is pure luck. The porcupine has no control over it, and it does not happen often.

The "quill pig" can lose several hundred quills in a single encounter with an enemy, without becoming handicapped. Very likely it started out with twenty to thirty thousand of them. The number varies considerably with the individual. As they are lost or moulted, others grow and take their place. Short white quills are always coming in down among the bases of the long, mature ones. These developing weapons are firmly rooted in the skin and do not come out easily. But they are painful deterrents to any carnivore that is tempted to grab the porcupine at a spot where mature quills are missing.

The final length of the quills depends on their location on the animal. The longest grow on the rump and the shortest on the cheeks. Measurements made on an adult yellow-haired (western) porcupine showed that quills on the cheek ranged from two-fifths to three-fourths of an inch in length. Those on the forehead were about one and one-fifth inches long; on the shoulders and middle of back, slightly more than two inches; on the rump, two and one-half inches; and along the side of the tail, two to two and one-third inches in length.

How can porcupines mate? Around stoves in old-time logging camps, one of the favorite topics of speculation was the possible methods by which porcupines could get together without spearing each other. Because of their prickly armament, it was almost universally believed that they could not possibly mate like other animals. Nature, however, has provided a simple means. Muscular control of the quills is so complete that the female is able to pull her quills down very tightly, or allow them to lie limply, and so avoid wounding the male. After some affectionate nose-rubbing, standing up on hind legs and embracing, the female twists her tail abruptly to one side or raises it directly over her back. Needless to say, mating does not take place unless the female is in complete agreement. In fact the male usually leaves it up to her to make the first advances. When ready, she is very aggressive. Whether she mates more than once during the season is unknown. If so, the unions must take place within three or four hours, after which she repels any suitor. Two males have been seen bristling their quills at each other while a female looked on without show of emotion.

During mating season, the porcupines lose their usual taciturnity. They chatter, grumble and whine. Little grunts, moans, miaows and even barks express the gamut of their emotions. Heard at night, these sounds are unlike anything that a porcupine could be expected to utter. As a result, eavesdroppers who are newcomers to the woods are often mystified.

Two Canada porcupines in southern New Hampshire once frequented the lawn and apple trees around a house for a number of weeks. On several nights the larger of the two animals was heard repeating over and over sounds like: "Dear, dear, dear." There was a human quality, becoming at times a distinct moan, that suggested a person in pain. However, it was moving briskly about in search of food. During one nocturnal occasion, the two animals seemed to be talking back and forth. One sounded like a querulous child, while the other moaned in lower tones that almost boomed. None of these sounds could be heard by human ears more than one hundred feet away.

In the latitude of northern United States, the eastern porcupine mates in late October, November, and possibly early December. The season for the yellow-haired species in northern Arizona is September to October.

The gestation period was unknown until recently and authorities disagreed on the vital statistics that determine the point. In New England the birth season is said to be during March. Most Ontario porcupines arrive in May, and a few during June. In the Southwest, yellow-haired porcupines are born in April or May. Their development period, therefore, would be six or seven months. While the rutting and birth periods undoubtedly are adjusted to latitude and altitude, the gestation period itself probably does not vary much in length. Dr. Albert R. Shadle has now determined that in the eastern species the development period is two hundred and nine days.

Each mother porcupine gives birth to one young. Twins are very rare. In fact there seems to be no authentic record of such an occurrence. The birthplace is the den in tumbled rocks, a hollow log, stump, windfall, brushpile, thicket, under the partial shelter of a fallen tree trunk, or between the exposed roots of a stump. The mother does not bother to make a nest or special bed for the event.

Because of its comparatively long development, it is no surprise that the young one comes into the world fairly well prepared. If the mother is a Canada porcupine (eastern species of North America), it is larger than a baby bear. It weighs between nine-tenths and one and one-tenth pounds, which is six or seven percent of the mother's weight. About twelve inches long from nose to end of tail, it is heavily clothed in long, dense black hair. Yellow-haired porcupines become yellow later. The beady black eyes are open and the tips of the blunt incisor teeth and some of the molars are already well past the gums.

In the fur are hundreds of quills, some of them as much as an inch long. Although said to be barbless, these juvenile spines are hard and sharp as needles as soon as they are dry. If there is any disturbance, the little porcupine will erect them defensively. It can walk unsteadily, and will wheel and swing smartly with its tail at an intruder. It does not have sufficient strength, however, to drive the spines into a human hand.

Young porcupines have lived when removed from the mothers by Caesarian operation, provided they were within a few days of normal birth. These little creatures exhibit the normal defense reaction within a few minutes of their forced arrival in the world.

Is the porcupine born head first? It is popularly supposed that this is essential; otherwise its backward-directed quills would kill the mother. Actually this is of little or no consequence, for the animal is born while still enclosed in the membranous sac.

Some Indian tribes believed that the mother porcupine drove her child away as soon as it was born, and never nursed it. As a matter of fact, she suckles it immediately after birth and tends it regularly for the next week. Then its increasing appetite for green herbs permits her to begin the process of weaning. This probably requires only a week or ten days, although well-fed mothers in captivity have been known to permit their young to nurse until they were more than three months old. The mother is not demonstrative, but sometimes rubs noses with her offspring and answers its whines with grunts.

From the second day of life, the young porcupine is able to climb. It does so cautiously, seldom going up more than half as high as the mother does until it is about six months old. It spends much time on the ground, sleeping curled up in hollow logs, stumps, or in heaps of brush. It is unlikely that mother and young remain together constantly after the latter is about six months of age. They probably drift apart by separating for periods of gradually lengthening duration until they finally meet as strangers.

During the first autumn, the young porcupine weighs about three and one-half pounds and measures one and one-half feet from nose to tail. A year later its weight has doubled or more, and it is about twenty-one inches long. It is now looking for a mate of its own age or older. Possibly some especially advanced porcupines breed when they are only six or seven months old.

Despite its lethargic manner, the porcupine is playful at times. Youngsters naturally are more frisky than grownups, but even a stodgy parent has been seen to dance. Standing on the hind feet and tail, it rolls or rocks, throwing the weight alternately on one foot while raising the other, then reversing and rocking to the other foot. Sometimes the front feet are waved and the head and shoulders swung from side to side. Young animals play together, wrestling and biting to the accompaniment of grumbles and whines. They frequently go through the motions of defending themselves from an imaginary enemy, whirling and slapping the tail as if in great danger. There is much difference in the behavior of various individuals. Some continue to be frivolous for years while others are serious from birth.

For all that it is such a dumpy creature, the porcupine is a ready swimmer. It often crosses streams of its own volition. Because the dense inner coat holds much air and because each quill is filled with air, it floats buoyantly. Of course the short legs cannot develop much speed.

On land, the bow-legged porcupine walks with a swinging waddle that reminds one of a very fat sailor. As each hind foot is moved forward close behind the front foot, the gait is almost pacing. The animal's back, hips and tail swing from side to side. Often the tail drags lightly on the ground. If alarmed, the animal breaks into a clumsy gallop. It always tries to get to the security of a tree or rock pile, for even a fat man can overtake a porcupine if the latter does not have too much advantage.

Most of the time the porcupine is not a sociable fellow. If it were gregarious, the forest would be depleted and the porcupine "herd" would be obliged to migrate or die. Except during mating season, under certain winter conditions, and where dens are scarce, the quill pig is seen alone, often a long distance from any other of its kind. For weeks it slowly plods or climbs alone, apparently quite content and without a thought for anything except its stomach. However, it is not disagreeable when other porcupines are around. Numbers often den together or use the same small rock pile for winter shelter. In northern Michigan during January, I have seen as many as seven porcupines feeding close together in the same or two or three adjacent trees. This was near the rock ledges which served as headquarters for the group.

In regions where piles of broken exposed rocks are scarce, porcupines may be forced to room together. The few available shelters sometimes accommodate large numbers of the animals in the course of a few months. While there may be room for no more than four or five porcupines at one time, the total number resorting to them may be much greater. More than one hundred have been consecutively removed from a New Hampshire mine dump that was only two hundred feet square. There seems to be no pride of ownership in these denning places and we have no indication that the porcupines fight for choice crevices or dens.

The porcupine is slow and deliberate. On the ground, only fright will force it out of a waddling walk into a lumbering gallop. In the trees it displays none of the swiftness or grace of the squirrels. It seems to consider every motion carefully. Once aloft, it will often climb higher to get away from danger, but seems to react too slowly to dodge missiles or to seek protection behind the trunk or larger limbs. Many biologists and the general public have supposed that its mental ability and alertness were sacrificed or lost because the coat of quills was adequate protection.

Apparently this is not true. Experimenters in porcupine psychology have found that it is adaptable. It is able to learn the way through a maze that proves too much for many other quicker witted animals. If captured young, porcupines frequently become delightful and affectionate pets. In one instance a pair of youngsters that were brought up on a bottle were left near their owner's cabin to make their own living through the winter. When the owner returned the next summer, after six months' absence, the porcupines recognized his voice. Coming to meet him, they held out their forepaws in greeting, and climbed up on him in search of food.

Part of the porcupine's reputation for stupidity is due to poor eyesight. I once watched a porcupine walking along a stream in central Alaska. When it stopped to take a drink, I ran up behind it with a camera. The noise of the rushing water drowned out the sound of my footsteps and prevented the keen ears of the porcupine from hearing me. When it turned on its haunches and caught sight of me only six feet away it obviously was in great perplexity. Watching me carefully, it did not stir until I moved. Only this told the porcupine that I was not a boulder.

On another occasion, Dr. H. H. T. Jackson stood still on a woods road in Wisconsin while a porcupine ambled up. Possibly mistaking the man's legs in their leather puttes for twin saplings, the animal started to gnaw on one of them. Dr. Jackson had to drive off the porcupine to save his puttees.

Although a little slow, the porcupine is persistent in working out any problem. Despite handicaps of physique, there is no doubt that it is a successful type. Porcupines are found on all five continents. Their center of abundance is in South America where scientists have described no less than six families and twenty-nine genera. All of these are tree-climbers. Some have long, prehensile tails which they use for grasping and climbing. The Old World porcupines live on the ground. The most spectacular are found in Africa and are provided with a great crest of black-and-white spines between twelve and fifteen inches long which arise from the shoulders and back.

Because the North American porcupine has quills something like those of the Old World hedgehog, it is frequently called a hedgehog. The spiny coat is almost the only feature that the two animals have in common. The true porcupine is a rodent, while the hedgehog is an insectivore and is closely related to the mole and the shrew. Needless to say, the same name should not be given to two very dissimilar animals.

The ancestors of North American porcupines emigrated from South America by way of the Isthmus of Panama. As long ago as the Pleistocene Age (one million years back), they were common all over the area that is now the United States. Although diversified into only two species, the present-day North American porcupines are numerous and with few exceptions are found nearly everywhere in forested areas. They are absent from the southeastern United States south of the Ohio River, from Newfoundland and the northern Arctic tundra, from much of the Great Plains, and the extreme Southwest.

Porcupines will take many conditions of climate and topography, all the way from hot chaparral to cold spruce forests. They are abundant in places in rocky canyons of the southwestern mountains. In central Alaska I have found them living contentedly in patches of scattered scrub timber and even along alder-bordered streams fully four miles from the nearest woodland.

In eastern America, porcupines are influenced most by human population and by forest fires and timber-cutting. They are scarce near the large cities, although it is surprising how often they manage to exist near smaller towns. They cannot survive intense fires or clear-cutting, but large sprout growth and open woodland are quite acceptable provided there are good sized den-trees or broken rock ledges for protection. Some of the densest populations of porcupines I have ever seen were in partially cut-over areas in the Upper Peninsula of Michigan.

In the West, the animals are most abundant on ridges. There are a number of reasons. The ground is apt to be snow-free longer than the flats. Ridges are natural trail routes. Ground vegetation is usually more diversified, and mistletoe, a great delicacy, is usually more abundant. However, these western porcupines may be found in as many different habitats as eastern ones, and occur on wooded plains as well as in the mountains. Rare wanderers have been seen on brushy deserts and arid grassland ten or more miles from the nearest hills or timber. In these journeys they take advantage of any cover or shelter, no matter how unusual. In treeless valleys they have been found in badger dens.

As a rule, porcupines make their home in a crevice in a ledge, a talus slope of broken rock, or a hollow tree or down log. Provided food trees are near by, the animals much prefer a rocky terrain to one that is smooth and unbroken. Sometimes they use good-sized caves in cliffs. Lava flows with their jagged, rough masses of rock, and caves, tubes, or "chimneys" are especially desirable. Porcupines often travel some distance to reach these rocky havens where they rest for several days before waddling back to their favorite trees. Dens frequently are marked by great piles of smooth pellets. Greenish brown at first, these droppings soon turn to a deep brown or blackish, then fade to light brown as they disintegrate.

Some of the porcupines' travels are short, such as those between dens and feeding areas. These trails, especially in snow, may be used repeatedly by the same or different individuals for more than three hundred feet. Other movements may be several miles long, as in mountainous country where numerous animals move to lower elevations during winter. These "migrations" often follow fairly definite routes. While the travel trails of porcupines are not easily seen, and, of course, are not beaten into the earth like the migration trails of elk, the general route often can be traced by the prevalence of barked trees which have served as lunch stations to generations of traveling porcupines. Most of these movements occur in spring and fall.

Once a porcupine picks on a wintering spot, it rarely wanders far away. Sometimes it will stay in one tree for weeks at a time during zero weather. The fur coat keeps it warm. Apparently it dislikes to face the task of hiking through soft snow without "snowshoes" to reach a den.

Most persons assume that porcupines live entirely on tree bark. Even during winter, when the animals live chiefly in trees, this is only partly true. They feed extensively on the inner bark of conifers, including most of the pines, tamaracks, spruces, hemlocks, firs, and northern white cedar; and on such hardwoods as oaks, maples, birches, cherry, beech, basswood, hornbeam (*Ostrya*), ash, cottonwood and other members of the poplar family, alders, and willows. However, porcupines in winter also eat considerable amounts of coniferous foliage, such as the needles of yellow and white pines and hemlock, and the flat sprays of cedar. Only the tender needles of the previous summer are taken. Mistletoe is a particularly favorite food of western porcupines during the cooler months.

Most porcupines prefer one tree species above all others. In the Northeast it is hemlock; in the Lake States, white pine; and in the West, yellow pine.

As spring comes, the porcupines seek out the red and sugar maples, for their cambium layer is full of sap. They are very fond of the catkins of poplars, alders and willows. With the disappearance of snow and the greening of the herbs, the porcupines come down to the ground for food. They eat the leaves of such shrubs as currants, gooseberries, buffalo berry, rose, thorn-apple, and buckbrush (*Ceanothus*); also grass, wild geranium, aster, lupine, cinquefoil, dandelion, dogbane and wood betony. In the northeastern United States, the animals have been seen wading into ponds to feed on water-lily pads and aquatic liverwort. The inner bark of trees is still eaten at times, but to a much less extent in summer than in winter. Oak acorns and beechnuts are sometimes taken in autumn. They may be gathered and consumed in the trees instead of waiting for frosts to bring them to the ground.

Although they are not known to eat meat, porcupines are very fond of bones. Presumably they need the minerals. The skeleton of any large mammal that dies, and the cast antlers of deer, elk or moose, will soon be chiseled away by the porcupines' teeth. The animals' fondness for salt is well known. Any ax or other tool that is left lying around a camp where porcupines can reach it will soon be minus a handle because of the salty perspiration. Tables or chairs on which salt has been spilled will be gnawed and devoured. Outdoor toilets may be partially eaten. Even larger buildings have tumbled down as a direct result of the porcupines' gnawing away the foundations. However, porcupines have been known to eat parts of the flooring around a bag of salt, but ignore the salt.

On the ground, the porcupine eats most plants just as it comes to them. As it encounters an herb, the animal sniffs it over briefly, then chews it noisily and thoroughly before swallowing it. Sometimes the porcupine rears back on its haunches and, if the plants are close together, may shuffle a step or two without dropping down to all fours.

In a tree, the porcupine is sure-footed but very slow. It greatly dislikes to jump in any direction, even as little as ten or twelve inches. Yet it balances and clings to twigs amazingly small. One marvels at its nerve as it climbs serenely with almost no support sixty feet above ground. If a desirable limb is overhead it will stand up at full height, reach with a front paw and bend the branch down to its mouth. Or, if the branch refuses to bend sufficiently, it cuts off the limb swiftly with its powerful chisel teeth. Any twigs that get in the way as it walks on the limbs are cut off and dropped to the ground, where they may become a welcome find for some hungry rabbit or deer. When feeding on twigs, tree flowers, or buds, the porcupine obviously relies much more on its nose than eyes to identify the tidbits. It sniffs quickly along the length of the branch to find out what is there.

Most of the porcupine's tree diet is taken from the larger branches or the trunk. It never eats while clinging, as the lighter bodied squirrels may do. Instead, it climbs the trunk, using all four clawed feet and flattened bristly tail, then finds a place to sit or rear on its haunches. Chipping or pulling off the loose outer bark, it drops the pieces to the ground. As soon as an area of soft inner bark is exposed it begins to eat. Its thorough chewing can be heard fifty to one hundred feet away. After eating its fill, it may sprawl out on a horizontal limb with all legs dangling, and rest for a time in perfect contentment.

The pale patches of wood with the marks of the porcupine's lower incisor teeth are conspicuous on the dark-barked trees. These "blazes" occur at any height above the ground. They may be smaller than a man's palm, or they may extend entirely around the tree and for several feet vertically. In regions where the snow depth is great they are concentrated on certain trees where the porcupines have wintered. Even in milder climates where the animals are not so much restricted, the "blazing" is not generally distributed over wide areas.

Forest managers often are worried by the damage done by porcupines to trees. The animals' girdling kills limbs, and even whole trees. Sometimes, in cutover lands, this may mean that seed trees die and gaps will occur in the future forest. The upper sections of trees that survive may grow gnarled or limby, spoiling that portion of the trunk for lumber or straight timbers. Loss of bark causes "cat-faces" and non-development of the underlying wood. It also permits the entrance of disease spores which may weaken or kill the tree.

However, the conspicuous nature of porcupine "work" often gives an exaggerated idea of its effect on the forest. A careful examination is necessary to appraise it accurately. Actually, girdling of side limbs rarely has much effect on the commercial timber which the tree ultimately will produce. Many trees recover after severe attacks. The loss of even a high percentage of seedling trees from a fully stocked stand means little, because they probably would be eliminated anyhow in the normal struggle for existence.

A study and appraisal of porcupine damage was once made in merchantable stands of red spruce in Maine. The number of porcupines ranged from twenty to twenty-eight a square mile. Slightly over one-half of one per cent of the total volume of timber had been lost as a result of their feeding, a monetary loss of only eleven and five-tenths to fifteen and seven-tenths cents an acre. In the yellow pine forests of the West the damage in places would be more costly. However, the expense of killing porcupines is worth while only in a small fraction of the woodland area, or under unusual circumstances. This may be accomplished by hunting and shooting, or by poisoning with salt which has been treated with strychnine or other lethal agent. This material should be placed well within the dens, not outside where other salt-loving mammals and birds can reach it.

Although the quills would seem to guarantee immunity against attack by any creature except man, the porcupine has its quota of natural foes. The red fox, bobcat, lynx, fisher and mountain lion are formidable enemies. Of course some of these predators, young or inexperienced, suffer terribly as a result of blundering encounters and leave the quill-pig strictly alone thereafter. Others, however, learn how to flip the spiny creature over on its back and rip open the defenseless soft belly. Occasionally, but not as often, this trick is also acquired by the wolf, coyote, wolverine, and the black and grizzly bears. The great horned owl, when starving, also has been known to attack the porcupine.

Other more insidious foes, but apparently much less dangerous ones, are tapeworms, roundworms, threadworms (*Filaria*), ticks and lice (*Mallophaga*). Practically all adult porcupines carry a large population of the first two internal parasites. An animal killed in northern Yellowstone Park contained about one hundred tapeworms and one hundred and twenty-five roundworms between three thirty-seconds and one inch long. Yet the animal was fat and apparently in good health. Porcupines are susceptible to a number of diseases, among which tularemia may be one of the worst. Tumors are of frequent occurrence. Sometimes the heart is attacked by parasites, or is shriveled and surrounded by a gelatinous fluid. The animals often have digestive disturbances, and are quite liable to infection from wounds received in climbing or from their own quills.

Severe forest fires burn or suffocate such slow-moving animals as porcupines. For several years following, the area has no attraction for possible immigrants.

What good is the porcupine? By monetary standards, very little. The quills are often used by Indians and white curio makers as ornamental work on native baskets, and other articles. Properly prepared, the meat is tasty. The animal is one of the very few woodland creatures that can be captured and killed by a lost person who is without firearms. In the West, its fondness for mistletoe is a real asset in reducing this parasitic plant which saps the vitality of so many trees. But it is too likely to undo this good work by eating the bark of the same trees and perhaps killing some of them. Despite all this, very few persons would like to exterminate the picturesque creature. Without the porcupine the forest would be a far less interesting place.

There are two main groups of quill-pigs:

1. The Canada porcupine (*Erethizon dorsatum*), which is blackish or dark brown, lives in eastern North America from Labrador to southern Pennsylvania and perhaps West Virginia, and west to Minnesota and the Hudson Bay region.

2. The yellow-haired porcupine (*E. epixanthum*) has a "frosting" of yellowish or greenish yellow due to the longer hairs being tipped with that color. It is found throughout western America within the range described.

General description. A large spiny rodent with small head, small eyes and ears, heavy, high-arched body, short, bowed legs, and heavy, short tail. Pelage made up of long, soft, woolly hair in which grow longer glistening guard hairs and, on back and tail, long, stiff, barbed spines. Color blackish to dark brownish, liberally sprinkled with whitish or yellowish tipped hairs; spines yellowish white tipped with brown or black. Total length, 27 to 40 inches; height at shoulder, about 12 inches; weight, 8 to 15 pounds, up to a maximum of 35 pounds.

Distinguishing characteristics. The spine-filled coat, high arched back, and clumsy movements.

Range. Most of northern North America, from Labrador to western Alaska; south to Massachusetts, southern Pennsylvania or possibly West Virginia, central Wisconsin, western South Dakota, southeastern Arizona, and the southern Sierra Nevada.

18. The Hares and Rabbits

PIKA—*OCHOTONA* SP.

The pika is one of the few mammals rugged enough to spend its entire life in the chill, high, barren mountains of the West. On summer days, when the sun shines warmly from a bright blue sky, the granite cirques and cliffs reflect the heat. The little meadows glow with the color of dozens of flowers, and through them murmur and gurgle the rivulets from melting snow banks.

Summer is short, clouds soon congeal around the peaks and drop their burden of snow and hail. Long plumes of snow stream from the crests and ridges, and icy winds beat and howl diabolically. The elk and coyotes flee to the valleys. The bighorns hunt for windswept slopes where the snow is shallow enough to paw down to the dried, brown herbage. Curled up in dens underground or in the ledges, bears, marmots and ground squirrels take refuge in a sleep so profound that some of them are almost lifeless.

But the little pika is not intimidated. It does not migrate, nor does it hibernate. Making no change in its schedule, the industrious animal hustles about its business under the deep snow. It looks like a medium-sized guinea pig in a soft gray or buffy gray coat. Known as the cony or rock rabbit, it is related to the rabbits and hares.

Its chosen home is where great piles of rocks of all sizes and shapes have been pried off the cliffs and mountainsides by alternating frost and heat, and come to rest below. A few renegades have been known to live in a sawmill slab pile or in a log jam on a mountain stream. Others have been found occupying burrows among trees. But most of their race do not feel at home away from broken rocks.

A couple of pika subspecies or geographic varieties live on the plains of northeastern California, eastern Oregon, and southwestern Idaho, in old lava fields. All other members of the tribe inhabit the mountains. In the United States they live as high as thirteen thousand six hundred feet (on Wheeler Peak in northern New Mexico). From the Columbia River northward, through western Canada and Alaska, they find temperature conditions suitable at lower elevations, down almost to sea level.

The rock slides of the high western mountains, which are so popular with

PIKA

pikas, support little plant life. A hardy shrub may gain a foothold, or a clump of grass, but rarely is there any vegetation except for the gray-green lichens that cling tightly to the rocks. Inhospitable places, the slides are shunned by most animals except the pikas, marmots, wood rats, and weasels. Even the alpine birds, the finches, juncoes, and pipits, alight only briefly.

"Ka-ack!" The slide that is almost inaccessible to man and apparently deserted comes to life. "Ka-ack!" High-pitched, the pika's cry has a rusty quality that is somewhat like a protesting door hinge. Lasting perhaps two or three seconds, the prolonged alarm signal sounds to me like the voice of a mechanical doll. It resounds, muffled, from the depths far below. Toward the head of the slide comes an echo, slightly different:

"Ka-chak!" Then, in a part of the rock field where the peculiar, squeaking bleat apparently did *not* originate, a bump of gray rock on a big slanting stone resolves itself into an animal. It is a pika, a ventriloquist.

Blending into the jumbled surroundings, the little creature is hard to distinguish. Only the head seems to move. It is merely lifted straight up as it looks around. The little eyes, set rather close to the high arched nose, can see on each side without turning the head, as well as straight ahead. The broad ears are efficient sound scoops. The nose trembles with excitement and the front feet shift nervously.

After the alarm has died away, there is no sound on the mountainside except the murmur of a distant stream or the far cry of an eagle. Then, from the rocks comes a series of short bleats. Spaced about two seconds apart, they have the same ventriloquial effect as the first alarm call. They come from all directions, but it is the pika in view that is making them. At each "ka" its hunched body and head moves upward and forward about an inch, and the ears twitch forward. As the series of bleats goes on, each note becomes a little fainter as if the pika were moving out of hearing distance. But there it is, opening and shutting its mouth. Perhaps it is running out of breath. Finally, after twenty-five or thirty notes, it becomes silent. Far across the slide, another animal may at last answer.

When danger appears too imminent, the pika may satisfy itself with one explosive "ka-ack!" and disappear like a flash into a crevice. However, if time and quiet are reassuring, it may continue its work. Hopping across the rocks, it moves in short, quick dashes, with a stiff, hobbling gait. Unlike the rabbits, the hind legs are as short as the fore legs, so it does not bound. The tiny, furred feet with the hairy soles give perfect traction. As it hops from slick slope to sharp ridge to peaked rock, it sticks at each contact almost as securely as a fly. Apparently it never sits up on its hind legs like its bigger relatives.

At the edge of the slide it pauses for one reassuring glance, then rushes to a favorite herb. Clipping it off with sharp incisors, it carries the plant to another and another. In less than a minute the pika has a bundle, almost as big as itself, crosswise in its mouth. Racing back to the slide, it hops across the rocks and lays the fresh bundle on a steadily increasing haystack for curing.

During late summer and fall the pika is very busy harvesting crops, for it seems to know that winter is approaching. Then it will be impossible to go beyond the jumbled rocks to the "hay fields." The pika is not fitted to tunnel through snow. It makes trip after trip for forage, rarely venturing more than a few yards from the edge of the rocks, although once in a great while it may be tempted as much as fifty or seventy-five feet away.

Some haystacks are small, but many contain as much as a bushel of dried material and represent numerous days of labor. Although the piles are sometimes located deep in the crevices of the rocks, they are usually so placed that the sun can get at them. Occasionally a tree trunk that has rolled down the slide may serve for overhead shelter, but generally a slanting rock keeps off rain and snow.

The pika collects many varieties of plants, the species depending on the locality and on the tastes of individual animals. Sometimes twigs and leaves are clipped from the lowest branches of trees, including aspen, lodgepole pine, Engelmann spruce, elder, and chokecherry. To get them the pika may climb briefly for two or three feet off the ground, and walk out on low horizontal limbs to reach choice bits. Among the shrubs identifiable in pika "hay piles" are currant, gooseberry, raspberry, rose, snowberry, syringa (New Mexico), blueberry (Yellowstone Park), serviceberry, *Holodiscus* (California), sagebrush (Oregon), and spirea of several species (Washington). Most of the pika's food is made up of grasses, sedges, and stems, leaves and blossoms of a great variety of other herbs. Some of these are nettles, thistles, lupine, phacelia, goldenrod, fireweed, aster, mountain avens, gentian, Indian tobacco, penstemon, bearberry, heather, knotweed, saxifrage, cinquefoil, yarrow, phlox, *Sieversia turbinata* and many ferns.

Of two stacks that I examined late one October day near the shore of Leigh Lake, Grand Teton National Park, one was made up mostly of elk sedge, Calamagrostis and poa grasses, bracken, and kinnikinick, with some twigs of snowbrush (*Ceanothus*), huckleberry (two kinds), leaves of alder and aspen, and several clusters of lichen. The other pile contained dwarf juniper, kinnikinick, pearly everlasting, lodgepole pine needles, elk sedge, huckleberry, spirea, honeysuckle (*Xylosteon*), aspen and elder leaves, and twigs of buffalo-berry and serviceberry.

Often the pika must run several hundred feet with its bundles of forage. Well-defined trails are beaten between the "hayfields," the several stacks, and the entrance to its home. Most of the work is done during the day, for it normally rests at night. However, it has been heard calling at night, possibly disturbed by an enemy, and is thought to work after dark if an approaching storm threatens to ruin an exposed stack.

Although the "haystack" is very compact, the material usually cures evenly. Apparently the little harvester cuts only enough each day to form a layer that is so thin as to dry properly. It often rests on the food pile, perhaps to enjoy the feel of increasing size. As a result great numbers of tiny, dry, pale yellowish-brown pellets are scattered through the stack on the layers, representing various days' work. These droppings, which are much like those of rabbits but far smaller, are also scattered about on the rocks, especially at favorite lookouts. The urine leaves whitish streaks on the stone.

Although early morning and late afternoon are devoted largely to making a living, the pika dearly loves siestas. It spends hours in the middle of the day perched on some sloping rock, its Roman nose just sticking above the skyline.

Pikas cannot endure heat. Those that live where the air goes above ninety or ninety-five degrees at midday always retire to the cool interior of the slides at that time.

As the pika sits hunched up, its little eyes, set in the blank, blunt head, look wise far beyond its really low intelligence. The attitude reminds one of a tiny old Indian huddling on a rock, drawing an imaginary blanket closer around the bent shoulders. It seems little wonder that some imaginative naturalist has given the animal the title of "little chief hare."

The small chief soaks up the ultraviolet rays, converses occasionally with neighbors, and watches for enemies. These are probably few, for the pika lives in an environment where a refuge from birds of prey and most carnivores is ordinarily never more than a yard away. There are almost no large snakes at high altitudes. Two enemies that are quick and agile, and capable of pursuing the pika into its rock passageways, are the marten and the weasel.

Whether pikas are actually sociable is unknown. Perhaps they do not go beyond passing the time of day. It seems likely that each home range and "hay pile" is guarded zealously from other adults. Possibly a mother and her brood may remain in the same territory and share a common food supply through the winter. In captivity pikas are difficult to keep together. They fight viciously, but sometimes live for a while in apparent harmony. Rabbitlike, the fighters face each other and kick at each other's back. They attempt to tear off fur and hide with the sharp claws of the hind feet. Incidentally, pikas have extremely thin skins which tear far more easily when being prepared by the taxidermist than even the delicate skins of rabbits.

On a typical rockslide in Yosemite National Park, Drs. Grinnell and Storer once estimated a population of about six pikas an acre. Each animal seemed to have a home territory of approximately seven hundred and fifty square yards.

According to the late Arthur H. Howell, far northern pikas, of Yukon Territory and Alaska, change their coats but once each year, in late summer. All of those living in the western states and southwestern Canada have two a year. The winter fur is shed in late June and early July, usually beginning on the head and progressing evenly and rapidly backward. This pale brownish fur is worn only for two months, or even less. Then it is replaced in a similar manner by the dark gray winter attire. As the blackish tips of these hairs wear away, by rubbing against rocks in the close quarters under the snow, the color grows steadily more grayish.

Although the feet are completely covered by hair, the pika apparently does not stop long on the snow. If it can reach a spot where the wind and sun have cleared the rocks, it will often run across snow patches to enjoy the midday rays when the temperature is still well below zero, provided the air is still.

Few naturalists are hardy enough to make a study of the pika's winter life. An intrepid investigator may walk, totter and crawl across the unstable jumble of rocks in the summer, but the wind is too cold and danger from snowslides is too great to tempt him during winter.

Very little is known of the details of family life. The young, usually numbering three or four but sometimes five, may be born in any month from late May to early September. They weigh about one-third of an ounce at birth. Like juvenile rabbits, they can be weaned and subsist entirely on vegetable matter when only one-fourth to one-third grown.

The low annual birth rate (low for a member of the rabbit tribe) is ample to offset the low death rate. Since they are so well protected from flesh-eaters, why don't they overrun the mountainsides? Perhaps the amount of food that can be reached safely from slide rock is one limiting factor. If the animals strictly police their little estates, as seems likely, fighting may further limit the population. Another probability is disease. Pikas in the Snowy Range of southeastern Wyoming were found to be infested with fleas. A considerable number contained tapeworms, sometimes to the extent that the parasites almost blocked the passage of food, and weighed as much as twenty-five per cent of the total contents of the intestines. Other pikas were afflicted with stomach worms. Possibly this uncomfortable fauna led some pikas to eat quantities of small, jagged bits of quartzite, which were found in their stomachs. I once watched a pika that had a round hole in one side of its head, midway between eye and ear, perhaps caused by a warble.

Pikas closely resembling our species are found all the way across Asia, as far south as the Himalayas and in the Ural Mountains on the borders of Europe. In Pleistocene times they ranged westward through northern Europe to England. The name "cony," which is widely used in western America, is European for the English rabbit. It is also the biblical term for the Syrian and African hyrax, a rock-dwelling creature which resembles an earless rabbit but is actually one of the hoofed mammals. "Pika," the European name, comes from an Asiatic tribe of people in northeastern Siberia. They pronounce it "pē-kah." In this country, the accepted pronunciation is "pī-keh."

In Western America, we do not find these little animals distributed over wide areas. Limited as they are practically to slides and piles of rock, only a couple of subspecies or geographic races are found on the valleys and plains between mountain ranges. These exceptions live in the old lava field of northeastern California, eastern Oregon, and southwestern Idaho. Even some perfectly good mountain systems are not inhabited. Between east-central British Columbia and southern Yukon is a vast area of hundreds of miles of jumbled mountains, apparently fine pika pastures, but not a pika in them.

General description. A small, tailless member of the rabbit family with short, broad, rounded ears, chunky body, and short legs whose front pair are but little shorter than the rear pair. Fur very soft and dense. Color buffy, reddish brown, or grayish, changing to whitish or pinkish buff on the under parts and feet; ears brownish to nearly black. Total length, 7 to 8 inches; height at shoulder, 3 inches; weight, 4 to 6½ ounces.

Distinguishing characteristics. Similar to a small, grayish guinea pig. Movements very abrupt. Found in rockslides, usually at high elevations. Has a shrill, short, bleating call.

Range. Mountainous regions of western North America, from northern New Mexico and Kern River, California, north and west to the Mount McKinley region, Alaska.

VARYING HARE
LEPUS AMERICANUS, L. WASHINGTONII, AND L. BAIRDII

Through the leafy woods a big brown hare hops down the trail. But for its upturned white tail, fluffy as a pompom, it can hardly be distinguished from the shadows. If you return to this spot in the dead of winter you may find the same animal. It is still almost invisible, but instead of being brown it is white as the snow that covers the bleak landscape. Only dark eyes and black-tipped ears prevent the camouflage from being complete. Because of this varying of color with the season, it is called the varying hare.

Its "snowshoes" have also given it the name of snowshoe hare. Like the Arctic hare, its long toes spread wide and the soles of the big feet are covered with coarse hair that is longer in winter than in summer. These "snowshoes" prevent its slipping on icy crusts and hold it up in soft snow. Even a light crust will not give away as it races through the swamps, and only the deepest and fluffiest snows will cut down its speed.

Other names for this graceful, fleet animal are white hare, gray hare, and gray rabbit. Strictly speaking, the term "rabbit" should be reserved for the cottontail (*Sylvilagus*). The ears and hind legs of rabbits are considerably shorter than those of hares, and the digestive tracts of the two groups have important

VARYING HARE

structural differences. At birth, rabbits are hairless and blind, while hares are well furred and their eyes are open.

Canada and Alaska, south of the tree limits, is the stronghold of the varying hare. Its range extends into the northeastern United States, south in the mountains as far as Virginia, and in the western highlands to central New Mexico and California. A forest animal, it rarely ventures far into open country. It is found not only in the big woods, but where there is plenty of underbrush for food and cover. Younger brushy growth, such as logged or burned areas that are coming back to forest are its favorite areas. Cedar, spruce and tamarack swamps, if not actually wet, and alder and willow thickets are sought, especially in winter. Many hares live at all seasons in spruce and fir thickets and mixed coniferous-deciduous woods. Slopes covered with a dense stand of young aspens or poplars are attractive to them, especially if they are interspersed with pines, spruces or firs.

The varying hare is the fleetest mammal in the forest. Its long hind legs push it over the ground or snow at thirty and more miles an hour. A "champion" may leap as much as twelve feet at a bound. As it whisks through a cedar swamp ahead of a panting dog, it seems to be traveling twice as fast as it really is. Even more startling is the hare's ability to burst almost instantly out of a relaxed sitting position into a dead run. It can also dodge bewilderingly at full speed. When running, it often makes high hops to look back at the pursuer.

In spite of its speed, this animal is content with a relatively small home territory. While the area varies with the density of cover and is larger in winter than in summer, the average hare will spend its entire life on less than a hundred acres of land. In Minnesota, repeated trapping of tagged animals showed that their range was only six hundred to thirteen hundred feet across, while the greatest distance covered by any hare was only a little over a mile. Many hares probably spend months without going farther than three hundred feet from "home."

Anyone who has hunted snowshoe hares knows that they will not go far from the point where they are started. A hare may take off at great speed, but soon commences to circle. I have seen it begin to turn even before it was out of sight through the woods. If pursued by a dog, the chase may come back and pass the initial point several times in eight or ten minutes, thus permitting the hunter who waits more than one opportunity to bag the game. To test the hare's persistence in clinging to its home range, a biologist once followed an animal in Wisconsin for an hour and a quarter. In spite of this disturbance and continuous pursuit, the hare refused to go outside an area of about ten acres.

If trapped and removed to a new area, many hares will leave, apparently in an attempt to find their old homes. Results of an experiment in Minnesota showed that they have little or no trouble in returning if the distance is less than a mile. But no hare was able to find the way back if liberated as much as three miles away. One animal was taken away seven times and released one-half mile from home. Each time it returned within two weeks.

If varying hares migrate *en masse,* it happens but rarely. Population pressure and scarcity of desirable food might cause such a movement. During early March, 1912, these conditions prevailed in the woods near Kelliher, northern Minnesota. A naturalist, W. T. Cox, recorded that all the hares that he saw in motion were traveling northwest, and all tracks led in the same direction. Crossing frozen Red Lake, he found that great numbers of hares were sitting on the ice within six or eight miles of the north shore, wherever patches of deeper snow afforded an opportunity of concealment. Apparently they had been overtaken on their travels by daylight and preferred to remain quiet until darkness should make it safer to continue. Near shore the number of hares was estimated at from twenty to fifty an acre.

"Home" to the average hare is a small depression in the leaf litter or ground which is made by the weight of its body resting there. This is called the "form." Because it likes to watch its surroundings for enemies, friends, or interesting happenings, it usually chooses a site on a knoll or slight elevation. This location also permits drainage and keeps the bed dry. It is usually overhung by protecting branches or is in a clump of shrubs or tall weeds. The varying hare probably will have other forms within its territory, but one will be used much more than the others.

While resting or watching, the varying hare generally sits with head, neck, and body drawn together compactly and all four feet gathered underneath but planted on the ground. The ears may be raised high, or laid back on the neck and shoulders. In the latter case the animal is especially hard to detect. Sometimes it lies on its side with all four legs extended lazily, or on chest and hips with only the hind legs sprawled out to one side. If something occurs at a distance it may sit up on its haunches, or even rise on the hind legs to see better. With front legs dangling or waving up and down, it may stand on tiptoe for several minutes.

Much time is spent in grooming its fur. As a preliminary, it may take a dust bath, preferably in a sunny spot. Ruffed grouse often use the same dusting places. Then the hare vigorously scratches and combs the fur, using the long claws of the hind feet. It scrubs its face with the forepaws, much like a cat, and finally washes its paws. Each hind leg and foot is extended, one at a time, far forward so that it can be cleaned without twisting its head.

Although it is not a digger, the varying hare sometimes takes shelter in an unused den of a skunk or a forest-dwelling woodchuck. It occasionally does a little scratching to make the "form" fit better, but it never makes a dugout. If a hollow log is available, the hare uses it—chiefly as a shelter from snow or rain.

The hare knows its domain well, and if an enemy appears it can take advantage of every natural means of retreat and concealment. If alarmed while abroad, it will dash for its favorite form. Here, motionless, blending into the landscape and surrounded by familiar shrubs and other objects, it feels safest. Despite this intense attachment for its "home," it seldom drives away neighboring hares even when they wander close to it. Hares sometimes quarrel during the courting season, but as a rule they get along without friction. No human knows how much this is due to indifference. Unlike the Arctic hares, the varying hares do not consort in stable groups, yet are not entirely oblivious to each other. On moonlit nights particularly, varying hares have been seen gathering in little clearings, where they sit quietly or occasionally chase each other briefly.

Once in a while a hare will thump from one to several times with a hind foot, a sound which carries with surprising clarity. Again, there will be a snorting grunt or a shrill scream. The last is a startling sound that can be heard for a hundred yards or more. Usually, if not always, it is a note of pain or fear. I have heard a varying hare, held fast in a wire snare but not seriously hurt, scream repeatedly as I approached on snowshoes. Each scream became fainter until the last was only a very weak bleat. A hare may make such an outcry if wounded badly by a shot or caught by a predator, or it may succumb without a sound.

The daylight hours are given over mostly to rest, although the hare may walk about slowly at times if hungry or restless. It prefers to feed at dusk or in darkness. Most excursions are made during the first hours of night and in the early morning. When it leaves the form, it stretches and hops off slowly and with seeming awkwardness. The forefeet are held close together and the big hind feet far apart. If moving along leisurely, the latter do not strike the ground ahead of the forepaws, although they may advance almost parallel to them. As it speeds up, the hind feet swing farther forward. At full run they hit the earth several feet ahead of the front paws. The long, terrifically powerful hind legs do most of the propelling at high speed; the forelegs serve mostly to hold up the front end of the animal.

Through custom, hares use a network of trails. Main roads are beaten down a foot or more in the sphagnum moss, while secondary trails are less distinct. Travel routes are especially conspicuous in winter. After a couple of weeks without a snowfall, the trails in a heavily populated swamp are packed down hard. The hares do not keep strictly to these runways, but leave them whenever they choose in order to reach promising patches of food. Especially fruitful spots, such as around "down" aspens or other tasty windfalls, may be packed hard over several square yards. On a small scale, the network of hare trails is similar to the "yard" of deer bands.

The varying hare is a fairly strict vegetarian. In summer it feeds chiefly on succulent herbs, including grasses, clovers, jewelweed, dandelion, and many others, and on tender buds and growing twigs of low woody plants. After herbaceous growth has been killed by cold, it may utilize the dried remains as long as it can get at them through the snow, but it places most dependence on shrubs and trees. It is fond of aspen, eating the twigs and bark as high as it can reach by standing on tiptoe. Other hardwoods used are willows, birches, alders and maples. It eats the bark, twigs and often the needles of conifers, including fir, cedar (*Thuja*), hemlock, spruce, tamarack or larch, and white pine. It has also been seen to partake of shoots of raspberry and blackberry canes.

In Canada, a biologist esimated that in one winter an average hare would eat the bark from fourteen aspen trees about two and one-half inches in diameter, with other foods serving as supplementary rations. Except for low-growing twigs, the accessible bark is limited to the trunk for a height of two feet above the snow level. This girdling kills the trees.

Once in a while, varying hares get a craving for meat. They will sometimes nibble at carrion, including dead bodies of their relatives. Apparently they are not aggressive to the extent of killing their food. It is very rare that captive varying hares destroy their own or another's young, as other caged animals often do, so we may infer that this rarely occurs in nature. In western Canada, trappers often are troubled by varying hares taking the baits and frequently springing the traps which are set for valuable furbearers. Sometimes half the traps of a line will contain only carcasses of careless, hungry hares.

I believe this appetite for flesh is variable. In northern Michigan I have noticed that a winter-killed deer might be visited by hares, while another carcass a few miles away was not utilized even though tracks in the surrounding woods showed them to be just as numerous. Hares are said to be averse to making the first cut into a body, and to feed only if the skin already has been torn open. This second carcass which the hares had not touched, however, had been opened and partly eaten by carnivores.

Like all lagomorphs, the hare chews with a wide sideward motion of the jaws. This is necessary because the lower jaw is much narrower than the upper, so that the two lower rows of molar teeth are considerably closer together than the two upper rows. When the animal's left molars are grinding a leaf, the right molars cannot meet because the lower tooth row is inside the upper row.

Many woodsmen claim that the hare never drinks after it is weaned, but this does not seem to be a fact. Perhaps green foods furnish it with most of the moisture requirement in summer, so that dew is enough to make up the remainder. I have seen varying hares eat snow, which probably must suffice in winter. Caged varying hares on a largely dry diet need from one-quarter to one-half pint of water each day.

Although it dislikes to get wet, the hare does not hesitate to leap into water if no other means of escape is open. On rare occasions it may swim voluntarily just to get to the other shore. One such hare was observed crossing a bay of the Kawishiwi River in northern Minnesota. Instead of choosing the shortest route, the animal crossed at the widest point—about one hundred and fifty yards. It swam easily, its head and level back above water, with regular, unhurried kicks of the hind legs. Apparently the front feet were not used. On leaving the river, it hopped up the beach and into the woods without stopping to shake the water from its fur. Another varying hare was seen to swim across the icy Hay River in Alberta, a trip of twelve to fifteen feet in a current traveling nine to ten miles per hour. Seemingly it was undertaken voluntarily.

In the northern United States, the hare's courtship season begins in early March. The female leads the male a merry chase through the woods, zigzagging and dodging violently. If the male is about to overtake her she may give a sudden bound upward, twist herself through one hundred and seventy degrees while in the air, and start running in the new direction on striking the ground. The male, of course, has passed underneath, but he turns as quickly as possible to follow.

Two weeks or even a month may pass with pursuits like this occurring from time to time before the female is ready to acquiesce. Then, suddenly, mating may take place a number of times in a few hours. There is nothing to indicate that the union lasts much longer. Both males and females are promiscuous. Quarrels between males seem to be uncommon. When they take place, the animals fight with their teeth and powerful hind feet and claws. Combat would seem to be almost pointless, for a female varying hare may accept the attentions of several males in rapid succession.

The young are born thirty-six to thirty-seven days after successful mating, or as late as forty days in delayed cases. The size of litter ranges from one to six, or rarely seven, eight, or even ten. Three or four is most common. The mother hare does not build a nest of any kind. She merely stops where she happens to be and rears on her haunches. Each birth requires only a slight muscular contraction. Then the mother tears open the membrane and eats it. As soon as the head and forequarters are exposed, the new-born hare, its eyes already open, starts to crawl toward its mother's breast. With the aid of a few nudges from her nose, it reaches her breast and begins to nurse. The mother then finishes freeing it from the birth sack, and licks it almost dry. There is only a brief interval between each birth. All of the young are usually born within half an hour. An hour afterward they are all dry. If anything happens to disturb the mother, they make low growling sounds and try to hide under her or each other.

Probably after the first nursing, the mother hare never suckles her offspring in daylight. She remains a short distance away, no doubt to avoid disclosing their whereabouts. Only at night does she return to feed them. In her casual manner she is a good mother. A captive hare has been seen to fight off bravely a weasel that was trying to get at her young. Contrary to a popular belief that little hares can get along from birth without any maternal care, they would die in a few days if deprived of milk. As a rule, they nurse about four weeks. They would like to continue longer, but are not permitted. As a matter of fact, they could probably survive if the mother were killed when they are only two weeks old. At that time they have been nibbling on tender grass and other herbs for two or three days.

Little hares of any species are sometimes called "leverets." They weigh two and one-half ounces at birth, with a possible variation from two to three and one-half ounces. They are fully covered with very fine, close brown fur which is about one-half to three-fourths of an inch long on the body. The ears, legs and noses are relatively short when compared with the mother's. They can walk and even hop soon after they are dry. At one week they have almost doubled in weight and are making short, exploratory trips around the "home" form. Hardy little creatures, they can survive several days of rain or snow.

They gain weight consistently and at a fairly uniform rate until they are about three months of age. A large number of young varying hares that were born and reared in captivity in Maine weighed an average of eleven ounces at three weeks, twenty-five ounces at six weeks, two pounds nine ounces at ten weeks, and three pounds at fifteen weeks. These weights are probably greater than those attained by hares under natural conditions in the wild, where meals are not served regularly nor quite so lavishly.

Young varying hares do not mate until they are mature, about a year after birth. While they have a possible life expectancy up to eight years, life is so hazardous that less than two in one hundred reach the age of five years. Only thirty per cent pass their first birthday (or fewer during a rapid population decline), and about fifteen per cent reach the age of two years.

Males cannot be distinguished from females in the field, but they differ in average weight and dimensions. Adult males are consistently about ten per cent heavier than females.

The populations of varying hares are subject to tremendous fluctuation. Periods of great abundance recur at intervals of about ten years, when the hares seem to be everywhere. Then, inevitably, the hordes melt away until it is hard to find a single animal.

The year 1886 was a period of remarkable hare abundance in western Canada. Seton estimated that in an area in Manitoba there were five thousand varying hares per square mile. By the end of the winter of 1886–7, the population was decimated and the country "was flecked with bodies of white-furred Hares."

This was truly extraordinary. Hares are considered abundant when they number five hundred to one thousand per square mile, although as many as three thousand four hundred have been found on such an area in Ontario. Following the cyclic peak, the decline is gradual for about two years. Then the population pitches downward sharply for about three years, reaching a low of possibly twenty-five to thirty animals per square mile. After this, it starts to climb gradually toward another peak.

When hares are abundant, their enemies feast and increase. Among the most important of these are the bobcat, lynx, coyote, wolf, red and white foxes, and weasel. Among the winged creatures are the great horned and great gray owls, the snowy owl, and the gyrfalcon. Near man's habitations, the hunting house-cat catches many young and subadult hares.

Sometimes the wild meat-eaters wreak havoc. One such instance was in northern Minnesota, when great horned, snowy and great gray owls gathered in the fringe of trees at the edge of a frozen lake. Here they picked off the hares as they crossed the ice. Lacking any cover, the hares were easily snatched up as fast as the owls could eat them. Along forty rods of shore line, an observer counted one hundred and nine little clusters of fur and blood which marked the spots where one hundred and nine hares met their end. Apparently thousands of migrating hares had been killed along a wide expanse. Yet survivors were abundant back in the protection of the forest. Actually, predation has little control over hare cycles which swing high and low with clocklike regularity. These fluctuations are not continent-wide. Instead, they are local, so that one region may have many hares at a time when other areas are depleted. Also, the fluctuations are extreme only in the northern and eastern portions of the range of the hare. In the western United States the population continues fairly constant from year to year.

What causes these clocklike fluctuations? Many pages have been written about the phenomenon. Because the varying hare is an important source of food for valuable fur animals, as well as human inhabitants of the northlands, many thousands of dollars have been spent in attempting to learn the facts about the declines and the factors controlling them.

Changes in the rate of reproduction have been suggested as a reason for the cycle. Female hares can mate immediately after giving birth to young, and if males are numerous they may do so. Three to five litters in a season may result. The first litter each year is smaller than subsequent broods. Therefore, as the number of litters in a season increases, the population rises disproportionately.· While change in rate of reproduction might account for the cyclic upswing, it is hardly sufficient to explain the sudden, swift declines. Some biologists have even tried to link the hare cycles with the increase and decrease of sunspots. Unfortunately for this theory, the rise and fall of the hare population occurs at different times in the various regions of the northland.

Declines appear to result almost entirely from disease. Varying hares are "genial hosts" to a number of parasites and disease-causing organisms. Coccidia, which are protozoans or one-celled animals, may affect the intestines or liver, causing poisoning or stoppage of the bile supply. Tapeworms, lungworms, stomach worms, ticks and fleas ordinarily do no harm but may be dangerous when they become abundant. A very important cause of mortality, which affects almost the entire hare population at times, has been termed "shock disease." Normal appearing animals suddenly go into convulsions, fall over, and die in a few hours or even minutes. A seizure may be brought on or hastened by violent exercise or fright. "Shock disease" is characterized by degeneration of the liver and consequent failure to store an adequate amount of sugar.

Like all its close relatives, the varying hare is well concealed as long as it stays perfectly still, a defensive measure which is often as useful as speed. With the exception of the Washington hare of the Pacific coast rain belt (where snow is generally of short duration) all varying hares change their brown coats for white winter ones. In late autumn the long, black guard hairs and the secondary yellow-and-black fur are replaced by white hairs. The reddish tipped gray underfur remains the same color as in summer. The shift is irregular and often occurs in patchwork fashion. It usually begins on the ears and feet and works upward and to the rear until the entire animal is clothed in ·iearly pure white with the exception of the black-tipped ears. Frequently the legs, ears and face are tinged with rust. The change generally requires ten weeks and is completed about the average time that the ground is covered with lasting snow.

To prevent the animal from becoming chilled by the steadily increasing cold, the winter hairs grow a little ahead of the shedding of the corresponding summer fur. This apparently means that there are two sets of hair roots, one of which sprouts in fall while the other is active only in spring.

In early spring the new reddish-brown dress begins to crowd out the winter suit. It reverses the order of the autumn change, beginning on the head and back and ending, at the very first of summer, on the ears and feet. Besides being different in color, the summer fur is shorter, lighter and more sparse than the winter coat.

Sometimes an early snow will find the hares still dressed mostly in brownish. Or a late fall may cause them to be glaringly conspicuous against the brown leaves. The varying hares do not change their coats according to the temperature or ground color. It is done entirely by the calendar. A captive hare kept in a heated room puts on the white heavy winter coat at the same time as the hares in the woods. Despite this occasional disservice, the change is definitely an advantage. Where varying hares and cottontails occur together, it is plain that the latter in their brownish-gray pelage are much more at a disadvantage on the snow-covered ground and must spend much of their time in dens or under brush heaps. The hares are well concealed even though they remain in the open.

The varying hare probably furnishes more sport than all the big-game species combined. It is also highly important in the winter diet of most northern Indian tribes, as well as of many white inhabitants of forests and rural districts. The meat, either roasted or parboiled and then fried, is excellent. The skins, cut into strips and plaited, are sometimes used by Indians for warm sleeping robes.

On the debit side, the hare girdles and kills many trees, including those that may be accessible in orchards. In the normal forest or brush country the loss of a certain percentage of seedlings or saplings merely thins the stand, so that ultimately the competition for survival is not as severe. After all, the forest and the hare have gotten along together very well for thousands of years. In plantations, however, hares may injure or kill a large percentage of the particular conifers whose survival is essential. Here measures must be taken either to destroy many of the hares or to guard the trees by other means.

Rabbits, hares and pikas were formerly included in the order of rodents. However, instead of the rodents' four incisor or chisel teeth, these animals have six. The extra pair are small and are placed directly behind the large pair in the upper jaw. These little teeth are rounded and lack a cutting edge. They are only moderately useful and cannot be seen without prying open the mouth and looking behind the large upper teeth. However, they constitute the scientific basis for placing these animals in a separate order, the lagomorphs. They have found their way by natural means to all parts of the world except Madagascar,

New Zealand, and Australia. European rabbits (*Oryctolagus cuniculus*) were transported to Australia and New Zealand, where they have proved so prolific and destructive that they are a major plague to farmers and stockgrowers.

The European hare (*Lepus europaeus*), a huge creature that sometimes attains a weight of thirteen pounds or more, is a native of central and western Europe, south of the Baltic (except the Spanish Peninsula). It was established at several points in North America before the First World War. It is now most abundant in southeastern Ontario and in the Hudson River Valley of eastern New York, as well as adjacent parts of Connecticut and Massachusetts. Introduced in the hope that it would serve as a desirable game animal, the European hare has only proven extremely destructive to orchards and other crops. In one New York county, the loss to fruit growers in a single winter was more than $100,000.

General description. A fairly large hare. In summer, grayish to brown, with blackish on rump and midline of back; throat buffy to reddish brown; tail blackish above, white underneath; abdomen and chin white. In winter, pure white with dusky tipped ears (except the varying hares of western Washington, the Cascades and Sierra Nevada, which do not turn white in winter). Total length, 16 to 20½ inches; height at shoulder, 8½ to 9 inches; average weight, 2 pounds 10 ounces, up to 4 pounds as a maximum.

Distinguishing characteristics. Typical rabbit form. Smaller than the Arctic hare. Generally larger than the cottontail rabbit, which has shorter ears and legs and never turns white in winter. In summer the varying hare generally is more reddish than the cottontail, and its hind feet are always much larger and have longer toes.

Range. Northern North America, mostly south of the tree limit, from Newfoundland to western Alaska; south to Connecticut, Virginia (in the mountains), central Michigan, central New Mexico (in the Rockies), and central California (in the Sierra Nevada).

ARCTIC HARE
LEPUS ARCTICUS AND L. OTHUS

In the American and Greenland Arctic where man can barely survive, these soft, fluffy, defenseless creatures flourish. Sometimes bands of twenty to sixty, or even a hundred Arctic hares gather on the barren hillsides. To the early explorers their flesh was a welcome change from the dried and salted beef and fat seal on which the expeditions subsisted. Occasionally it saved them from starvation.

An adult Arctic hare of the smallest species weighs about twice as much as the average three-and-one-half-pound varying (snowshoe) hare. On the Alaska Peninsula, where the largest hares are found, a big fat specimen may scale up to twelve or possibly fifteen pounds and measure twenty-eight inches from the tip of its blunt nose to the end of its short, fluffy tail. This one will also have the biggest hind feet in the family, seven inches from the tip of toenail to the back of heel. Except for extraordinary size the Arctic hare is a typical hare, with long hind legs, long ears, and soft, fine-spun fur that covers even the soles of the feet. To keep out the deadly cold of the Arctic, its coat is much thicker than that of the rabbit that lives in a temperate climate.

Each spring and fall the Arctic hare gets a new coat. Throughout most of the year, it wears an all-white coat with black eartips. While the pelage of the fox and bear is tinted with yellowish, that of the hare is like new-fallen snow. It is so white that the Eskimo hunter insists on using it to cover the sail of his

ARCTIC HARE

little boat when he wants to drift within range of the wily seal. This greatly hunted prey is said to be so sharp-eyed that it can detect a fox- or bearskin sail by contrast with the pure white snow.

In the southern Arctic, summer lasts three months. The ground is bare long enough to make it worth while for the Arctic hare to put on a dark coat. Most southerly ranging hares (those of Newfoundland and southwestern Alaska) are brown to brownish gray, with white legs, feet and tail, and brownish-black ears during the summer. Farther north the summer coats become progressively less brown and more gray. In southern Greenland and northern Baffin Island they are bleached to a pale smoky gray, sometimes washed with pale buff or with black hairs sprinkled over the back and top of the head. Only the ears are darker. Finally, hares of Ellesmere Island and northern Greenland remain white throughout the year. These animals, some of which are within seven degrees or less than four hundred and fifty miles from the North Pole, live where the ground is exposed only for a few short weeks in summer. Even then the brown earth and rock are often hidden briefly by snowstorms. Brown coats in this territory would be a handicap.

Although the summer coats here are the same color as the winter ones, they are lighter in weight. The hairs are sparser and shorter. Change from winter to summer apparel is gradual and very irregular with all Arctic hares. On Baffin Island the spring shift is completed in early June. This dark coat is worn less than three months. Often it is discarded before the end of August. When snow is delayed until October, the hare is as conspicuous as an elephant. The Eskimos take advantage of the easy hunting and feast on rabbit stew.

Against a snow-covered landscape the white-garbed hare is almost invisible. With yellow eyes nearly closed and black-tipped ears laid backward, it crouches, immobile and at ease. There are no shadows in the long Arctic night, and even when the sun is above the southern horizon it is often obscured or dimmed by fog and haze. Consequently, even at close range the hare is a part of the monotonous whiteness.

Possibly this is one of the reasons for its lack of fear during the colder months. Then, by moving quietly and slowly, a person is able to catch the animal with his hands. In summer, when the ground is bare, the same hare may become so wary that a hunter can hardly stalk within gunshot range.

Arctic hares are circumpolar in range. They are found on most of the larger islands as well as the northern fringe of the continents fronting on the polar ocean. The biggest of those that live above the Arctic Circle are not in the south around Hudson Bay, but nearest the Pole. There, on the most northerly islands in the world, they are at times very numerous. The abundance of all Arctic hares, like that of other hares and rabbits, varies in cycles. High populations are followed by extremely low ones. The distribution is also rather sporadic. Hares may be numerous in some places but absent from others where conditions seem just as favorable or even better. They are found from sea level up to the summits of the mountains—as high as three thousand feet, for instance, on Baffin Island.

Except when they are perhaps driven down to the flat tundra to find emergency winter subsistence on the dwarf willows, most Arctic hares live on the slopes and ridges of rocky hills and low mountains. There the wind blows the snow down to a few inches in depth. Only a few Arctic hares live the year round on open tundra and sometimes just to the south in the scattered scrub forest, the "land of the little sticks" as the Indians call it.

The footprints of Arctic hares look at first glance like those of small deer due to the development of claws on the two middle toes.

Very little food is found above the snow in winter. The plants cannot stand the fierce Arctic gales and must keep under cover. As long as the snow is loose, the hares have little trouble. When it crusts, they must break it or starve. But the front legs are strong and the feet are furnished with short, heavy claws. Hammering with rapid blows, they break the crust. To make elbow room they tumble the hard chunks out of the hole with their paws, or pick them up with their mouths. Then they tunnel down with noses and feet.

In that harsh, rocky country, food plants are often widely spaced. Digging just anywhere would frequently be a great deal of wasted labor. The hares, however, have a sense, probably smell, so keen that they can detect food through a foot or two of snow. Sometimes a hare, running at full speed across the hills, will jerk to a stop as though pulled by an underground magnet. Burrowing through the undisturbed snow it will pull up a tasty willow twig from its concealment flat on the earth.

In northern Greenland and Ellesmere Island, the hares have been given by Nature a special device for extracting cold-stunted plants from the hard, wind-pounded snow and rock crannies. The animals' jaws are long and tapering. From them the four big incisor teeth, two above and two below, project forward obliquely like the teeth of a thumb-sucking child. Jaws working like long-nosed pliers, the animals work their sharp teeth into crevices in the crust and rock to get every available bit of food.

Willow is the hare's basic diet. They eat it summer and winter—leaf, bud, bark, twig, and root. The latter, when the ground is not frozen, is dug and pulled up and eaten to the last, tiniest morsel. Besides willow, the principal summer foods are grasses, mountain sorrel (*Oxyria*), flowers, stems and leaves of saxifrage, and buds and twigs of crowberry. When these foods are depleted, the animals can get along for a while on dried grass and moss.

Those hares that happen to live near the sea coast come down to the ocean at low tide to feed on the tough, leathery kelp as well as other marine plants that may be washed ashore. They will also eat carrion, at least in winter, and have been known to get into fox traps while feeding on the meat baits. Others, attracted by stores of blubber, have boldly invaded igloos and wooden buildings. For water they eat snow, which is the only form in which it may be found in the Arctic during more than half the year. Whether they drink in summer is unknown, but many Eskimos claim that they will travel long distances to eat from a snow bank.

Ordinarily the hare feeds in the morning and evening. Only storms will keep it "home" then. Until the weather calms, it crouches in the lee of a sheltering rock and dozes away the hours. It does not make a "form" as southern rabbits do. Perhaps the intense cold does not permit the slight body heat, that escapes through the dense fur, to melt the snow. Sometimes the wind will heap snow around it so that it is partly protected. Only occasionally does it tunnel into the drifts, but if necessary it can burrow a number of feet.

As the spring sun moves higher above the horizon the hare will follow it from one side of the rock to the other. Only the strongest winds will make it forego sunbaths. It needs a great deal of vitamin D after the long months of continuous dusk and darkness.

This new energy does things to the bands of hares. After a winter of amiable sociability, the males suddenly become antagonistic. They snap at each other with their teeth. Rising up on the hind legs they box furiously. Long sharp claws of their front feet tear out wads of fur and slash through thin, delicate skins. Beginning about the first of April in the south, or a month later on northern Ellesmere Island, the breeding season lasts about two weeks. Then the bands break up. According to certain observers, the hares sometimes move by pairs to the tundra or seacoast. Others have found that the animals stay on the same range throughout the year.

Apparently, like other rabbits, Arctic hares vary in their behavior. Sometimes they are exceedingly watchful and shy throughout the spring. Others are less suspicious of danger than during the winter. Even during the summer, they are not always consistently alert and wild. Some explorers have noticed that they are extremely fearful of sled dogs. The Norwegian, Otto Sverdrup, however, found that the hares on southwestern Ellesmere Island were enormously abundant and quite unafraid. He wrote that his "dogs became almost unmanageable. They gave chase time after time; and the hares themselves were so dazed that they had not the wit to keep out of the way. They did not appear to be afraid; they hopped about only a few yards in front of the teams. . . . As if to incite the dogs to the utmost, the hares came and settled down a few yards from them, and then stood on two legs and stared at us. . . . After a good deal of trouble we succeeded in driving away the greater number, and were at last able to go on."

Especially careless hares may be struck with devastating suddenness by either the snowy owl or the great gray owl. If the first attack misses, or if the hare has prior warning, it will endeavor to find shelter against a cliff or among broken rocks. The owls, being adapted to attack by diving, do not know how to hop along the ground or to thrust their powerful talons into crevices after prey. Among other enemies of the hare are the great tundra brown bears, grizzlies, wolf, lynx and weasel. The latter may be carried a long distance by the screaming hare before the weasel is able to sever enough blood vessels in his victim's neck. The white fox is the hare's worst foe. Fortunately, during the late spring mating season and the early summer when the young hares are growing up, the fox is occupied with easy and abundant food—the eggs and young of ground-nesting birds.

The hare's sight is not good and little dependence is placed upon it. The keen nose and hearing generally give warning of trouble. If uncertain of the location or degree of danger, the hare rises on its hind legs to its greatest height and, with forelegs carried either loosely or close to the chest, hops on tiptoe up the ridge. Sometimes it stands like this for many minutes with the wind blowing so hard that it threatens to sweep a man off his feet. But the hare is perfectly poised and gets a more satisfactory scent. Every muscle is tense, the big ears twist this way and that, and the nostrils twitch rapidly.

If satisfied that an attack by a fox or wolf is imminent, the hare drops to all fours and races off at great speed. If on the tundra, it can dodge and change course like flashes of lightning. This is apt to discourage a clumsy pursuer. In mountainous country the hare always races directly up the steepest slope with such speed and endurance that any predator is soon convinced it should look elsewhere for dinner. For this reason foxes and wolves are most likely to attack from above. This gives them the advantage in out-rushing the prey, who usually must start from a standing or prone position. As a defense measure, the hare habitually faces up-hill. If while feeding it wishes to sample some plants growing down the slope, it runs down—then immediately turns so as to face up-grade once more.

There is only time in the brief Arctic summer to rear one litter of young. It may contain as few as two or a maximum of eight, but the usual size is five to seven. Young hares are born sometime between early May and early July. The exact time depends on the latitude, general weather conditions, and other circumstances. The majority arrive in June and the last week of May. They are born with a full woolly coat which is similar in general color to their parents at that season. Their eyes are wide open. For several weeks they are helpless and confined to the nest. On hearing any strange sound they flatten and "freeze" with eyes closed and ears pressed back on their necks. By the time they are half grown, they have developed some running ability and try to flee from trouble. They tire easily, however, and are soon reduced to ineffectual dodging to escape a pursuer. Eskimo children have great fun chasing young hares. When finally captured, the animals are breathless and paralyzed with fear.

Arctic hares, like their southern relatives, insist on following a trail. Instead of jumping over an obstacle, they always try to go under it. For this reason Eskimos capture many animals by stretching nooses across the runways. Modern Eskimos also use ordinary steel traps, into which hares will step without fear or suspicion.

Except in spring, the flesh of hares is excellent. For soup or boiled meat, it is greatly enjoyed by Eskimos as a change from a year-round diet of seal. Every scrap is eaten, even the ear cartilage and the marrow which is sucked from the broken bones. Any Indian knows that chewing the milk-filled glands of a mother hare will mend an upset stomach!

The fur is very warm and is used by Eskimos to staunch the flow of blood and bind up wounds. They plait strips of hare hide into blankets and sleeping bags, which are lightweight and wonderfully warm. The skin is fragile and will not stand heavy use, but it is sometimes used to make imitation bear-skin trousers. Turned inside out, it makes good stockings for cold weather. But if it is used too soon after being taken off the animal, it may give the human wearer a fine infestation of fleas. These insects often inhabit the hares in great numbers, causing them to hop and scratch in annoyance and even pain. Their presence does not mean that the animals are dirty. On the contrary, they are fastidious about their fur. If it becomes soiled in digging for willow roots in the muddy ground, a hare will immediately try to comb out the mud, or will rub itself vigorously in a snowbank or clump of grass. Both adults and young eat and stay healthy in captivity, but do not reproduce.

General description. A large, heavy hare. In summer, white or grizzled grayish, reddish, or brownish, with blackish rump, black ear-tips, and white tail, feet, and under parts. In winter, pure white except for black ear-tips. Total length, 20 to 28 inches; height at shoulders, 11 to 12 inches; weight, 6 to 12 pounds or more.

Distinguishing characteristics. Large size (averaging about 23 inches in length from nose to end of tail); underfur is completely white in winter, while that of the varying hare has buffy tips.

Range. Arctic America, mostly north of the tree limit, from Newfoundland and Labrador west to western Alaska (including the Alaska Peninsula but excluding the Arctic coast from Horton River to Point Barrow); from northern Ungava, York Factory, and Great Slave and Great Bear Lakes north to the Arctic coast, many of the islands of the Arctic Ocean, and the coasts of Greenland.

JACK RABBIT
LEPUS SP.

The jack rabbit is not a rabbit. It is a hare. (See pp. 583–585.) Jackass ears are partly responsible for the name. They are much larger than those of any other mammal, for its size. Covered with fine hair, they are great scoops of thin cartilage. Those of the twenty-four-inch-long antelope jack rabbit rise eight and one-quarter inches above the head—more than one-third of its total length!

As the jack rabbit bobs off across the plains in great easy bounds, the ears stand up like twin busbys on a hop-skipping grenadier. Sensitively they twist and turn to catch every sound of pursuit. The long hind legs and big feet strike the ground together. They can drive it ahead at the rate of thirty to thirty-five miles an hour. Then the ears are flattened back against the neck and shoulders. In times of stress, an exceptional jack rabbit may increase its speed to forty-five miles an hour.

Sometimes a jack rabbit will start running while the enemy is still far off. On another occasion it will permit itself to be almost stepped upon. This is especially likely if it is a white-tailed jack rabbit. The sudden flash of white as the unseen hare explodes into full flight is likely to fluster even a nerveless hunter like the coyote. A second's uncertainty on the predator's part may be long enough for the hare to get away.

Only a greyhound can run down a fleet jack rabbit in fair chase. Slower runners, such as the coyote and even the fox, must use their wits to supplement their heels. Sometimes they succeed in stealing up on a dozing jack rabbit. If the intended victim races off, a smart hunter may be able to figure out its probable circling course and cut across to intercept it.

The jack rabbit is a top notch broad-jumper. A black-tail jack may cover the

BLACK-TAILED JACK RABBIT

ground in leaps of fifteen feet, while a white-tail sometimes extends this to twenty-one feet. One of the latter, which had been shot through the abdomen, once made a leap of twenty-two feet four inches by actual measurement.

I know a young man in western South Dakota who learned the hard way about the leaping powers of a jack rabbit. Dressed in his Sunday best, Mike was driving down the highway at about fifty miles an hour intent upon calling on his girl. A big white-tailed jack rabbit, startled by the car, commenced to race ahead on the roadside. As Mike approached and started to pass, the rabbit gave a mighty leap to cross the road in front of the car. It cleared the hood but crashed through the windshield and against the chest of the driver. Mike was almost knocked unconscious, but managed to stop the car. He found the interior, as well as himself, spattered with blood and festooned with yards on yards of intestines. This rabbit, spurred by fear, had made a high jump of almost four and one-half feet.

Between long leaps the jack rabbit generally makes two or three short jumps perhaps five or six feet in length. When closely pursued, it digs in its toes and runs low to the ground with less bounding motion.

If not too hard pressed, it generally leaps higher every fourth or fifth bound to check on its pursuer's progress. The height of this observational or "spy" hop depends on the kind of ground cover. It may be only a little higher than the rest of the bounds, or it may be as much as four feet above the ground in order to clear bushes or tall grass. This leap also varies with the species of rabbit. The black-tailed jack uses it under nearly all conditions. The white-tailed relative may make extra high jumps only in dense vegetation.

Sometimes the white-tail, in order to see over the grass, starts off bounding on its hind feet. Standing upright, it makes four to six long hops and then drops to all fours.

The ordinary running leaps of the jack rabbit generally are not more than a couple of feet off the ground. A fence two and one-half feet high will keep most jack rabbits out of a lawn or cultivated field. An exceptional animal, however, has been seen to bound over a five and one-half-foot fence with great ease and no more incentive than its appetite.

Jack rabbits inhabit open, treeless regions of western America. Attempts to establish them in the East (Pennsylvania and Virginia) have failed. Depending upon whether the upper surface of the tail is black or white, they are classified as either black-tailed or white-tailed jacks (see page 611). The ranges of the two groups overlap, although that of the white-tail extends much farther to the north than the warmth-loving black-tail. The white-tail also lives in the "parks" and on open slopes of the mountains as well as on plains, and has been found well above timberline at elevations as great as twelve thousand feet.

One of the most remarkable of the several species is the antelope jack rabbit, a member of the black-tailed tribe. This exceptionally large hare of the southwestern desert can flash signals like the antelope (pronghorn), by shifting the white hairs on its rump. When it runs away in fright, muscles pull the loose skin of the hind quarters forward and up, exposing a large area of white fur, first on one hip and then on the other. At the same time the hairs "bristle," thus reflecting more light. As the animal zigzags, the white flashes from hip to hip. It always appears on the side that is momentarily toward the object from which it is fleeing. Caused by fear, these "signals" are automatic. Possibly they warn other rabbits to "Look out!"

The more northerly white-tailed jack rabbit puts on a white coat for winter wear. At this time, a novice might mistake a jack from western Canada, or from the higher slopes of the United States Rockies, for a misplaced Arctic hare. By shooting one, blowing aside its long, fine, and very thick guard-hairs and then finding the inner fur tipped with buff, he can be sure that it is actually a jack rabbit. As one goes southward, or descends the southern mountains, the summer and winter coats of the white-tailed jack show less difference. Finally, wherever snow lasts only a short time, the winter coat of this rabbit is still white but is distinctly brownish on the top of the head and along the back. The black-tailed jack rabbit's gray to brownish gray coat is much the same summer and winter, except as the old fur fades and wears and then is replaced in spring and fall by new, bright fur.

In addition to powerful legs built for great speed, the jack rabbit has a number of structural adaptations which help it to survive. The body is long and lean and the dull, nondescript coat blends well with the surroundings. To take advantage of this, the animal "freezes" at the first hint of trouble. In fact, it is motionless much more often than not. In the resting position, with ears laid back on the shoulders, the animal is very hard to see. Its sensitive hearing apparatus can pick up a stealthy footfall or the sound of fur brushing lightly against the trailside brush, even while the coyote or other enemy is still some distance away. Its nose, which seems to be always quivering, is of great value in detecting foes and in the less exciting job of selecting food. A pair of large, soft brown eyes complete the defense equipment. They can detect even a slight movement at a great distance, although they do not seem to pick out an enemy readily so long as he remains absolutely still. At night the eyes reflect lights, such as an auto headlamp, with a pink glow.

The jack rabbit is not particular about its range. Almost any area in the West will do, provided grass is plentiful. There can be a good deal of shrubby growth; in fact, jacks are often numerous on the mesquite-studded deserts of the Southwest. Too-dense shrubbery is avoided because it is a handicap to an animal whose best defense is speed. The black-tailed jack rabbit prefers but does not always require that the country be a plain. It crosses arroyos readily, and uses them as well as hills for shelter from strong winds. A bank is useful for shade from the hot sun. Of course the white-tailed jack rabbit is often found on steep mountain slopes.

It is surprising that an animal that can rival the antelope in speed restricts itself to a relatively small territory. A circle of two miles diameter is probably enough for all ordinary purposes. As long as good food is available the rabbit may not leave this area for weeks or months. Like other mammals, it is a creature of habit, wearing trails into the grass by repeated use. In arid regions, a heavy rain storm will soak a narrow belt across country and so waken the seeds which may have awaited moisture for several years, while all around the vegetation remains sparse. Then the rabbits may move in from as much as ten miles away, but they stay only long enough to feed. Sometimes they come into towns or farms to find green lawns, hedges, or alfalfa, particularly if the arid plains are struck by drought.

A migration of thousands of jack rabbits was once seen in Malheur County, Oregon. The animals were moving into the face of a heavy snowstorm, and were going from a high elevation toward lower country. Perhaps they were made restless and anxious by the storm, and the cold that also prevailed. Such a migration is very rare among jack rabbits.

Living as most of them do on arid or semi-arid plains, jack rabbits seldom drink. Much of their moisture intake comes from succulent vegetation. Although they enter water most reluctantly, they will do so to escape serious trouble. With ears laid back, they strike out apparently with all four feet. Swimming as fast as a dog, they often emerge from the water with their back fur still dry.

Are jack rabbits sociable? At times they are found in scattered groups, feeding along in apparent amity. Perhaps the food is particularly succulent and tasty, or strong winds may drive them from the upland plain into a sheltered valley. During mating season, several males may collect about a single female. All of these gatherings are of brief duration.

The jack rabbit feels safer at night and prefers to feed at that time or when the sun is low. However, it may go out for food at any time during the day, especially if it is cloudy. As a rule, it waits until the shadows are long in the afternoon before leaving its form, and quiets down two or three hours after sunrise. The time varies with the weather. If it is excessively hot, cold, or windy, the jack rabbit retires earlier and does not resume feeding until nearly sunset.

Each jack rabbit has several forms distributed throughout its range. They are the simplest kind of scratched spots, four to six inches wide and ten to eighteen inches long. Made by the animal twisting and scratching about in order to clear a comfortable surface for resting, they may be as deep as three and one-half inches. Some forms are under thick brush, so that the occupant is inconspicuous, and completely sheltered from attack from above. Only rarely, however, is the resting place as well concealed as that of the cottontail. Usually it is screened only from one side. Sometimes it is completely in the open, yards from any shrub or grass clumps.

A favorite form may be used for a few days or a week before the rabbit moves to another part of its territory. Or it may serve for only a single day before the owner selects another.

If hard pressed by an enemy, a young jack rabbit will often take shelter in an abandoned burrow, or even spend the day in such a place. The adult will seldom do so. A full-grown black-tailed jack rabbit that I once saw near Rodeo, New Mexico, was one of the exceptions. As I passed a badger hole about two feet deep, I caught a glimpse of gray fur. Looking in, I saw the rabbit crouched down, its ears flattened back on the shoulders. Although wide awake, it made no sign that it saw me. The loud bang of my Graflex shutter did not make it jump when I took a photograph. About two hours later, when I passed the spot again, it was still there in the same position. Apparently it had not moved a muscle. Each day for several days thereafter I looked in the hole, but never saw it again.

Although jack rabbits almost never dig any earth shelters more pretentious than open forms, the white-tailed jack rabbit in the North makes burrows in the snow. To escape the bitter winter gales, it claws into the drifts for three or four feet. One rabbit may have several tunnels located at strategic points over its range. An especially big drift which is supported and stabilized by shrubbery may house a dozen or more rabbits. During the worst cold, each rabbit still has its own tunnel. Apparently they do not want to huddle together, even for warmth. These snow tunnels serve not only for shelter from the wind but as good hiding places from winged enemies such as the snowy and gray owls.

In shallow snow the white-tailed jack rabbit sits heading into the wind. In this way the dense fur coat sheds the cold air instead of rumpling up and admitting it. A plowed field is a favorite resort of this species in winter.

The female weighs more than her mate of the same age, but the difference is not so great as to be appreciable to the eye. There is no color difference in the sexes.

The mating season is long, extending from early spring until at least mid-summer. It probably lasts only about four months in the North. In Arizona, the jack rabbits may mate during any month of the year, but the majority do so between January and September. There is considerable chasing and sparring, and frequently pitched battles between rival males. Standing erect on the tip-toes of their hind feet, a pair of buck rabbits box each other furiously. Usually there is no sound except the thud of rapid-fire blows. Occasionally, however, there is a grunting or growling sound deep in the throat. Clumps of fur begin to litter the ground. In their excitement they strike out at each other with a hind foot at every opportunity. A blow with one of these weapons, which is jagged with heavy sharp claws, may tear an opponent wide open. Sometimes the rabbits even go at each other with their teeth. Soon one of the fighters begins to weaken. He races off, pursued only briefly by the victorious one. Many rabbits, especially males, have torn ears, the result of fighting or of carelessness in rushing through their thorny habitat.

Little is known about the mating habits of jack rabbits. Most of them pair at night; very likely they are completely promiscuous. One rabbit is interested in another probably no longer than a few hours or a night or two at most.

About six weeks afterward, the expectant mother prepares a nest by digging out a bowl in the earth under an overhanging bush or in thick grass. Ordinarily the depression may be very shallow, but may be as much as eight inches deep. It is oval in outline, between four and nine inches across, and lined with fur which the mother pulls out of her own coat.

One antelope jack rabbit in Arizona chose a barrel cactus about sixteen inches in diameter. She dug out the top to a depth of some fourteen inches. The long sharp spines made a fence around the nursery.

A black-tailed jack rabbit may have up to six young at a birth, but many of them bear only one to three. The average seems to be two or three. White-tailed jack rabbits are more prolific. The broods contain between one and seven or even eight young, with four as an average. The young of both species are born fully covered with mottled brownish gray fur, and their eyes wide open. They vary greatly in size, depending to some extent on the bulk and vitality of the mother, but even more on the size of the litter. A lone youngster is often three times as heavy as the largest member of a multiple birth. Often there is a difference of fifty per cent in the weights of brothers and sisters.

New-born jack rabbits are five and one-half to eight inches long and weigh two to six ounces. Their lower incisor teeth are well developed and the uppers are breaking through the gums. Their ears are disproportionately small, but these soon "catch up." In less than five minutes after birth, the young are nursing. They can stand up and even take a few steps. After they are fed, the mother covers them with fine grass or with a blanket of her own fur. She then settles down in a form from which she can watch the nursery, but far enough away so that no clue to its location would be given to a wandering enemy. Except in case of dire need, she returns to her family, even to nurse them, only under cover of night.

No one knows when they leave the birth nest. It is possible that the mother herself distributes them, one in a place, when they are a few days old. At that time they begin to show an interest in tender green leaves and grass-tips. They are independent of maternal care in three or four weeks, or perhaps less. Adrey E. Borell, of the Soil Conservation Service, used to see them frequently on his farm in California when they were very young and apparently had left their nest. At least no nests were ever found. While perhaps not "wet behind the ears," at least their ears were still short. He thinks that they may become independent when only a week old. Usually jack rabbits are not seen until they are more than half-grown. They attain adult stature when two months old, but take much longer to get their full weight.

If succulent food is available, the mother jack rabbit will usually rear several litters of young each year. During favorable times on the southern plains she may have possibly four or more. In the far north and at high altitudes in the mountains she may breed only once. The most powerful checks on the jack rabbit population are drought and coyotes.

Although jack rabbits are said to feed sometimes on carrion, they are almost invariably vegetarians. Even the few insects that they pick up seem to be accidentally trapped in leafy food. The list of plants eaten by such widely distributed mammals is naturally too long to be detailed here. It includes the buds, leaves, fruits, twigs, bark and even roots of numerous trees and shrubs. Among them are greasewood, rabbitbrush, shadscale (*Atriplex*), mesquite, catclaw, palo verde, sagebrush, willow, and aspen. In the Southwest, mesquite provides between one-third and one-half of all the food eaten during the year.

In arid regions the jack rabbit eats a good deal of cactus during the drier months. It prefers the less spiny kinds such as prickly pear. Visnaga, cholla, hedgehog cactus, and saguaro are taken also. In tackling the worst of these, such as the cholla, the rabbit first chews around a patch of spines and carefully pulls it away. Then, poking its nose very slowly into the opening, it bites out a bit of pulp. In spite of all its care the cruel spines sometimes enter the flesh and break off.

Grass and herbs are the preferred foods. As long as they are available, the rabbit lives on them to the exclusion of other growth. The most succulent and tender sprigs are selected and the coarser, older parts left untouched. A very thorough study by Drs. Vorhies and Taylor of the food of Arizona jack rabbits has shown that between one-quarter and one-half of their year-long food is grass. From twelve to seventeen per cent is portulaca. Miscellaneous plants including gilia, caltrop, composites (daisy family), ragweed, boerhaavias, and herbs of the Figwort, Borage and Eriogonum families comprise eight to fifteen per cent of the diet.

Like other herbivores, rabbits seem to require minerals. Just as cattle, buffalo and deer use licks, rabbits patronize spots where they eat earth. Approximately half of a large number of stomachs of southern Arizona rabbits examined contained sand or gravel.

It is little wonder that in many parts of the West the jack rabbit is disliked. In years of peak abundance, farmers may be forced to take harsh measures to protect their crops. Strychnine-treated baits are scattered, and thousands of the big hares are poisoned. Organized drives and hunts account for hundreds or thousands more. During a day and a half near Lamar, Colorado, one hundred and one gunners once killed five thousand one hundred and forty-two jack rabbits. By forming long lines of beaters and driving the animals into enclosures, as many as twenty thousand have been killed at one time in the San Joaquin Valley of California. In 1915, Harney County, Oregon, offered five cents bounty for each rabbit scalp. That year the county treasurer paid out the sum of fifty-one thousand four hundred and fifty-nine dollars and ten cents for the enormous total of one million twenty-nine thousand one hundred and eighty-two scalps. Most of these great slaughters were confined to black-tailed jack rabbits, which are usually more abundant and destructive than the white-tails. However, a community hunt in western Hettinger County, North Dakota, in December 1924 resulted in destroying seven thousand five hundred and fifty white-tails on an area only twenty to thirty miles square.

Of course jack rabbits are not always destructive, and in reasonable numbers they are an asset. They serve as food for valuable fur-bearers and as a "buffer species" between game birds, poultry and livestock, and their predatory enemies. Although the lean black-tailed jacks are considered by many people to be inferior as food, they are eaten by Indians and many of the poorer but more discerning elements of our population. The white-tailed jack rabbit ranks on a higher plane and is used more widely for food. Actually, the young meat of both species is excellent but, like the flesh of other rabbits, it must be well-cooked to kill any possible tularemia bacteria.

The jack rabbit is fond of alfalfa, clover, and irrigated grasses, and in dry seasons will travel far to feed on them. At such a time, hordes of rabbits have been known to leave the deserts of eastern Oregon and flock into the cultivated valleys. "Bands" estimated to number several hundred animals have destroyed a crop in a single night, and then retired to the surrounding sagebrush to spend the day. After autumn rains revived the wild grasses and herbs on the desert, however, the rabbits left the farming districts and returned to their wild and more flavorsome food. During winter they sometimes came back and lived on the crowns of the surviving forage plants, stacked hay, and the twigs and bark of fruit trees.

Jack rabbits have hearty appetites. They nibble away almost constantly from the time they begin to forage in late afternoon until they retire the following morning. Because their food is digested so rapidly, they must eat continuously to keep their stomachs full. Experiments on captives have shown that fifteen antelope jack rabbits (*Lepus alleni*) or thirty Arizona jack rabbits (*L. californicus eremicus*), will eat as much valuable forage as one sheep. It takes only seventy-four of the former, or twice as many Arizona jack rabbits, to eat as much as a cow. In addition to the grass that they consume, they cut down and waste a good deal. They also encourage an increase in less desirable range plants at the expense of the grassy areas.

In most regions jack rabbit populations fluctuate in cycles that average about seven years in length, but may vary between five and ten. At the peaks the animals may become very numerous. A total of twenty million jack rabbits has been estimated in the half of the state of Oregon which is inhabited by the species. Drs. Vorhies and Taylor once calculated that five thousand to ten thousand rabbits lived on a fifty thousand-acre area in southeastern Arizona.

Hunting jack rabbits is fine sport. They are so fast that they can out-distance all except the fastest dogs. It is surprising that the sport of running jack rabbits with greyhounds is not more popular. Their bounding gait makes them an erratic and difficult target for even a crack marksman. Tame and fairly unsuspicious when protected, they quickly become wild when hunted. Perhaps the most unpleasant feature of killing them is the loud, despairing scream that they frequently give when badly wounded. This shrill cry often continues until the animal is killed.

A market has developed in this country in recent years for wild rabbit skins. Thousands of pounds of jack rabbit hides have been used for hatters' fur. A small number of the best grades of white-tailed skins are used for trimming inexpensive cloth coats. The price of the skins has varied greatly, but in the past few years has been about seven cents each. The carcasses of many of the rabbits have gone to fur and poultry farms for use as feed.

Thousands of years ago, pueblo and cliff-dwelling Indians learned how to make warm garments and robes from rabbit skins. Archaeologists have found these fur blankets in ancient burials.

Jack rabbits have a great many enemies in addition to man. The most potent of the four-footed predators are the coyotes. In New Mexico, research has shown that fifty-five per cent of coyote diet is composed of jack rabbits and cottontails. Many ranchers have remarked on the increase of rabbits that often follows a coyote eradication campaign. Jack rabbits are among the most popular items of the diet of bobcats, and they are also killed by wolves and foxes. Rattlesnakes, bull snakes, king snakes and other hunters among the reptiles seek out and swallow baby rabbits. The larger predatory birds such as the bald and golden eagles, great horned, Arctic, and great gray owls, and the red-tailed and rough-legged hawks swoop down from the air. Diseased or crippled jack rabbits are especially subject to attack by a host of meat-eaters, even the slow-moving skunk or the little weasel.

The lesser but potent enemies are fleas, lice, ticks, and the flies whose larvae, known as "warbles," develop in living flesh. During an infestation of these huge larvae in rabbits at Malheur Lake, Oregon, in 1920, a naturalist counted as many as seven in the head of one rabbit. Some animals were blinded by the parasites which destroyed the eyes or crowded the eye sockets. Tapeworms and roundworms are serious pests at times. Among other diseases, tularemia is one of the most important.

The probable length of life of the jack rabbit is unknown. In view of all the enemies, very few are likely to die of the infirmities of old age.

Jack rabbits commonly are classified according to the color of the upper surface of the tail:

1. The white-tailed jacks (*Lepus townsendii*) are buffy or grayish in summer. Their tails are completely white, although sometimes with a mixture of black hairs or a blackish middle line on the upper side. All animals of this species become much paler in winter, and those living in the north or at high elevations are almost pure white and somewhat resemble the Arctic hare. They weigh six to nine pounds, up to a maximum of thirteen pounds. The range extends from central Saskatchewan to northern New Mexico, and from western Wisconsin to central Washington and the Sierra Nevada of California.

2. The black-tailed jack rabbits (*Lepus californicus, L. alleni, L. gaillardi*) have white tails with the upper surface more or less black. They are grayish and smaller than the preceding, generally weighing four to six pounds and a maximum of seven and one-half pounds. The group is often subdivided into gray-sided jacks. (*L. californicus*) and white-sided jacks (*L. alleni* and *L. gaillardi*). They all prefer more southerly regions and arid plains than do the white-tailed jacks, ranging from northern Oregon, central Nebraska and western Missouri south to central Mexico.

General description. A large hare with very long ears and long, powerful hind legs. Pale grayish to dark buffy brown above; white below; tail all white or white with a black upper surface. Some species become very pale gray or even white in winter. Total length, 20 to 26 inches; height at shoulder, 9½ to 12 inches; weight, 4 to 8 pounds, up to a possible 12 to 14 pounds.

Distinguishing characteristics. Larger than the varying hare, with larger, longer ears. The summer coat is grayer than the distinctly brown fur of the varying hare; only those jacks that live in the north or at high altitudes become white in winter. The jack rabbit is larger and has longer ears and legs (especially hind legs) than the cottontail.

Range. Western United States and southwestern Canada; central Saskatchewan and western Wisconsin to central Washington and the coast of California, south to southern Baja California, Chiapas (Mexico), and eastern Texas. Introduced and established in western Oregon.

COTTONTAIL RABBIT

SYLVILAGUS SP.

"The courage of a rabbit!" is not necessarily an insult.

I once had a cottontail rabbit that practically bearded a "lion" in its den. For scientific reasons it was placed in a cage with a big male bobcat. The predator, which was three times as large, reached out to snatch his prey. Instantly the rabbit struck him in the face with its hind foot. Completely astounded, the big cat sat back on his haunches and stared. Not until hours later did he recover his aplomb sufficiently to kill and eat the cottontail.

From fur-lined cradle to bloody grave (usually in some carnivore's stomach), the cottontail is beset by adversity. All of the meat-eaters, from the weasel and black snake to the wolf and great horned owl, are constantly hunting it. Man, the greatest predator of all, kills its kind by the millions every year. The cottontail has a short life, little more than one chance in twenty of attaining its first birthday.

Yet, despite all hazards, this soft little creature, from eleven to twenty-one inches long, is one of our most common animals. Everyone knows the small hunched figure, clothed the year round in grizzled brownish fur. Big dark eyes and typical rabbit ears (but considerably shorter than those of the hares) supplement a twitching nose to detect approaching danger. As it scurries off, zigzagging on short legs, the raised under side of the fluffy short tail, like a fully opened cotton boll, proclaims its identity. The pure white "cottontail" is lacking in a few species of this group, but in general it is a distinctive family badge.

Every mature female does her best to fill the hedgerows of the continent with her progeny. She may begin before she is a year old. Completely promiscuous, her attentions are easily won. By January each year, even in the northern states, amorous pursuits have become as important as food. Scattered tufts of fur mark the location of occasional fights between suitors.

Courting rabbits often engage in hopping contests. A pair will face each other. Then one rabbit leaps straight up in the air and the other dashes underneath. Turning about, they may repeat the routine several times. Sometimes an especially desirable female may acquire a retinue of four or five males. Whether she accepts more than one of them during a single period is unknown.

A day or two after pairing off, she acquires an active dislike for her current mate and turns on him violently. Biting mouthfuls of fur from his flanks and back, she chases him out of her territory. A month later her resulting litter is born and she may mate again before they are a day old. In this hasty fashion she can achieve three or four or even five families each season. The rutting period lasts until perhaps the middle of September when most of the animals abandon their mating interests and concentrate on getting into condition to meet the rigors of winter.

A seven-month mating season is the general rule over the northern half of the United States. Farther south, and on the Pacific Coast, cottontails may breed during any month of the year. Of course no female wild rabbit rears young continuously, even in the tropics. Supplies of food, vitamins and hormones impose limitations on reproductive desires and capacities. In the north, weather

COTTONTAIL

is an additional factor which limits the broods of young if not the mating instincts of the parents. Nestlings have been found frozen stiff in southern Michigan during February. Young cottontails have been seen in the nest in the same region as late as September twelfth, and a New York mother has been found with two-fifths-grown embryos on September sixteenth. It seems doubtful that such late-arriving rabbits would have much chance of surviving the winter. Most northern cottontails are born in late April, May, June, or July.

While twenty-eight to thirty days ordinarily elapse between mating and the birth of the young, the period may be as brief as twenty-five days or as long as thirty-two days. Three or four days before her time, the female cottontail picks out a nest site for the coming family. Perhaps she has special requirements in mind—if so, they are individual ideas. One female will select a spot amid shrubbery, another will nestle between the spreading roots of an old tree, while still a third prefers the cover of a large clump of grass. Some nests are in woods, others in orchards or brushy pastures. Most rabbits, however, build in open fields, and many choose a spot that is completely barren except for leaves and other plant debris.

With her forepaws the expectant mother digs a hole six or seven inches long, five inches wide, and three to four inches deep. She scratches chiefly from the same end of the hole. If the ground slopes, she stands on the downhill side so that the hole often is a little slanting and undercut at one end. As slightly more of the sides are dug away under the surface, the hole takes the shape of a shallow bowl. The rabbit lines this with bits of grass and with fur which she pulls out of her breast and abdomen with her teeth. Then she goes away.

More often than not, the rabbit saves herself some work by making over a depression such as a cow or horse track or an old skunk digging. One nest was found in a deep bed of straw. By scooping it out to a depth of four or five inches this improvising rabbit made a fine springy cradle without the trouble of tearing a hole in the hard earth. Western cottontail mothers frequently dig until the bowl becomes a shallow burrow, or may move into the abandoned den of some other animal.

Probably the most remarkable nest site known was in a willow tree on the bank of the Niagara River in western New York. The trunk was a huge one, more than four feet in diameter, and leaned at an angle of forty-eight degrees. Many small sprouts covered it and made it possible for even a rabbit to walk up the upper side. Twelve feet above the base the trunk forked, and in the crotch a cottontail built a nest of bluegrass and fur. Almost buried in a scraggly growth of sprouts, the nest was hidden and—more important—held safely. It was nine and one-half feet above the ground measured perpendicularly. Here five young were tended and reared until they were able to climb to the ground and take up a normal terrestrial existence.

Sometimes a nervous female is so anxious to have a nest all ready for her young that she starts building as much as two weeks before the event. Then she may abandon this project after a number of days and build another. Any rabbit is likely to make a second or rarely a third nest if the hole or bedding is disturbed before the birth of the young. Even plundering mice, looking for material for their own homes, may cause her to leave.

This is a precaution which the cottontail instinctively uses to thwart predators that might return later and eat her precious brood. Once the young are born and in the nest, however, the mother may disregard a great deal of disturbance of the bedding, and even the killing of a part of her family, without abandoning or moving the survivors. Another mother, however, has been known to move her young to a new location, even though nothing has molested the nest. She presumably had good rabbit reasons for making the change.

The mother has little advance warning that her brood is about to arrive. Perhaps she is in her form, taking her daytime rest. Or, if it is evening or night, she is probably off along the wood border getting a meal of grass and tender raspberry shoots. She may be a full hundred yards from the nest that she has prepared so carefully. No matter; as soon as the last youngster is born and fed, she carries each one in her mouth, one at a time, to the cradle.

During the day, and even at night when she is not actually nursing the little ones, the mother cottontail does not hover over her young. She stays at a little distance where she can watch the nest without attracting attention to it. Since this does not keep the children warm on chilly spring days, she covers them with a felted blanket of bits of grass and more fur from her under side.

When she returns to feed the young under the concealment of night, she carefully draws back the fragile cover. Then she squats over the opening with her feet spread apart, while the hungry youngsters reach up to the small nipples. When they are satisfied, she replaces the bedcover, scatters a few leaves and grasses over it, and goes away. The babies are now totally concealed, and the nest looks just like a nondescript patch of leaf and grass litter.

A family of young cottontails numbers anywhere from one to eight. The average varies from year to year between four and five and five-tenths. The largest litters are generally born in spring or early summer. The young are blind and deaf at first. Only lines show where the eyelids eventually will open. The short, shriveled ears, about one-half inch long, lie flat on the tiny heads and the auditory openings are sealed. The babies measure four to four and three-quarter inches long and weigh five-sevenths to one and one-quarter ounces. Only the lower ends of the incisors can be seen and the molars are invisible. In a few hours after birth the deeply pink skins begin to fade. By the following day the fast-developing hair causes the back and flanks to darken perceptibly. At this time a scant, short fuzz can be seen over the entire animal. By the fourth day the fur is so far developed on the top of the head that the first mottling can be noticed. At one week the little animals are well clothed and their color pattern is apparent for the first time.

There is considerable difference in the time that ears and eyes open, both in various species and in members of the same litter, and even in the organs on either side of the head of the same animal. Precocious cottontails begin to glimpse daylight on their sixth day, and each eye may require twenty-four to thirty-six hours before it can be opened wide. The eye-opening process in a five-rabbit brood may extend over three days. The ears commence to function at about the same time as the eyes. As they do so, they begin to stand upright. Although feeble at first, they acquire strength and rigidity, and in about a week they are much like adult ears in miniature. Brush rabbits apparently require ten or eleven days, or two to three days longer than other cottontails, before acquiring their sight and hearing.

Up to the time that they can see and hear, young rabbits are quiet little creatures. They snuggle together, twisting away from any sunbeams that straggle into the nest through rents in the slowly disintegrating coverlet, and sleep most of the time. Even when hungry, they squeak only faintly, and mill around by pushing themselves restlessly on their bellies. However, by the time they are ten days old they squeal loudly on occasion, sometimes for minutes at a time. If removed from the nest they hop about instead of crawling.

Despite their dawn-to-dusk fasts between nursings, the little rabbits grow rapidly. Undoubtedly they are fed several times between sunset and sunrise. At two weeks of age they have quadrupled their birth weight and scale approximately three and one-half ounces.

Even though the mother stays away from her nest between nursings, the young are very much on her mind. She will answer a call for help and will take great risks to try to drive away an enemy that may be molesting her brood. If a squirrel or an adult rabbit wanders too near the nest she will charge the intruder viciously and drive it off.

When the young are about twelve days old they venture out of their nest for the first time. For several days they do not wander more than a few yards from home. They pick at tempting green sprouts, learning to like them and to augment their mother's milk. Most of the daylight hours they stay in little forms. Each youngster has its separate place in the grass or under shrubs. At night they return again to the nest to sleep, huddling together for warmth. Their increasing bulk and spirit of independence makes them dissatisfied, and when fourteen to sixteen days of age they leave their nursery forever.

For some time thereafter the youngsters feed and play in their mother's territory. Sometimes two or more wander about in each other's company or with her. Of course the arrival of the next litter brings cares that occupy her full time, but she seems not to resent the continued proximity of the older children. However, they wander farther and farther away until at last they find separate ranges of their own where they settle down.

Young cottontails attain the weight of small adults, two pounds to two pounds three ounces when they are about five months old. Females are almost always heavier than males. Both sexes may be capable of breeding as early as six months of age. Generally, most North American cottontails do not bear young until the following spring when they are at least nine or ten months old. There are a few exceptions: the marsh and swamp rabbits of the southern states and cottontails (including the Audubon species) of the Southwest. In these regions the breeding season extends practically throughout the year, and a young cottontail does not need to wait for winter's passing before propagating.

The average young rabbit probably finds a satisfactory home within a mile of its birthplace. If food and cover are suitable it is likely to remain here for the rest of its life. Several attempts have been made to determine the size of the cottontail's home range. In a study that was made in Michigan, it was found that the summer home of the average female covered about twenty-two and one-half acres. During winter this was reduced to fourteen acres. Immature rabbits of both sexes required between thirteen and fifteen acres. Adult males roamed widely and covered possibly more than one hundred acres. In Connecticut and Missouri very different figures were obtained. In the former, adults of both sexes needed an average of only eight to nine acres, while in Missouri they were content with slightly over one acre.

With the exception of females with young, cottontails are tolerant of each other. The feeding territories of males and of non-breeding females are shared in common with very little friction. A mother rabbit, however, will not allow any other grown-up female on her home range. Trespassing beyond a border or neutral zone will cause a fight.

This competition for territory by breeding females may act as a limitation on the population. Certainly the number of ranges which are furnished with suitable cover and dens or other shelters have a decided influence on the number of rabbits. The fortunate animals that win and can hold the best ranges are comparatively immune to attack by most enemies, while those on poorer areas suffer the greatest losses. The need for proper shelter seems to be the only reason that rabbits move from open uplands to brushy lowlands to spend the winter. These movements are short (usually less than a mile) and are the only migrations ever performed by these usually sedentary animals.

The cottontail makes use of forms like those of the snowshoe hare and jack rabbit. They are smaller, of course, about six inches wide by nine or ten inches long. The rear end is often against a mass of shrubs or base of a small tree. During summer the rank grass or overhanging shrubbery serves to screen the form from prying eyes. During winter the rabbit may still patronize a bed surrounded by grass if the stalks have not been crushed by snow. Almost always, there will be more substantial shelter within safe reach. This may be a tangle of dense brush, a woodcutter's pile of slash, a den in broken rocks, or a burrow in the ground. Any one or several are the rabbit's chief reliance in winter, while open forms are ordinarily used during most of the summer.

The rabbit does not make its own burrow. It takes over an old badger digging, the abandoned home of a skunk, woodchuck, prairie dog, or fox. It may be in bad repair and partly collapsed, but the new tenant is not fussy. It does not require a deep tunnel and often is content with little more than an overhanging roof. Usually a den is the exclusive possession of one rabbit, but I have heard of as many as five animals being routed out of one such shelter.

Brush piles seem to be shared by two or more cottontails more often than dens. The bottom of a long-used pile is honeycombed with runways. The animals make these by clipping off twigs with their teeth until they can pass through the pile in almost any direction. Inside are several scratched-out forms where the rabbit or rabbits can sit in comfort. Evidently they feel very secure in such places. Hunters often fail to scare them out even by leaping up and down on top of the heap. They usually flee from an open form if an enemy approaches within ten feet.

Generally the cottontail spends most of the daylight hours sleeping or resting in the form or other shelter. It begins to stir a couple of hours before sunset, and by the time the sun goes down is hopping briskly along the faint trails, and picking at choice bits of food. When busily feeding it moves from plant to plant in short hops, the hind feet paired. Sometimes it steps alternately with each foot like a cat or dog. (When moving slowly, the marsh rabbit is particularly apt to walk like most other quadrupeds.) It may or may not take a rest for several hours in the middle of the night. Sunrise generally sees it back in bed. It has no deep aversion for bright light, however. It is not uncommon in summer to see the cottontail abroad even at midday. During the winter it is more likely to stay in the form, den, or burrow throughout the day.

Fluffy, deep snow is a great handicap to the cottontail whose hind feet are not adapted for snowshoeing like those of the varying hare. The cottontail sinks down in the feathery stuff and soon becomes exhausted. A slight crust is enough to hold up the small body, but too much ice seals away all the food below the snow-level and also supports swift enemies such as the fox and coyote.

Altogether, winter is an uncomfortable season for the cottontail. The female is especially likely to stay huddled in her burrow or form during storms and does not seek any food until they are over. To some extent this is also true of the male. As a result, Michigan cottontails have been found to weigh one to four ounces less in late winter than in the early part of that season. Females lose more than twice as much weight as males, presumably because they are more easily scared into shelter by bad weather.

In spite of hard winters, by simple mathematics the world should have been knee-deep in rabbits long ago. If each adult female produced four litters a year, each containing five young, there would be twenty-two rabbits at the end of the season instead of the original pair. As the population is divided equally between males and females, the next year should see a further increase of two hundred and twenty or a total population of two hundred and forty-two. If all survived, the number in five years would be more than three hundred and twenty-two thousand for each original pair!

Of course rabbit populations do not pyramid in this unrestrained fashion. Except for rather minor cyclic changes (see page 621) and local disease epizootics, rabbit numbers remain fairly constant. The fact is that each annual increase of rabbits is generally lost before the next breeding season begins.

Life's hazards crowd around every cottontail. Many of them in their baby nests are destroyed by plowing, cultivating, haying, or other farm operations. Four-footed predators are sometimes successful in finding the nests. Crows and large snakes, including rattlers and gopher snakes, occasionally devour baby rabbits,—even the red squirrel has been known to eat them. Dogs and cats are especially destructive in settled regions.

Heavy rains may flood the sunken nest, drowning or at least chilling the occupants. The mother cottontail's habit of preparing her nest a number of days before the young are born, and then leaving it uncovered, may give them pneumonia if the weather in the meantime is rainy. She does not hesitate to put the babies into a soaking wet bed and then cover them with a quilt of damp, clammy grass and fur. Observation of large numbers of rabbit nests in Pennsylvania has revealed that approximately thirty-five per cent of the broods fall victim to one hazard or another before the youngsters are ready to leave.

Once out of the nest, the cottontail finds that almost every meat-eating bird and mammal of any size has incessant designs on its life. Human hunters probably head the list; the weasel comes next, followed by the red, gray and kit foxes, coyote, domestic dog and cat, and mink. Great horned, barred, and barn owls, as well as marsh, red-tailed, and broad-winged hawks swoop out of the air with clutching talons. As everyone knows who has traveled the highways, great numbers of cottontails are crushed to death by automobiles. Most of this destruction occurs at night when the animals are blinded and confused by car headlights.

Even against such potent enemies as the weasel and fox, the cottontail is far from helpless. Although its first impulse is always to shrink unnoticed by "freezing," it is usually ready to dash away if necessary. It is not a distance runner, but relies instead on sprinting fast enough to reach a burrow or brush pile. Its scurrying hops, heading first to the left, then to the right, are strikingly different from the long rapid bounds of the jack rabbit and varying hare, but are effective in carrying it through the shrubbery of its chosen home.

Thick brush, standing or in piles, is essential to ensure safety from the larger carnivores and rapacious birds such as hawks and owls. Of course the weasel can follow into any place that a cottontail can squeeze. When trailed into a burrow and seemingly cornered, the cottontail has been known to rush past the weasel, bowling it over and escaping to the open. In actual combat the cottontail lashes out vigorously with its hind feet. Equipped with stout sharp nails, they are effective weapons against the smaller predators.

Many rabbits are unwilling or unconscious hosts to a great variety of parasites, most of which may weaken or kill if they become abundant or virulent. Ticks, fleas and mites infest the fur and skin. Warble-fly larvae burrow into the flesh, and during the warmer months of the year are common. Flukes and a number of species of tapeworms and roundworms make trouble internally. Protozoans also cause coccidiosis, a common disease which destroys the lining of the intestines and occasionally eats into the liver.

Tularemia is another rabbit disease which has been widely publicized since it was first recognized in 1910, because it is highly infectious to man. Caused by a tiny microbe whose scientific name is *Pasturella tularensis* (or *Bacterium tularensis*), it is highly lethal to rabbits, hares, ground squirrels, and many other rodents. The mortality rate in man is about four per cent of all cases. The disease is spread from rabbit to rabbit by physical contact and by ticks, lice, fleas, and biting flies. Humans may contract it by handling infected animals or eating the meat when not well cooked. The resulting fever is often very severe, and lasts on the average about two months even if not fatal. A "must" precaution against contracting tularemia or "rabbit fever" is to have nothing to do with any cottontail that looks or acts sick.

Wherever hunting is intensive, the life of the average cottontail is especially short. In southern Michigan, a biologist marked and released seventy rabbits during January, February, and March. By the next November only twelve of them could be found. Two months later apparently only five were alive. Thus only seven and one-tenth per cent of the rabbits that had already survived the vicissitudes of youth were able to live another year. In the same region, just two out of two hundred and twenty-six marked cottontails attained the age of two and one-half years.

In a Michigan refuge which was closed against hunting, seventy-three adult rabbits were ear-tagged. At least twenty-five per cent lived another year. This indicates that when protected from man the natural life of a cottontail is about two years. (Compare this to less than a year for the average rabbit. See page 619.) Exceptionally long-lived individuals may see their third birthday.

State game departments have obtained some interesting information on the numbers of cottontails on lands where protection from hunters permits a natural increase. On Grosse Isle, an island of six thousand six hundred and eighty-one acres in the Detroit River between Michigan and Ontario, a six-year closed season resulted in the rabbits doing serious damage to gardens and shrubbery. In a few days, hunters killed two thousand and ninety-six. Many others survived, so the original population must have been at least one rabbit for each two acres of land. In Pennsylvania, the state game commission in one year trapped two hundred and sixty-five cottontails from a sixty-acre island in the Schuylkill River, leaving an estimated fifty animals. In this case, there were more than five cottontails per acre. Five or six rabbits hopping about on every square of land measuring two hundred and ten feet on a side is a dense population!

An average number in Middle Western farming country is perhaps one rabbit for each two or three acres. Of course, many acres of highly cultivated land are not suitable habitat, so the population in favorable spots is much greater.

Variations in cottontail abundance occur from time to time, especially in the north. However, they are not nearly as extreme nor as clearly defined as the cycles of the varying hare. Actually, little is known about them. The increase or decrease in one area does not seem to be related to that which may be occurring in the next county.

Probably the cottontail eats a greater variety of vegetable food than any other North American mammal. Every naturalist agrees that it is easier to name the foods which it leaves untasted than those which are eaten. The coast-to-coast range complicates the task of listing even the favorite items. Cottontails sometimes have individual preferences, and in one region may eat voraciously a shrub or herb that is utilized only moderately elsewhere.

We can generalize by saying that in temperate climates three-quarters of the summer food is herbs. The bulk of this (almost one-half of the total diet) is grass and sedge. The cottontail is well known for its fondness for clover and prefers it to most other domesticated forage plants. After the grasses, it picks a great variety of herbaceous plants such as goldenrod, plantain, chickweed, sorrel, and strawberry. Then, in much smaller quantity, come the leaves and fruits of shrubs, vines and trees. The range of these foods may be shown by listing birch, maple, apple, wild cherry, blackberry, blueberry, spirea, viburnum, and grape.

As the autumn frosts mow down succulent plants and older grasses dry up, the cottontail is forced gradually onto its winter diet. This consists very largely of the twigs and bark of many woody plants, as well as buds and needles of a number of coniferous trees. The favorite species in the northeastern states are hazel, black and gray birch, beech, white, red and black oak, American elm, barberry, sassafras, spice bush, witch-hazel, apple, chokecherry, rose, black cherry, staghorn sumac, bittersweet, red and sugar maple, dogwood, blueberry, red and white pine, and white spruce. Cottontails are fond of blackberry and raspberry canes, and often cut them down and eat all of the previous season's growth. Dried goldenrod and other herbs are taken sparingly. Waste grains, especially corn, are relished whenever they can be found. The change from winter to summer diet is abrupt, showing how much cottontails prefer green herbs to woody material.

Rabbits sometimes commit depredations in truck gardens where they eat lettuce, beans, peas and other vegetables, especially when the plants are young and tender. Most of the plants nibbled grow near the edge of fields, for cotton-tails seldom feed farther than a hundred feet or so from brushy cover. More lasting damage is done in winter, when dire necessity at times forces the animals to eat berry canes and to girdle apple, cherry, and other fruit trees, and orna-mental shrubs. Man may keep these infractions to minor proportions by fencing, by providing more appetizing winter food such as apple tree thinnings (the twigs are more relished than the tough bark of the trunks), or by shooting or trapping the overabundant animals.

All the trouble that the cottontail causes fades into insignificance in view of its value as a game animal. It furnishes sport for more hunters than all of the deer, moose, bears and other big-game species combined. In 1938, almost three hundred and forty-seven thousand men and boys went rabbit hunting in Michi-gan alone. Only one hundred and seventy thousand, or forty-nine per cent of that number, hunted the white-tailed deer. The number of cottontails killed annually in the United States has never been told accurately, but certainly runs into many millions. In 1938, the estimated number taken in Michigan was two and one-half millions; in Pennsylvania, three millions; in Ohio, four millions; and in Missouri, four and one-half millions. (The record kill of deer in one year in Michigan was seventy-five thousand six hundred and eighty-two, established in 1941.)

Even at the low price of twenty-five cents each, the value of this meat is enormous. The small bunny is big business to the game departments of most states, especially those east of the Great Plains.

Cottontails live throughout the southern half of the North American continent, and thence into northern South America. Perhaps their dislike of winter limits their northward range. In any event, above the United States boundary they are found only in southern Ontario and in southwestern Saskatchewan. With this exception, cottontails thrive in a great variety of climates and habitats. Cool uplands, burning deserts, grasslands, even suburban lots of the largest cities. A few patches of shrubs, either on a town lot or along the slope of a western arroyo, suffice for necessary cover from enemies.

With a few exceptions, cottontails do not care for the deep forest. They are typically inhabitants of brushy areas and woodland borders. Two species, the swamp rabbit (*Sylvilagus aquaticus*) and the marsh rabbit (*Sylvilagus palustris*), live in wet lowlands of the southern United States and thence into South America. These are capable swimmers, and the swamp rabbit is a good diver. It has big feet with widely spreading toes to enable it to walk easily on soft, oozy mud. At the other extreme is the Rocky Mountain cottontail (*Sylvilagus nuttallii*) which is found as high as eleven thousand five hundred feet in the Pikes Peak region of Colorado.

The European rabbit (*Oryctolagus cuniculus*) was originally a native of the western Mediterranean countries. With some help from man, it has spread over all of Europe except the cold northern countries. For centuries it has been domesticated and more varieties have been developed than any other mammal except the dog. Many types of fur color and texture have been produced. Breeding has developed so-called "hares" which are four times as large as the wild rabbit. Even the brain has been reduced in proportion to the bulk of the animal, and its skeleton has been changed noticeably.

These tame species are familiar as children's pets and as meat animals. All the domesticated rabbits in North America are the European species, not the native American.

Like their wild relatives that have made themselves such a nuisance in Australia and elsewhere, these domesticated bunnies can make their own living if necessary in mild climates. When introduced to some of the mid-Pacific islands, they multiplied and destroyed nearly all the vegetation. As a result, the soil blew away, flightless species of birds were exterminated, and the islands were converted from lush tropical forests to barren wastes.

To a lesser degree, European rabbits have had the same effect when released on some of the small San Juan Islands in Puget Sound. In a few years, the rabbit hordes had eaten all the succulent plants close to the ground. One entire island of fifty-eight acres was literally honeycombed with burrows. The openings were only a few feet apart. Gradually the island was slipping into the sea. The birds, which had formerly nested there by the thousands, had been dispossessed. To save a naval radio compass station from being undermined, poisoned baits were distributed and gas was pumped into the burrows. In a few days an estimated two thousand rabbits were destroyed.

For convenience, the pigmy rabbit (genus *Brachylagus*) has been included in the group of cottontails. It is not strictly a cottontail, however. Its chief distinguishing feature is an entirely buffy tail. Only eleven to twelve inches long, it is found from central Nevada to southern Idaho, and in southeastern Oregon and northeastern California.

The true cottontails (genus *Sylvilagus*) are divided into the following groups:

1. The eastern cottontails (*S. floridanus*) are brownish, and occur from the Atlantic coast to southeastern Wyoming, extreme southeastern Arizona, and much of Central America to Costa Rica.

2. The Rocky Mountain cottontails (*S. nuttallii*) are grayer than the above. Their range extends from western North Dakota and central New Mexico west to the Cascades and the Sierra Nevada.

3. The Audubon cottontails (*S. audubonii*) are rather large, browner than the animals of the preceding group, but not as brightly colored as the eastern cottontails. Most of the species live in the southwestern United States and northwestern Mexico, from central Oklahoma and Texas to the Pacific coast of California, thence south to Sinaloa and the Mexican Plateau. One species ranges north to central Montana.

4. The marsh rabbits and swamp rabbits (*S. palustris* and *S. aquaticus*) are clothed in dark fur that is short and thin. The tail is small and usually is dingy (not white) beneath. They live in marshy places; the former in the Atlantic and Gulf coastal regions from southeastern Virginia to southern Florida and

southern Alabama; the swamp rabbits from the western Gulf coast (Alabama to southern Texas) to northern Alabama, southern Illinois, and southern Oklahoma. Other species of the group are found in eastern Mexico and south to Patagonia.

5. The brush rabbits (*S. bachmani*) are small and dark, with short legs and short, brownish tails. They inhabit the Pacific Slope from the western foothills of the Sierra Nevada to the coast, and from Oregon to southern California.

General description. A medium-sized rabbit with fairly long ears and medium-long hind legs. Fur soft, reddish brown to grayish brown above, white on under parts except the brownish throat; the short tail is brown above and pure white beneath, except some of the marsh rabbits whose tails are gray on the underside, and the brush rabbit and pigmy rabbit whose tails are brownish or buffy. Size varies with the species; total length, 11 to 22 inches; height at shoulders, 6½ to 7½ inches; weight, generally 2 to 3½ pounds, or rarely up to 6 pounds.

Distinguishing characteristics. The cottontails are smaller than the jack rabbits and other hares; the hind feet are considerably smaller and the ears are shorter. Because they range south of the varying hares (with some overlapping) their fur is thinner and shorter, and their winter coat is not white. Varying hares becomes white in winter and their coats are long and thick.

Range. Southern North America, coast to coast, and much of South America; from central New Hampshire, southern Ontario, North Dakota, southwestern Saskatchewan, and northeastern Washington, south to Patagonia.

19. The Vanishing Mermaid

THE MANATEE—*TRICHECHUS LATIROSTRIS*

Cities of pearl! Mountains of gold and sugar! Fishes that fly! MERMAIDS! These were the reports that early sailors brought back to Europe from tropical seas.

There was no doubt about the mermaids. They lived along the equatorial coast of Africa. They beckoned across the Atlantic near the shores of New Spain and among the newly discovered West Indies. They lured adventurers pushing beyond these horizons to the Red Sea, the Indian Ocean, and along the northern coast of Australia.

Eventually some misanthropic sailor killed a mermaid. What bitter disillusionment followed for his shipmates! At close range, not even the most unsophisticated sailor could find a mermaid enchanting.

The creature was about ten feet long. Too big to be petted! She had tested the tackle with more than half a ton of dead weight. Instead of being delicate and fair, her skin was rough and gray. Her thick, round-shouldered body tapered away to a horizontal, graceful fluke. But not even the loneliest sailor could desire to be held in her bungling flipper-arms. She had no fingers. Three little flat nails indicated where they should have been.

Where were those floating tresses the sailors thought they had seen from a distance? The siren was bald-headed! Not a hair on her seallike head. And until the men looked for a pair of languishing eyes, they missed the tiny, soulless orbs almost buried in wrinkles. Two valvelike slits were her nostrils and she had no ears. A broad muzzle with a greatly swollen upper lip divided in two lobes. On both lips were a number of short, stiff bristles, practically the only hairs on her whole body. A mermaid with whiskers! Sprawled out on the deck, she looked rather like a small, wrinkled whale.

All in all, it seemed to be the end of the mermaid story. But no! One of the animals was at last dragged into a museum. Sober scientists examined it, dissected it and named its family—Sirenia! Romance dies hard, even in a museum.

Men began to learn more about "sirens." The Atlantic species went by the Indian name of manatee. Their relatives, the dugongs, lived in the Pacific and Indian Oceans and the Red Sea.

The largest of this race was the Steller sea-cow. Inhabiting the Bering Strait between Russia and Alaska, this husky mermaid reached the enormous length of twenty-five feet and weighed a couple of tons. She was much sought after by Russian sealers and whalers, not for her charm, but for her fat. The thick coat of blubber protected her from the icy waters but finally proved her undoing. About 1868, only twenty-seven years after her discovery, the last Steller sea-cow vanished unromantically into the rendering tanks.

Our American mermaids, the manatees, are no more beautiful than the rest of their family. About nine to fifteen feet long, they weigh six hundred to perhaps two thousand pounds. Haunting the Florida coast and lagoons, these buxom sirens are slow-moving, harmless vegetarians. Drifting up to a patch of waving slender river grass, they seem to be sitting upright, their heads above the water. Methodically they reach for lunch with flipper-hands. Their great swollen upper lips pull the coarse food into their mouths. Too indolent to fully

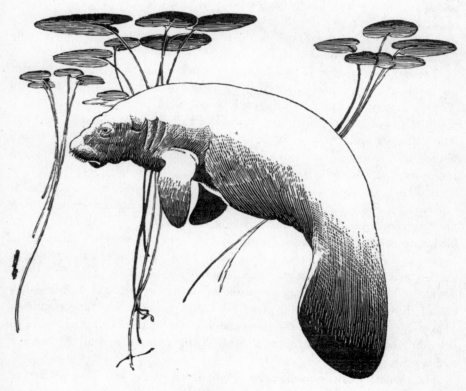

MANATEE

utilize their small sets of oversize cheek teeth, they swallow their food half chewed. Nevertheless, on a still night you can hear their flapping lips and crunching teeth two hundred yards away. They sound like a herd of horses feeding in a pasture.

Ordinarily the manatees are typical natives of the tropics, sluggish and drowsy. Like sleepy human dwellers of those climes, who sprawl against a sunny wall, heads bowed in slumber, the manatees also sag into human U-shaped positions. But the water dwellers have the advantage that their world is all wall. No matter how they droop, the water is always there to give support. So wherever they go, the manatees loll comfortably, heads and tails hanging. Every five to fifteen minutes, their shoulders rise above the surface, their heads follow and they breathe two or three times. Then their heads fall forward, the shoulders sink slowly out of sight, and they return to their dreamy contemplation of the brightly colored fish swimming about them.

Life is not always peaceful, even in this watery Garden of Eden. Manatees are so timorous that a sudden shower of rain or a leaf dropping on the water may cause a brief panic. There are real dangers as well. Sharks and huge crocodiles are always hungry and are glad to tackle an enormous dinner whose only defense is thrashing, lunging flight.

The mother manatee scoops up her baby, tucks it under her arm and makes off, while the father and relatives create a furious confusion, plunging in all directions. Fortunately, a chance whack of one of their thrashing tails, with a half ton of bone and muscle behind it, will make even a hungry crocodile retreat. The manatees run first and—if they think—think afterward. Apparently they never become aggressive enough to disagree among themselves, even over a choice meal of water plants.

In March or April the manatee mother looks for a sheltered place that is safe from sharks, killer whales and sawfish. It may be a lagoon—provided it is not a crocodile resort—or behind a mass of driftwood or wreckage. This is the birthplace of the little manatee (occasionally twins). About thirty inches long, it can—and must—swim immediately. Being born in the water, this is one of the few mammal young that needs no swimming lessons.

The mother manatee nurses her young by sitting up, her head and shoulders out of the water, and clasping it to her breast between her flipper-arms—a Madonna of the Sea! She is affectionate and, as manatee courage goes, brave in defending her baby from danger. At least, she never leaves it behind when she rushes off to safety.

The manatees usually dislike the rough waters of the sea. They prefer the bays and larger rivers from Florida through Central America and the West

Indies to the Amazon. Sometimes they venture along the coasts, especially be-hind reefs and islands that break the force of the rollers.

Very rarely a manatee may forsake the quiet waters of remote rivers and take up residence in a noisy harbor. Such an adventuress was the manatee that lived for years in the Miami River in the heart of that mecca of frost-bitten Yankees. Crusted with oily scum and refuse, the old lady ignored the whirling propellers of launches and the satire of loungers who watched her from the bridge. What a mermaid! Or was "she" a merman?

When mermaids were first discovered there was considerable argument as to whether they were fish or mammal. Some hard-pressed sailors tried eating one. Being used to a diet of fat pork pickled in vats of brine, they decided that fresh manatee meat was not half bad.

Eventually a Friday dawned that found a crew reduced to eating manatee or nothing. The chaplain raised the question of the propriety of good Catholic seamen eating meat in violation of the Holy Father's edict. Hunger, however, sharpened lay wits and the padre bowed to the view that any creature which spent its life in the water must be a fish.

Under less drastic circumstances, this theory was challenged. The lean meat and the fat seemed more like that of an ox or hog than of a fish. The blood was thick and deep red. The bones were heavy enough to be carved into "ivory" weapons. The manatee undoubtedly breathed air. So, at last, both religion and science got together and decided that the manatee was a mammal and not to be eaten by Catholics on Fridays.

All this time and for centuries before, the unconverted natives of America had been eating manatee without regard for the day of the week. Paddling a small dug-out canoe to a "grazing ground" of manatees, they hurled spears into the herd of "sea-cows." As soon as a weapon was buried in one of the bodies, the rawhide rope attached to the thrower pulled taut. Wildly the tiny boat was dragged about by the wounded manatee. Back and forth, round and round, it whirled with the mad gyrations of the frenzied animal. A deep dive would founder the dug-out and spill the hunters into the water, where crocodiles some-times devoured them. But with luck, the Indians, battering and slashing with spears at every appearance of the manatee's head, would soon put an end to the unfortunate creature.

Then the whole village feasted. Red steaks from the rump! Light-colored meat from the breast, back and tail muscles! Fat slabs of spareribs! And finally the lardlike oily fat so much prized in cooking. Had they only known it, they were eating pounds of excellent substitute for cod-liver oil. In those days they got their vitamins without benefit of drugstores.

Although still numerous in wilder parts of Central and South America, manatees are very scarce in North America. They are exceedingly rare, if indeed they still exist, along the Gulf coast from the Rio Grande to the Turner River of Florida. A few manatees still doze away the days in the lagoons of the Thousand Islands and Florida Bay. Others drift about in Biscayne Bay and north to Fort Lauderdale, but the tribe is very small.

Cold winters have taken their toll. A couple of near-freezing nights is probably enough to bring double pneumonia. The American mermaids lack the blankets of blubber that kept their extinct relatives, the Stellar sea-cows, cozy despite the icebergs. The freezes of 1895, 1917, and 1937 are known to have been hard on the population. But much more serious has been shooting. Although protected by law, fresh manatee meat and oil are tempting to the swamp "conch" who may be on short rations. So-called "sportsmen" shoot at the bobbing heads just for fun. Propellers of motorboats have fatally wounded others. The placid, easygoing manatees have never learned to be wary of the pale-faced men in the huge canoes, from whose rails the thunder sticks spit fire and death, and from whose hulls come slashing agony.

General description. A large aquatic animal with thick, rounded body; head small, grotesque, with thick pendulous upper lip divided medially; eyes small; external ears absent; forelimbs modified into broad fingerless flippers; hind limbs absent; body terminating in a broad rounded tail or "fluke." Skin finely wrinkled, almost hairless (except muzzle, which is provided with numerous stiff bristles). Color dark gray above, sometimes shading to dirty whitish gray below. Total length, 7 to 15 feet (extreme); weight, 500 to possibly 2000 pounds.

Distinguishing characteristics. A large mammal inhabiting coastal areas and river estuaries of the tropics and subtropics, distinguished from other aquatic mammals such as porpoises and whales by sluggish behavior, upright position and head more often above water.

Range. West Indies, coasts of the Atlantic Ocean and Gulf of Mexico from Central America north to southern Florida and, very rarely, Virginia and North Carolina.

20. Two Seafarers

THE WHALE—ORDER *CETACEA*

The largest animal in the history of the world is the whale. But there are whales and whales. Big whales and little ones; whales that navigate the oceans; whales that cruise in harbors and rivers. The largest of the family is the Blue Whale, which may be one hundred and six feet long and weigh over one hundred and twenty-five tons. Some of its little relatives are only five feet long with a feather weight of seventy pounds.

There are two families of whales, the Toothless and the Toothed. Instead of teeth, the toothless whales have strainers. Hundreds of strips of whalebone, frayed with a mass of long thick fringe, hang from the gum of its upper jaw. Acting as strainers, these plates are about a quarter of an inch apart, not more than a foot wide and, including the fringe, two to over ten feet long. Whalebone is not like real bone, but is a horny substance that is quite flexible. It is also called baleen.

Of course, you remember Jonah and the Whale. If you believe Kipling, you may believe that these whalebone strips are made by Jonah's raft and tied into the whale's mouth by Jonah's suspenders. This was just to be sure that the whale could never swallow Jonah or any other man again.

Actually, the throats of whalebone whales are too small (only a few inches in diameter) to swallow anything larger than a herring. The strainers are a great convenience in getting dinner. The whalebone whale has only to swoosh through the water with its mouth open. The sea pours in. Along come barrels of sea food. With its huge tongue the whale forces the water back out through the side strainers and swallows the food that is left.

Whalebone whales feed almost entirely on small animal life of the upper levels of the sea. This teeming life consists of little creatures, many of which are shrimplike forms less than two inches long! Existing in shoals of untold millions, it is known collectively as plankton or, to whalers, as "krill." It takes a lot of these small organisms to satisfy the appetite of the largest animal in the world. Just an ordinary sized whale will eat a ton of sardines topped off with a variety of other small fish and crustaceans for breakfast.

Streaking through the water with gustatory delight, the whalebone whale

GRAY WHALE

occasionally pays dearly for indifference to other traffic. A few years ago, a small finback followed a school of fish into Los Angeles Harbor. So preoccupied was it in swallowing the fish as fast as it could that a man in a skiff was able to row up and throw a rope around its flukes. The finner was enraged at this indignity. It was not used to being lassoed. Furiously it tore around the harbor, thrashing its tail with anger and throwing up great waves. The man was in the same predicament as the chap who grabbed the bear by the tail, but he held on. In a blind dash, the maddened whale finally ran onto the beach. Struggling and gasping for air, it collapsed and suffocated.

You can recognize a whalebone whale by its double nostril. The toothed whales have only a single blowhole. The toothless whalebone whales have another curious difference from most other mammals. The females are as large and often considerably larger than the males. You may be sure they don't put up with any harems.

There are some whales which could actually have swallowed Jonah and his raft. These are the toothed whales, which have large throats and no baleen. But Jonah couldn't have "danced and pranced and howled and prowled, and danced hornpipes where he shouldn't." He would have been digested in no time at all by the powerful gastric juices.

The teeth of these toothed whales are uniform, usually cone-shaped, but varied in number, depending on the species. Some have two, others have a hundred.

Toothed whales have a different diet from the toothless whalebone whales. The great sperm whale, for example, lives almost entirely on large cuttlefish or squids that grow up to thirty feet long. Even the wounds that these struggling creatures inflict with their long beaks and tentacles do not deter its appetite. It also likes fish. A toothed whale can swallow a six-foot seal or a ten-foot shark whole.

Probably once a land mammal, the whale has completely adapted itself to water during the last few thousands of centuries. A long time ago it discarded the hairy coat of its remote ancestors, with the technical exception of a few whiskers on the muzzle. To keep warm, it acquired a long undercoat of blubber. This fat is sometimes twelve inches thick in places. It also keeps the whale from going hungry when food is scarce. Through disuse, the hind legs have disappeared completely except for one or two bones which are buried deep in the body. The forelegs have developed into flippers which it uses as paddles for balancing and steering. The greatest improvement is the large flat fin, the flukes, on the end of its tail. This is the propeller.

The large whales cannot travel at as great a speed as the small ones. Some of them, however, can attain a rate of thirty miles an hour for short distances. We can hardly conceive the tremendous power that is needed to drive the huge bulk of a sixty-foot sei or pollock whale through the water at such a speed. Ordinarily they cruise much more slowly, perhaps at about eight miles an hour.

Like most other mammals that live in the water, the whale no longer has an external ear. It can hear perfectly well, although sounds are transmitted to the hearing apparatus through a very tiny opening. Even in a one-hundred-foot whale this aperture is barely large enough to admit the end of a pencil. It automatically closes when the whale dives or "sounds."

Living in the sea has brought about some modifications in the whale's eye. Since the eyeball is fixed, the whale must move its whole body to shift the line of sight. Its eye lens is set permanently at one focus, perhaps because the entire eye, like the rest of the animal, is built to withstand the enormous pressures of the deep. The whale sheds greasy tears. A set of glands supply a soothing oily substance that protects its eyes from the irritation of salt water.

Whalers have argued interminably over the ability of their prey to see through the air. Some whales, notably the sperm and the killers, frequently rear partly out of water and seem to look around. It is possible that this is only to secure an extra-deep lungful of air.

The whale probably can't smell, but this isn't important. Some scientists think it doesn't sleep, because it will follow a ship for days at a time. Perhaps instead of being a sleep-walker, it is a sleep-swimmer!

Don't ever think it has become a fish. Besides being nursed at the mother's breast, it still has five fingers buried in each flipper, a four-chambered heart that pumps warm blood, and a set of large lungs. It has to come up for air.

Because of its life under the water, the whale's respiratory tract is a special job, built for the purpose. The ordinary swimmer would get its lungs full of water if it ploughed through the sea with its mouth wide open as the whalebone whales do when feeding. The whale's air ducts are not connected with its mouth or throat as are other mammals'. The single or paired nostrils are located far back on the highest part of its head. A set of valves automatically closes the blowhole when submerged. In this way no water can get in. The air duct runs back to the chest, which holds a roomy set of unlobed lungs.

When it is undisturbed and at peace with the world, the whale follows a fairly regular procedure in breathing and submerging. A big sperm whale, for example, stays on the surface for about ten minutes. During this period it breathes about sixty or seventy times. The last inhalation is a long, full one, enough to last for an hour or even more under water. Most whales, however, will stay down ordinarily only eight to twelve or fifteen minutes, and they breathe only four or five times between deep dives or "soundings."

Many a tall tale has been related about the diving ability of the whale. Undeniably, some great depths are reached. A sperm whale once became entangled in a cable at a depth of three thousand two hundred and forty feet. Apparently it did not mind the pressure of fourteen hundred pounds per square inch. But, caught in the cable, it drowned. Probably only a sperm or a beaked whale would dive to this depth.

The whale does not spout water. On coming to the surface after a deep dive, it empties its lungs with a mighty rush. The warm, moisture-laden breath expands violently into the cooler air. Condensing into a geyserlike spout, it may rise twenty feet or more and can be seen for several miles. During calm weather, it can be heard at least a mile away.

You can tell a whale by its spout. The rorqual's is high and slender. The humpback's is short and broad. The sperm's is slanting instead of rising straight up like the others.

In the Arctic the spout of a whale will hold together as a cloud for several minutes in the cold air. I have seen spouts so dense in Alaskan waters that they screened the portion of the mountainside directly behind them.

We do not know a great deal about the whale's mating life. Some whales are thought to be monogamous, while others are polygamous or even promiscuous. It is difficult to check up on them. How can you track them across trackless oceans? How can you recognize them as individuals?

Identification disks of monel metal have been shot into whales by harpoon guns. When the marker is later found either in the hide or the bottom of a rendering tank, it is returned with statistics for a reward and recording to the Colonial Office in London. These records and years of whaling observations have given us considerable information about their travels and age, but not their mating.

We know that most whales pair in winter or spring, when they are in the warmer waters near the earth's fat middle. The whales have different methods of courtship, depending on the species. Dr. Remington Kellogg knows more about this and whales in general than any other American scientist.

The blue whale is very discreet. It probably carries on all mating completely under water. The finback is a little more exuberant and once in a great while so far forgets itself as to leap above the surface of the water.

Perhaps the humpbacks are the most passionate of all the whales. There is no decorum about a young humpback whale during the mating season. Gamboling and rolling lustily on top of the ocean, he shows off his repertoire of sea tricks to attract the female's immovable eye. He often leaps completely out of water. The resulting crashes of his fifty-foot-long body could leave no female entirely indifferent.

Once having got together, humpbacks have been seen to lie side by side, stroking each other with their long fins. Ardently they strike alternate "gentle" blows with their great arms. The sound of these love pats can be heard for miles.

The whalers call the humpback female the prostitute of the sea. Like her mate, the blue whale female is more inhibited. Or perhaps just coy. Anyhow, she never, never pursues the male. Apparently cool and indifferent, she ignores him. The blue whale male must do all the pursuing and perhaps he likes it that way.

Most whale mothers are pregnant longer than human mothers. They carry their embryonic youngsters about ten to twelve months, depending on the species. When born, the baby is immense, even in comparison with its big mother. A seventy-foot whale may give birth to a calf twenty-four feet long.

The calves are born without any long undercoat of blubber. Perhaps that is the reason the mothers have their deliveries in warm waters where the babies won't catch cold.

Twins are rather rare in the whale world. Normally only one calf is produced at birth. The mother lavishes on it all the affection of which her huge bulk is capable. And a seventy- to ninety-foot whale can hold a lot of anything. Even though normally timid, she will brave great dangers in attempts to guard her calf. Before international agreements forbade the killing of mothers and calves, whalers took advantage of this maternal trait by harpooning the calf and towing the body to their ship. The bereaved mother would usually follow and could be killed easily.

Like all other mammal mothers, the whale nurses her young. When the baby is hungry, it noses the mother's flanks. Responding to this prompting, she rolls toward one side and raises the rear of her body almost out of water. The two nipples, which are normally carried in recesses in the body near the back of the abdomen, are pushed out. Her young then can nurse with its nostrils above the water. It doesn't have to work as hard as the human baby. The milk is forced into its mouth by the contraction of the mother's muscles. Sometimes it comes too fast. Spilling into the ocean, it clouds the water for yards around.

Young whales grow up with astounding speed. The baby blue whale doubles its birth length of twenty-four feet in seven months. Certainly it is big enough now to start rustling its own food. Other whale young may nurse until they are a year old.

At about thirty months the calf may be eighty feet long and beginning to wander after the young cows. He is now ready to take on whatever responsibilities a whale male assumes, which are probably very few. His mate is the principal guardian of their child and her cares are so great that she calves only every other year.

If any creature could be immune to trouble, it would seem to be the largest one in the world. But even the whale has its enemies and vicissitudes. The killer whale, which is a dolphin fifteen to thirty feet long (one of the small whales), has no fear or compunction in assaulting the large whales. The dolphins also hunt in packs for their great relatives. Ganging together, they will tear at the tongue and lips of a big whale until it bleeds or is hacked to death.

To run aground is usually a catastrophe for a whale. Adapted to life in water, which provides support, its chest framework is weak. When left high and dry by a falling tide, the chest collapses and it cannot breathe. A few cetaceans, such as the California gray whale, like to roll in the breakers. They will survive stranding in two or three feet of water until the rising tide floats them off. Most stranded whales soon suffocate.

Not even the whale is immune to parasites. Barnacles and other parasitic crustaceans attach themselves to the skin, especially when the whale is in warm waters. If abundant, these shells may impede the mammal just as they retard the speed of ships. The whale cannot go into dry dock to have its hull scraped, but it does make for the cold oceans where barnacles grow numb and drop off. Whales—especially gray whales—have lice which cling to the mighty body with hooklike legs.

The sperm whale is said to be worn out by eating a ton of clawing squids and octopuses each day, and to die at the tender age of eight or nine. Recently, however, evidence has been found that female sperm and "whale bone" whales had borne as many as fifty calves. They may have been over a hundred years old.

Of course man is the worst enemy of the whale. For more than a thousand years, he has scoured the seas in ships, pursuing the great creature into the farthest corners of the world. Before petroleum was discovered to light man's lamps, whale oil was much in demand for this purpose and for the manufacture of candles. As much as three hundred and five barrels could be obtained from a single blue whale.

Women must keep an illusion of their figures. In the past they have demanded great amounts of whalebone for corsets. The price went up to seven dollars a pound for good quality plates. A single large whale was worth twelve thousand dollars at top prices. Whalers redoubled their efforts to kill whales faster. Then came the kerosene lamp, electric lights, steel corset "bones," and nylon girdles. Edison and Dupont gave the whales a brief respite.

But this breathing spell was short. Whale oil is still valuable for soap-making, lard and margarine substitutes, fuel and explosives. Sperm oil, which is composed chiefly of waxes rather than fats, is still in demand for lubricating light machinery, for use in the leather trade and for the production of face creams. Even the flesh is eaten, especially by Japanese too poor to buy beef.

Ambergris, a fatty, grayish substance from the intestines of sick sperm whales (probably the result of eating too many cuttlefish!) is valued as a fixative for perfume. It has been worth up to twenty dollars an ounce. One lucky crew captured a whale that was carrying around a lump of ambergris weighing seven hundred and fifty pounds!

Whaling equipment was originally very crude. In the old days when the whalers sighted a whale, they left their ship and pursued the animal and its companions in small row boats. When near enough, they hurled harpoons into one of their prey. Maddened with pain, the giant thrashed about sending up great waves, often smashing or capsizing the boat. Many a whaler was lost overboard. Only the whales that would float after death could be hunted. The great finner family (finbacks, rorquals and humpbacks) sank to the depths after being killed and would drag the boat after them.

Whaling today is greatly improved and mechanized. Large floating factories steam to the last great whaling grounds—the Antarctic. Killer boats pursue and capture the fastest whales by explosive harpoons fired from a powerful gun. Attached to the harpoon is a heavy rope that is hauled in or let out by a steam winch. Air is then pumped through a hose into the whale to keep the dead body afloat. If other whales are still in sight, a marker is placed on the dead whale to indicate ownership and the killer boat goes after the rest of the school.

When the dead whales are towed to the factory ship, they are drawn into the hull by a steam winch, stripped of their blubber, cut up and rendered into oil, cattle food and fertilizer. The whales are full of oil. Not only their tears, their mothers' milk and their blubber, but their flesh and bones. Although the best grade of oil comes from the blubber, lesser grades are secured from the meat and bones.

Whales have been killed at an appalling rate. Some one has calculated that the world catch of whales for the first hundred years after 1517 was about a thousand animals. In 1936–37, more than forty-six thousand whales were killed in the Antarctic alone. Here more than twelve thousand men were engaged in whaling during the brief polar summer of three months.

National and commercial interests became alarmed. Surely no animal, reproducing at the rate of only one calf every two years, could stand such a slaughter. Commercial whaling in North American waters had long since almost ceased. In 1935 an international agreement came into force regulating the killing of whalebone whales, defining the seasons, species, and length of whales that may be taken and prohibiting the molesting of immature animals and of mother whales with their calves.

Despite these restrictions, the slaughter of whales continued unabated until World War II. It seemed likely that some species would vanish entirely. Other whales were expected to become so scarce that hunting them, at least with expensive equipment, would become unprofitable.

World War II increased the whales' chances of survival temporarily. When men became so preoccupied in killing each other, they had little time to kill whales. Japanese whaling boats were used for troop transports and oil tankers. Britain could not spare ships and our own factory ships, killer boats and workers were devoted largely to the war effort.

Instead of the seven hundred whaling ships that had sailed out of United States ports in 1850, there were only three in 1943. The annual eight-million-dollar catch of a hundred years ago had dwindled to a mere forty-four thousand.

Because there are many whales, with many popular names for each whale, a sketch of the "family tree" may straighten out some of the confusion. Only the more important members will be listed, and only one popular name for each member.

I WHALEBONE WHALES

(Suborder *Mysticeti*). Toothless whales with paired nostrils, huge mouths and small throats.
1. Right Whales (*Eubalæna glacialis* and *Balæna mysticetus*).
2. Gray Whale (*Rhachianectes glaucus*).
3. Finbacks, Humpbacks and Rorquals (Family *Balænopteridæ*). (Includes Blue Whale and Sei Whale).

II TOOTHED WHALES

(Suborder *Odontoceti*). Single nostril, smaller mouths, teeth, and relatively huge throats.
1. Sperm Whale (*Physeter catodon*).
2. Pigmy Sperm Whale (*Kogia breviceps*).

3. Dolphins and Porpoises (Family *Delphinidæ*). Includes Killer Whale, Blackfish, White Whale, Narwhal.

4. Beaked Whales (Family *Ziphiidæ*). Includes Bottlenose Whale.

WHALEBONE WHALES

RIGHT WHALES

As with all whalebone whales, the female right whale is larger than the male. Traveling at low speed, near the surface of the water, occasionally leaping into the air, carrying huge quantities of oil and whalebone, these whales were once very numerous and "just right" for the whalers. Thus their name!

The right whales of the North Atlantic and North Pacific oceans wear formal black suits. Even the whalebone that clutters up their mouths is black. One out of five wear white vests. A horny, irregularly shaped "bonnet" above the muzzle is usually studded with lice, parasitic worms and barnacles. These whales have no dorsal (back) fin, and the pectoral (shoulder) fins are broad. Usually about forty-five or fifty feet long, an occasional old female has grown to sixty-five feet.

GRAY WHALE

Summering in the Arctic, wintering as far south as Mexico, the gray whale is sometimes known as the Devil Fish. Its dark body is covered with white scars probably caused by barnacles. It also lacks a dorsal fin. Unlike the right whales, the pectoral fins are narrow and its baleen (whalebone) is yellowish white or yellow.

FINBACKS, RORQUALS, AND HUMPBACKS

Usually enormous creatures with comparatively small heads, these whales live in both the Atlantic and Pacific oceans. They all have a dorsal fin. You can recognize them by the family crest. This is a set of many long parallel grooves on the outside of throat and chest. Their length varies from thirty to one hundred and six feet.

TOOTHED WHALES

SPERM WHALE

Moby Dick was a sperm. The sperm that swallowed Jonah was probably just a third-rater, compared to Moby Dick. The head of the sperm whale is enormous, almost one-third of the length! In this head is a great cavity filled with as much as a ton of fine oil which, on exposure to the air, hardens into a waxy mass. The largest of the toothed whales, the male is sometimes sixty-five feet long. His mate is considerably smaller and supposed to be more amiable.

Indigestion, probably caused by the tons of sharp pronged cuttlefish jabbing through the intestines, sometimes produces ambergris, the valuable perfume fixative. The upper jaws are toothless, but the lower ones sprout twenty to thirty heavy molars. These gray colored whales run in schools in both the Atlantic and Pacific Oceans. The females and calves stay in tropical waters the year round, but each year the adult males spend their summer vacations as bachelors, as far south as the Antarctic, and as far north as the Bering Sea.

PIGMY SPERM WHALE

The pigmy sperm is small, nine to thirteen feet long. However it has two more teeth in its upper jaw than the big sperm, which has none. The twenty-eight to thirty teeth in the lower jaws are very pointed and slender. An intrepid mariner, it navigates all the oceans, but is rarely seen. The sickle-shaped dorsal fin is the family badge.

PORPOISES AND DOLPHINS

The porpoises and dolphins are among the smaller cetaceans. Most of them are from five to fourteen feet long, but included in the family are several "whales," the white whale or beluga, the killer whale, and the narwhal that may be up to thirty feet long. Because this is an especially interesting family, a separate section has been allotted to them (see pp. 642–645).

BEAKED WHALES

The ten kinds of beaked whales have long snouts and grooved throats. Almost toothless, they have only one or two teeth at the end of each lower jaw. The Cuvier's Beaked Whale has various colored and patterned suits. During mating season, he may go completely berserk and not only attack his male rivals but also females and offspring.

Description. A very large, fish-shaped mammal highly adapted for aquatic, chiefly oceanic, life. Body rounded, tapering to the tail which is a broad horizontal fin or "flukes"; neck region not constricted, body merging directly into the large head; fore limbs modified into uniform paddle flippers; no external hind limbs; eyes small, nostrils opening via a single or paired opening near crown of head; no external ears. Skin practically hairless, smooth and shining.

Color varies with species: black, bluish, brownish or gray, paler or nearly white underneath. Size varies greatly with the species; total length, 30 to over 106 feet; weight, up to 125 tons and more.

Distinguishing characteristics. An extremely large fish-shaped mammal, found only in the ocean or sometimes in bays and the lower portions of the larger rivers. Adults (with the exception of the pigmy sperm whale, the dolphins and porpoises) are usually over 30 feet. The pigmy sperm, and dolphins and porpoises are usually under 30 feet.

Range. The oceans of the world.

DOLPHIN
FAMILY *DELPHINIDÆ*

Anyone who has taken a sea voyage of any length has seen dolphins or porpoises. From far out toward the horizon, one or two or perhaps a dozen dolphins come tearing in at more than thirty miles an hour to join the ship. Like great shiny fat fish, they break the surface, clear the water in graceful arcs, and disappear cleanly only to leap again a few moments later. Sometimes, just to demonstrate their skill and speed, they may drop back and allow the ship's bow to forge ahead. Then, with a rush, they flash forward. cross the bow contemptuously, and hurtle away to look for more exciting ventures.

The dolphins appear to be merry souls. Convivial creatures, they almost always travel in company. A perpetually pleasant, insouciant expression heightens the impression of good will. Cavorting through the waves, they seem to be bursting with joy. Actually they are the most voracious mammals of the sea. Their great mouths with rows of sharp teeth mean snapping death to most fish and their appearance inevitably throws a school into frenzy. Without qualms, they devour the wounded and feeble members of their own family.

One of the large dolphins, the killer whale, is the most predacious of them all. The wolf of the sea, it travels with the pack and will gang up on one of the great whales. Tearing at the lips and tongue, the killers leap and slash. The bloody sea is churned into froth by the struggle. Frequently the victim seems to be paralyzed with fright, and merely turns on its side while being hacked to pieces.

These killers have threatened men standing on ice floes by shattering the ice around them. They have even menaced them on board ship. Probably the catch of seals was the lure, not the men.

DOLPHIN

One morning in Glacier Bay, Alaska, I came face to face with a black killer. Hanging over the rail, I was anxiously watching the icebergs scrape the paint off our boat. A killer suddenly broke water so close to me that it could almost have touched me. It was more than half as long as our thirty-six-foot boat. Then it sank back into the water. One of those sudden Alaskan fogs dropped over us and we could not see, but felt or imagined the presence of it and its gang, at every lap of water.

The killer has an enormous appetite. When opened, one killer (only sixteen feet long) was found to have eaten thirteen porpoises and fourteen seals for dinner. Penguins are incidental tidbits. Eskimos at Cape Prince of Wales say that they have seen a killer throw a two thousand pound walrus completely out of water.

Probably no mammal except a human dares to attack the killer. Great numbers of so-called killer whales have been swept ashore by high winds and their blind greed for food. In 1935, between two hundred and three hundred of these gangsters terminated their bloody careers on the beach about fifty miles from Capetown. Another group of twenty killers died on a rocky beach at Estevan Point, Vancouver Island, British Columbia, on June 12 or 13, 1945. It was presumed that they were in pursuit of fish or other food when they stranded. But these were only "false killer whales" (*Pseudorca*). Real killers are probably too smart and too powerful to get themselves into such a fix.

Dolphins, porpoises, the killer whale, blackfish, white whale, narwhal and others all belong to the dolphin family. They are, of course, small whales. Like the rest of the toothed whales, they have a single blowhole in their foreheads. Most of these dolphins are from five to fourteen feet long, but some species may be up to thirty feet in length. You can distinguish them from the other whales by their smaller size.

With the exception of the black finless porpoise, white whale and narwhal, all have dorsal fins. Those of the dolphins curve backward at a rakish angle; the porpoises' and the killers' are more triangular in shape. The common dolphins are recognized by their long jaws, forming "beaks," which the rest of the family do not have.

The main facts of the dolphins' lives are much the same as the larger whales'. They have some outstanding differences, however.

While the big whales usually prefer their own company or a few boon companions at the most, the dolphins surround themselves with friends. As many as eight hundred white whales (a species of dolphin) have been seen swimming together up the St. Lawrence River.

On rare occasions, North American dolphins may take excursions up rivers farther than whales ever venture. At least one school of dolphins ascended the Hudson River as far as Poughkeepsie. Dead common dolphins have also been found in the Hudson at Highland, seventy-three miles north of New York Harbor, and at Van Wies Point, one hundred and forty-five miles above New York.

Although the largest of the dolphin family are sometimes sought for their oil, most of the group are regarded as too small for commercial "whaling." At one time, however, a fishery for the common bottle-nosed dolphin was carried on at Cape Hatteras. They were netted in some numbers, one thousand two hundred and sixty-eight being caught during one winter.

The common porpoise, which weighs from one hundred to one hundred and twenty pounds, was once used extensively for food. During medieval times, it was considered a royal dish. In the days when men were men, strong-smelling fat meat was not objectionable!

General description. Small, toothed whales with single blowholes. Color and patterns vary with the species: black, bluish, gray, white and sometimes brownish or yellowish. Total length, 4 to 30 feet (extremes); most dolphins range in size from 5 to 14 feet. Weight, 70 pounds to several tons, generally 500 to 1,000 pounds.

(Some of the larger dolphins are dignified by the name of "whale." Among these are the killer whale, which has a blunt snout and high dorsal fin, and is black above and white below; the white whale of the Arctic; also the narwhal, which is unique in having a spirally twisted tusk, occasionally 9 feet long, projecting from the left upper jaw.)

Distinguishing characteristics. At a distance, can be distinguished from the big whales only by smaller size and generally more active movements.

Range. The oceans of the world; occasionally in bays and the lower courses of large rivers.

List of References

The following books and articles contain much valuable information on the lives of North American mammals. The list is by no means complete, but it includes many of the more significant recent publications and some of the older standard references. Facts were drawn from most of them, as well as from minor sources and the experience of the author, in writing the foregoing chapters of this book.

GENERAL REFERENCES

Allen, Glover M. 1942. Extinct and vanishing mammals of the western hemisphere. pp. vii–xv, 1–620. Amer. Committee for International Wild Life Protection.

Anderson, R. M. 1934. Mammals of the eastern Arctic and Hudson Bay. In Canada's Eastern Arctic, pp. 67–108. Dept. Interior, Ottawa.

Anderson, R. M. 1937. Mammals and birds of the Western Arctic District, Northwest Territories, Canada. Reprinted from Canada's Western Northland, pp. 97–122; map., illus. Dept. of Mines and Resources, Ottawa.

Anderson, R. M. 1939. Mammals of the province of Quebec. Ann. Rpt. Provancher Soc. Nat. Hist., Quebec, for 1938. pp. 50–114. Quebec.

Anthony, H. E. 1928. Field book of North American mammals. pp. iii–xxv, 1–625; illus. G. P. Putnam's Sons, N. Y.

Arthur, Stanley C. 1928. The fur animals of Louisiana. Bull. No. 18. Dept. of Conservation, State of Louisiana, pp. 1–433; illus. New Orleans, La.

Audubon, John J., and Bachman, John. 1846–1854. The viviparous quadrupeds of North America. 3 vols. Vol. 1, 389 pp., 1846; vol. 2, 334 pp., 1851; vol. 3, 384 pp., 1854.

Bailey, Alfred M., and Hendee, Russell W. 1926. Notes on the mammals of northwestern Alaska. Jour. of Mammalogy, vol. 7, no. 1, pp. 9–28; illus. Feb., 1926.

Bailey, Vernon. 1905. Biological survey of Texas. North Amer. Fauna No. 25. 222 pp.; illus. Wash., D. C.

Bailey, Vernon. 1923. Mammals of the District of Columbia. Proc. Biol. Soc. of Washington, vol. 36, pp. 103–138. May 1, 1923.

Bailey, Vernon. 1926. A biological survey of North Dakota. North Amer. Fauna No. 49, 226 pp.; illus. U.S.D.A., Wash., D. C.

Bailey, Vernon. 1928. Animal life of the Carlsbad Cavern. 195 pp., illus. Williams and Wilkins Co., Baltimore, Md.

Bailey, Vernon. 1930. Animal life of Yellowstone National Park. 241 pp., illus. Charles C. Thomas, Springfield, Ill., and Baltimore, Md.

Bailey, Vernon. 1931. Mammals of New Mexico. North Amer. Fauna No. 53. 412 pp.; illus. U.S.D.A., Wash., D. C.

Bailey, Vernon. 1936. The mammals and life zones of Oregon. North Amer. Fauna No. 55. 416 pp.; illus. U.S.D.A., Wash., D. C.

Baird, Spencer Fullerton. 1857. Mammals of North America. In: Reports of Explorations and Surveys for a Railroad from Mississippi River to Pacific Ocean, vol. 8, pt. 1, pp. xv–xlviii, 1–757; illus. Wash., D. C.

Barnes, Claude T. 1927. Utah mammals. Bulletin, Univ. of Utah, vol. 17, no. 12, 183 pp.; illus.

Beard, Daniel B. et al. 1942. Fading Trails—the story of endangered American wildlife. pp. vii–xv, 1–279; illus. The Macmillan Company, N. Y.

Bennitt, Rudolf, and Nagel, Werner O. 1937. A survey of the resident game and furbearers of Missouri. Univ. of Missouri Studies, vol. 12, no. 2, pp. 1–215. Columbia, Mo.

Boone & Crockett Club; Alfred Ely, Chairman. 1939. North American big game. pp. vii–xxii, 1–533; illus. Charles Scribner's Sons, N. Y.

Burt, William Henry. 1934. The mammals of southern Nevada. Trans. San Diego Soc. of Nat. Hist., vol. 7, no. 36, pp. 375–427.

Cahalane, Victor H. 1943. Meeting the mammals. pp. 1–133; illus. The Macmillan Co., N. Y.

Cary, Merritt. 1911. A biological survey of Colorado. North Amer. Fauna No. 33, pp. 1–256; illus. Wash., D. C.

Cary, Merritt. 1917. Life zone investigations in Wyoming. North Amer. Fauna No. 42, 95 pp.; illus. Wash., D. C.

Caton, John Dean. 1877. The antelope and deer of America. 426 pp. Forest & Stream Publishing Co., N. Y.

Chittenden, Hiram M. 1902. The American fur trade of the far West. 3 vols.; illus. Francis P. Harper, N. Y.

Clarke, C. H. D. 1940. A biological investigation of the Thelon game sanctuary. Bul. No. 96, Biological Series No. 25, Nat. Museum of Canada, Ottawa. pp. 1–135; illus.

Cooke, Fannye A. 1943. Game animals of Mississippi. Miss. State Game and Fish Comm. Survey Bull. pp. i–v; 1–42 (mimeog.).

Cory, Charles B. 1912. The mammals of Illinois and Wisconsin. Field Museum of Natural History, Zool. Series Vol. XI, Publication 153, pp. 1–502. Chicago, Ill.

Coues, Elliott. 1877. The fur-bearing animals of North America: a monograph of American Mustelidæ. 348 pp.; illus. Wash., D. C.

Cowan, Ian McTaggart. 1939. The vertebrate fauna of the Peace River District of British Columbia. Occas. Papers British Columbia Provincial Museum, no. 1, pp. 1–102. Victoria, B. C.

Cross, E. C., and Dymond, J. R. 1929. The mammals of Ontario. Royal Ontario Museum Zool., Handbook no. 1, pp. 1–56; illus.

Davis, William B. 1939. The recent mammals of Idaho. Contrib. of the Mus. of Vertebrate Zool., Univ. of Calif., Berkeley. 400 pp.; illus. The Caxton Printers, Caldwell, Idaho.

Dearborn, Ned. 1932. Foods of some predatory fur-bearing animals in Michigan.

Univ. of Michigan, School of Forestry & Conservation. Bulletin No. 1. pp. 1–52. Ann Arbor, Mich.

Degerbøl, Magnus, and Freuchen, Peter. 1935. Report of the Fifth Thule Expedition 1921–24. vol. 11, no. 4–5. (Mammals). pp. 1–278. Gyldendal, Copenhagen.

Dice, Lee Raymond. 1919. The mammals of southeastern Washington. Jour. of Mammalogy, vol. 1, no. 1, pp. 10–21. Nov., 1919.

Dice, Lee Raymond. 1920. Notes on the mammals of interior Alaska. Jour. of Mammalogy, vol. 2, no. 1, pp. 20–28. Feb., 1920.

Dice, Lee Raymond. 1927. A manual of the recent wild mammals of Michigan. Univ. of Michigan, Mich. Handbook series No. 2, 63 pp.; illus. Ann Arbor.

Dixon, Joseph S. 1938. Birds and mammals of Mount McKinley National Park. Fauna of the National Parks No. 3. 236 pp.; illus. Wash., D. C.

Duck, L. G., and Fletcher, Jack B. A survey of the game and furbearing animals of Oklahoma. Pittman-Robertson Series No. II, State Bulletin No. 3, 144 pp.; illus. Oklahoma Game & Fish Commission. (No date.)

Dufresne, Frank. 1942. Mammals and birds of Alaska. U. S. Dept. of Interior, Fish and Wildlife Service Circular No. 3, pp. 1–37; illus. Wash., D. C.

Dufresne, Frank. 1946. Alaska's animals and fishes. pp. 1–309; illus. A. S. Barnes and Company, New York.

Elton, Charles. 1935. Animal ecology. 209 pp.; illus. The Macmillan Co., N. Y.

Gabrielson, Ira N. 1941. Wildlife conservation. 250 pp.; illus. The Macmillan Co., N. Y.

Goode, George Brown. 1887. The fisheries and fishery industries of the United States. Section 1; Natural history of useful aquatic animals. pub. 1884. Section 5; History and methods of the fisheries. (vol. 2). 881 pp. Section 9: The seal-islands of Alaska, by Henry W. Elliot. Wash., D. C.

Goodwin, George Gilbert. 1935. The mammals of Connecticut. State Geological and Natural History Survey Bulletin No. 53, 221 pp.; illus. Hartford, Conn.

Gray, Prentiss N. 1932. Records of North American big game. pp. iii–viii, 1–178; illus. Derrydale Press, N. Y.

Grinnell, J. 1913. A distributional list of the mammals of California. Proc. Calif. Acad. Sci., 4th ser., vol. 3, pp. 265–390; illus. San Francisco, Calif.

Grinnell, J.; Dixon, Joseph S., and Linsdale, Jean M. 1937. Fur-bearing mammals of California, their natural history, systematic status, and relations to man. 2 vols., 777 pp.; illus. Contribution from the Museum of Vertebrate Zool., Univ. of California. Berkeley, Calif.

Hahn, Walter Louis. 1909. The mammals of Indiana. Thirty-third annual report of Indiana Dept. Geol. Nat. Resources, for 1908. vol. 33, pp. 417–663; illus.

Hall, E. Raymond. 1946. Mammals of Nevada. pp. v–xi, 1–710; illus. Univ. of Calif. Press, Berkeley and Los Angeles.

Hamilton, W. J., Jr. 1935. The fur-bearers of New York in their relation to agriculture. Cornell Extension Bulletin 319. N. Y. State College of Agric., Ithaca, N. Y. pp. 1–25; illus. March, 1935.

Hamilton, W. J., Jr. 1939. American mammals: their lives, habits, and economic relations. 434 pp.; illus. McGraw-Hill Book Co., N. Y.

Hamilton, W. J., Jr. 1943. The mammals of eastern United States: an account of recent land mammals occurring east of the Mississippi. 432 pp.; illus. Comstock Publishing Co., Ithaca, N. Y.

Harper, Francis. 1927. The mammals of the Okefinokee Swamp region of Georgia. Proc. Boston Society of Natural History, vol. 38, no. 7, pp. 191–396; illus. Boston, Mass.

Heller, Edmund. 1925. The big game animals of Yellowstone National Park. Roosevelt Wild Life Bull. vol. 2, no. 4, pp. 405–467; illus. Syracuse, N. Y., Feb., 1925.

Herrick, C. L. 1892. The mammals of Minnesota. Bull. No. 7, Geol. & Nat. Hist. Survey of Minn., 301 pp.; illus. Minneapolis.

Hornaday, William T. 1927. The American natural history. xxv–449 pp.; illus. 15th ed. rev. Chas. Scribner's Sons, N. Y.

Howell, A. Brazier. 1930. Aquatic mammals. 338 pp.; illus. Charles C. Thomas, Springfield, Ill. & Baltimore, Md.

Howell, A. Brazier. 1944. Speed in animals. pp. iii–xii, 1–270; illus. Univ. of Chicago Press.

Howell, Arthur H. 1921. A biological survey of Alabama. I. Physiography and life zones. II. The mammals. North Amer. Fauna No. 45, pp. 1–88; illus. Wash., D. C.

Jackson, Hartley H. T. 1908. A preliminary list of Wisconsin mammals. Bull. Wisconsin Nat. Hist. Society, no. 6, pp. 13–34. Milwaukee, Wis.

Jackson, Hartley H. T. 1944. Big-game resources of the United States, 1937–1942. Research Report 8, pp. 1–56. U.S.D.I., Wash., D. C.

Jordan, David Starr. 1929. Manual of the vertebrate animals of the north-eastern United States, inclusive of marine species. 446 pp. World Book Co., N. Y.

Kennicott, Robert. 1857. The quadrupeds of Illinois injurious and beneficial to the farmer. Ex. Doc. 32, 35th Congress, 1st session: Rept. Commissioner Patents 1856 (Agriculture). pp. 52–110; illus. Washington, 1858.

Komarek, Edwin V., and Komarek, Roy. 1938. Mammals of the Great Smoky Mountains. Bull. Chicago Acad. Sci., vol. 5, no. 6, pp. 137–162; illus.

Ligon, J. Stokley. 1927. Wild life of New Mexico, its conservation and management. 212 pp.; illus. State Game Commission, Dept. of Game & Fish, Santa Fe, N. M.

Lowery, George H., Jr. 1943. Check-list of the mammals of Louisiana and adjacent waters. La. State Univ., Occ. Papers of Mus. of Zool., No. 13. pp. 213–257. Baton Rouge, Nov. 22, 1943.

Lyon, Marcus Ward, Jr. 1936. Mammals of Indiana. Amer. Midland Naturalist, vol. 17, no. 1, pp. 1–384; illus. Notre Dame, Indiana.

Manning, T. H. 1943. Notes on the mammals of south and central west Baffin Island. Jour. of Mammalogy, vol. 24, no. 1, pp. 47–59. Feb., 1943.

McGowan, Dan. 1936. Animals of the Canadian Rockies. 302 pp.; illus. Dodd, Mead & Co., N. Y.

Mearns, Edgar Alexander. 1907. Mammals of the Mexican boundary of the United States. Smithsonian Inst., U. S. Nat. Mus. Bull. 56, pt. 1, pp. i–xv, 1–530. Wash., D. C.

Miller, Gerrit S., Jr. 1924. List of North American recent mammals, 1923. U. S. Nat. Museum Bull. 128. pp. xvi, 1–673. Wash., D. C.

Miller, Gerrit S., Jr., and Gidley, J. W. 1931. Mammals and how they are studied. In Smithsonian Scientific Series, vol. 9, pp. 171–385; illus. Wash., D. C.

Necker, Walter L., and Hatfield, Donald M. 1941. Mammals of Illinois. Chicago Acad. Sci. Bull., vol. 6, no. 3, pp. 17–60.

Nelson, E. W. 1930. Wild animals of North America. 254 pp., illus.; rev. ed. National Geographic Society, Wash., D. C.

Norton, Arthur H. 1930. The mammals of Portland, Maine, and vicinity. Proceedings of the Portland Soc. Nat. Hist., vol. 4, pt. 1, pp. 1–151.

Osgood, Wilfred H. 1900. Results of a biological reconnaisance of the Yukon region; General account of the region. Annotated list of mammals. North Amer. Fauna No. 19, pp. 1–100; illus. Wash., D. C.

Osgood, Wilfred H. 1904. A biological reconnaissance of the base of the Alaska Peninsula. North Amer. Fauna No. 24, pp. 1–96; illus. Wash., D. C.

Osgood, Wilfred H. 1909. Biological investigations in Alaska and Yukon Territory. North Amer. Fauna No. 30, pp. 1–86. Wash., D. C.

Osgood, Wilfred H.; Preble, Edward A., and Parker, George H. 1915. The fur seals and other life of the Pribilof Islands, Alaska, in 1914. Public Doc. 820, from Bull. of the Bureau of Fisheries, vol. 34, 1914, 172 pp.; illus. Wash., D. C.

Over, William H., and Churchill, Edward P. 1941. Mammals of South Dakota, pp. 1–56, index. Univ. of South Dakota, Vermillion. (mimeog.).

Palmer, L. J. 1944. Food requirements of some Alaskan game mammals. Jour. of Mammalogy, vol. 25, no. 1, pp. 49–54. Feb., 1944.

Pratt, Henry S. 1923. A manual of land and fresh water vertebrate animals of the United States (exclusive of birds). pp. xv, 1–422. P. Blakiston's Son & Co., Philadelphia.

Preble, Edward A. 1908. A biological investigation of the Athabaska-Mackenzie region. North Amer. Fauna No. 27. 574 pp.; illus. Wash., D. C.

Preble, Edward A. 1923. Mammals of the Pribilof Islands. North Amer. Fauna No. 46, pp. 101–120. Wash., D. C.

Rhoads, Samuel N. 1903. The mammals of Pennsylvania and New Jersey. 266 pp.; illus. Philadelphia. (Privately published.)

Romer, Alfred Sherwood. 1945. Vertebrate paleontology. 687 pp.; illus. (second edition). Univ. of Chicago Press.

Ruth, Clara. 1937. Preserves and ranges maintained for buffalo and other big game. Biological Survey, Bureau of; Wildlife Research and Management Leaflet BS–95. 20 pp.; illus. Sept., 1937.

Saunders, William E. 1932. Notes on the mammals of Ontario. Trans. Royal Canadian Institute, vol. 18, pt. 2, no. 40, pp. 271–309.

Scott, William B. 1924. A history of the land mammals of the western hemisphere. pp. ix–xiv, 1–693; illus. The Macmillan Co., N. Y.

Seton, Ernest Thompson. 1929. Lives of game animals. 4 vols. Vol. 1, 640 pp.; vol. 2, 746 pp.; vol. 3, 780 pp.; vol. 4, 949 pp.; illus. Doubleday, Doran & Co., Garden City, N. Y.

Sheldon, Charles. 1930. The wilderness of Denali. 412 pp.; illus. Charles Scribner's Sons, N. Y.

Soper, J. Dewey. 1942. Mammals of Wood Buffalo Park, northern Alberta and District of Mackenzie. Jour. of Mammalogy, vol. 23, no. 2, pp. 119–145. May, 1942.

Soper, J. Dewey. 1944. The mammals of southern Baffin Island, Northwest Territories, Canada. Jour. of Mammalogy, vol. 25, no. 3, pp. 221–254; illus. September, 1944.

Stephens, T. C. 1922. Mammals of the lake region of Iowa. Bull. Okoboji Protective Assoc., pp. 47–64.

Stone, Witmer, 1908. The mammals of New Jersey. Annual Report of the New Jersey State Mus. for 1907. pp. 33–110. Trenton, N. J.

Stone, Witmer; and Cram, William Everett. 1902. American animals: a popular guide to the mammals of North America north of Mexico, with intimate biographies of the more familiar species. 318 pp.; illus. Doubleday, Page & Co., N. Y.

Stoner, Dayton. 1918. The rodents of Iowa. Iowa Geological Survey Bull. No. 5, 172 pp.; illus. Des Moines.

Surber, Thaddeus. 1932. The mammals of Minnesota. Bull. of Minnesota Dept. of Conservation, Div. of Game and Fish, St. Paul. 84 pp.; illus.

Sutton, George Miksch, and Hamilton, William J. 1932. The mammals of Southampton Island. Mem. Carnegie Museum, vol. 12, pt. 2, sec. 1, pp. 9–111; illus.

Swanson, Gustav; Surber, Thaddeus, and Roberts, Thomas S. 1945. The mammals of Minnesota. Technical Bull. No. 2, Minnesota Dept. of Conservation. 108 pp.; illus.

Swarth, H. S. 1922. Birds and mammals of the Stikine River region of northern British Columbia and southeastern Alaska. Univ. of California Publ. in Zool., vol. 24, no. 2. pp. 125–314.

Swenk, Myron H. 1908. A preliminary review of the mammals of Nebraska. Student Zool. Lab., Univ. of Neb. No. 89, 88 pp. Lincoln.

Texas Game, Fish and Oyster Commission. 1945. Principal game birds and mammals of Texas, their distribution and management. 149 pp.; illus. Pub. by the Commission, Austin, Texas.

Warren, Edward R. 1921. The small mammals of Colorado. Colorado Mtn. Club Pub. No. 7, 31 pp.; illus. June, 1921.

Warren, Edward R. 1942. The mammals of Colorado: their habits and distribution. 330 pp.; illus. 2nd rev. ed. Univ. of Oklahoma Press, Norman, Okla.

Williams, Samuel Howard. 1928. The mammals of Pennsylvania. 163 pp.; illus. Univ. of Pittsburgh Book Store, Pittsburgh, Pa.

Yellowstone National Park. 1924–1942. Yellowstone Nature Notes, vols. 1. no. 1, to vol. 19, nos. 1 & 2. Issued in pamphlet. (mimeog.).

REFERENCES TO SPECIFIC MAMMALS

PECCARY

Walker, M. V. 1941. These little pigs have a way. Region 3 Quarterly, vol. 3, no. 3, pp. 15–18; illus. (mimeog.) National Park Service, Santa Fe, New Mexico. July, 1941.

THE DEER FAMILY

Cahalane, Victor H. 1939. Deer of the world. National Geographic Magazine, vol. 76, no. 4, pp. 463–510; illus. October, 1939.

ELK

Cahalane, Victor H. 1943. Elk—food—and winter. Outdoor America, vol. 8, no. 3, pp. 4–5, 16; illus. Chicago, Ill. February, 1943.

Rush, W. M. 1932. Northern Yellowstone elk study. Montana Fish & Game Commission, Helena. 131 pp.; illus.

Schwartz, John E. —— Range conditions and management of the Roosevelt elk on the Olympic Peninsula. U.S.D.A., Forest Service. pp. 1–65; illus. (mimeog.)

Sheldon, Charles. 1927. The conservation of the elk of Jackson Hole, Wyoming. National Conference on Outdoor Recreation, Wash., D. C. pp. 1–36; illus. July, 1927.

Skinner, Milton P. 1936. Browsing of the Olympic Peninsula elk in early winter. Jour. of Mammalogy, vol. 17, no. 3, pp. 253–256. August, 1936.

Young, Vernon A., and Robinette, W. Leslie. 1939. A study of the range habits of elk on the Selway Game Preserve. Univ. of Idaho Bull., vol. 34, no. 16; School of Forestry Bull. No. 9, pp. 3–48; illus. Moscow. December, 1939.

WHITETAIL DEER

Bartlett, I. H. 1938. Whitetails: presenting Michigan's deer problem. Mich. Dept. of Conservation, Lansing, Mich. pp. 1–64; illus.

Cook, David B., and Hamilton, W. J., Jr. 1942. Winter habits of white-tailed deer in central New York. Jour. of Wildlife Management, vol. 6, no. 4, pp. 287–291; illus. October, 1942.

Foote, Leonard E. 1945. The Vermont deer herd: a study in productivity. State Bulletin, Pittman-Robertson Series No. 13. pp. 1–125; illus. Vermont Fish & Game Service, Montpelier.

Hammerstrom, F. N., Jr., and Blake, James. 1939. Winter movements and winter foods of white-tailed deer in central Wisconsin. Jour. of Mammalogy, vol. 20, no. 2, pp. 206–215. May, 1939.

Maynard, L. A.; Darrow, Robert; Bump, Gardiner, and Woodward, J. C. 1935. Food preferences and requirements of the white-tailed deer in New York State. Bull. No. 1, N. Y. State Conservation Dept. and N. Y. State College of Agriculture. pp. 1–35; illus.

Newsom, William Monypeny. 1926. Whitetailed deer. pp. xviii, 3–288; illus. Charles Scribner's Sons, N. Y.

MULE DEER

Dixon, Joseph S. 1934. A study of the life history and food habits of mule deer in California. Calif. Fish & Game, vol. 20, nos. 3 & 4, pp. 181–282; 315–354; illus. Sacramento, July & Oct., 1934.

Hall, E. Raymond. 1927. The deer of California. Calif. Fish & Game, vol. 13, no. 4, pp. 233–259; illus. Sacramento, October, 1927.

Russell, Carl Parcher. 1932. Seasonal migration of mule deer. Ecological Monographs, vol. 2, no. 1, pp. 1–46; illus. January, 1932.

Sheldon, H. H. 1933. The deer of California. Santa Barbara Museum of Natural History, Occasional Papers No. 3. pp. 1–71; illus. Santa Barbara, Calif., Nov. 1, 1933.

BLACKTAIL DEER

Einarsen, Arthur S. 1946. Management of black-tailed deer. Jour. of Wildlife Management, vol. 10, no. 1, pp. 54–59; illus. Jan., 1946.

MOOSE

Hickie, Paul F. —— Michigan moose. pp. 1–57; illus. Mich. Dept. of Conservation, Lansing, Mich.

Merrill, Samuel. 1916. The moose book. pp. iii–xv, 3–399; illus. (second edition). E. P. Dutton & Co., N. Y.

CARIBOU

Dugmore, A. A. Radclyffe. 1913. The romance of the Newfoundland caribou. pp. viii, 1–191; illus. William Heinemann, London.

Hadwen, Seymour, and Palmer, Lawrence J. 1922. Reindeer in Alaska. U.S.D.A. Bull. No. 1089. 75 pp.; illus. Wash., D. C.

Murie, Olaus J. 1935. Alaska-Yukon caribou. North Amer. Fauna No. 54, pp. 1–93; illus. U.S.D.A., Wash., D. C. June, 1935.

Palmer, Lawrence J., and Rouse, Charles H. 1945. Study of the Alaska tundra with reference to its reactions to reindeer and other grazing. U.S.D.I., Fish and Wildlife Service, Research Report 10; pp. 1–48; illus.

ANTELOPE

Bailey, Vernon. 1920. Old and new horns of the prong-horned antelope. Jour. of Mammalogy, vol. 1, no. 3. pp. 128–129; illus. May, 1920.

Einarsen, Arthur S. 1938. Life history and management of antelope in Oregon. Transactions, Third N. A. Wildlife Conference, pp. 381–387; map. Wash., D. C.

Fisher, Lee William. 1942. Live trapping Texas antelopes. Jour. of Wildlife Management, vol. 6, no. 3, pp. 231–236; illus. July, 1942.

Leister, Claude W. 1932. The pronghorn of North America. Bull. N. Y. Zoological Society, vol. 35, no. 6, pp. 183–193; illus. Nov.-Dec., 1932.

Nelson, Edward W. 1925. Status of the pronghorned antelope, 1922–1924. U.S.D.A. Dept. Bull. No. 1346, pp. 1–64; illus. August, 1925.

Nichol, A. A. 1942. Gathering, transplanting, and care of young antelopes. Jour. of Wildlife Management, vol. 6, no. 4, pp. 281–286; illus. October, 1942.

Noback, Charles V. 1932. The deciduous horns of the pronghorn antelope. Bull. N. Y. Zoological Society, vol. 35, no. 6, pp. 195–207; illus. Nov.-Dec., 1932.

Skinner, M. P. 1922. The prong-horn. Jour. of Mammalogy, vol. 3, no. 2, pp. 82–105; illus. May, 1922.

BUFFALO

Allen, J. A. 1877. History of the American Bison, *Bison americanus*. Ninth Annual Report of the U. S. Geological & Geographical Survey of the Territories, pp. iii–vii, 441–587. Wash., D. C.

Branch, E. Douglas. 1929. The hunting of the buffalo. pp. v–vii; 1–240; illus. D. Appleton & Co., N. Y.

Garretson, Martin S. 1938. The American bison: the story of its extermination as a wild species and its restoration under Federal protection. 254 pp.; illus. New York Zoological Society, N. Y.

Haines, Francis D. 1940. The western limits of the buffalo range. Pacific Northwest Quarterly, vol. 31, no. 4, pp. 389–398. Oct., 1940.

Hornaday, William T. 1889. The extermination of the American bison, with a sketch of its discovery and life history. Annual Report of U. S. Nat. Museum for 1887, pp. 367–548; illus.

Soper, J. Dewey. 1941. History, range, and home life of the northern bison. Ecological Monographs, vol. 11, no. 4, pp. 347–412; illus. October, 1941.

MUSKOX

Hone, Elisabeth. 1934. The present status of the muskox in Arctic North America and Greenland. Special Publication No. 5, Amer. Committee for International Wild Life Protection, pp. 1–87; illus. Cambridge, Mass.

Yarham, E. R. 1941. Canada's fight for the musk oxen. Amer. Forests, vol. 47, no. 9, pp. 424–425, 448; illus. Sept., 1941.

Young, Stanley P. 1941. The return of the musk oxen. Amer. Forests, vol. 47, no. 8, pp. 368–372; illus. Aug., 1941.

BIGHORN

Davis, William B. 1938. Summer activity of mountain sheep on Mt. Washburn, Yellowstone National Park. Jour. of Mammalogy, vol. 19, no. 1, pp. 88–94. February, 1938.

Davis, William B., and Taylor, Walter P. 1939. The bighorn sheep of Texas. Jour. of Mammalogy, vol. 20, no. 4, pp. 440–455; map. November, 1939.

Honess, Ralph F., and Frost, Nedward M. 1942. A Wyoming bighorn sheep study. Wyoming Game and Fish Department Bull. No. 1, pp. i–vi, 1–126. Cheyenne, July 1, 1942.

Mills, Harlow B. 1937. A preliminary study of the bighorn of Yellowstone National Park. Jour. of Mammalogy, vol. 18, no. 2, pp. 205–212. May, 1937.

MOUNTAIN GOAT

Cooney, R. F. 1942. Trapping and transplanting mountain goats. Proceedings of the 22nd Annual Conference of West. Assoc. of State Game and Fish Commissioners. pp. 55–57. (mimeog.)

Harmon, Wendell H. 1944. Notes on mountain goats in the Black Hills. Jour. of Mammalogy, vol. 25, no. 2, pp. 149–151. May, 1944.

OPOSSUM

Lay, Daniel W. 1942. Ecology of the opossum in eastern Texas. Jour. of Mammalogy, vol. 23, no. 2, pp. 147–159. May, 1942.

Reynolds, Harold C. 1945. Some aspects of the life history and ecology of the opossum in central Missouri. Jour. of Mammalogy, vol. 26, no. 4, pp. 361–379. February, 1946.

ARMADILLO

Kalmbach, E. R. 1943. The armadillo: its relation to agriculture and game. pp. ii–iv, 1–61; illus. Game, Fish & Oyster Commission, Austin, Texas.

Strecker, John K. 1926. The extension of range of the nine-banded armadillo. Jour. of Mammalogy, vol. 7, no. 3, pp. 206–10. Aug., 1926.

Taber, F. Wallace. 1939. Extension of the range of the armadillo. Jour. of Mammalogy, vol. 20, no. 4, pp. 489–493. Nov., 1939.

Taber, F. Wallace. 1945. Contribution on the life history and ecology of the nine-banded armadillo. Jour. of Mammalogy, vol. 26, no. 3, pp. 211–226. Aug., 1945.

MOLE

Arlton, A. V. 1936. An ecological study of the mole. Jour. of Mammalogy, vol. 17, no. 4, pp. 349–371; illus. Nov., 1936.

Eadie, W. Robert. 1939. A contribution to the biology of *Parascalops breweri*. Jour. of Mammalogy, vol. 20, no. 2, pp. 150–173; illus. May, 1939.

Hamilton, William John, Jr. 1931. Habits of the star-nosed mole, *Condylura cristata*. Jour. of Mammalogy, vol. 12, no. 4, pp. 345–355; illus. Nov., 1931.

Silver, James, and Moore, A. W. 1941. Mole control. Conservation Bulletin No. 16, U. S. Dept. of Interior, pp. 1–17; illus. Wash., D. C.

SHREW

Blossom, Philip M. 1932. A pair of long-tailed shrews (*Sorex cinereus cinereus*) in captivity. Jour. of Mammalogy, vol. 13, no. 2, pp. 136–143. May, 1932.

Jackson, Hartley H. T. 1928. A taxonomic review of the American long-tailed shrews. North Amer. Fauna No. 51, pp. 1–238; illus. Wash., D. C.

Lawrence, Barbara. 1945. Brief comparison of short-tailed shrew and reptile poisons. Jour. of Mammalogy, vol. 26, no. 4, pp. 393–396. February, 1946.

Moore, Joseph C. 1943. A contribution to the natural history of the Florida short-tailed shrew. Proc. Florida Acad. Sci., vol. 6, pp. 155–166. Dec., 1943.

Pearson, Oliver P. 1942. On the cause and nature of a poisonous action produced by the bite of a shrew (*Blarina brevicauda*). Jour. of Mammalogy, vol. 23, no. 2, pp. 159–166. May, 1942.

BAT

Allen, Glover Morrill. 1940. Bats. Harvard Univ. Press, Cambridge, Mass. pp. 1–368; illus.

Griffin, Donald R. 1945. Travels of banded cave bats. Jour. of Mammalogy, vol. 26, no. 1, pp. 15–23. Feb., 1945.

Gudger, E. W. 1945. Fishermen bats of the Caribbean region. Jour. of Mammalogy, vol. 26, no. 1, pp. 1–15; illus. Feb., 1945.

Miller, Gerrit S., Jr. 1907. The families and genera of bats. U. S. Nat. Mus. Bul. 57, pp. 1–282; illus. Wash., D. C.

Wimsatt, William A. 1945. Notes on breeding behavior, pregnancy, and parturition in some Vespertilionid bats of the eastern United States. Jour. of Mammalogy, vol. 26, no. 1, pp. 23–33. Feb., 1945.

THE BEARS
Skinner, M. P. 1925. Bears in the Yellowstone. pp. 1–158; illus. A. C. McClurg Co., Chicago.

BLACK BEAR
Beatty, M. E. 1943. Bears of Yosemite. Yosemite Nature Notes, vol. 22, no. 1, pp. 1–16; illus. January, 1943.
Stevens, C. L. 1943. The black bear in New Hampshire. Separate from the The Granite State Forester. No. 5, pp. 37–65. Univ. of N. H., Durham. (mimeog.)

GRIZZLY BEAR
Holtzworth, John M. 1930. The wild grizzlies of Alaska. pp. v–xxi, 1–417; illus. G. P. Putnam's Sons, N. Y.
Wright, William H. 1909. The grizzly bear: the narrative of a hunter-naturalist, historical, scientific and adventurous. pp. vii–x, 3–274; illus. Chas. Scribner's Sons, N. Y.

POLAR BEAR
Jackson, Hartley H. T. 1932. The polar bear, nomad of the ice fields. Home Geographic Monthly, vol. 2, no. 1, pp. 19–24; illus. July, 1932.

RACCOON
Giles, LeRoy W. 1940. Food habits of the raccoon in eastern Iowa. Jour. of Wildlife Management, vol. 4, no. 4, pp. 375–382. Oct., 1940.
Stuewer, Frederick W. 1943. Raccoons: their habits and management in Michigan. Ecological Monographs, vol. 13, pp. 203–258; illus. April, 1943.
Whitney, Leon F. 1931. The raccoon and its hunting. Jour. of Mammalogy, vol. 12, no. 1, pp. 29–38. Feb., 1931.
Whitney, Leon F. 1933. The raccoon—some mental attributes. Jour. of Mammalogy, vol. 14, no. 2, pp. 108–114. May, 1933.

COATI
Taber, F. Wallace. 1940. Range of the coati in the United States. Jour. of Mammalogy, vol. 21, no. 1, pp. 11–14. Feb., 1940.

RINGTAIL
Richardson, William B. 1942. Ring-tailed cats. (*Bassariscus astutus*): their growth and development. Jour. of Mammalogy, vol. 23, no. 1, pp. 17–26; illus. Feb., 1942.

FISHER
Rand, A. L. 1944. The status of the fisher, *Martes pennanti* (*Erxleben*), in Canada. The Canadian Field-Naturalist, vol. 58, no. 3, pp. 77–81. May-June, 1944.

WEASEL
Hamilton, W. J., Jr. 1933. The weasels of New York. American Midland Naturalist, vol. 14, no. 4, pp. 289–344; illus. July, 1943.

Quick, H. F. 1944. Habits and economics of the New York weasel in Michigan. Jour. of Wildlife Management, vol. 8, no. 1, pp. 71–78; illus. Jan., 1944.

Young, Stanley P. 1940. "Black boots" of the prairie. American Forests, vol. 46, no. 1, pp. 16–18; illus. Jan., 1940.

MINK

Anon. 1941. Mink raising. Wildlife Leaflet 191, Fish & Wildlife Service, U.S.D.I., Wash., D. C. May, 1941. pp. 1–10. (mimeog.)

Errington, Paul L. 1943. An analysis of mink predation upon muskrats in north-central United States. Research Bulletin 320, Iowa Agricultural Experiment Station, Ames, Iowa. pp. 798—924; illus.

SEA OTTER

Barabash-Nikiforov, I. 1935. The sea otters of the Commander Islands. Jour. of Mammalogy, vol. 16, no. 4, pp. 255–261. Nov., 1935.

Elliott, Henry W. 1887. The sea-otter fishery. The fisheries and fishery industries of the U. S. Sect. 5, vol. 2, pp. 483–491. Wash., D. C.

Fisher, Edna M. 1939. Habits of the southern sea otter. Jour. of Mammalogy, vol. 20, no. 1, pp. 21–36; illus. Feb., 1939.

Fisher, Edna M. 1941. Prices of sea otter pelts. Calif. Fish & Game, vol. 27, no. 4, pp. 261–265. Oct., 1941.

Ogden, Adele. 1941. The California sea otter trade—1784–1848. pp. i–xi, 1–251; illus. Univ. of Calif. Press, Berkeley and Los Angeles.

STRIPED SKUNK

Allen, Durward L. 1939. Winter habits of Michigan skunks. Jour. of Wildlife Management, vol. 3, no. 3, pp. 212–228; illus. July, 1939.

Cuyler, W. Kenneth. 1924. Observations on the habits of the striped skunk (*Mephitis mesomelas varians*). Jour. of Mammalogy, vol. 5, no. 3, pp. 180–189. August, 1924.

Shaw, William T. 1928. The spring and summer activities of the dusky skunk in captivity. N. Y. State Museum Handbook No. 4, pp. 5–91; illus. Albany.

SPOTTED SKUNK

Crabb, Wilfred D. 1944. Growth, development and seasonal weights of spotted skunks. Jour. of Mammalogy, vol. 25, no. 3, pp. 213–221; illus. Sept., 1944.

BADGER

Hamlett, G. W. D. 1932. Observations on the embryology of the badger. Anatomical Record, vol. 53, no. 3, pp. 283–303; illus. August, 1932.

RED FOX

Errington, Paul L. 1935. Food habits of Mid-west foxes. Jour. of Mammalogy, vol. 16, no. 3, pp. 192–200; August, 1935.

Errington, Paul L. 1937. Food habits of the red fox in Iowa. Journal Papers No. J-353, 354 of the Iowa Agric. Exper. Sta., reprinted in Amer. Wildlife, vol. 26, nos. 1 & 2, pp. 5, 6, 13, 24, 30, 31; illus. Jan.-Feb. & Mar.-April, 1937.

Murie, Adolph. 1936. Following fox trails. Univ. of Mich. Museum of Zoology Miscl. Public. no. 32, pp. 1–45; illus.

Seagears, Clayton B. 1944. The fox in New York. Educational Bulletin, N. Y. Conservation Dept. 85 pp.; illus. Albany, N. Y.

COYOTE

Dice, Lee R. 1942. A family of dog-coyote hybrids. Jour. of Mammalogy, vol. 23, no. 2, pp. 186–192; illus. May, 1942.

Murie, Adolph. 1940. Ecology of the coyote in the Yellowstone. U.S.D.I. National Parks Fauna Series No. 4, pp. iii–x; 1–206; illus. Wash., D. C.

Murie, Olaus J. 1935. Food habits of the coyote in Jackson Hole, Wyo. U.S.D.A. Circular 362, pp. 1–24. Oct., 1935. Wash., D. C.

Murie, Olaus J. 1945. Notes on coyote food habits in Montana and British Columbia. Jour. of Mammalogy, vol. 26, no. 1, pp. 33–40. Feb., 1945.

Nordyke, Lewis. 1944. Coyote cunning. Nature Mag., vol. 37, no. 3, pp. 121–124; illus. March, 1944.

Sperry, Charles C. 1939. Food habits of peg-leg coyotes. Jour. of Mammalogy, vol. 20, no. 2, pp. 190–194. May, 1939.

Sperry, Charles C. 1941. Food habits of the coyote. U.S.D.I., Fish & Wildlife Service, Wildlife Research Bulletin 4, pp. 1–70. Wash., D. C.

Young, Stanley P. 1943. What was the early Indian dog? American Forests, vol. 49, no. 12, pp. 571–573, 594, 603; illus. Dec., 1943. (Concluded in vol. 50, no. 1, pp. 26–28, 32, 45; illus. January, 1944.)

WOLF

Criddle, Norman. 1925. The habits and economic importance of wolves in Canada. Dominion of Canada, Dept. of Agriculture, Bulletin No. 13—New Series. pp. 1–24; illus. Ottawa, March, 1925.

Murie, Adolph. 1944. The wolves of Mount McKinley. U.S.D.I. National Parks Fauna Series No. 5, pp. iii–xix, 1–238; illus. Wash., D. C.

Young, Stanley P. 1940. It's "red," but truly American. Western Sportsman, vol. 5, no. 6, pp. 10–11, 26; illus. Denver, Nov., 1940.

Young, Stanley P., and Goldman, Edward A. 1944. The wolves of North America. pp. v–xx, 1–588; illus. American Wildlife Institute, Wash., D. C.

THE CATS

Cahalane, Victor H. 1943. King of cats and his court. National Geographic Mag., vol. 83, no. 2, pp. 217–259; illus. Feb., 1943.

COUGAR

Hibben, Frank C. 1937. A preliminary study of the mountain lion (*Felis oregonensis* sp.). Univ. of New Mexico Bull. Whole No. 318, Biol. Series, vol. 5, no. 3, pp. 3–59. Albuquerque, Dec. 15, 1937.

Musgrave, M. E. 1926. Some habits of mountain lions in Arizona. Jour. of Mammalogy, vol. 7, no. 4, pp. 282–285. Nov., 1926.

Young, Stanley P. 1943. Early wildlife Americana. Amer. Forests, vol. 49, no. 8, pp. 387–389, 414; illus. August, 1943.

Young, Stanley P., and Goldman, Edward A. 1946. The puma, mysterious American cat. pp. xiv + 358; illus. American Wildlife Institute, Wash., D. C.

JAGUAR

Nelson, E. W., and Goldman, E. A. 1933. Revision of the jaguars. Jour. of Mammalogy, vol. 14, no. 3, pp. 221–240. August, 1933.

BOBCAT

Rollings, Clair T. 1945. Habits, foods and parasites of the bobcat in Minnesota. Jour. of Wildlife Management, vol. 9, no. 2, pp. 131–145; illus. April, 1945.

THE FINFEET

Allen, Joel Asaph. 1880. History of North American pinnipeds, a monograph of the walruses, sea-lions, sea-bears and seals of North America. U. S. Geol. and Geographic Survey of the Territories, Miscl. Publ. No. 12. pp. xvi–785. Wash., D. C.

SEA LION

Rowley, John. 1929. Life history of the sea-lions on the California coast. Jour. of Mammalogy, vol. 10, no. 1, pp. 1–36; illus. Feb., 1929.

Scheffer, Victor B. 1946. Growth and behavior of young sea lions. Jour. of Mammalogy, vol. 26, no. 4, pp. 390–392; illus. Nov., 1945.

EARLESS SEALS

Bartlett, Robert A. 1927. Newfoundland seals. Jour. of Mammalogy, vol. 8, no. 3, pp. 207–212. August, 1927.

Darling, F. Fraser. 1939. I lived with seals. Discovery, n.s. vol. 2, no. 12, pp. 112–120; illus. March, 1939.

Scheffer, Theo. H., and Sperry, Charles C. 1931. Food habits of the Pacific harbor seal, *Phoca richardii*. Jour. of Mammalogy, vol. 12, no. 3, pp. 214–226. August, 1931.

Scheffer, Victor B., and Slipp, John W. 1944. The harbor seal in Washington State. Amer. Midl. Nat., vol. 32, no. 2, pp. 373–416; illus. Sept., 1944.

SEA ELEPHANT

Anthony, A. W. 1924. Notes on the present status of the northern elephant seal, *Mirounga angustirostris*. Jour. of Mammalogy, vol. 5, no. 3, pp. 145–152; illus. August, 1924.

Huey, Laurence M. 1924. Recent observations on the northern elephant seal. Jour. of Mammalogy, vol. 5, no. 4, pp. 237–242; illus. Nov., 1924.

Walker, Lewis W. 1932. Elephants of the sea. Nature Mag., vol. 19, no. 3, pp. 173–4; illus. March, 1932.

Williams, Woodbridge. 1941. Jumbo of the deep. Natural History Mag., vol. 48, no. 3, pp. 144–149; illus. Oct., 1941.

WALRUS

Allen, Glover M. 1930. The walrus in New England. Jour. of Mammalogy, vol. 11, no. 2, pp. 139–145. May, 1930.

Collins, Grenold. 1940. Habits of the Pacific walrus (*Odobenus divergens*). Jour. of Mammalogy, vol. 21, no. 2, pp. 138–144. May, 1940.

THE 'CHUCKS AND GROUND SQUIRRELS

Howell, Arthur H. 1938. Revision of the North American ground squirrels. U.S.D.A. North Amer. Fauna No. 56, pp. 1–256; illus. Wash., D. C.

Wade, Otis. 1930. The behavior of certain spermophiles with special reference to aestivation and hibernation. Jour. of Mammalogy, vol. 11, no. 2, pp. 160–188; illus. May, 1930.

WOODCHUCK

Anon. 1943. Control of woodchucks. U.S.D.I., Fish & Wildlife Service, Wildlife Leaflet 237. pp. 1–4. Chicago, Ill. April, 1943. (mimeog.)

Hamilton, W. J., Jr. 1934. The life history of the rufescent woodchuck *Marmota monax rufescens* Howell. Annals of the Carnegie Museum, vol. 23, pp. 85–178; illus. July 5, 1934.

Schoonmaker, Walter J. 1938. The woodchuck: lord of the clover field. Bull. N. Y. Zool. Society, vol. 41, no. 1, pp. 3–12; illus. Jan.-Feb., 1938.

Twichell, A. R. 1939. Notes on the southern woodchuck in Missouri. Jour. of Mammalogy, vol. 20, no. 1, pp. 71–74. Feb., 1939.

MARMOT

Couch, Leo King. 1930. Notes on the pallid yellow-bellied marmot. The Murrelet, vol. 11, no. 1, pp. 1–6; illus. May, 1930.

Howell, Arthur H. 1915. Revision of the American marmots. North Amer. Fauna No. 37, pp. 1–80; illus. U.S.D.A., Bureau of Biological Survey, Wash., D. C.

Kitchin, E. A. 1942. Marmota. pp. 1–20; illus. Privately printed.

COLUMBIAN GROUND SQUIRREL

Alcorn, J. R. 1940. Life history notes on the Piute ground squirrel. Jour. of Mammalogy, vol. 21, no. 2, pp. 160–170. May, 1940.

Shaw, William T. 1918. The Columbian ground squirrel. The Monthly Bulletin, vol. 7, nos. 11–12, pp. 710–720; illus. Calif. State Commission of Horticulture. Nov.-Dec., 1918.

Shaw, William T. 1925. Breeding and development of the Columbian ground squirrel. Jour. of Mammalogy, vol. 6, no. 2, pp. 106–113; illus. May, 1925.

Shaw, William T. 1925. Tracking the Columbian ground squirrel to its burrow. Nat. Geographic Mag., vol. 47, no. 5, pp. 587–596; illus. May, 1925.

Shaw, William T. 1926. Age of the animal and slope of the ground surface, factors modifying the structure of hibernation dens of ground squirrels. Jour. of Mammalogy, vol. 7, no. 2, pp. 91–96; illus. May, 1926.

STRIPED GROUND SQUIRREL

Baldwin, Francis Marsh, and Johnson, Kenneth LeRoy. 1941. Effects of hibernation on the rate of oxygen consumption in the thirteen-lined ground squirrel. Jour. of Mammalogy, vol. 22, no. 2, pp. 180–182. May, 1941.

Hisaw, Frederick L., and Emery, Frederick E. 1927. Food selection of ground squirrels, *Citellus tridecemlineatus*. Jour. of Mammalogy, vol. 8, no. 1, pp. 41–44. February, 1927.

Johnson, George E. 1931. Early life of the thirteen-lined ground squirrel. Transactions Kansas Acad. of Science, vol. 34, pp. 282–290; illus.

Wade, Otis. 1927. Breeding habits and early life of the thirteen-striped ground squirrel, *Citellus tridecemlineatus* (Mitchill). Jour. of Mammalogy, vol. 8, no. 4, pp. 269–276; illus. Nov., 1927.

ROCK SQUIRREL

Edge, Elton R. 1931. Seasonal activity and growth in the Douglas ground squirrel. Jour. of Mammalogy, vol. 12, no. 3, pp. 194–200; illus. Aug., 1931.

MANTLED GROUND SQUIRREL

Gordon, Kenneth. 1938. Observations on the behavior of Callospermophilus and Eutamias. Jour. of Mammalogy, vol. 19, no. 1, pp. 78–84; illus. Feb., 1938.

Gordon, Kenneth. 1943. The natural history and behavior of the western chipmunk and the mantled ground squirrel. Monograph Studies in Zoology No. 5, pp. 1–104; illus. Oregon State College, Corvallis.

Hatt, Robert T. 1927. Notes on the ground squirrel, Callospermophilus. Mich. Univ., Mus. of Zool. Occas. Papers 185, 22 pp.; illus. June 29, 1927.

PRAIRIE DOG

Cates, E. C. 1927. Notes concerning a captive prairie-dog. Jour of Mammalogy, vol. 8, no. 1, pp. 33–37. Feb., 1927.

Clapp, Kennedy N. 1941. Prairie dogs. Region Three Quarterly, National Park Service, vol. 3, no. 2, pp. 21–25; illus. April, 1941. Santa Fe, N. M.

Hollister, N. 1916. A systematic account of the prairie-dogs. North Amer. Fauna, No. 40, pp. 1–37; illus. Wash., D. C.

Kelso, Leon H. 1939. Food habits of prairie dogs. U.S.D.A. Circular No. 529, pp. 1-15. Wash., D. C. June, 1939.

Longhurst, William. 1944. Observations on the ecology of the Gunnison prairie dog in Colorado. Jour. of Mammalogy, vol. 25, no. 1, pp. 24–36; illus. Feb., 1944.

Soper, J. Dewey. 1938. Discovery, habitat and distribution of the black-tailed prairie-dog in western Canada. Jour. of Mammalogy, vol. 19, no. 3, pp. 290-300; illus. Aug., 1938.

Stockard, A. H. 1929. Observations on reproduction in the white-tailed prairie-dog (*Cynomys leucurus*). Jour. of Mammalogy, vol. 10, no. 3, pp. 209–212. August, 1929.

Taylor, Walter P., and Loftfield, J. V. G. 1924. Damage to range grasses by the Zuni prairie dog. U.S.D.A. Dept. Bull. No. 1227, pp. 1-16; illus. Aug. 10, 1924. Wash., D. C.

THE CHIPMUNKS AND SQUIRRELS

Dennis, Wayne. 1930. Rejection of wormy nuts by squirrels. Jour. of Mammalogy, vol. 11, no. 2, pp. 195–201. May, 1930.

Goodrum, Phil. 1937. Notes on the gray and fox squirrels of eastern Texas. Trans. Second N. A. Wildlife Conference, pp. 499–504. Wash., D. C.

Lang, Herbert. 1925. How squirrels and other rodents carry their young. Jour. of Mammalogy, vol. 6, no. 1, pp. 18–24; illus. Feb., 1925.

EASTERN CHIPMUNK

Allen, Elsa G. 1938. The habits and life history of the eastern chipmunk, *Tamias striatus lysteri*. N. Y. State Museum Bulletin No. 314, pp. 1–122; illus. Albany, N. Y., Sept., 1938.

WESTERN CHIPMUNK

(See Mantled Ground Squirrel above)

RED SQUIRREL

Cram, William Everett. 1924. The red squirrel. Jour. of Mammalogy, vol. 5, no. 1, pp. 37–41; illus. Feb., 1924.

Hatt, Robert T. 1929. The red squirrel: its life history and habits, with special reference to the Adirondacks of New York and the Harvard Forest. Roosevelt Wild Life Annals, vol. 2, no. 1, pp. 1–146; illus. Roosevelt Wild Life Forest Experiment Station, College of Forestry. Syracuse, N. Y. March, 1929.

Hatt, Robert T. 1943. The pine squirrel in Colorado. Jour. of Mammalogy, vol. 24, no. 3, pp. 311–345; illus. Aug., 1943.

Hayward, C. Lynn. 1940. Feeding habits of the red squirrel. Jour. of Mammalogy, vol. 21, no. 2, pg. 220. May, 1940.

Ingram, William Marcus. 1940. Red squirrels chased by robins. Jour. of Mammalogy, vol. 21, no. 2, pp. 219–220. May, 1920.

Klugh, A. Brooker. 1927. Ecology of the red squirrel. Jour. of Mammalogy, vol. 8, no. 1, pp. 1–32; illus. February, 1927.

Murie, Olaus J. 1927. The Alaska red squirrel providing for winter. Jour. of Mammalogy, vol. 8, no. 1, pp. 37–40; illus. February, 1927.

Petrides, George A. 1941. Snow burrows of the red squirrel (*Tamiasciurus*). Jour. of Mammalogy, vol. 22, no. 4, pp. 393–394. Nov., 1941.

Shaw, William T. 1936. Moisture and its relation to the cone-storing habit of the western pine squirrel. Jour. of Mammalogy, vol. 17, no. 4, pp. 337–349; illus. Nov., 1936.

Yeager, Lee E. 1937. Cone-piling by Michigan red squirrels. Jour. of Mammalogy, vol. 18, no. 2, pp. 191–194. May, 1937.

GRAY SQUIRREL

Chapman, Floyd B. 1938. Summary of the Ohio gray squirrel investigation. Trans. Third N. A. Wildlife Conference, pp. 677–684. Wash., D. C.

Fitzwater, William D., Jr., and Frank, William J. 1944. Leaf nests of gray squirrel in Connecticut. Jour. of Mammalogy, vol. 25, no. 2, pp. 160–170. May, 1944.

Hungerford, K. E., and Wilder, N. G. 1941. Observations on the homing behavior of the gray squirrel (*Sciurus carolinensis*). Jour. of Wildlife Management, vol. 5, no. 4, pp. 458–460. Oct., 1941.

Merriam, C. Hart. 1930. A nest of the California gray squirrel (*Sciurus griseus*). Jour. of Mammalogy, vol. 11, no. 4, pg. 494; illus. Nov., 1930.

Nichols, John Treadwell. 1927. Notes on the food habits of the gray squirrel. Jour. of Mammalogy, vol. 8, no. 1, pp. 55–57. Feb., 1927.

Seton, Ernest Thompson. 1920. Migrations of the graysquirrel (*Sciurus carolinensis*). Jour. of Mammalogy, vol. 1, no. 2, pp. 53–58. Feb., 1920.

Terres, J. Kenneth. 1939. Gray squirrel utilization of elm. Jour. of Wildlife Management, vol. 3, no. 4, pp. 358–359. Oct., 1939.

TASSEL-EARED SQUIRRELS

Goldman, E. A. 1928. The Kaibab or white-tailed squirrel. Jour. of Mammalogy, vol. 9, no. 2, pp. 127–129; illus. May, 1928.

McKee, Edwin D. 1941. Distribution of the tassel-eared squirrels. Plateau, vol. 14, no. 1, pp. 12–20; illus. July, 1941.

FOX SQUIRREL

Allen, Durward L. 1942. Populations and habits of the fox squirrel in Allegan County, Michigan. Amer. Midland Naturalist, vol. 27, no. 2, pp. 338–379; illus. Mar., 1942.

Allen, Durward L. 1943. Michigan fox squirrel management. pp. 1–404; illus. Game Division, Dept. of Conservation, Lansing, Mich.

Baumgartner, Luther L. 1938. Population studies of the fox squirrel in Ohio. Trans. Third N. A. Wildlife Conference, pp. 685–689. Wash., D. C.

Baumgartner, Luther L. 1939. Foods of the fox squirrel in Ohio. Trans. Fourth N. A. Wildlife Conference, pp. 579–584. Wash., D. C.

Baumgartner, Luther L. 1939. Fox squirrel dens. Jour. of Mammalogy, vol. 20, no. 4, pp. 456–465; illus. Nov., 1939.

Baumgartner, Luther L. 1943. Fox squirrels in Ohio. Jour. of Wildlife Management, vol. 7, no. 2, pp. 193–202; illus. April, 1943.

Brown, Louis G., and Yeager, Lee E. 1945. Fox squirrels and gray squirrels in Illinois. Bulletin, vol. 23, art. 5, Ill. Nat. Hist. Survey. pp. 449–536; illus. Urbana, Sept., 1945.

Cahalane, Victor H. 1942. Caching and recovery of food by the western fox squirrel. Jour. of Wildlife Management, vol. 6, no. 4, pp. 338–352. Oct., 1942.

Stoddard, H. L. 1920. Nests of the western fox squirrel. Jour. of Mammalogy, vol. 1, no. 3, pp. 122–123; illus. May, 1920.

Svihla, Ruth Dowell. 1931. Captive fox squirrels. Jour. of Mammalogy, vol. 12, no. 2, pp. 152–156. May, 1931.

FLYING SQUIRREL

Cowan, Ian McTaggart. 1936. Nesting habits of the flying squirrel *Glaucomys sabrinus*. Jour. of Mammalogy, vol. 17, no. 1, pp. 58–60. Feb., 1936.

Hatt, Robert T. 1931. Habits of a young flying squirrel (*Glaucomys volans*). Jour. of Mammalogy, vol. 12, no. 3, pp. 233–238. Aug., 1931.

Howell, Arthur H. 1918. Revision of the American flying squirrels. North Amer. Fauna No. 44, pp. 1–64; illus. Wash., D. C.

Sollberger, Dwight E. 1940. Notes on the life history of the small eastern flying squirrel. Jour. of Mammalogy, vol. 21, no. 3, pp. 282–293. Aug., 1940.

Sollberger, Dwight E. 1943. Notes on the breeding habits of the eastern flying squirrel (*Glaucomys volans volans*). Jour. of Mammalogy, vol. 24, no. 2, pp. 163–173. June, 1943.

Svihla, Ruth Dowell. 1930. A family of flying squirrels. Jour. of Mammalogy, vol. 11, no. 2, pp. 211–213; illus. May, 1930.

THE CHISEL TEETH—PART 1

Bradt, G. W. 1932. The mammals of the malpais, an area of black lava rock in the Tularosa Basin, New Mexico. Jour. of Mammalogy, vol. 13, no. 4, pp. 321–328. Nov., 1932.

Elton, Charles. 1942. Voles, mice and lemmings. pp. ii, 1–496. Oxford Univ. Press, London.

Garlough, F. E., and Spencer, Donald A. 1944. Control of destructive mice. Conservation Bulletin No. 36, U. S. Dept. of Interior. pp. 1–37; illus. Wash., D. C.

POCKET GOPHER

Barrington, B. A., Jr. 1942. Description of birth and young of the pocket gopher, *Geomys floridanus*. Jour. of Mammalogy, vol. 23, no. 4, pp. 428–430; illus. Nov., 1942.

Breckenridge, W. J. 1929. Actions of the pocket gopher (*Geomys busarius*). Jour. of Mammalogy, vol. 10, no. 4, pp. 336–339; illus. Nov., 1929.

Criddle, Stuart. 1930. The prairie pocket gopher, *Thomomys talpoides rufescens*. Jour. of Mammalogy, vol. 11, no. 3, pp. 265–280; illus. Aug., 1930.

Dice, Lee R. 1939. Thomomys the engineer—friend or foe? Amer. Forests, vol. 45, no. 10, p. 512. Oct., 1939.

Dixon, Joseph. 1929. Control of pocket gophers and moles in California. Calif. Agric. Extension Service Circular 29, pp. 1–16; illus. Univ. of Calif., College of Agric., Berkeley.

Dixon, Joseph. 1929. The breeding season of the pocket gopher in California. Jour. of Mammalogy, vol. 10, no. 4, pp. 327–328; illus. Nov., 1929.

English, Pennoyer F. 1932. Some habits of the pocket gopher, *Geomys breviceps breviceps*. Jour. of Mammalogy, vol. 13, no. 2, pp. 126–132; illus. May, 1932.

Hubbell, T. H., and Goff, C. C. 1939. Florida pocket gopher burrows and their arthropod inhabitants. Proc. of the Florida Academy of Sciences, vol. 4, pp. 127–166.

Johnson, Charles Eugene. 1926. Notes on a pocket gopher in captivity. Jour. of Mammalogy, vol. 7, no. 1, pp. 35–37. Feb., 1926.

Scheffer, Theo. H. 1931. Habits and economic status of the pocket gophers. U.S.D.A. Technical Bulletin No. 224, pp. 1–26; illus. Wash., D. C.

Warren, Edward R. 1937. Notes on pocket gophers. Jour. of Mammalogy, vol. 18, no. 4, pp. 473–477; illus. Nov., 1937.

Wight, H. M. 1930. Breeding habits and economic relations of the Dalles pocket gopher. Jour. of Mammalogy, vol. 11, no. 1, pp. 40–48. Feb., 1930.

SPINY MOUSE
Goldmar. Edward A. 1911. Revision of the spiny pocket mice. North Amer. Fauna No. 34, pp. 1–70; illus. U.S.D.A., Wash., D. C.

POCKET MOUSE
Bailey, Vernon. 1939. The solitary lives of two little pocket mice. Jour. of Mammalogy, vol. 20, no. 3, pp. 325–328. Aug., 1939.
Blair, W. Frank. 1937. The burrows and food of the prairie pocket mouse. Jour. of Mammalogy, vol. 18, no. 2, pp. 188–191. May, 1937.
Osgood, Wilfred H. 1900. Revision of the pocket mice of the genus *Perognathus*. U.S.D.A. North Amer. Fauna No. 18, pp. 1–73; illus. Wash., D. C.
Scheffer, Theo. H. 1938. Pocket mice of Washington and Oregon in relation to agriculture. U.S.D.A. Tech. Bull. No. 608, pp. 1–15; illus. Wash., D. C.

KANGAROO RAT
Compton, Lawrence V., and Hedges, R. Frank. 1943. Kangaroo rat burrows in earth structures. Jour. of Wildlife Management, vol. 7, no. 3, pp. 306–316; illus. July, 1943.
Grinnell, Joseph. 1932. Habitat relations of the giant kangaroo rat. Jour. of Mammalogy, vol. 13, no. 4, pp. 305–320. Nov., 1932.
Hall, E. Raymond, and Linsdale, Jean M. 1929. Notes on the life history of the kangaroo mouse (*Microdipodops*). Jour. of Mammalogy, vol 10, no. 4, pp. 298–305; illus. Nov., 1929.
Hawbecker, Albert C. 1940. The burrowing and feeding habits of *Dipodomys venustus*. Jour. of Mammalogy, vol. 21, no. 4, pp. 388–396; illus. Nov., 1940.
Hawbecker, Albert C. 1944. The giant kangaroo rat and sheep forage. Jour of Wildlife Management, vol. 8, no. 2, pp. 161–165; illus. April, 1944.
Howell, A. Brazier, and Gersh, I. 1935. Conservation of water by the rodent *Dipodomys*. Jour. of Mammalogy, vol. 16, no. 1, pp. 1–9. Feb., 1935.
Monson, Gale, and Kessler, Wayne. 1940. Life history notes on the banner-tailed kangaroo rat, Merriam's kangaroo rat, and the white-throated wood rat in Arizona and New Mexico. Jour. of Wildlife Management, vol. 4, no. 1, pp. 37–43. Jan., 1940.
Monson, Gale. 1943. Food habits of the banner-tailed kangaroo rat in Arizona. Jour. of Wildlife Management, vol. 7, no. 1, pp. 98–102. Jan., 1943.
Shaw, William T. 1934. The ability of the giant kangaroo rat as a harvester and storer of seeds. Jour. of Mammalogy, vol. 15, no. 4, pp. 275–286; illus. Nov., 1934.
Tappe, Donald T. 1941. Natural history of the Tulare kangaroo rat. Jour. of Mammalogy, vol. 22, no. 2, pp. 117–148; illus. May, 1941.
Taylor, Walter P. 1936. The banner-tail and other burrowers. Amer. Forests, vol. 42, no. 2, pp. 68–70, 93; illus. Feb., 1936.
Vorhies, Charles T., and Taylor, Walter P. 1922. Life history of the kangaroo rat, *Dipodomys spectabilis spectabilis* Merriam. U.S.D.A. Bull. No. 1091, pp. 1–40; illus. Wash., D. C. Sept. 13, 1922.

BEAVER

Bailey, Vernon. 1926. How beavers build their houses. Jour. of Mammalogy, vol. 7, no. 1, pp. 41–44; illus. Feb., 1926.

Bailey, Vernon. 1927. Beaver habits and experiments in beaver culture. U. S. Dept. of Agric., Tech. Bull. No. 21, pp. 1–39; illus. Wash., D. C. Oct., 1927.

Bradt, Glenn W. 1938. A study of beaver colonies in Michigan. Jour. of Mammalogy, vol. 19, no. 2, pp. 139–162. May, 1938.

Bradt, G. W. 1939. Breeding habits of beaver. Jour. of Mammalogy, vol. 20, no. 4, pp. 486–489. Nov., 1939.

Cook, David B. 1940. Beaver-trout relations. Jour. of Mammalogy, vol. 21, no. 4, pp. 397–401. Nov., 1940.

Couch, Leo K. 1942. Trapping and transplanting live beavers. U. S. Dept. of Interior Conservation Bull. No. 1730, pp. 1–20; illus. Wash., D. C.

Dugmore, A. Radclyffe. The romance of the beaver. 225 pp.; illus. J. B. Lippincott Co., Philadelphia.

Hiner, Laurence E. 1938. Observations on the foraging habits of beavers. Jour. of Mammalogy, vol. 19, no. 3, pp. 317–319. Aug., 1938.

Johnson, Charles Eugene. 1927. The beaver in the Adirondacks. Roosevelt Wild Life Bulletin, vol. 4, no. 4, pp. 499–641; illus. Syracuse, N. Y.

Leighton, Alexander H. 1932. Notes on the beaver's individuality and mental characteristics. Jour. of Mammalogy, vol. 13, no. 2, pp. 117–126. May, 1932.

Leighton, Alexander H. 1933. Notes on the relations of beavers to one another and to the muskrat. Jour. of Mammalogy, vol. 14, no. 1, pp. 27–35. Feb., 1933.

Morgan, Lewis H. 1868. The American beaver and his works. pp. i–xv, 17–330; illus. J. B. Lippincott & Co., Philadelphia, Pa.

Soper, J. Dewey. 1937. Notes on the beavers of Wood Buffalo Park, Alberta. Jour. of Mammalogy, vol. 18, no. 1, pp. 1–13; illus. Feb. 1937.

Warren, Edward R. 1926. (1) A study of the beaver in the Yancey region of Yellowstone National Park. (2) Notes on the beaver colonies in the Longs Peak region of Estes Park, Colorado. Roosevelt Wild Life Annals, vol. 1, nos. 1–2, pp. 1–234; illus. Oct., 1926.

Warren, Edward R. 1927. The beaver. pp. xx, 1–177; illus. Williams & Wilkins Co., Baltimore, Md.

Warren, Edward R. 1932. The abandonment and reoccupation of pond sites by beavers. Jour. of Mammalogy, vol. 13, no. 4, pp. 343–346; illus. Nov., 1932.

GRASSHOPPER MOUSE

Bailey, Vernon, and Sperry, Charles C. 1929. Life history and habits of grasshopper mice, genus *Onychomys*. U.S.D.A. Technical Bull. No. 145, pp. 1–19; illus. Wash., D. C.

HARVEST MOUSE

Howell, Arthur H. 1914. Revision of the American harvest mice. North Amer. Fauna No. 36, pp. 1–97; illus. U. S. Dept. of Agriculture, Wash., D. C.

Leraas, Harold J. 1938. Observations on the growth and behavior of harvest mice. Jour. of Mammalogy, vol. 19, no. 4, pp. 441–444. Nov., 1938.

Smith, Clarence F. 1936. Notes on the habits of the long-tailed harvest mouse. Jour. of Mammalogy, vol. 17, no. 3, pp. 274–278. Aug., 1936.

WHITE-FOOTED MOUSE

Behney, W. H. 1936. Nocturnal explorations of the forest deer-mouse. Jour. of Mammalogy, vol. 17, no. 3, pp. 225–230; illus. Aug., 1936.

Blair, W. Frank. 1941. Observations on the life history of *Baiomys taylori subator*. Jour. of Mammalogy, vol. 22, no. 4, pp. 378–383. Nov., 1941.

Blair, W. Frank. 1943. Activities of the Chihuahua deer-mouse in relation to light intensity. Jour. of Wildlife Management, vol. 7, no. 1, pp. 92–97; illus. Jan., 1943.

Clark, Frank H. 1938. Age of sexual maturity in mice of the genus Peromyscus. Jour. of Mammalogy, vol. 19, no. 2, pp. 230–234. May, 1938.

Cogshall, Annetta Stow. 1928. Food habits of deer mice of the genus Peromyscus in captivity. Jour. of Mammalogy, vol. 9, no. 3, pp. 217–221. Aug., 1928.

Dice, Lee R. 1932. The prairie deer-mouse. Cranbrook Institute of Science Bulletin No. 2, pp. 1–8; illus. Bloomfield Hills, Mich.

Dice, Lee R. 1933. Longevity in *Peromyscus maniculatus gracilis*. Jour. of Mammalogy, vol. 14, no. 2, pp. 147–148. May, 1933.

Dice, Lee R. 1935. Inheritance of waltzing and of epilepsy in mice of the genus *Peromyscus*. Jour. of Mammalogy, vol. 16, no. 1, pp. 25–35. Feb., 1935.

Huestis, R. R. 1933. Maternal behavior in the deer mouse. Jour. of Mammalogy, vol. 14, no. 1, pp. 47–49; illus. Feb., 1933.

Murie, O. J., and Murie, Adolph. 1931. Travels of *Peromyscus*. Jour. of Mammalogy, vol. 12, no. 3, pp. 200–209. Aug., 1931.

Nicholson, Arnold J. 1941. The homes and social habits of the wood-mouse (*Peromyscus leucopus noveboracensis*) in southern Michigan. American Midland Naturalist, vol. 25, no. 1, pp. 196–223; illus. Jan., 1941.

Osgood, Wilfred H. 1909. Revision of the mice of the genus *Peromyscus*. North Amer. Fauna No. 28, pp. 1–285; illus. U.S.D.A., Wash., D. C.

Summer, F. B., and Karol, J. J. 1929. Notes on the burrowing habits of *Peromyscus polionotus*. Jour. of Mammalogy, vol. 10, no. 3, pp. 213–215; illus. Aug., 1929.

Svihla, Arthur. 1932. A comparative life history study of the mice of the genus *Peromyscus*. Univ. of Mich., Museum of Zoology Miscl. Public. No. 24, pp. 1–39. July 8, 1932.

Svihla, Arthur. 1934. Development and growth of deermice (*Peromyscus maniculatus artemisiae*). Jour. of Mammalogy, vol. 15, no. 2, pp. 99–104. May, 1934.

RICE RAT

Goldman, Edward A. 1918. The rice rats of North America. N. A. Fauna No. 43, pp. 1–100; illus. U.S.D.A., Wash., D. C.

Svihla, Arthur. 1931. Life history of the Texas rice rat (*Oryzomys palustris texensis*). Jour. of Mammalogy, vol. 12, no. 3, pp. 238–242; illus. Aug., 1931.

COTTON RAT

Komarek, E. V. 1937. Mammal relationships to upland game and other wildlife. Trans. Second North Amer. Wildlife Conference, pp. 561–569. Wash., D. C.

Meyer, Bert J., and Meyer, Roland K. 1944. Growth and reproduction of the cotton rat, *Sigmodon hispidus hispidus,* under laboratory conditions. Jour. of Mammalogy, vol. 25, no. 2, pp. 107–129; illus. May, 1944.

Strecker, John K. 1929. Notes on the Texas cotton and Attwater wood rats in Texas. Jour. of Mammalogy, vol. 10, no. 3, pp. 216–220. August, 1929.

Svihla, Arthur 1929. Life history notes on *Sigmodon hispidus hispidus.* Jour. of Mammalogy, vol. 10, no. 4, pp. 352–353. Nov., 1929.

WOOD RAT
(See also Kangaroo Rat and Cotton Rat, above)

Donat, Fae. 1933. Notes on the life history and behavior of *Neotoma fuscipes.* Jour. of Mammalogy, vol. 14, no. 1, pp. 19–26. Feb., 1933.

English, Pennoyer F. 1923. The dusky-footed wood rat (*Neotoma fuscipes*). Jour. of Mammalogy, vol. 4, no. 1, pp. 1–9; illus. Feb., 1923.

Feldman, Horace W. 1935. Notes on two species of wood rats in captivity. Jour. of Mammalogy, vol. 16, no. 4, pp. 300–303. Nov., 1935.

Gander, Frank F. 1929. Experiences with wood rats, *Neotoma fuscipes macrotis.* Jour. of Mammalogy, vol. 10, no. 1, pp. 52–58. Feb., 1929.

Goldman, Edward A. 1910. Revision of the wood rats of the genus *Neotoma.* North Amer. Fauna No. 31, pp. 1–124; illus. Wash., D. C.

Horton, Jerome S., and Wright, John T. 1944. The woodrat as an ecological factor in southern California watersheds. Ecology, vol. 25, no. 3, pp. 341–351; illus. July, 1944.

Lay, Daniel W., and Baker, Rollin H. 1938. Notes on the home range and ecology of the Attwater wood rat. Jour. of Mammalogy, vol. 19, no. 4, pp. 418–423. Nov., 1938.

Newcombe, C. L. 1930. An ecological study of the Allegheny cliff rat (*Neotoma pennsylvanica* Stone). Jour. of Mammalogy, vol. 11, no. 2, pp. 204–211; illus. May, 1930.

Poole, Earl L. 1936. Notes on the young of the Allegheny wood rat. Jour. of Mammalogy, vol. 17, no. 1, pp. 22–26; illus. Feb., 1936.

Poole, Earl L. 1940. A life history sketch of the Allegheny woodrat. Jour. of Mammalogy, vol. 21, no. 3, pp. 249–270; illus. Aug., 1940.

Richardson, William B. 1943. Wood rats (*Neotoma albigula*): their growth and development. Jour. of Mammalogy, vol. 24, no. 2, pp. 130–143; illus. June, 1943.

Spencer, Donald A., and Spencer, Alice L. 1941. Food habits of the white-throated wood rat in Arizona. Jour. of Mammalogy, vol. 22, no. 3, pp. 280–284. Aug., 1941.

Svihla, Arthur, and Svihla, Ruth Dowell. 1933. Notes on the life history of the wood-rat, *Neotoma floridana rubida* Bangs. Jour. of Mammalogy, vol. 14, no. 1, pp. 73–75. Feb., 1933.

Vestal, Elden H. 1938. Biotic relations of the wood rat (*Neotoma fuscipes*) in the Berkeley Hills. Jour. of Mammalogy, vol. 19, no. 1, pp. 1–36; illus. Feb., 1938.

Vorhies, Charles T., and Taylor, Walter P. 1940. Life history and ecology of the white-throated wood rat, *Neotoma albigula albigula* Hartley, in relation to grazing in Arizona. Univ. of Arizona, Agr. Exp. Sta. Tech. Bull. No. 86, pp. 455–529; illus. Tucson.

Warren, Edward R. 1920. Notes on wood rat work. Jour. of Mammalogy, vol. 1, no. 5, pp. 233–235; illus. Nov., 1920.

Warren, Edward R. 1926. Notes on the breeding of wood rats of the genus *Neotoma*. Jour. of Mammalogy, vol. 7, no. 2, pp. 97–101. May, 1926.

THE CHISEL-TEETH—PART 2
(See also Part 1)

Piper, Stanley E. 1928. The mouse infestation of Buena Vista Lake basin. Monthly Bulletin, vol. 17, no. 10, pp. 538–560; illus. Calif. Dept. of Agriculture, Sacramento. Oct., 1928.

LEMMING

Allen, Glover M. 1919. The American collared lemmings (*Dicrostonyx*). Bull. of Mus. of Comp. Zool. at Harvard College, vol. 62, no. 13, pp. 509–540; illus. Cambridge, Mass. Feb., 1919.

Shelford, V. E. 1943. The abundance of the collared lemming (*Dicrostonyx groenlandicus* (Tr.) var. *richardsoni* Mer.) in the Churchill area, 1929 to 1940. Ecology, vol. 24, no. 4, pp. 472–484; illus. Oct., 1943.

MEADOW MOUSE

Bailey, Vernon. 1900. Revision of American voles of the genus *Microtus*. North Amer. Fauna No. 17, pp. 1–88; illus. U.S.D.A., Wash., D. C.

Bailey, Vernon. 1924. Breeding, feeding, and other life habits of meadow mice (*Microtus*). Jour. Agric. Research, vol. 27, no. 8, pp. 523–535; illus. Feb. 23, 1924.

Blair, W. Frank. 1940. Home ranges and populations of the meadow vole in southern Michigan. Jour. of Wildlife Management, vol. 4, no. 2, pp. 149–161. April, 1940.

Benson, Seth B., and Borell, Adrey E. 1931. Notes on the life history of the red tree mouse, *Phenacomys longicaudus*. Jour. of Mammalogy, vol. 12, no. 3, pp. 226–233; illus. Aug., 1931.

Burt, W. H. 1928. Additional notes on the life history of the Goss lemming mouse. Jour. of Mammalogy, vol. 9, no. 3, pp. 212–216; illus. Aug., 1928.

Criddle, Stuart. 1926. The habits of *Microtus minor* in Manitoba. Jour. of Mammalogy, vol. 7, no. 3, pp. 193–200. Aug., 1926.

Graham, Samuel A. 1929. The larch sawfly as an indicator of mouse abundance. Jour. of Mammalogy, vol. 10, no. 3, pp. 189–196. Aug., 1929.

Hamilton, W. J., Jr. 1937. Activity and home range of the field mouse, *Microtus pennsylvanicus pennsylvanicus* (Ord.). Ecology, vol. 18, no. 2, pp. 255–263. April, 1937.

Hamilton, W. J., Jr. 1937. The biology of microtine cycles. Jour. of Agric. Research, vol. 54, no. 10, pp. 779–790. May 15, 1937.

Hamilton, W. J., Jr. 1937. Growth and life span of the field mouse. Amer. Naturalist, vol. 71, pp. 500–507. Sept.–Oct., 1937.

Hamilton, W. J., Jr. 1938. Life history notes on the northern pine mouse. Jour. of Mammalogy, vol. 19, no. 2, pp. 163–170; illus. May, 1938.

Hamilton, W. J., Jr. 1940. Life and habits of field mice. Scientific Monthly, vol. 50, pp. 425–434; illus. May, 1940.

Hamilton, W. J., Jr. 1941. Reproduction of the field mouse *Microtus pennsylvanicus* (Ord.). Cornell Univ. Agric. Exper. Sta. Memoir 237, pp. 1–23; illus. Ithaca, N. Y.

Hatfield, Donald M. 1935. A natural history study of *Microtus californicus*. Jour. of Mammalogy, vol. 16, no. 4, pp. 261–271. Nov., 1935.

Hatt, Robert T. 1930. The biology of the voles of New York. Roosevelt Wild Life Bulletin, vol. 5, no. 4, pp. 509–623. Aug., 1930. Syracuse, N. Y.

Howell, A. Brazier. 1926. Voles of the genus *Phenacomys*. North Amer. Fauna No. 48, pp. 1–66; illus. U.S.D.A., Wash., D. C.

Howell, A. Brazier. 1927. Revision of the American lemming mice. North Amer. Fauna No. 50, pp. 1–38; illus. Wash., D. C.

Linsdale, Jean. 1927. Notes on the life history of *Synaptomys*. Jour. of Mammalogy, vol. 8, no. 1, pp. 51–54. Feb., 1927.

Shaw, William T. 1924. Alpine life of the heather vole (*Phenacomys olympicus*). Jour. of Mammalogy, vol. 5, no. 1, pp. 12–15; illus. Feb., 1924.

WATER RAT

Harper, Francis. 1920. The Florida water-rat (*Neofiber alleni*) in Okefinokee Swamp, Georgia. Jour. of Mammalogy, vol. 1, no. 2, pp. 65–6; illus. Feb., 1920.

MUSKRAT

(See also citation under Mink)

Bailey, Vernon. 1937. The Maryland muskrat marshes. Jour. of Mammalogy, vol. 18, no. 3, pp. 350–354; illus. Aug., 1937.

Bellrose, Frank C., and Brown, Louis G. 1941. The effect of fluctuating water levels on the muskrat population of the Illinois River valley. Jour. of Wildlife Management, vol. 5, no. 2, pp. 206–212. April, 1941.

Elton, Charles, and Nicholson, Mary. 1942. Fluctuations in numbers of the muskrat (*Ondatra zibethica*) in Canada. Jour. of Animal Ecology, vol. 11, no. 1, pp. 96–126. May, 1942.

Errington, Paul L. 1937. Habitat requirements of stream-dwelling muskrats. Trans. Second North Amer. Wildlife Conference, Amer. Wildlife Institute, pp. 411–416.

Errington, Paul L. 1937. The breeding season of the muskrat in northwest Iowa. Jour. of Mammalogy, vol. 18, no. 3, pp. 333–337. Aug., 1937.

Errington, Paul L. 1937. Drowning as a cause of mortality in muskrats. Jour. of Mammalogy, vol. 18, no. 4, pp. 497–500. Nov., 1937.

Errington, Paul L. 1939. Reactions of muskrat populations to drought. Ecology, vol. 20, no. 2, pp. 168–186. April, 1939.

Errington, Paul L. 1939. Observations on young muskrats in Iowa. Jour. of Mammalogy, vol. 20, no. 4, pp. 465–478. Nov., 1939.

Errington, Paul L. 1941. Versatility in feeding and population maintenance of the muskrat. Jour. of Wildlife Management, vol. 5, no. 1, pp. 68–89. Jan., 1941.

Hollister, N. 1911. A systematic synopsis of the muskrats. North Amer. Fauna No. 32, Bur. of Biol. Surv., U.S.D.A., pp. 1–47; illus. Wash., D. C.

Johnson, Charles E. 1925. The muskrat in New York: its natural history and economics. Roosevelt Wild Life Bulletin, vol. 3, no. 2, pp. 199–320; illus. March, 1925. Syracuse, N. Y.

Lay, Daniel W. 1945. Muskrat investigations in Texas. Jour. of Wildlife Management, vol. 9, no. 1, pp. 56–76. Jan., 1945.

McCann, Lester J. 1944. Notes on growth, sex and age ratios, and suggested management of Minnesota muskrats. Jour. of Mammalogy, vol. 25, no. 1, pp. 59–63. Feb., 1944.

Mizelle, John D. 1935. Swimming of the muskrat. Jour. of Mammalogy, vol. 16, no. 1, pp. 22–25. Feb., 1935.

Mohr, Erna. 1933. The muskrat, *Ondatra zibethica* (*Linnaeus*), in Europe. Jour. of Mammalogy, vol. 14, no. 1, pp. 58–63. Feb., 1933.

Storer, Tracy I. 1938. The muskrat as a native and alien: a chapter in the history of animal acclimatization. Calif. Fish & Game, vol. 24, no. 2, pp. 159–175. Sacramento. April, 1938.

Svihla, Arthur, and Svihla, Ruth Dowell. 1931. The Louisiana muskrat. Jour. of Mammalogy, vol. 12, no. 1, pp. 12–28; illus. Feb., 1931.

HOUSE MOUSE
(See also The Chisel-Teeth—Part 2, above)

Buck, C. W., Tolman, N., and Tolman, W. 1925. The tail as a balancing organ in mice. Jour. of Mammalogy, vol. 6, no. 4, pp. 267–271. Nov., 1925.

Dice, Lee R. 1932. The songs of mice. Jour. of Mammalogy, vol. 13, no. 3, pp. 187–196. Aug., 1932.

Schwarz, Ernst, and Schwarz, Henriette K. 1943. The wild and commensal stocks of the house mouse, *Mus musculus* Linnaeus. Jour. of Mammalogy, vol. 24, no. 1, pp. 59–72. Feb., 1943.

HOUSE RAT

Lantz, David E. 1909. The brown rat in the United States. Biol. Survey, Bull. No. 33, pp. 1–54; illus. U.S.D.A., Wash., D. C.

Silver, James. 1941. The house rat. U.S.D.I. Wildlife Circular No. 6, pp. ii–iv, 1–18; illus. Govt. Print. Office, Washington, D. C.

Silver, James, and Garlough, F. E. 1941. Rat control. U. S. Dept. of Interior, Conservation Bull. No. 8, 27 pp.; illus. Wash., D. C.

Zinsser, Hans. 1935. Rats, lice and history. 301 pp. Little, Brown & Co.

MOUNTAIN BEAVER

Anthony, H. E. 1916. Habits of Aplodontia. Bulletin of the Amer. Mus. of Nat. Hist., vol. 35, art. 6, pp. 53–63; illus. New York, April 1, 1916.

Scheffer, Theo. H. 1929. Mountain beavers in the Pacific Northwest: their habits, economic status, and control. U.S.D.A. Farmers' Bulletin No. 1598, pp. 1–18; illus. Wash., D. C., Aug., 1929.

JUMPING MOUSE

Blair, W. Frank. 1940. Home ranges and populations of the jumping mouse. Amer. Midland Naturalist, vol. 23, no. 1, pp. 244–250. Jan., 1940.

Hamilton, W. J., Jr. 1935. Habits of jumping mice. Amer. Midland Naturalist, vol. 16, no. 2, pp. 187–200.

Preble, Edward A. 1899. Revision of the jumping mice of the genus *Zapus*. North Amer. Fauna No. 15, Bureau of Biol. Surv., U.S.D.A., pp. 1–42; illus. Wash., D. C.

Sheldon, Carolyn. 1934. Studies on the life histories of *Zapus* and *Napaeozapus* in Nova Scotia. Jour. of Mammalogy, vol. 15, no. 4, pp. 290–300. Nov., 1934.

Sheldon, Carolyn. 1938. Vermont jumping mice of the genus Zapus. Jour. of Mammalogy, vol. 19, no. 3, pp. 324–332; illus. Aug., 1938.

Sheldon, Carolyn. 1938. Vermont jumping mice of the genus *Napaeozapus*. Jour. of Mammalogy, vol. 19, no. 4, pp. 444–453; illus. Nov., 1938.

Snyder, L. L. 1924. Some details on the life history and behavior of *Napæozapus insignis abietorum* (Preble). Jour. of Mammalogy, vol. 5, no. 4, pp. 233–237; illus. Nov., 1924.

Svihla, Arthur, and Svihla, Ruth Dowell. 1933. Notes on the jumping mouse *Zapus trinotatus trinotatus* Rhoads. Jour. of Mammalogy, vol. 14, no. 2, pp. 131–134. May, 1933.

PORCUPINE

Batchelder, Charles Foster. 1930. The voice of the porcupine. Jour. of Mammalogy, vol. 11, no. 2, pp. 237–239. May, 1930.

Campbell, Sam. 1943. Adventure with porcupine. Amer. Forests, vol. 49, no. 9, pp. 426–427, 463–464; illus. Sept., 1943.

Curtis, James D. 1944. Appraisal of porcupine damage. Jour. of Wildlife Management, vol. 8, no. 1, pp. 88–91. Jan., 1944.

Curtis, James D., and Kozicky, Edward L. 1944. Observations on the eastern porcupine. Jour. of Mammalogy, vol. 25, no. 2, pp. 137–146. May, 1944.

Gabrielson, Ira N. 1928. Notes on the habits and behavior of the porcupine in Oregon. Jour. of Mammalogy, vol. 9, no. 1, pp. 33–38; illus. Feb., 1928.

Garlough, F. E., Gabrielson, Ira N., and Horn, E. E. 1938. Porcupine control in the western states. U.S.D.A. Leaflet No. 60, pp. 2–8; illus. Wash., D. C.

Murie, Olaus J. 1926. The porcupine in northern Alaska. Jour. of Mammalogy, vol. 7, no. 2, pp. 109–113; illus. May, 1926.

Shadle, Albert R. 1944. The play of American porcupines (*Erethizon d. dorsatum* and *E. epixanthum*). Jour. of Comparative Psychology, vol. 37, no. 3, pp. 145–150. June, 1944.

Shadle, Albert R. 1946. Copulation in the porcupine. Jour. of Wildlife Management, vol. 10, no. 2, pp. 159–162; illus. April, 1946.

Shadle, Albert R., and Ploss, Wm. R. 1943. An unusual porcupine parturition and development of the young. Jour. of Mammalogy, vol. 24, no. 4, pp. 492–496. Nov., 1943.

Struthers, Parke H. 1928. Breeding habits of the Canadian porcupine (*Erethizon dorsatum*). Jour. of Mammalogy, vol. 9, no. 4, pp. 300–308; illus. Nov., 1928.

Taylor, Walter P. 1935. Ecology and life history of the porcupine (*Erethizon epixanthum*) as related to the forests of Arizona and southwestern United States. Univ. of Arizona, Biol. Sci. Bull. No. 3, pp. 5–177; illus. Tucson.

THE HARES AND RABBITS

Couch, Leo King. 1929. Introduced European rabbits in the San Juan Islands, Washington. Jour. of Mammalogy, vol. 10, no. 4, pp. 334–336; illus. Nov., 1929.

Day, Albert M. 1937. Sylvatic plague. Transactions Second North Amer. Wildlife Conference, pp. 555–560. Wash., D. C.

Garlough, F. E., Welch, J. F., and Spencer, H. J. 1942. Rabbits in relation to crops. U.S.D.I. Conservation Bull. 11, pp. 1–20; illus. Wash., D. C.

Johnson, Charles Eugene. 1925. The jack and snowshoe rabbits as swimmers. Jour. of Mammalogy, vol. 6, no. 4, pp. 245–249. Nov., 1925.

Nelson, E. W. 1909. The rabbits of North America. North Amer. Fauna No. 29, pp. 1–314; illus. Wash., D. C.

PIKA

Dice, L. R. 1927. The Colorado pika in captivity. Jour. of Mammalogy, vol. 8, no. 3, pp. 228–231, Aug., 1927.

Grinnell, Joseph, and Storer, Tracy I. 1917. The Yosemite cony—a chapter in the natural history of the Yosemite National Park. Sierra Club Bulletin, vol. 10, no. 2, pp. 159–164; illus. Jan., 1917.

Howell, Arthur H. 1924. Revision of the American pikas. North Amer. Fauna No. 47, pp. 1–57; illus. U.S.D.A., Wash., D. C.

Martin, Ken. 1943. The Colorado pika. Jour. of Mammalogy, vol. 24, no. 3, pp. 394–396. Aug., 1943.

VARYING HARE

Aldous, C. M. 1937. Notes on the life history of the snowshoe hare. Jour. of Mammalogy, vol. 18, no. 1, pp. 46–57; illus. Feb., 1937.

Cox, W. T. 1936. Snowshoe rabbit migration, tick infestation, and weather cycles. Jour. of Mammalogy, vol. 17, no. 3, pp. 216–221. Aug., 1936.

Grange, Wallace B. 1932. Observations on the snowshoe hare, Lepus americanus phaeonotus Allen. Jour. of Mammalogy, vol. 13, no. 1, pp. 1–19; illus. Feb., 1932.

Grange, Wallace B. 1932. The pelages and color changes of the snowshoe hare, Lepus americanus phaeonotus Allen. Jour. of Mammalogy, vol. 13, no. 2, pp. 99–116; illus. May, 1932.

Green, R. G., and Larson, C. L. 1938. A description of shock disease in the snowshoe hare. Amer. Jour. of Hygiene, vol. 28, no. 2, pp. 190–212; illus. Sept., 1938.

Orr, Robert T. 1934. Description of a new snowshoe rabbit from eastern Oregon, with notes on its life history. Jour. of Mammalogy, vol. 15, no. 2, pp. 152–154. May, 1934.

Severaid, Joye Harold. 1942. The snowshoe hare: its life history and artificial propagation. pp. 1–95; illus. Maine Dept. of Inland Fisheries and Game. Augusta.

Severaid, Joye Harold. 1945. Pelage changes in the snowshoe hare (Lepus americanus struthopus Bangs). Jour. of Mammalogy, vol. 26, no. 1, pp. 41–63; illus. Feb., 1945.

Soper, J. Dewey, 1921. Notes on the snowshoe rabbit. Jour. of Mammalogy, vol. 2, no. 2, pp. 101-108; illus. May, 1921.

ARCTIC HARE

Howell, Arthur H. 1936. A revision of the American Arctic hares. Jour. of Mammalogy, vol. 17, no. 4, pp. 315–337; illus. Nov., 1936.

8 LIST OF REFERENCES 675

Sverdrup, Otto. 1904. New land; four years in the Arctic regions. Translated by Ethel Harriet Hearn. 2 vols., pp. 496 and 504. Longmans, Green & Co., N. Y.

JACK RABBIT

Taylor, Walter P., Vorhies, Charles T., and Lister, P. B. 1935. The relation of jack rabbits to grazing in southern Arizona. Jour. of Forestry, vol. 33, no. 5, pp. 490–498; illus. May, 1935.

Vorhies, Charles T., and Taylor, Walter P. 1933. The life histories and ecology of jack rabbits, *Lepus alleni* and *Lepus californicus* ssp., in relation to grazing in Arizona. Univ. of Arizona Coll. Agric., Agric. Exper. Sta. Technical Bulletin No. 49, pp. 471–587; illus. Tucson, May 31, 1933.

Wood, Kerry. 1944. Prairie jack. Fauna, vol. 6, no. 2, pp. 42–47; illus. June, 1944.

COTTONTAIL RABBIT

Allen, Durward L. 1939. Michigan cottontails in winter. Jour. of Wildlife Management, vol. 3, no. 4, pp. 307–322; illus. Oct., 1939.

Beule, John D., and Studholme, Allen T. 1942. Cottontail rabbit nests and nestlings. Jour. of Wildlife Management, vol. 6, no. 2, pp. 133–140; illus. April, 1942.

Blair, W. Frank. 1936. The Florida marsh rabbit. Jour. of Mammalogy, vol. 17, no. 3, pp. 197–207. Aug., 1936.

Dalke, Paul D., and Sime, Palmer R. 1941. Food habits of the eastern and New England cottontails. Jour. of Wildlife Management, vol. 5, no. 2, pp. 216–228. April, 1941.

Dice, L. R. 1927. The transfer of game and fur-bearing mammals from state to state, with special reference to the cottontail rabbit. Jour. of Mammalogy, vol. 8, no. 2, pp. 90–96. May, 1927.

Elder, William H., and Sowls, Lyle K. 1942. Body weight and sex ratio of cottontail rabbits. Jour. of Wildlife Management, vol. 6, no. 3, pp. 203–207. July, 1942.

Hamilton, W. J., Jr. 1940. Breeding habits of the cottontail rabbit in New York state. Jour. of Mammalogy, vol. 21, no. 1, pp. 8–11. Feb., 1940.

Haugen, Arnold O. 1942. Home range of the cottontail rabbit. Ecology, vol. 23, no. 3, pp. 354–367; illus. July, 1942.

Haugen, Arnold O. 1942. Life history studies of the cottontail rabbit in southwestern Michigan. Amer. Midland Naturalist, vol. 28, no. 1, pp. 204–244; illus. July, 1942.

Haugen, Arnold O. 1943. Management studies of the cottontail rabbit in southwestern Michigan. Jour. of Wildlife Management, vol. 7, no. 1, pp. 102–119; illus. Jan., 1943.

Hickie, Paul. 1940. Cottontails in Michigan. 109 pp. & append.; illus. Game Division, Michigan Dept. of Conservation, Lansing, Mich.

Hosley, N. W., editor. 1942. The cottontail rabbits in Connecticut. State of Connecticut Public Document No. 47; Geol. and Nat. Hist. Survey Bulletin No. 65, 97 pp., illus. Hartford, Connecticut.

Ingles, Lloyd G. 1941. Natural history observations on the Audubon cottontail. Jour. of Mammalogy, vol. 22, no. 3, pp. 227–250; illus. Aug., 1941.

Lantz, D. E. 1916. Cottontail rabbits in relation to trees and farm crops. U.S.D.A. Farmers' Bulletin 702, 13 pp., illus. (Revised 1922, 1924). Wash., D. C.

Morgan, B. B., and Waller, E. F. 1940. A survey of the parasites of the Iowa cottontail (*Sylvilagus floridanus mearnsi*). Jour. of Wildlife Management, vol. 4, no. 1, pp. 21–26. Jan., 1940.

Orr, Robert T. 1942. Observations on the growth of young brush rabbits. Jour. of Mammalogy, vol. 23, no. 3, pp. 298–302. Aug., 1942.

Schwartz, Charles W. 1941. Home range of the cottontail in central Missouri. Jour. of Mammalogy, vol. 22, no. 4, pp. 386–392. Nov., 1941.

Schwartz, Charles W. 1942. Breeding season of the cottontail in central Missouri. Jour. of Mammalogy, vol. 23, no. 1, pp. 1–16; illus. Feb., 1942.

Svihla, Ruth Dowell. 1929. Habits of *Sylvilagus aquaticus littoralis*. Jour. of Mammalogy, vol. 10, no. 4, pp. 315–319; illus. Nov., 1929.

Sweetman, Harvey L. 1944. Selection of woody plants as winter food by the cottontail rabbit. Ecology, vol. 25, no. 4, pp. 467–472. Oct., 1944.

Todd, John B., M.D. 1927. Winter food of cottontail rabbits. Jour. of Mammalogy, vol. 8, no. 3, pp. 222–228. Aug., 1927.

Tomkins, Ivan R. 1935. The marsh rabbit: an incomplete life history. Jour. of Mammalogy, vol. 16, no. 3, pp. 201–205; illus. Aug., 1935.

Trippensee, R. E. 1936. The reproductive function in the cottontail rabbit (*Sylvilagus floridanus mearnsii* Allen) in southern Michigan. Proceedings, North Amer. Wildlife Conference, pp. 344–350. Wash., D. C.

TWO SEA FARERS

Allen, Glover M. 1916. The whalebone whales of New England. Vol. 8, No. 2, Memoirs of the Boston Society of Natural History, pp. 107–322; illus. Boston, Mass.

Beddard, F. E. 1900. A book of whales. 312 pp.; illus. G. P. Putnam's Sons, New York.

Bonnot, Paul. 1929. The whales of California. Calif. Fish and Game, vol. 15, no. 3, pp. 203–215; illus. July, 1929.

Kellogg, Remington. 1928. A history of whales, their adaptation to life in the water. Quarterly Review of Biology, vol. 3, no. 1, pp. 29–76, and vol. 3, no. 2, pp. 174–208.

Kellogg, Remington. 1940. Whales, giants of the sea. National Geographic Mag., vol. 77, no. 1, pp. 35–90; illus. Jan., 1940.

Norman, John R., and Fraser, Francis C. 1938. Giant fishes, whales and dolphins. 361 pp.; illus. W. W. Norton & Co., New York.

Scammon, C. H. 1874. The marine mammals of the northwestern coast of North America, together with an account of the American whale fishery. 312 pp.; illus. John H. Carmany & Co., San Francisco, and G. P. Putnam's Sons, New York.

Spears, John R. 1910. The story of the New England whales. The Macmillan Co., New York.

WHALES

Andrews, Roy Chapman. 1916. Whale hunting with gun and camera. 332 pp.; illus. D. Appleton & Co., New York.

Kellogg, Remington. 1929. Migrations of whalebone whales. Smithsonian Inst. An. Rept. for 1928, pp. 467–494.

Index

Actinomycosis, 64
Alaska Game Commission, 87–88
Albrecht, C. J., 8
Alces: americanus, 44–53; *gigas,* 44–53
Alexis, Grand Duke, of Russia, 73
Alopex lagopus, 241–245
American Museum of Natural History, 8
Antelope, 62–70, 140
Antilocapra americana, 62–70, 140
Antrozous, 133
Aplodontia rufa, 550–556
Arizona, University of, 278
Armadillo, 108–113
Ashbrook, Frank G., 8
Audubon, John James, 187

Badger, 66, 222–227
Bailey, Vernon, 357
Baiomys, 479
Balæna mysticetus, 639, 640
Balænopteridæ, 633, 635–640
Bang's disease, 46
Bassariscus astutus, 165–169
Bat, 126–133; big brown, 133; free-tailed, 131, 133; hoary, 130; leaf nosed, 126–127, 132; little brown, 131, 133; lump-nosed, 133; mastiff, 133; pale, 133; pipistrelle, 133; Refinesque, 133; red, 133; silver-haired, 130, 133; spotted, 133; yellow, 133
Bats, "Molossid," 132–133; "Vespertilionid," 133
Bean, Robert, 268
Bear, 134–155; Barren Ground, 144–150 (grizzly bear); big brown, 144–150 (grizzly bear); black, 134–143; blue, 143 (glacier bear); brown, 134–143 (black bear); cinnamon, 134–143 (black bear); glacier, 143; grizzly, 19, 20, 38, 143, 144–150; ice, 150–155, 241 (polar bear); Kermode's, 143; "kodiak," 144–150 (grizzly bear); polar, 150–155, 241; water, 150–155, 241 (polar bear)
Bear's Small Cousins, The, 156–169
Beaver, 452–462
Beaver, mountain, 550–556
Bell, William B., 8
Beluga, 640, 644, 645 (white whale)

Benson, Jack (Norman J.), 45
Bighorn, 88–98, 232, 287
Biological Survey, U. S., 270
Bison, 71–82 (buffalo); *bison athabascæ,* 81; *bison bison,* 81
"Black Death," 547 (bubonic plague)
Blackfish, 640, 644
Blarina, 124
Bobcat, 290–297, 612
Boomer, 550–556 (mountain beaver), 389–400 (red squirrel)
Boone, Daniel, 71
Borell, Adrey E., 9, 607
Brachylagus, 624
Brown, J. R., 430
Bruce, Jay (J. C.), 268, 269
Bubonic plague, 547
Buffalo, 71–82; plains, 71–82; wood, 73, 76, 81
Bummer, 389–400 (red squirrel)
Burroughs, John, 382

Cacomixtle, 165–169 (ringtail)
Calculus, 39
Callorhinus, 298–303
Campbell, Charles D., 269
Canis, 245–263
Capybara, 454
Caribou, 53–61, 86, 88, 232; Barren Ground, 56–57, 58, 59–60; woodland, 56–57
Carlsbad Caverns, 129
Carnegie Museum, 8
Castor, 452–462
Cats, The, 264–297. See also Civet, Lynx cat, Pennant's cat, Ringtail, Spotted king cat
Cervus, 15–23, 140; *canadensis canadensis,* 22; *canadensis occidentalis,* 22–23; *nannodes,* 23
Cetacea, 631–645
Chaetodipus, 442
Chamois, European, 98
Chehalis, 550–556 (mountain beaver)
Chicago Museum of Natural History, 8
Chicago (Brookfield) Zoo, 268
Chickaree, 170, 389–400 (red squirrel); Douglas, 399
Chipmunk, 359–363, 377–389; alpine, 388; antelope, 359–363 (antelope squirrels); "cen-

tral," 388; eastern, 377–383; least, 388; Townsend, 388; western, 383–389
Chipmunks and Squirrels, The, 377–424
Chippie, 377–383 (eastern chipmunk)
Chisel-teeth, 425–576
'Chucks and Ground Squirrels, The, 328–376
Citellus: beecheyi, 358; columbianus, 341–349; lateralis, 363–368; leucurus, 359–363; tridecemlineatus, 349–355; variegatus, 355–359
Civet, 165–169 (ringtail)
Clarke, C. H. D., 9, 418, 460, 556
Classification of mammals, 6–7
Clethrionomys, 518
Coati, 161–165
Coatimundi, 161–165 (coati)
Cody, "Buffalo Bill" (William Frederick), 73
Colter, John, 458
Condylura, 118–119
Conopatus, 216–218
Conservation, 1–2
Cony, 577–583 (pika)
Coon, 156–161 (raccoon)
Coronado, Francisco Vasquez de, 71
Corynorhinus, 133
Couch, Leo K., 8
Cougar, 38, 264–272, 277
Cox, William T. 586
Coyote, 35, 62, 66, 245–255
Crater Lake National Park, 365
Cratogeomys, 433–434
Cryptotis, 124
Cynomys, 375
Cystophora cristata, 312–313

Darling, F. Fraser, 317
Dasypterus, 133
Dasypus novemcinctus texanus, 108–113
Deer, 15–61, 250, 296, 398; Arizona whitetail, 32 (Coues deer); blacktail, 29, 30, 38, 40–44; Coues, 32; dwarf whitetail, 32 (Coues deer); mule, 33–40, 252–253; Sonora whitetail, 32 (Coues deer); Virginia, 23–33, 37 (whitetail deer); whitetail, 23–33, 37
Definition of mammals, 3–4
Delphinidæ, 634, 637, 640, 641, 642–645
De Solis, Antonio, 71
Dicrostonyx, 501–507
Didelphis, 104–108, 113
Dipodomys, 442–452; ingens, 447; merriami, 447, 449; spectabilis, 448
Diseases, 18, 46, 64, 95, 96, 101, 103, 233, 253, 547, 592
Dixon, Joseph S., 431
Dog, domestic, 106–112
Dog, prairie, 66, 368–376
Dogs, The Wild, 228–263

Dolphin, 637, 640, 641, 642–645; common, 644–645
Dugong, 626

Eagle, golden, 96, 102, 232
Economic uses, 2
Einarsen, Arthur S., 42
Elk, 15–23, 140; California, 23; dwarf, 23; Olympic, 22–23; Rocky Mountain, 22; Roosevelt, 22–23; tule, 23
Elton, Charles, 289
Enhydra lutris, 203–209
Eptesicus, 133
Erethizon: dorsatum, 564, 567, 568, 571, 574, 575; epixanthum, 564, 566, 567, 568, 571–572, 576
Erignathus barbatus, 315–316
Ermine, 180–188 (weasel)
Euarctos americanus, 134–143
Eubalæna glacialis, 639, 640
Euderma, 133
Eumetopias jubata, 303–308
Eumops, 133
Eutamias, 383–389; alpinus, 388; amoenus, 388; minimus, 388; quadrivittatus, 388; townsendii, 388
Eyra, 282–284 (jaguarundi)

Fable, 124, 126, 134, 269, 270, 275, 276, 306, 325, 328, 370–371, 455, 503, 541, 566, 568, 589, 590
Felis: cacomitli, 282–284; concolor, 38, 264–272, 277; onca, 12, 273–278; pardalis, 278–282; weidii, 281
Ferret, black-footed, 187
Finfeet, The, 298–327
Fish and Wildlife Service, 8, 9, 87–88, 175, 302
Fisher, 175–180
Florida, University of, 9
Fly, nose, 30
Flyer, The, 126–133
Forest Service, U. S., 266, 409
Fouke Fur Company, 302
Fox, Arctic, 241–245; "bastard," 233; black, 233; blue, 243, 245; "cross," 233; gray, 237–240; kit, 235–237; "platinum," 234; red, 228–234; "samson," 233; silver, 233; swift, 235–237 (kit fox)

Geomyidæ, 425–434
Geomys, 433
Glacier National Park, 144, 338
Glaucomys, 416–424; sabrinus, 423; volans, 423
Goat, mountain, 98–103
Goldman, Edward A., 273
Goose, Canada, 20

Gopher, chestnut-faced pocket, 433–434; eastern pocket, 433; pocket, 66, 425–434; western pocket, 433

"Gopher," striped, 349–355 (striped ground squirrel)

Grand Canyon National Park, 168, 409

Grand Teton National Park, 144, 580

Grimm, Rudolph, 148

Grinnell, Joseph, 581

Groundhog, 328–336 (woodchuck)

Ground squirrel, 66, 225, 341–368, 377–383; antelope, 359–363 (antelope squirrel); California, 358; Columbian, 343–349; Franklin's, 349; golden-mantled, 363–368; mantled, 363–368 (golden-mantled ground squirrel); Richardson's, 348; rock, 355–359; round-tailed, 349; spotted, 348–349; striped, 349–355, 377–383 (eastern chipmunk); thirteen-lined, 349–355 (striped ground squirrel); Townsend's, 348; Washington, 348

Gulo, 193–198

Hackie, 377–383 (eastern chipmunk)

Halichœrus grypus, 316–318

Hall, E. Raymond, 8, 433

Hamilton, William J., Jr., 352

Hands, John, 277–278

Hare, Arctic, 594–601; European, 594; gray, 181, 583–594 (varying hare); little chief, 577–583 (pika); marsh, 537 ("marsh hare"); snowshoe, 181, 583–594 (varying hare); varying, 181, 583–594; white, 181, 583–594 (varying hare)

Hares and Rabbits, The, 577–625

Hedgehog, 570

Heliographer, The, 62–70

Hemorrhagic septicemia, 95

Heppenstall, Caroline A., 8

Hill, J. Eric, 8

History of mammals, 5–6

Homodontomys, 499

Hornaday, William T., 73

Horns and antlers, 65–66

Howell, Arthur H., 581

Hudson's Bay Company, 289, 461

Humboldt, Alexander, 276

Hyrax, 582

Insect Hunters, The, 114–125

Isle Royale National Park, 46–47, 48, 51

Jack rabbit, 601–612; antelope, 603; black-tailed, 603, 604, 606, 607, 609, 611; white-tailed, 601–603, 604, 606, 607, 609, 610, 611

Jackson, Hartley H. T., 9, 570

Jaguar, 12, 273–278

Jaguarundi, 282–284

Jones, "Buffalo" (Charles J.), 87

Kansas, University of, 8

Kean, Edmund, 271

Kellogg, Remington, 8, 635

Kipling, Rudyard, 631, 633

Klugh, A. Brooker, 398

Kogia breviceps, 639, 641

Lagurus, 518

La Hontan, Baron de, 337

Lasionycteris, 130, 133

Lassen Volcanic National Park, 386

Legend, 124, 126, 134, 269, 270, 275, 276, 306, 325, 328, 370–371, 455, 503, 541, 566, 568, 589, 590

Lemming, 242, 501–507; banded, 507 (collared lemming); bog, 519 (lemming mouse); brown, 507 (common lemming); collared, 507; common, 507; pied, 507 (collared lemming); Unalaska Island, 504

Lemmus, 501–507

Leopard cat, 278–282 (ocelot)

Lepus: alleni, 611; *americanus,* 583–594; *arcticus,* 594–601; *bairdii,* 583–594; *californicus,* 611; *europaeus,* 594; *gaillardi,* 611; *othus,* 594–601; *townsendii,* 611; *washingtonii,* 583–594

Leucorossuromys, 375

Liomys irroratus texensis, 434–436

Livestock, Original American, 71–103

"Lumpy-jaw," 64 (actinomycosis)

Lutra, 198–203

Lynx, 96, 284–290

Lynx canadensis, 96, 284–290

Lynx cat, 290–297, 612 (bobcat)

Lynx rufus, 290–297, 612

McAtee, Waldo L., 8

Macrotus, 132

Madsen, Charles, 326–327

"Madstone," 39

Manatee, 626–630

Margay, 281

Marmot, 170, 336–341; hoary, 336, 338, 339, 340, 341; yellow-bellied, 337, 338, 339, 340, 341

Marmota: caligata, 336–341; *flaviventris,* 336–341; *monax,* 328–336

"Marsh hare," "marsh rabbit," 537 (muskrat)

Marten, 170–175

Martes, 170–175 (marten); *pennanti,* 175–180

Mephitis, 209–216

Mermaid, The Vanishing, 626–630

Mice, 29, 66, 230. See also Mouse

Michigan, University of, 411–412
Microchiroptera, 126–133
Microdipodops, 451
Microsorex, 124
Microtus, 508–519
Mink, 113, 188–193; sea, 192
Mirounga angustirostris, 318–322
Mole, 114–119, 229–230; common, 114, 115, 116, 117, 118; European, 116; hairy-tailed, 114, 115, 117, 118; shrew, 115, 119; star-nosed, 114, 115, 116, 117, 118–119; western, 114, 115, 118, 119
"Mollosid" bats, 132–133
Montezuma, 71
Moose, 44–53
Mount McKinley National Park, 91, 195, 232, 259, 287, 289, 336, 511
Mountain beaver, 550–556
Mountain goat, 98–103
Mountain lion, 38, 264–272, 277 (cougar)
Mountain sheep, 88–98, 232, 287
Mouse: Baird's pocket, 439; beach, 479; bean, 516; California parasitic, 472; California pocket, 437; canyon, 476, 479; deer, 479; desert, 472, 479; field, 508–519 (meadow mouse); golden, 479; gopher, 475, 479; grass-hopper, 462–466; grassland jumping, 562; harvest, 466–470; house, 538–544; jumping, 556–563; Kansas pocket, 439; lemming, 519; "lemming," 519 (tree mouse); meadow, 508–519; Pacific pocket, 437; pine, 518; pocket, 437–442; prairie deer, 475, 477; red-backed, 518; scorpion, 462–466 (grasshopper mouse); Sonoran white-footed, 464; spiny, 434–436; tree, 519; white-footed, 470–479; woodland jumping, 562. See also Mice
Muridæ, 548
Murie, Adolph, 9, 20, 181
Murie, Olaus J., 9, 138
Mus musculus, 538–544
Musk-carriers, The, 170–227
Muskox, 82–88
Muskrat, 188–189, 201, 523–538
Mustela, 180–188 (weasel); *erminea*, 187; *frenata*, 187–188; *macrodon*, 192; *rixosa*, 187; *vison*, 113, 188–193
Myotis, 131, 133
Mysticeti, 631–639

Nahuel Huapi National Park, 276
Napæozapus, 556–563
Narwhal, 640, 644, 645
Nasua narica, 161–165
National Bison Range, 76
National Museum, U. S.. 8

National Park Service, 8, 136, 269
National Zoological Park, 76, 261, 268
Necrotic stomatitis, 18, 95–96, 103
Nelson, Edward W., 124, 273
Neofiber alleni, 519–523
Neotoma, 487–500
Neotomia, 499
Neürotrichus, 119
Notiosorex, 124–125
Nycteris, 130, 133
Nycticeius, 133

Ocelot, 278–282
Ochotona, 577–583
Odobenus, 153, 322–327
Odocoileus: columbianus, 29, 30, 38, 40–44; *couesi*, 32; *hemionus*, 33–40, 252–253; *virginianus*, 23–33, 37
Odonatra, 188–189, 201, 523–538
Odontoceti, 633–640
Ontario Fisheries Research Laboratory, 418
Ontario, Province of, 9
Onychomys, 462–466; *leucogaster*, 465; *torridus*, 465
Opossum, 104–108, 113
Oreamnos americanus, 98–103
Oryctolagus cuniculus, 594, 623–624
Oryzomys palustris, 479–483
Osgood, Wilfred H., 8
Otter, 198–203; sea, 203–209
Overly, Fred, 336–337
Ovibos moschatus, 82–88
Ovis: canadensis, 88–98; *dalli*, 89, 91, 93, 95, 97, 98, 232, 287
Owl, burrowing, 113

Panther, 38, 264–272, 277 (cougar)
Parascalops, 118
Parks. See Crater Lake National, etc.
Peary expeditions, 86
Pecari angulatus, 10–14
Peccary, 10–14
Pekan, 175–180 (fisher)
Pennant's cat, 175–180 (fisher)
Peritonitis, 101
Perognathus, 437–442
Peromyscus, 470–479; *californicus*, 472; *eremicus*, 472; *leucopus*, 472
Phenacomys, 519
Philadelphia Zoo, 292
Phoca fasciata, 314; *grœnlandica*, 313; *hispida*, 313–314; *vitulina*, 309–311
Phocidae, 308–318
Physeter catodon, 633, 634, 635, 637, 638, 639, 640–641

Picket pin, 341–368 (ground squirrel)
Pig, The Wild, 10–14
Pika, 577–583
Pine-marten, 170–175 (marten)
Pipistrellus, 133
Pitymys, 518
Plautus, Titus Maccius, 541
Polar bear, 150–155, 241
Porcupine, 29, 66, 140, 176–177, 195, 240, 296, 563–576; Canada, 564, 567, 568, 571, 574, 575 (eastern porcupine); eastern, 564, 567, 568, 571, 574, 575; western, 564, 566, 567, 568, 570, 571, 574, 576 (yellow-haired porcupine); yellow-haired, 564, 566, 567, 568, 570, 571, 574, 576
Porpoise, 640, 641, 642–645; common, 645
Prairie dog, 66, 368, 376; black-tailed, 372, 374–375; white-tailed, 372, 374–375
Primeval conditions, 1
Prince Albert National Park, 137
Procyon lotor, 156–161
Pronghorn, 62–70, 140 (antelope)
Puma, 38, 264–272, 277 (cougar)

Quill pig, 29, 66, 140, 176–177, 195, 240, 296, 563–576 (porcupine)

Rabbit: Audubon cottontail, 617, 624; brush, 625; cottontail, 113, 182, 612–625; domestic, 594, 623–624; eastern cottontail, 624; European, 594, 623–624; gray, 181, 583–594 (varying hare); jack, 601–612; marsh, 617, 618, 623, 624; pigmy, 624; rock, 577–583 (pika); Rocky Mountain cottontail, 623, 624; snowshoe, 181, 583–594 (varying hare); swamp, 617, 623, 624; white-tailed jack, 601–603, 604, 606, 607, 609, 610, 611
Rabbits, 29, 583–585
Rabies, 233, 253
Raccoon, 156–161
Rangifer, 53–61, 232
Rat: barn, 544–550 (house rat); black, 546, 548, 549; brown, 546, 548, 549–550; cotton, 113, 483–487; dwarf kangaroo, 451; giant kangaroo, 447; gray, 544–550 (house rat); house, 544–550; kangaroo, 442–452; Merriam kangaroo, 447, 449; Norway, 544–550 (house rat); pack, 487–500 (wood rat); rice, 479–483; roof, 546, 548, 549 (black rat); sewer, 544–550 (house rat); trade, 487–500 (wood rat); Tulare kangaroo, 451; water, 519–523; wharf, 544–550 (house rat); wood, 487–500
Rattus: norvegicus, 544–550; *rattus*, 544–550
Red and gray cat, 282–284 (jaguarundi)

Reindeer, 60, 86, 88
Reithrodontomys, 466–470
Rhachianectes glaucus, 637, 639, 640
Ringtail, ringtail cat, 165–169
Rock rabbit, 577–583 (pika)
Rockchuck, 336, 338, 339, 340, 341 (yellow-bellied marmot)
Rogers, Edmund B., 20
Russell, Carl P., 8

Sable, 170–175 (marten)
Scalopus, 118
Scapanus, 119
Sciurus: alberti, 406–410; *arizonensis*, 416; *carolinensis*, 400–405; *chiricahuae*, 416; *griseus*, 400–405; *kaibabensis*, 406–410; *niger*, 410–416
Schmidt, Karl P., 8
Sea-cow, Steller, 627; 626–630 (manatee)
Sea elephant, 318–322
Sea lion, 303–308; California, 307; northern, 307; southern, 307; Stellar, 307
Sea mink, 192
Sea otter, 203–209
Seafarers, Two, 631–645
Seals, 152, 298–327; bearded, 315–316; bladder-nose, 312–313 (hooded seal); eared, 299–308; earless, 308–327; elephant, 318–322 (sea elephant); fjord, 312–313 (ringed seal); fur, 298–303; gray, 316–318; Greenland, 313 (harp seal); Guadalupe fur, 303; hair, 309–311 (harbor seal); harbor, 309–311; harp, 313; hooded, 312–313; leopard, 309–311 (harbor seal); ribbon, 314; ringed, 312–313; "true," 308–327; West Indian, 309
Sequoia National Park, 185
Seton, Ernest Thompson, 2, 72–73, 591
Sewellel, 550–556 (mountain beaver)
Shadle, Albert R., 567
Sheep, black, 97, 98 (bighorn); Dall, 89, 91, 93, 95, 97, 98 (bighorn); mountain, 88–98, 232, 287 (bighorn); northern, 97 (bighorn); Stone, 97, 98 (bighorn)
Sheldon, Charles, 287, 289
Sheridan, General "Phil" (Philip H.), 73
Sherman, Harley B., 9, 131
Shock disease, 592
Showt'l, 550–556 (mountain beaver)
Shrew, 119–125; common, 124; Crawford, 124–125; gray, 124–125; "little," 124; long-tailed, 121, 124; pigmy, 124; short-tailed, 119–121, 124; water, 123, 124
Siemel, Sascha, 276
Sierra Diablo, 93
Siffleur, 328–336 (woodchuck)

Sigmodon, 113, 483–487
Skunk, 113; badger, 216–218 (hog-nosed skunk); hog-nosed, 216–218; hooded, 215–216; spotted, 218–222; striped, 209–216
Skunk-bear, 193–198 (wolverine)
Soil Conservation Service, 9
Sorex, 124
Soricidæ, 119–125
Spilogale, 218–222
Spotted king cat, 12, 273–278 (jaguar)
Squirrel: antelope, 359–363; antelope ground, 359–363 (antelope squirrel); Arizona gray, 415; California ground, 358; chipping, 377–383 (eastern chipmunk); Chiricahua, 411, 416; Columbian ground, 343–349; Durango, 406; federation, 349–355 (striped ground squirrel); flying, 416–424; fox, 410–416; Franklin's ground, 349; gray, 400–406; ground, 66, 225, 341–368; northern red, 391, 399; pine, 399; red, 170, 389–400; rock, 355–359; tassel-eared, 406–410
Steller, Georg Wilhelm, 305
Stomatitis, necrotic, 18, 95–96, 103
Storer, Tracy I., 581
Sumner, Lowell, 290–291
Survivors of Ancient Orders, The, 104–113
Sutton, George M., 506
Sverdrup, Otto, 598–599
Swift, 235–237 (kit fox)
Sylvilagus, 612–625; *aquaticus*, 624–625; *audubonii*, 624; *bachmani*, 625; *floridanus*, 624; *nuttallii*, 624; *palustris*, 624–625
Synaptomys, 519

Tadarida, 129, 131, 133
Talpidæ, 114–119
Tamias striatus, 377–383
Tamiasciurus, 389–400; *douglasii*, 399; *fremonti*, 399; *hudsonicus*, 399
Tapeworm, cat, 293
Taxidea taxus, 66, 222–227
Taxocara cati, 293
Taylor, Walter P., 608
Teonoma, 499
Thalarctos maritimus, 150–155, 241
Thomomys, 433
Tiger cat, 278–282 (ocelot)
Trichechus latirostris, 626–630
Tularemia, 620–621
Tule Lake National Wildlife Refuge, 36

Urocyon: cinereoargenteus, 237–240; *littoralis*, 237–240
Ursus, 19, 20, 38, 143, 144–150

Voles, 508, 517–519
Vorhies, Charles T., 608
Vulpes, 228–234; *macrotis*, 235–237; *velox*, 235–237

Wainwright National Park, 76
Walrus, 153, 322–327
Wapiti, 15–23, 140 (elk)
Weasel, 180–188, 513–514
Whale, 241, 631–642; beaked, 635, 640, 641; blue, 631, 635, 636, 639; bottlenose, 640; California gray, 637; finback, 633, 635, 638, 639, 640; gray, 637, 639, 640; humpback, 635–636, 638, 639, 640; killer, 634, 637, 640, 641, 644; pigmy sperm, 639, 641; pollock, 634; right, 639, 640; rorqual, 635, 637, 639, 640; sei, 634, 639; sperm, 633, 634, 635, 637, 638, 639, 640–641; toothed, 633–645; whalebone, 631–639; white, 640, 644, 645
Whistle-pig, 328–336 (woodchuck)
Whistler, 550–556 (mountain beaver)
Wight, Howard M., 429–430
Wild Pig, The, 10–14
Wildcat, 290–297, 612 (bobcat)
Wilderness Society, 9
Wind Cave National Park, 79, 80
Wolf, 59, 62, 83–84, 96, 102, 242–243, 256–263, 566
Wolf, brush, 35, 62, 66, 245–255 (coyote)
Wolverine, 193–198
Wood Buffalo Park, 81
Wood, J. A., 137
Woodchuck, 328–336

Yagouaroundi, 282–284 (jaguarundi)
Yak, 88
Yellowstone National Park, 20, 22, 31, 50, 73, 92, 136, 138, 143, 144, 148, 149, 172, 173, 174, 182, 190, 225, 249, 253, 339, 367, 386, 575
Yosemite National Park, 173, 201, 581

Zalophus californianus, 305–308
Zaphus, 556–563
Zion National Park, 269
Ziphiidæ, 640